JAPAN

TOKYO

CHINA

TAIWAN

SINGAPORE

IFALUK   TRUK

a
eaux
Iroquois   NEW
YORK

PERU

m. w. johnson

CULTURE
AND
MENTAL HEALTH   *Cross-Cultural Studies*

THE MACMILLAN COMPANY
NEW YORK · CHICAGO
DALLAS · ATLANTA · SAN FRANCISCO
LONDON · MANILA
IN CANADA
BRETT-MACMILLAN LTD.
GALT, ONTARIO

CULTURE
AND
MENTAL HEALTH

Cross-Cultural Studies

Edited by
MARVIN K. OPLER

New York | THE MACMILLAN COMPANY

Library of Congress catalog card number: 59-9305

The Macmillan Company, New York
Brett-Macmillan Ltd., Galt, Ontario

Printed in the United States of America

LIST OF CONTRIBUTORS

G. Morris Carstairs | (Chapter 16)
William Caudill | (Chapter 8)
Bingham Dai | (Chapter 9)
George De Vos | (Chapter 14)
Jacob Fried | (Chapters 5 and 22)
Thomas Gladwin | (Chapter 7)
A. Irving Hallowell | (Chapters 1 and 2)
E. Gartly Jaco | (Chapter 21)
Abram Kardiner | (Chapter 18)
Edward A. Kennard | (Chapter 17)
Tsung-yi Lin | (Chapter 10)
J. B. Loudon | (Chapter 15)
Margaret Mead | (Chapter 23)
Simon D. Messing | (Chapter 13)
Horace Miner | (Chapter 14)
H. B. M. Murphy | (Chapter 12)
Marvin K. Opler | (Introduction, Chapters 4 and 19)
Morris E. Opler | (Chapter 11)
Victor D. Sanua | (Chapter 20)
Seymour B. Sarason | (Chapter 7)
Melford E. Spiro | (Chapter 6)
Anthony F. C. Wallace | (Chapter 3)
Eric D. Wittkower | (Chapter 22)

BIOGRAPHICAL NOTES ON THE CONTRIBUTORS

Of the following contributors, seven presented initial drafts of these papers at the fifty-sixth annual meeting of the American Anthropological Association in Chicago, December, 1957: Marvin K. Opler, chairman and organizer of the symposium; William A. Caudill; Jacob Fried; Edward A. Kennard; H. B. M. Murphy; Morris E. Opler; and Anthony F. C. Wallace. The other contributors were then requested to add to the cross-cultural or world coverage of this volume.

G. MORRIS CARSTAIRS is both a psychiatrist and social anthropologist, currently Assistant Director of the Medical Research Council's Social Psychiatry Research Unit at Maudsley Hospital, London. Publications include *The Twice Born: A Study of a Community of High-Caste Hindus* (Hogarth Press, London, 1957; Indiana University Press, Bloomington, 1958); "Medicine and Faith in Rural Rajasthan" (in *Health, Culture and Community,* edited by B. D. Paul, Russell Sage Foundation, New York, 1955); "A Census of Psychiatric Cases in Two Contrasting Communities" (with G. W. Brown, *Journal of Mental Science,* 1958, Vol. 104, pp. 72–81).

WILLIAM CAUDILL is Lecturer on Social Anthropology, Department of Social Relations at Harvard University, and Research Associate, Department of Psychiatry at Harvard Medical School. Dr. Caudill has done research on the Japanese-Americans in this country and has studied the social structure of psychiatric hospitals in the United States and Japan. He is author of *The Psychiatric Hospital as a Small Society* (Harvard University Press, Cambridge, and the Commonwealth Fund, New York, 1958); "Japanese-American Personality and Acculturation" (*Genetic Psychology Monographs,* 1952, Vol. 45, pp. 3–102); and several journal articles on topics in anthropology and psychiatry.

BINGHAM DAI received his Ph.D. in sociology from the University of Chicago, following undergraduate work in China. From 1933 to 1935, he

vii

was connected with the Chicago Institute for Psychoanalysis. He is now Professor of Psychology in the Department of Psychology and Professor of Mental Hygiene in the Department of Psychiatry, Duke University. He is the author of *Opium Addiction in Chicago* (Commercial Press, Shanghai, 1937) and many papers published on problems of culture-personality relationships, particularly in Chinese culture. He is also a consultant for the World Federation for Mental Health.

GEORGE DE VOS is Lecturer in Social Welfare at the School of Social Welfare of the University of California at Berkeley. With Professor Miner, he is coauthor of a forthcoming book on Algeria. He is the author with Dr. Caudill, another contributor, of "Achievement, Culture and Personality: The Case of the Japanese-Americans" (*American Anthropologist,* 1956, Vol. 58, pp. 1102–1126). As a psychologist interested in ethnic differences, he has also published "A Quantitative Rorschach Assessment of Maladjustment and Rigidity in Acculturating Japanese-Americans" (*Genetic Psychology Monographs,* 1955, Vol. 52, pp. 51–87) and other studies on projective techniques.

JACOB FRIED is an anthropologist in the Department of Sociology and Anthropology at McGill University, and a collaborator with Dr. Eric D. Wittkower of the Allan Memorial Institute of Psychiatry in the Section of Transcultural Psychiatric Studies. He has done field research in Hawaii, northern Mexico, and among American Indians. With Dr. Wittkower, he edits *Transcultural Research in Mental Health Problems* (a Newsletter). In the work here reported, he was connected with the Department of Neuropsychiatry, Hospital Obrero of Lima, Peru.

THOMAS GLADWIN is Social Science Consultant, Community Services Branch of the National Institute of Mental Health. He received his doctorate from Yale in anthropology and psychology. His publications include *Truk, Man in Paradise* (with Seymour B. Sarason, Viking Fund Publications in Anthropology, New York, 1953); "Psychological and Cultural Problems in Mental Subnormality" (with Seymour B. Sarason, *Genetic Psychology Monographs,* 1958, Vol. 57, pp. 3–290).

A. IRVING HALLOWELL is Professor of Anthropology at the University of Pennsylvania and Professor of Anthropology in Psychiatry at its medical school. He is also Curator of Social Anthropology at the University Museum. He was Chairman of the Division of Anthropology and

Psychology, National Academy of Sciences, National Research Council, 1946–1949, and is a past president of the American Anthropological Association, American Folklore Society, and Society for Projective Techniques. In 1955, Dr. Hallowell received the Viking Medal and Award in General Anthropology. Dr. Hallowell is author of *Culture and Experience* (University of Pennsylvania Press, Philadelphia, 1955); and *The Role of Conjuring in Saulteaux Society* (University of Pennsylvania Press, Philadelphia, 1942).

E. GARTLY JACO is Associate Professor of Sociology in the Departments of Neuropsychiatry and Preventive Medicine and Public Health, and Director of the Division of Medical Sociology in the University of Texas Medical Branch. He is editor of *Patients, Physicians and Illness* (The Free Press of Glencoe, Ill., 1958); "The Social Isolation Hypothesis and Schizophrenia" (*American Sociological Review*, 1954, Vol. 19, pp. 567–577); "Social Factors in Mental Disorders in Texas" (*Social Problems*, April, 1957, Vol. 4, pp. 322–328); and other articles in medical sociology. He is now completing a monograph on the social epidemiology of mental disorders in Texas.

ABRAM KARDINER is Attending Psychiatrist at the Psychiatric Institute of Columbia University, and was formerly Director of its Psychoanalytic Clinic from 1955–1957. He was also Clinical Professor of Psychiatry at Columbia for several years, and before that an Associate in Anthropology in the Columbia University Graduate School. Among Dr. Kardiner's books are the following: *The Individual and His Society* (Columbia University Press, New York, 1939); *The Traumatic Neuroses of War* (Paul B. Hoeber, Inc., New York, 1941); *The Psychological Frontiers of Society* (with R. Linton, Cora DuBois, and James West, Columbia University Press, New York, 1945); and *Sex and Morality* (Bobbs-Merrill, New York and Indianapolis, 1954).

EDWARD A. KENNARD is Chief, Anthropology Service, Veterans Administration Hospital at Perry Point, Maryland. Previously, he served in the same capacity, from 1954 to 1958, at the Downey Hospital in Illinois. One of his publications in the field of social psychiatry is "Psychiatry, Administrative Psychiatry, Administration" in *The Patient and the Mental Hospital* (edited by M. Greenblatt, D. J. Levinson, and R. H. Williams, The Free Press of Glencoe, Ill., 1957).

TSUNG-YI LIN is Professor and head of the Department of Psychiatry and Neurology, National Taiwan University, and Director of the Taipei

Children's Mental Health Center. Dr. Lin was Research Fellow at Harvard University Medical School from 1950–1952, after having been Chief Psychiatrist at the National Taiwan University Hospital. He is the author of several studies, including "Anthropological Study of the Incidence of Mental Disorder in Chinese and Other Cultures" (*Psychiatry*, 1953, Vol. 16, p. 313).

J. B. LOUDON is both a psychiatrist and social anthropologist, who has been associated with the Institute of Psychiatry at Maudsley Hospital, London. Dr. Loudon has also directed a Social Psychiatry Research Unit at Llandough Hospital studying two different populations in South Wales, one rural and one urban. Earlier, he spent two years among the Zulu of South Africa.

MARGARET MEAD, formerly president of the World Federation for Mental Health (1956–1957), is Associate Curator of Ethnology at the American Museum of Natural History and Adjunct Professor of Anthropology at Columbia University. In 1957, she was chosen Viking Medalist in General Anthropology. Among her relevant publications are *Childhood in Contemporary Cultures* (coedited with Martha Wolfenstein, University of Chicago Press, Chicago, 1955); *New Lives for Old* (William Morrow and Company, New York, 1956); and *Cultural Patterns and Technical Change* (editor, Mentor Books, New York, 1955; UNESCO, Paris, 1953). Dr. Mead has written many monographs on the results of her field work in regions of the South Pacific, including Samoa, the Admiralty Islands, Indonesia, and New Guinea.

SIMON D. MESSING is an anthropologist teaching in the Department of Sociology, Hiram College, Ohio. He was Harrison Fellow of the University of Pennsylvania, 1950–1951, where he received his doctorate in cultural anthropology. He is author of several papers on Ethiopian ethnology, including some on psychological topics. Before his Harrison Fellowship, he did research on technological change and social adjustment in a Pennsylvania town. He has published as coauthor several handbooks on Jordon, Syria, and Lebanon for the Human Relations Area Files (1956).

HORACE MINER is Professor of Sociology and Anthropology at the University of Michigan. He is author of *St. Denis: A French-Canadian Parish* (University of Chicago Press, Chicago, 1939); *The Primitive City of Timbuctoo* (Princeton University Press, Princeton, 1953); and is coauthor of a forthcoming volume on Algerian culture and personality in transition.

H. B. M. MURPHY combines the fields of public health in which he holds a doctorate with studies in social psychiatry. He has been associated with the Milbank Memorial Fund as a Fellow, and previously was the Director of the Student Health Service of the University of Malaya in Singapore (1952–1957). Dr. Murphy was also medical consultant to the International Refugee Organization (1947–1950). He is now completing various studies on mental health in Southeast Asia. Trained in Edinburgh and London, his publications include *Flight and Resettlement* (UNESCO, Paris, 1955); "The Mental Health of Singapore: Suicide" (*Medical Journal of Malaya,* 1954, Vol. 9, p. 1); and "Einwirkungen von Emigration und Flucht auf die psychische Verfassung" (in *Geistige Hygiene, Forschung und Praxis,* edited by Pfister, Basle, 1955).

MARVIN K. OPLER is an anthropologist and sociologist who has worked in the field of social psychiatry since 1938. He is now Professor of Social Psychiatry in the Department of Psychiatry, University of Buffalo School of Medicine, and Professor of Sociology in the Department of Sociology, University of Buffalo Graduate School. He is a coauthor of *Acculturation in Seven American Indian Tribes* (with R. Linton, editor, Appleton-Century-Crofts, New York, 1940); author of *Culture, Psychiatry and Human Values* (Charles C Thomas, Publisher, Springfield, Ill., 1956); coauthor of *The Symposium on Preventive and Social Psychiatry* (Government Printing Office, Walter Reed Army Institute of Research, Washington, D.C., 1958); and coauthor of *Clinical Studies in Culture Conflict* (edited by G. Seward, Ronald Press, New York, 1958); and has made various other contributions on topics in anthropology, sociology, and psychiatry in both book and journal form. He was recently associated for six years with Dr. T. A. C. Rennie as a professor in the Department of Psychiatry, Cornell University Medical College, and was a principal investigator at Cornell in the Community Mental Health Research Study. He is Associate Editor of *The International Journal of Social Psychiatry.* His publications in anthropology and social psychiatry include such groups as those in the Midtown Community Mental Health Research Study (New York), Japanese, Ute Indians, and Puerto Ricans. Dr. Opler has taught at the William Alanson White Institute of Psychiatry, Psychoanalysis,

and Psychology in New York City, at the Los Angeles Institute of
Psychoanalysis, and as a professor in the New School for Social Research, in the Harvard University Department of Social Relations,
and at Stanford University.

MORRIS E. OPLER is Professor of Anthropology at Cornell University,
Ithaca. He is author of *An Apache Life-Way* (University of Chicago
Press, Chicago, 1941); and of various studies in the ethnology of the
American Southwest and India. He has directed the Cornell University projects relating to India; has done extensive fieldwork among
Apache tribes and peoples of India; and has published widely on
both areas. He is also the author of *Social Aspects of Technical Assistance in Operation* (UNESCO, Paris, 1954).

VICTOR D. SANUA attended the American University at Cairo and took his
doctorate in psychology at Michigan State University. He was a research clinical psychologist at the Institute of Physical Medicine and
Rehabilitation of New York University–Bellevue Medical Center, before joining the staff at Cornell University Medical College as Russell
Sage Fellow in cross-cultural research in association with Dr. Marvin K. Opler. He is now a Fellow (postdoctoral researcher) in the
Department of Social Relations at Harvard. Among Dr. Sanua's publications is a study in 1957 on "Problems in Vocational Rehabilitation
of Disabled Puerto Ricans in New York City" (*Rehabilitation Monograph*, No. 12, New York University, Bellevue Medical Center).

SEYMOUR B. SARASON is Professor of Psychology at Yale University and
Director of its Training Program in Clinical Psychology. His books
include *Psychological Problems in Mental Deficiency* (Harper &
Brothers, New York, 2nd ed., 1953); *The Clinical Interaction* (Harper
& Brothers, New York, 1954); and *Truk, Man in Paradise* (with
Thomas Gladwin, Viking Fund Publications in Anthropology, New
York, 1953).

MELFORD E. SPIRO is Professor of Anthropology at the University of Washington. Besides his study with E. G. Burrows, called *An Atoll Culture*
(Human Relations Area Files, New Haven, 1953), he has published
two volumes on research in *kibbutz* culture and personality: *Kibbutz,
Venture in Utopia* (Harvard University Press, Cambridge, 1956) and
Children of the Kibbutz (Harvard University Press, Cambridge, 1958).

ANTHONY F. C. WALLACE is Senior Research Associate in Anthropology
at the Eastern Pennsylvania Psychiatric Institute and also Research

Associate Professor of Anthropology at the University of Pennsylvania. He is the author of "The Modal Personality Structure of the Tuscarora Indians" (*Bureau of American Ethnology*, Bulletin 150, 1952); "Stress and Rapid Personality Changes" (*International Record of Medicine*, 1956, Vol. 169, pp. 761–774); "Revitalization Movements" (*American Anthropologist*, 1956, Vol. 58, pp. 264–281); and other books and monographs.

ERIC D. WITTKOWER is Associate Professor of Psychiatry at McGill University and Associate Psychiatrist at the Royal Victoria Hospital and Montreal General Hospital. Dr. Wittkower was trained as a biochemist, psychiatrist, and psychoanalyst. He has been a consulting psychiatrist at the National Sanatorium, Beneden, Kent. His publications include *A Psychiatrist Looks at Tuberculosis* (National Association for Prevention of Tuberculosis, New York, 1949); *Emotional Factors in Skin Diseases* (with Brian Russell, Paul B. Hoeber, Inc., New York, 1953); and *Recent Developments in Psychosomatic Medicine* (with R. A. Cleghorn, J. B. Lippincott Co., Philadelphia, 1954).

EDITOR'S PREFACE

By definition, social psychiatry is a complex combination of disciplines. From medicine come psychiatry, psychoanalysis, and public health. From the behavioral or social science side come anthropology, social psychology, and sociology. Each one of these special fields dealing with man, health, and community is indispensable. Each one is represented in this volume, usually by more than a single contributor. The contributors have each, in their turn, worked in close association with psychiatry for a considerable period of time.

I have aimed at such representation in planning a volume on *Culture and Mental Health*. It was my intention to gather over twenty such interdisciplinary contributions. I hoped to have the studies represent not only Europe but the four other major continents, North America, South America, Africa, and Asia. Island areas like Formosa and the South Pacific (Micronesia) also seemed possible for inclusion. Because research on culture and personality has often involved groups near at hand in the United States, such as American Indian and American ethnic groups, several such studies were also included. Each one of these objectives was reached in this volume.

While the central theme of this volume is the variable effect of culture or cultural stress on mental health, it is hoped that appropriate methods for such study are also represented. This, too, seems to be the case in the present volume. Besides public health epidemiology, one finds psychoanalysis, psychological and social science methods. Further, one could call the approach of Wallace ethnohistorical as well as psychiatric, or call Murphy's study epidemiological, although it obviously is based upon cultural studies of ethnic groups in Singapore. Or one could contrast the approaches of Sarason, Gladwin, and Spiro in nearby areas of Micronesia which combine field observation, life history, and psychological testing with the Miner–De Vos work on Algeria which is only roughly similar, while the equally sensitive work of Messing on Abyssinia is strikingly different. It was decided that methodological rubrics

xv

emphasized the variety of analytic tools used in such research without indicating the consistent or uniform focus in all the studies on the importance of cultural background in mental functioning. Other modes of organization, such as grouping Fried's acculturation study with Lin's analysis of the changing Formosan scene, seemed equally distracting from the main purpose. The clearest method of organization, from the reader's point of view, seemed to be the simple geographic method of organizing studies according to region, such as African or Asian-Formosan, American ethnic groupings, or American Indian studies. Therefore, one can find the studies from Truk or Ifaluk grouped together, just as studies of the American Negro like Kardiner's are placed with studies of Italian and Irish in the New York scene, and with these Mexican-American and American-Jewish intergeneration studies.

My association with Dr. T. A. C. Rennie and others at Cornell University Medical College in social psychiatry extended from 1952 to 1958 and served to convince me of the necessity for a culture and mental health volume. None such exists. In 1956, it was decided to develop a cross-cultural volume with contributors from the many disciplines and areas listed above. In 1957, at the request of the American Anthropological Association, a symposium on this subject was held in Chicago with only seven of the final two dozen studies represented. The regional areas represented at Chicago were Japan (William Caudill), Peru (Jacob Fried), an American hospital (Edward A. Kennard), Mexico (Oscar Lewis), Singapore (H. B. M. Murphy), American ethnic groups (Marvin K. Opler), India (Morris E. Opler), and an Iroquois study (Anthony F. C. Wallace). The response to this preview of the intended cross-cultural volume encouraged me when the papers were first in process to add well over a dozen other contributions based on the experience of persons working in the social science and medical fields. To emphasize the exploratory nature of current studies and the practical programs in social psychiatry developed through such agencies as the World Health Organization, I added one further paper by Eric D. Wittkower and Jacob Fried on transcultural research programs, and another by Margaret Mead on mental health in world perspective.

M. K. O.

February, 1959

ACKNOWLEDGMENTS

Of the twenty-three studies in this book, most are original accounts which have not appeared elsewhere. A few are reprinted. For A. Irving Hallowell's two essays which pioneered in this field, we wish to thank the author and the *Journal of Social Psychology* for permission to reprint from Volume 9, and the *American Journal of Psychiatry* relative to Volume 92, also reprinted with permission from Dr. Hallowell's *Culture and Experience*, University of Pennsylvania Press, Philadelphia, 1955. The essay by Eric D. Wittkower and Jacob Fried is reprinted from *The International Journal of Social Psychiatry*, Volume 3, and hereby acknowledged. Tsung-yi Lin's paper will appear coincidentally in the *British Journal of Delinquency*, as will my Chapter 19 in *The Psychiatric Quarterly*, both gratefully acknowledged. Bingham Dai's paper appeared recently in Volume 4 of *Social Problems* and is reprinted with permission. Special acknowledgments are also made to the Wenner-Gren Foundation for Anthropological Research and to *Sociometry* for parallel studies, having somewhat different emphasis, respectively, by Thomas Gladwin and Seymour B. Sarason and by Horace Miner and George De Vos. A quotation from *Psychiatry* is acknowledged by Melford E. Spiro in his essay. In brief, sixteen of these studies, the decided majority, are new and a few find parallels elsewhere.

The editor is grateful to Mrs. Marion W. Johnson for the excellent end-map illustrating the location of the various peoples here discussed.

CONTENTS

SECTION VII:
World Perspectives

Marvin K. Opler

Department of Psychiatry
University of Buffalo School of Medicine
and
Department of Sociology
University of Buffalo

INTRODUCTION

THE CULTURAL BACKGROUNDS OF MENTAL HEALTH

With the year 1960 designated as Mental Health Year in international world health organization circles, it becomes necessary to take stock of the position of behavioral sciences concerning this enormous problem. There has been no consistent attack on problems of mental illness around the world. While no continent or island area has been immune from the scourges of mental disorders, the scientific world has seemed content to study limited problems in the relationship of culture to mental health in restricted and often localized areas. For this reason, both in research and in action programs a broad world perspective on mental health has been seriously lacking.

A search of the literature and discussions with others active in the field of social psychiatry indicate that the existing studies and programs have to date been scattered and inconclusive. For example, the World Health Organization in 1953 published a study in ethnopsychiatry called, not too appropriately, *The African Mind in Health and Disease*. A psychiatrist and public health expert, J. C. Carothers, brought together no less than 191 references to the literature on Africa with his own wide experience in Kenya—and, even so, the results unleashed widespread controversy. Of course, although social scientists, psychiatrists, and others entered the fray, the central difficulty lay in the paucity of rounded studies which fulfilled the behavioral science requirements of these various fields. Among the 191 references, not a single one could be cited which conclusively filled such requirements and successfully resolved the difficulty.

The present volume must therefore travel widely around the world

1

carefully selecting studies which are well informed by both the social
and psychological or psychiatric disciplines.

In each essay referring to some region of the world, we have authors
who have trained themselves, or taught, or contributed heavily in psychiatric settings and in the literature. Some themselves are primarily
psychiatrists, like Lin of Formosa, who have conducted extensive anthropological research. While the matter of credentials as interdisciplinary behavioral scientists is clear, it may be less apparent to a casual
reader that these are intended to be pioneering studies in world mental
health, each of which establishes important findings within a more total
pattern of basic questions concerning mental health. It is easy to miss
these fundamental challenges and to call this, instead, a round-the-
world survey of mental health, which it most certainly is not.

Published fieldwork on the Iroquois tribes is richer in historical depth
and coloring than for most nonliterate peoples. There are few tribes
anywhere for whom the descriptions of psychiatric and social phenomena
are so complete down through the years. It is interesting that such descriptions go beyond personal documents and psychological insights,
provided by such relatively "modern" figures as Handsome Lake of
the Iroquois, to accounts of the larger setting of cathartic and control
mechanisms in social and religious life as presented by Wallace. Even
more striking is the contrast between earlier methods of acting out
pressures and stresses within the early Iroquois culture and later values
and emphases on control mechanisms once that culture was subject to
the conditions of conquest. However, the persistence of cultural environment as a partly going concern is seen in Hallowell's essays on
the Ojibwa and my own account of Ute Indian dream analysis. The
shattering effects of migration into the urban scene of the Peruvian Indians, studied by Fried in his account of their psychiatric adjustments
in acculturation, provide a warning to American Indian administrators
at a time when the government is planning the rapid relocation and
detribalization of its oldest American citizens. In this sense it can be
seen that the essays on various American Indian groups have been developed into a pattern which tests out the problems implicit in the
changing culture of our Indian tribes, both from the point of view
of their intrinsic cultural strengths and the impact of two periods of
white contact, one early and involving internal modifications, like the
psychological adaptations of the Iroquois, and the other involving a
process which is unfortunately uprooting Indians such as those in Peru.

It will be noted that none of these essays just discussed, which trace typical processes affecting American Indians from periods of early contact on, brings in individual cases for full consideration. This is because they focus upon the larger scene in which the individual is involved. It is therefore appropriate next to present two matched and balanced studies from a single region (Micronesia). Here two authors, Gladwin and Sarason, focus upon a continuum of more or less adjusted cases within their larger study of Trukese personality. The selection is from a normative range of men and women within this cultural group. These are contemporary "well" people of the South Pacific. They contrast with a few from Ifaluk, also in Micronesia, who represent a total census of the psychotics studied intensively by Spiro. There are, of course, differences between these two cultures as well as similarities, but our intention was not to develop a control study of Ifaluk's psychotics in Trukese normative personality. Rather the studies are grouped together because they illustrate in rich depth that both the normative and psychotic personalities are moored in culture and subject to the conditions of cultural existence. For instance, Spiro's least adjusted personalities in his atoll culture are triggered into psychotic manifestations after particular jarring experiences at the hands of Japanese. But not many persons in Ifaluk are so afflicted. Further, his case of the chief's son illustrates specific hazards in this relatively rare status role among the Ifaluk.

These are but a few examples of the effects of cultures on mental functioning. So far as social psychiatry is concerned, they suggest that the next major developments in mental health planning will probably occur on an administrative as well as a theoretical basis. The chapters by Caudill on Japan, Carstairs on London, or Kennard on a midwest American hospital illustrate some major variations already in effect. In Japan, psychiatric institutions are small, while in the United States they have grown far too large. In addition, Carstairs, writing from the vantage point of social rehabilitation of English patients, finds that this society places particular demands upon the individual emerging from the treatment milieu. However, our cultural contrasts from around the world disclosed that not only do hospitals and treatment milieus differ, but that even the paths into illness have a different topography in each culture. Indeed, as Lin shows in his study of Formosan delinquency types, variations in class identity or in the pace of acculturation of class segments may produce differences in deviant types. Similarly,

Miner and De Vos, in their study of Algerian personality types, find some variation between the people of desert and oasis social environments. When we trace the Asian studies which have been presented here from Japan through China and India, there are evidences that the cultural backgrounds and forms of illness covary apart from the question of how these illnesses are treated. For example, Dai presents stresses implicit in the more traditional Chinese family. When, further, we trace these patterns even in scattered examples from Japan, Formosa, China, or North India down to the single city of Singapore, as Murphy describes it, we find that Hindus, Chinese, and Malays appear to have differing amounts and types of disorders, each depending on their cultural existence.

American traditions in this area have based an approach to treatment largely upon behavioristic ideas of rewarding good patient activities with privileges or imposing punishments in the form of stricter custodial and closed ward supervision. We have varied this pragmatic stimulus and response, reward and punishment Lockean system, emphasizing behaviorism, with only a slight amount of clinical treatment in depth, or psychotherapy, largely reserved for the upper classes. A. B. Hollingshead and F. C. Redlich, in their study of social class and mental illness, have shown how such differing treatment is meted out in a New England city according to class lines (3).

G. Allport in his book, *Becoming*, on the basic considerations for a psychology of personality, has contrasted this behavioristic tradition derived from Locke with a Leibnizian tradition which views the mind or mental functioning as striving or attempting to cope with environment (1, 5). On the European continent, rather than in America, we find this last tradition today more strongly represented in psychiatry by a variety of existentialist movements (5).

However, the existentialist and phenomenological movements in psychiatry, while emphasizing the individual's subjective ties to environment (*Umwelt*) and his personalized interpretations of experience, have said all too little about the role of culture in guiding the formation of such meanings and environments.

On the continent, again, one finds the striking experiments in foster-home care of mental patients and in home treatment. In Gheel, Belgium, this town since the Middle Ages has shouldered a mission to care for the mentally disturbed who have sought asylum there. Some 2,500 patients live in Gheel in foster homes even today, and this is based upon the particular tenet that in a first or subsequent trial a family can be found in which a patient will find a temporary home. The town is districted into four wards, each with medical and nursing facilities. As in other forms of medicine, the hospital is only a last resort in emergencies, and the physician's calls are made in the home scene.

In the city of Amsterdam, Dr. A. Querido, a psychiatrist, has worked since 1930 in a larger urban area of over a million people to develop full-time psychiatric teams administering home treatment. Querido's interest in developing particular assets in the patient and in his own family and community relationships is based upon a philosophy that the adaptation or adjustment should be accomplished in the original family setting. Consequently, this method also develops inpatient arrangements only in the technical circumstances requiring hospital observation and treatment. Querido feels that removing the patient from his meaningful social and cultural environment avoids the crucial questions in a disturbed adaptation. While we do not intend to discuss such organizational arrangements in Gheel, in Amsterdam, in Denmark's programs for psychiatric nursing, or in Israel's varied program utilizing community resources, all of these systems aim at an action program within a live social and cultural scene, rather than within a dispirited custodial institution. These are obviously programs interested in the amelioration, prevention, or cure of serious human problems involving an existing structure of social and human relations which have become distorted. Applied social psychiatry therefore has a range of application going beyond the individual to the family and to social and cultural organization. It resembles an existential, phenomenological interest in that it centers attention upon the structure of symbolized meanings resident ultimately in the individual personality. But it does not stop there since a system of human values, of one type or another, is important in the functioning of any individual. Therefore, a science or philosophy of human values in which cultural or social backgrounds are specified becomes crucial in understanding the individual's functioning. That these backgrounds affect certain groups in a culture is illustrated in J. B. Loudon's account of emotional hazards for women among the Zulu.

Following our studies in this symposium of various contrasts from Asia, Africa, Oceania, and Europe, we next focus down on particular problems of American subcultural groups, such as Irish and Italians, the children of immigrant Jewish parents, the American Negro, and

Spanish Americans. The point here is that modern heterogeneous society contains a series of subcultural groups, some of which, like the American Negro, have their total cultural identity with the American scene blocked by a towering barrier of social and economic discrimination. The culture of colored people is a deeply ingrained American culture, but the opportunity to identify as Americans rather than second-class citizens is denied, of course with psychological results. That Kardiner is hopeful about a gradual emancipation from this economic and psychological bondage, as colored people continue to move into more secure placement because of professional, artistic, or technical attainments is not the whole point. Their more complete emancipation may continue to come slowly or the leap may hopefully come sooner and involve a more widespread emancipation. But psychiatry, in the meantime, must treat individuals now and then on whom the mark of oppression has been laid. It cannot do so without noting a subcultural variation which grows out of the discriminatory pattern.

Many existentialists have held that the number of environments (*Umwelten*) is equal to the number of individuals. This is an ultimate dignification of unique meanings of experience for individuals which distracts attention from typologies in family, in culture, and in society. While no two individuals are the same, and we may speak of the uniqueness of a person, a family, or a culture, the very term "environment" becomes meaningless unless it is seen as the prevailing conditions modifying existence for the individual, family, or cultural group. Therefore, we have included studies which document the difference between male Irish and Italian schizophrenics (M. K. Opler) or between first- and second-generation Jewish persons in the American scene (V. D. Sanua). All this points to the need for a newer differential psychology and anthropology which does not get lost in the welter of individual differences. Further, we have included an account by E. Gartly Jaco of Spanish Americans in Texas, who on first inspection appear to have an enviable mental health status, despite their minority label, when compared with white and nonwhite Texans who are their neighbors. If we lost sight of the fact that this minority group had the deepest cultural roots of all Texans in the area and lived close to the Mexican sources of their cultural tradition, we might speak of them hastily as a people caught in the throes of acculturation or rapid cultural change. But one has only to look back and contrast them with the uprooted Peruvian Indians or the people of Ifaluk after Japanese invasion, to realize that it is the cultural group in process of rapid relocation or reacting to conquest which provides the less stable psychological picture.

We have just looked ahead to a range of studies marshaled for this volume. Without fully anticipating the importance of their content or the special points which each makes, this is to provide a first glance, or overview, of what comes later. But first we must provide a rationale for the approach to personality through culture.

There is a difference between culture-personality study and scientific research into the cultural backgrounds of mental illness. The latter, indeed, requires additional special knowledge of pathological behavior as developed through such sciences as psychiatry, psychology, and anthropology. But nevertheless, as such major movements as the psychoanalytic or existentialist would contend, a science of man and culture forms a fundamental basis for both the studies of personality in society and of mental dysfunction. Science itself is a type of human behavior which, as we know, deals with experience according to certain assumptions and methods. At the same time, sciences have typical limits set according to the phenomena being investigated. In dealing with experience, one must include its relevant aspects. In the physical and organic areas of existence, among nonhuman phenomena, culture is irrelevant although it may play some role in the perspectives of particular "scientific" men. When, however, we cross the line to human experience, culture is never irrelevant. It does not matter whether we are studying normative personality or a rising toll of mental illness linked with cultural disorganization and social decay. Both culture-personality study and the study of mental disorders require a basic unified science concerned with man and culture. This generalizing behavioral science is required, as Cassirer and others interested in a philosophy of symbolization have proposed, simply because all culture depends upon the human exercise of a symbolic faculty. While E. Sapir once wrote on the topic "why cultural anthropology needs the psychiatrist," it is even more important today to understand why psychiatry requires the anthropologist. It matters little whether such a unified and generalizing behavioral science appears under the rubric of "social psychiatry" or "cultural anthropology" so long as it is understood to be interested in the discovery of regularities in processes affecting man's fate, health, and cultural survival on various evolutionary levels of cultural development around the world.

Culture is, in part, a symbolic organization of behavior in which the meaning of that behavior is expressed in interpersonal processes stemming from cultural traditions. It is no wonder, then, that political figures interested in a widespread tampering with that behavior, like Goering in Hitler's Germany, should have found even the word "culture" highly offensive since it represented deep strivings and regularities in the social process. Our point here is that such widespread meanings as are adumbrated in cultural symbols do not require identical interpretations on the part of all culture carriers in order to be effective. Between the unique or even "idiosyncratic" meanings of experience for the individual and the norms of everyday conduct at its most commonplace, the symbolic cultural world operates constantly to inject its traditional forms of structured meanings and experiences with greater or less effect upon the individual (6). How this cultural reinforcement may operate, in one instance, is documented in M. E. Opler's account from India.

In the past, the focus of psychiatry has been upon the individual case, classified under diagnostic headings which changed in time or historically, or else were modified by the particular outlooks and even the kinds of training a practitioner received. To introduce a general order into such a confusing array of observational and interpretive yardsticks, the Freudian system adopted a genetic historical approach to each individual resting upon a biological and hedonistic interpretation of his motivations. More recently, and even within that movement, sensitive observers faced with the perplexities of almost unreachable schizophrenic behavior (like F. Fromm-Reichmann) attempted to develop interpretations of that behavior *from within* the curiously distorted and constricted patterns of the patient. Both existential and phenomenological interpretations on the continent, while often blithely dispensing with Freudian constructs of unconscious motivation, again proceed usually by reconstructing experiences, meanings, and symbols in a wholly individualized manner. There have been claims that this valuable and sensitive search has disposed of the abstract and unnecessary dichotomy between the subject and the object. While this last position also represents a stimulating challenge to certain rigid repetitions of formulae among certain Freudians, it can be questioned whether this method does not resolve itself into a wholly individualized subjectivism. Freudianism is more systematic. We too feel that subject and object dichotomies may become ways of missing the importance of meanings, symbols, and interpretations of environments on the part of the individual. But we discover repeatedly that mental disorders vary both in quantity and quality according to different environments, and that they have even changed within one tradition, like the Western European. Therefore, it may be stated that the cultural environment is an active causal force in determining stress systems, family typologies, and even to an extent the kinds of personalized meanings which operate within a cultural setting.

Social psychiatry is therefore interested in the larger vista of people around the world and even in remote places as a massive laboratory for the study of the relations of culture to mental health and illness according to various designs for living.

Social psychiatry is as concerned about the impact of varying cultural and social environments upon human psychology as it is in the more descriptive problem of the incidence or differences in psychopathology among various peoples. It may contain, as this volume does, studies which approach these problems of incidence and differences in psychopathology from a quantitative standpoint. Or social psychiatry may go beyond the stage of counting such resultants to depth studies illustrating how culture, social system, and personality become connected variables, dependent in the long run upon the material conditions and social organization under which the culture operates. As phenomenology has demonstrated, the behavioral sciences have only just begun to study the cultural symbol. We know it enters into the totality of patterned family and social influences acquired and transmitted in a cultural tradition. We know less about the significant and discernible values of such systems of symbols for the individual. In short, while we know that culture includes traditional systems transmitted as methods for regulating behavior, ethics, and attitudes, this transmission through families and social units has only recently become a subject for research. We also know that this transmission does not occur with perfect regularity and that the elements which ultimately are incorporated from the culture into personal functioning may, in a range of families and individuals, produce a series of problems best called mental illness. But while individuals do not live a life span in a constant and unvarying relationship with a total cultural environment, there is enough constancy to be able to speak of normative patterns in every cultural scene.

The evidence is increasing also on the patterning of mental disorders. A culture is often enough in flux, or divided in its structures, to contain serious conflicts in values and in action patterns, throwing whole families and individuals into states of empty, unsatisfying, or disturbed functioning. We are not speaking of a constant and static relationship with total environment, but simply saying that the conditions within the culture affect family and social units and through them produce the subtle and unique characteristics of individuals.

There can therefore be a psychodynamic view of how a culture typically operates. This culturally dynamic point of view indicates a special role for social and preventive psychiatry. The fact that cultures differ in their evolutionary status and vary in their effects upon individuals produces vivid and dramatic contrasts in societies presented in the pages which follow. While Ute Indian practitioners conduct dream analyses with patients, they are also looked upon as the organized and even religiously sanctioned custodians of all health within the society, and they function in group-oriented settings guaranteeing the total welfare of a Ute band as well as in individual cases. One could hardly find such parallels in psychoanalytic practice. Nor would one find the same activist orientation as the Ute shamans illustrate when they conduct their energetic and spirited attack upon the illness in the songs and dances marking later stages in therapy. Such contrasts in societies count heavily if we are thinking of practical programs applied to communities as well as to families and individuals. While cultures vary in their effects on individuals, there are normative or statistical trends defining health and illness in any community and determining not only the style of disorder, but the manner of prevention and treatment (3, 6).

In social psychiatry, attention must be shifted to processes involving society, personality, and mental illness in their relationships. A. N. Whitehead has called all nature a structure of evolving processes. Of course, this includes the human world as well. In a mature behavioral science system, or a philosophy of science, such evolving processes and their relationships become the reality to be studied. In an earlier volume called *Culture, Psychiatry and Human Values,* the author stated that mental disorders were also processes which had changed markedly in human history. A study of such illnesses discussed in the literature up to 1956 disclosed that their social and cultural origins had changed. For some disorders, the developmental course of illness had changed. It was claimed that methods of prevention and techniques of therapy would probably change in a parallel fashion. Viewing the history of psychiatry and its present expansion in social psychiatry, we were forced to conclude that new methods, theories, and practical applications must emerge in this medical and behavioral science discipline (6).

Psychiatry in the past has been far too greatly preoccupied with descriptive tasks of classifying illness on the basis of restricted Western European and American practice. Such illness nomenclature in psychiatry dates back to the last century. Description and classification have now begun to penetrate the contributions of culture-personality studies in other parts of the world. In general, culture-personality analysis in anthropology has not yet been widely incorporated as an essential part of the method and theory of social psychiatry. Too often the anthropologist has derived his clinical models from the existing schools and assumptively applied them to the materials on personality from diverse cultures. Ideally, the development of personality in society and culture, or of mental health or illness, must be studied by a combination of such behavioral science methods as are illustrated in this volume. These include the cultural anthropologist's view of strikingly different societies as well as our own contemporary cultures. The clinical psychologist's investigation of individual personality balances can be helpful. The sociological and quantitative data are needed but require additional knowledge of social psychiatry and medical history concerning the changing styles of behavioral disorders. In its broadest scope, this is a broadly oriented scientific exploration of varying human needs and values in changing social and cultural settings. Recently, some persons involved in social psychiatry have become greatly concerned with the definition of "a case," often seeking to force such descriptions into the prevailing nomenclature developed within one cultural tradition. The necessity is to look behind such labels as are used in diagnoses. Others have merely "rated cases" to discover gross quantitative measures of the extent of disorder. Here again social psychiatry requires more convincing demonstrations of empirical rating as a method of classifying psychiatric data. Too often the framework for rating, as for diagnostic labels, is determined by the background and outlook of given practitioners. The only framework that locates new and realistic categories for diagnostic and therapeutic purposes is the naturalistic one that includes the factors operating in human existence, namely, the cultural, social, and experiential factors which make an individual what he is.

It is obvious that the individual is not a product of historically derived diagnostic terms or individually biased ratings and outlooks. Processes or events, along with qualities or relations, are more basic categories for understanding the world. There was a time when matter and motion, or substance and attribute, were used as descriptive categories for early scientific naturalism. Although these are far from dead and buried, just as diagnostic categories are still partly revealing in psychiatry, they have been supplanted in a more analytic spirit of inquiry which is far more interested in the structure of evolving processes. Descriptive labels like schizophrenic are still congenial concepts like matter and substance, but it cannot be assumed that essential qualities and relationships in the human world are really explored by such terms. Description requires further analysis, just as the case described or provisionally rated cannot be understood until it is seen in its meaningful setting and relationships. Simplifications of Freudian theory down to biological need cannot be used to bridge the gap between living organisms and cultures. One cannot use a system of analysis which is nine-tenths biological and one-tenth psychological and intend to encompass cultural anthropology with its wide reference to diverse forms of human living. In the second half of this century, when we are far down the path of seeking environmental as well as biological factors in mental illness, social and cultural factors cannot be called the epiphenomena of biological "givens." The social and cultural are given too, and must be analyzed in their distinct effects on human biology.

In social psychiatry it cannot be presumed that a Freudian energy-distribution theory, or any other system exclusively based on organic premises, is enough to understand and interpret the various social and cultural processes or relationships that influence behavior. What our studies show in various ways is that mental processes and disorders have a cultural and social setting always implicitly and essentially related to these resulting forms of behavior. In this way we move beyond an exclusively organicist theory, or indeed beyond a subjectively rigid psychological one.

Psychologists like E. Hilgard have already defined social character as having the function of organizing human energies in the operation of given social systems. Linton's familiar term of "status personality" likewise classifies specific influences which derive from a group's more or less conscious attempt to train individuals for particular social roles in such systems (4). Freud, much earlier, in The Ego and the Id, defined his notion of a superego as the heir of the Oedipus complex and stated it embodied ethical standards of mankind. Such concepts illustrate movements in psychology, anthropology, and psychiatry which can accommodate an interest in process and relations and in which cultural settings and relationships are seen as profoundly influencing the development of mental disorder. While each concept may be incomplete in itself, it illustrates an interest in such settings and relationships, together with the resulting mental developments as constituting the real process in the individual with which social psychiatry must deal.

In approaching the widespread problems represented in this volume, it is obvious that there are not enough psychiatrists nor psychoanalytic hours to accommodate this mass of seriously disturbed people. In the recent studies in the midtown section of New York City, our group working with T. A. C. Rennie found that both the ethnic groups and the lower classes who received the least treatment had the most serious disorders both in quantity and quality (7). The study by Hollingshead and Redlich, to which we have referred above, is strictly limited to the prevalence and distribution of mental disorders already receiving treatment (3). Our study goes a step further in that it includes people from the midtown communities who either were in treatment or who required psychiatric help without having received it. When we expand this view of a serious and largely neglected psychiatric problem in the biggest city in the United States, with better-than-average facilities and many psychiatrists, to the larger view we have presented in this volume, then the vastness of the world problem in mental health becomes apparent.

Social psychiatry is interested in these variations among ethnic groups and classes in our own society as well as throughout the world because differences in incidence, prevalence, and type of disorder provide a practical basis in planning for mental health problems and give insight into the necessary ingredients of preventive techniques. While not enough is known today about all of these variations and their origins in cultural circumstances, the studies in this volume point out what methods may be used in such research and the kinds of differences which may be expected. At this point, social and preventive psychiatry become aspects of public health and intercultural education. While mental disorders often take a toll through psychosomatic and organic channels, the opportunity of correcting the often irreversible organic changes by preventing them has not been applied in communities. Thus, social psychiatry has an indirect organic emphasis. In addition to its organic and psychological scope, social psychiatry also has a role to play with reference to appropriate action programs in community organization. Here, however, as every anthropologist knows, the methods most suited to one's society may run counter to the attitudes and values of another. For example, in Carstairs' essay on rehabilitation of English patients, there is considerable emphasis upon the modifications or use of specific institutions following the patient's discharge. English social psychiatry has also had a practical emphasis on other institutional modifications, such as the open hospital and experiments with "day" or "night" hospitals. This emphasizes the use of experimentation with therapeutic milieus. In other societies, for example, in the Peruvian case, the need for pre-existing family and community relationships is more noticeable. Or the society may itself, as in the case of the Zar cult reported by Messing, establish appropriate therapeutic milieus within its own institutional frameworks. In Ute Indian dream analysis, the shaman accomplishes this in subsequent ceremonies where he invokes the support of kin groups in his conduct of therapy. Psychiatry has hardly begun to investigate these modes of organization for their therapeutic and supportive content, and it is clear that no one institutional model meets the needs within all societies, with their different systems of stress, types of breakdown, and varying therapeutic requirements.

There are, of course, transcultural values, universal needs of mankind, and generic similarities in disorders around the world. If one speaks of human adaptation or adjustment to environment, one is discussing a continuum or range of adaptation within this context. However, it would be erroneous to regard the notion of such a continuum as having exactly the same characteristics in all societies. Further, so little is known of actual human potentialities that any such continuum should be open-ended on the side of positive adjustment. Such a newer classification, which includes human potentialities for improvement and which points to the possibilities of a different range of problems in various social environments, is an altogether different conception from the usual diagnostic systems in effect in psychiatry. The rigidities of the usual diagnostic system developed within Western European society do not allow for an emphasis on the varying degrees of different psychiatric problems in communities.

Most psychiatric illnesses are usually admixtures from the point of view of a strict Kraepelinian type of differential diagnostic system. The usual illness nomenclature and concern with labels, rather than with the epidemiological extent of problems and their specific types, can promote not only therapeutic nihilism, but increase the distance between psychiatric training and the variations in illness found in different cultural and class groupings. Further, a more positive emphasis on human potentialities raises questions about our vague notions of normality. In our Midtown Study in New York City, for example, a discussion of "averages," "norms," and even "medians" would have portrayed the typical individual of midtown, not as healthy and positively adjusted or adapted, but as a somewhat sick individual more characteristic of the problems of our times. Since evaluations or ratings of such adjustment or adaptation for epidemiological purposes rarely consider people's assets along with their liabilities, much is lost in many studies concerning human potentialities or even human resistances to illness.

We know that needs exist not only within individuals but in families, communities, and even whole societies. Besides the assessment of the extent of these needs, we must understand how they arise since their etiology and dynamics are the central concern of a behavioral science. Social psychiatry typically locates the disorder, consequently, not merely in the individual, but in the context of family and culture. Mental health or psychiatric disorder therefore becomes a special part or aspect of a sociocultural system. Just as we are interested in the possibilities of more optimum mental health in a community, so an interest in the development of disorders goes beyond the mere detection and tabulation of the numbers of cases to a consideration of the probable development of a widespread form of disorder. Theories and conceptual models which claim a simple homeostatic relationship between the individual and his environment lose sight of the related processes occurring both on the social and the individual levels. It is more useful to speak of "balances and imbalances" coexisting in various degrees in all persons, and affected, at the same time, by stress-producing factors in the social and cultural environment.

These balances in individuals, connected with environmental factors, must not be subordinated to diagnostic labels, on the one hand, or to oversimplified theories of homeostasis, on the other. Earlier writers, like L. K. Frank, have suggested that society is "the real patient" rather than the individual. E. Fromm has suggested that "socially patterned defects" can be found as much in society and culture as in the individual (2). While the Freudian system has, at times, approached such a model, it has focused on the individual and consequently tended to ignore the varying cultural effects of different types of stress. To bring these various positions together in a larger synthesis, it can be proposed that a feedback mechanism, involving continued relationships between the individual and his culture, is constantly in operation so that inordinate stress, excessive in time, in amount, or in impact upon the person, produces disorder. C. Bernard's "internal environment" connected with an external environment, or W. B. Cannon's homeostasis, are similar concepts although they have less reference to the importance of the symbolism, the values, and the family systems that underpin and form a basis for a particular culture and background.

The task of such a relational science of personality is to account for the cross-cultural variations in mental health with as few general constructs and laws as possible, but without destroying the conception of these essential relationships. Purely individualistic theories or essentially psychogenetic ones ignore the areas of meanings and values useful to the anthropologist in discussing an environment, and they tend to substitute theories of individual motivation. But motivation cannot substitute totally for the content of mental functioning or for particular knowledge of how people adapt in socially and culturally different situations. As phenomenology has shown, the variations in human symbolic processes, or in meanings from one group to another, suggest that the line between personality and environment is an abstraction. Whether we are speaking of protective habits, defenses, symptoms, or even diagnoses, we require a further knowledge of the total settings of personality. Rather than an "interior environment" in any sense separable from outside influences, or the idea of a "balanced system" within the individual, we would prefer to call these open systems involving physiology, personality, and the wider systems of meaning derived from subcultures and classes. In modern societies, we must also realize that such groups as families, peer groups, and neighborhoods are sometimes the very units in a culture least able to function effectively in promoting useful balances, growth, and maturation. A society in which such groups show pathology is one that requires a specific localized analysis and the mobilization of scientific information to prevent further decay.

We have also stated above, in our discussion of rigid and "catch-all" scientific nomenclature, that existing terms for illness derived from the nineteenth and early twentieth centuries do not encompass these cultural and class variations. Perhaps it is more crucial that they fail in pointing adequately to the social and cultural roots of individual problems. Today we require the addition of persons trained to understand the patient or troubled member of the community in his social and cultural milieu.

In the perspective of world mental health, it is obvious that such personnel are still rare, and research of this type has only just begun. It is hoped that this volume will suggest many of the techniques and conceptions useful in such an undertaking. In this sense, these pioneering studies from around the world are dedicated to the deepest hopes and aspirations of an International Mental Health Year. But they point far beyond 1960 to the paths social psychiatry will follow in the next decades.

BIBLIOGRAPHY

1. Allport, G.: *Becoming*. New Haven: Yale University Press, 1955.
2. Fromm, Erich: *Escape from Freedom*. New York: Rinehart and Company, 1941.
3. Hollingshead, A. B., and Redlich, Fredrick C.: *Social Class and Mental Illness*. New York: John Wiley and Sons, 1958.
4. Linton, Ralph: *The Study of Man*. New York: Appleton–Century Co., 1936.
5. May, R.; Angel, E.; and Ellenberger, H. F., eds.: *Existence: A New Dimension in Psychiatry and Psychology*. New York: Basic Books, 1958.
6. Opler, Marvin K.: *Culture, Psychiatry and Human Values*. Springfield, Ill.: Charles C Thomas, Publisher, 1956.
7. Rennie, T. A. C.; Srole, L.; Opler, M. K.; and Langner, T.: "Urban life and mental health." *American Journal of Psychiatry*, 1957, vol. 113, pp. 831–836.

THE AMERICAN INDIAN —NORTH AND SOUTH AMERICA

A. Irving Hallowell

Department of Anthropology
University of Pennsylvania

1

PSYCHIC STRESSES AND CULTURE PATTERNS *

A thorough understanding of the incidence, etiology, symptomatology and forms of certain classes of mental disorder requires a serious attempt to evaluate the influence of nonorganic factors, the relevance of which is thrown into sharp relief once the data of history and ethnology are taken into account, in addition to clinical observations. When a human perspective is substituted for the more narrowly circumscribed outlook that implicitly identifies human behavior with the characteristic behavior of man in contemporary western civilization, it becomes evident that mental disorders exhibit variations which cannot altogether be attributed to organic factors alone. Fenichel, for instance, refers to "the demands of present day civilization with its contemporary manifestations which we find in the neurotic patients of today who come to seek treatment. So far as we know, other civilizations had produced neuroses, but these differed from the neuroses of today, because these civilizations demanded different instinctual privations. The taboo which we now designate 'compulsion neurosis' is normal in civilizations other than ours; a 'devil neurosis of the seventeenth century,' once studied by Freud could not be fitted into our present diagnostic scheme. Indeed we are able to observe how the clinical pictures presented by the neuroses of today are changing, obviously parallel with changes in society and morality. It is the morality which prevails at the time which is directed against instinct in individuals, and morality is a relative power the nature of which depends on the structure of society. It is at this point that the psychologist must admit his inadequacy and agree that the prob-

* This paper was originally published in the *American Journal of Psychiatry*, 1936, vol. 92, pp. 1291–1310, and was later included in *Culture and Experience*. Philadelphia: University of Pennsylvania Press, 1955. Reprinted by permission.

lem of the etiology of neuroses is not a purely individual medical problem and that it needs supplementary sociological considerations." *

To the anthropologist, at least, it is a commonplace that, despite the phylogenetic unity of man and the specific identity of contemporary races of our kind, the acquired behavior patterns that characterize the human species show an amazing diversity of forms. Transmitted from generation to generation in the form of the folkways, mores, customs, beliefs, and techniques of particular groups of mankind, they comprise the cultural, as opposed to the organic, heritage of Man. Broadly viewed, the extremely varied character of human culture patterns, when considered in connection with the fundamental organic unity of mankind, presents a phenomenon unique among living things. Man's behavior is everywhere canalized, restricted, and defined by customary procedures that are imposed upon each new generation of human individuals in accordance with the demands of different culture patterns. Verbal communication is patterned by conventional linguistic forms. Beliefs, among other things, offer a standardized interpretation of the meaning of physical phenomena of the outer world, often a reification of mythological beings. Interpersonal relations are guided by the traditional forms of the social and economic order. Even perception itself and mental imagery are not free from the influence of culture patterns, nor are motor habits, gestures, the expression of the emotions, and the motivations of the individual.

It seems likely then, that as a result of differences in the social pressures imposed by varying cultural configurations, qualitative differences in cultural values bear some relation to the incidence and character of psychic stresses in different human societies, quite additional to situational and organic factors. We are not yet in a position to elucidate these relations in any precise detail, but the hypothesis is one that poses an important problem for investigation.

So far as the gross incidence of clinically recognized mental disorders is concerned, it has been casually asserted from time to time that there is an increase in mental disease as a marked symptom of the stress and strain of modern life in western civilization in contrast to a relatively low incidence of such disorders among so-called primitive peoples. In view of the fact, however, that reliable information is not available on the incidence of mental diseases in primitive societies, such a sweeping

* Fenichel, O: *Outline of Clinical Psychoanalysis.* New York: W. W. Norton & Co., 1934, pp. 3–4.

statement is unwarranted. White (6) queried it a number of years ago, and on the basis of Mead's observations on functional disorders in Samoa, it has more recently been challenged by Winston (7). Nevertheless, it may very well be that the gross incidence of mental disorders will be found to vary in different culture provinces, if sufficiently reliable information is ever obtained upon which to base comparisons.

The consideration of differences in the forms and symptoms of mental disorders in various societies, in the same society at different periods, and in different contemporary classes of the population of a given society, would seem to offer a more tangible approach to possible relations between these disorders and prevalent culture patterns.

There is one intrinsic difficulty, however, which makes the diagnosis of mental disorder in societies other than our own anything but a simple matter. If "normal" behavior, as defined in our culture, is taken as an absolute standard of reference and the behavior of individuals conditioned to the values of another culture are compared with it, then of course it is even possible to speak of "group psychoses and neuroses" as manifested by the individuals of the exotic society. If, however, we acquaint ourselves with the modal behavior of individuals in a series of totally different cultures and develop norms based on such a standard of reference, we discover that there always are individuals deviant from the norm in every society, and some of these exhibit definite pathological symptoms. This procedure offers a genuine parallel to the study of personality deviation in our own society because it takes account of the cultural forces which mold the normal individual in the society. "Cultural anthropology," as Sapir has said, "has the healthiest of all scepticisms about the validity of the concept 'normal behavior.' It cannot deny the useful tyranny of the normal in a given society but it believes the external form of normal adjustment to be an exceedingly elastic thing. . . .

"It is valuable because it is constantly rediscovering the normal. For the psychiatrist and for the student of personality in general, this is of the greatest importance, for personalities are not conditioned by a generalized process of adjustment to the 'normal' but by the necessity of adjusting to the greatest possible variety of idea and action patterns according to the accidents of birth and biography." *

---

* Sapir, Edward: "Cultural anthropology and psychiatry." *Journal of Abnormal and Social Psychology*, 1932, vol. XXVII, no. 3, p. 235. Cf. Benedict, Ruth: "Anthropology and the abnormal." *Journal of General Psychology*, 1934, vol. X.

The reification of dream or vision experiences, for example, is not in accord with the culture patterns of contemporary western civilization. Individuals who interpret dreams in this manner may therefore be characterized as aberrant. But among the Saulteaux Indians with whom I have been in personal contact, as well as among many other native Americans, the deviant individual would be one to whom certain dream experiences were not believed to bring one into direct contact with spiritual entities of the cosmos. Without a knowledge of the cultural background of an individual the psychological significance of dream reification in terms of "normality" or "abnormality" has little or no meaning.

Thus, while the beliefs of an individual are always relevant to an understanding of his behavior, the source of these beliefs is of great importance. It is chiefly in reference to the beliefs regarding the nature of the external world and the normality of interpersonal relationships that are engendered by certain traditions in our culture that the belief systems of primitive peoples appear to be "flights from reality," comparable with the delusional systems of psychotic individuals in our society. But can the concept of "reality" itself be regarded as having any absolute content? Just as the psychotic person acts as if his delusional system constituted reality (as it truly does for him), so the individuals inculcated with the belief systems of primitive societies act as if such beliefs were true. But whereas the psychotic reifies a specific personal version of reality, the normal individual of a primitive society reifies the generic beliefs typical of the cultural heritage to which he has been subjected. Thus, while there are many analogies between the delusional systems of psychotics and the beliefs of some of the so-called primitive peoples, the sources of these beliefs are very decidedly to be distinguished. The reality of the psychotic is a unique, subjective, and highly personal configuration, the meaning and psychological significance of which is often unintelligible or even incommunicable to his fellows. The reality, on the other hand, that is culturally defined, embodying meanings and values which are shared in common by whole series of individuals, has been communicated to the person along with many other ideas and behavior patterns as part of a unified cultural heritage. The delusional system of an individual of a primitive society must be evaluated with reference to the definition of "reality" characteristic of his culture and not that of some other.

Once reality is intellectually accepted as a relative term the meaning and content of which is to be sought in culturally defined terms, considerable insight is obtained into the behavior of individuals acculturated to different reality patterns. The paradox seems to be that the deflation of reality in an absolute sense of the term offers a genuine realistic approach to problems of both normal and abnormal behavior. Reality for the Bushmen of South Africa is not the equivalent of reality for the Navajo any more than medieval cosmology and demonology are accredited realities in western civilization today. And the reality of the psychotic of our culture is not the equivalent of any of these.

Science in our culture aims at an interpretation of celestial, meteorological, terrestrial, biotic, and psychological phenomena which is more definitive in an absolute sense than anything ever known before in human history. At the same time, the scientific point of view looks with equanimity upon a changing interpretation of phenomena. It is authoritative without being finalistic. Hypotheses are tested and retested and new interpretations emerge. Yet even in western culture, scientifically defined reality has not completely displaced some aspects, at least, of the older and more tenacious traditional versions of reality deeply rooted in the ideology and mores of our society. The recurrent "conflict between religion and science" is symptomatic of this lag. Among individuals of the educated classes, the mental habit of viewing the external objects of what we call the natural world in terms of established scientific knowledge about them has so completely divorced our minds from other possible attitudes that we are even apt to attribute our point of view to innate intelligence or common sense, instead of to a traditionally acquired mode of thought. Hence the charge of stupidity, childishness, or naïveté, sometimes flung at primitive man, is a boomerang that may some day be found at our own feet. Whatever the ultimate status of scientifically defined reality may prove to be, the psychological fact remains that just as we act in accordance with this pattern of reality, or its derivatives, so primitive man acts with respect to his concepts of reality.* If we seek to understand the determinants of human behavior, this must be recognized as one of the psychological imponderables, the specific weight of which can hardly be challenged. Moreover, its specific influence in concrete forms of individual behavior can readily be observed, once we establish the proper frame of reference.

* For which the individuals who entertain these concepts find plentiful support in their actual experience. See Hallowell, A. Irving: "Some empirical aspects of Northern Saulteaux religion." *American Anthropologist*, 1934, vol. 36.

When we recognize that the traditional culture patterns of any specific group of human beings provide a frame of reference that not only defines the phenomenal universe but delimits the ambit of interpersonal relations, we see that some psychic stresses which result in "abnormal" behavior of the individual are to be viewed as resultants of inner psychic forces and social pressures productive of aberrant, instead of modal, behavior. The differential factors involved in such cases are, of course, the crux of the matter. Before these factors are to be envisaged, however, one must consider the correlative, if not primary, question as to the relation between specific culture patterns and the modal forms of personality structure and character traits which these seem to favor. Certainly, quite aside from mental disorder, character traits inculcated by one culture may seem deviant or abnormal to persons of another culture, a fact usually thrown into relief when even individuals of different cultures are brought into more or less intimate contact.

Ever since the westward movement of Ojibwa-speaking peoples into Manitoba in the eighteenth century, one of the names by which they have been known is Bungi. Etymologically, this name seems to have been derived from a native term meaning *a little of something*. The Indians were always asking the whites for a little of this and a little of that; pangi tobacco, pangi tea, pangi flour, etc. In short, from the point of view of the white man, they were persistent and annoying beggars. If we were to render the name by which the Indians became known into an English metaphor, beggar would best convey its meaning. To the whites, the outstanding character trait of the Indian was begging. And I have often heard them reviled for this same characteristic today. In my opinion, the relation of this trait to the cultural background of the Indians is quite clear. It is simply the obverse side of the positive emphasis laid in their native culture upon *giving*. Food, articles of clothing, pipes, and other items circulate freely among those who need them. If children are given food or candy, for instance, they will share it at once with their playmates. Among adults, those who have anything always share what they have with the "have nots." It is not surprising that the Indians should have carried over their culturally determined habits in their social intercourse with traders, missionaries, and settlers. How could they have done otherwise, particularly in view of the fact that they found themselves in the "have-not" class with respect to so many novelties that the white man possessed. So to the white man, with quite different institutional patterns of distributing commodities, and hence a different evaluation of the character trait exhibited by the Saulteaux, they became Bungi—Beggars.

Benedict (1), considering cultures as integrated wholes, has shown how they operate with gross selectivity in respect to the encouragement of certain human temperaments and psychological trends, and the consequent discouragement of others.* All cultures, indeed, because of their very emphasis on characteristic sets of values, must inevitably generate psychic stress in the individuals who from temperament, experience, or by reason of some inner conflict find such values uncongenial. There are societies in which homosexuality has been culturally integrated, others in which it is tolerated, and others in which it is suppressed with vigor. We know cultures in which dissociative psychic states or hysteria have been one qualification for religious leadership † or even sainthood; and with the latter, we might contrast societies where there are no culturally approved channels for the expression of such psychic phenomena outside of a mental hospital.

Knowing so little about the genetic processes of cultural conditioning and personal symbolisms, to say nothing of the conflicting inner forces that the psychoanalysts emphasize, we encounter enormous difficulties in elucidating the relationship of psychic stresses to culture patterns in complex and stratified societies where the relationship of individuals to a variety of cultural patterns is so intricate. I should like to make the point, however, that *pari passu* with the investigation either of generic culture configurations which in one society may permit, or even exploit, what in another may be regarded as pathological manifestations, or of the relation of cultural configurations to the problem of mental disorder in any society, there must also be considered the role which specific culture patterns may play in bringing about psychic stresses of a much less spectacular sort.

It seems to me that the elucidation of these less serious forms of psychic stress, especially in the simpler and culturally homogeneous societies, should be of some value in throwing light on the funda-

* In "The problem of feminine masochism." *Psychoanalytic Review*, 1935, vol. 22, Karen Horney discusses the relative weight of anatomico-physiological components as contrasted with cultural factors and concludes that feminine masochism cannot be related to the former alone "but must be considered as importantly conditioned by the culture-complex or social organization in which the particular masochistic woman has developed."

† Cf. Seligman, Brenda Z.: "The part of the unconscious in social heritage." Essays presented to C. G. Seligman, 1934.

mental mechanisms involved in both the genesis and resolution of such states of mind under varying conditions, as well as offering the possibility of testing some of the psychological concepts and interpretations advanced to explain the behavior of individuals habituated to the culture patterns of western civilization.[*]

I shall attempt to demonstrate this by the analysis of some case material that shows how some characteristic culture patterns of the Berens River Saulteaux [†] seem to have functioned in relation to the psychic stresses of certain individuals. For the most part, only minor tensions are involved, although a few of these cases might possibly be considered to verge on clinically recognizable disorders. It would seem that the creation, as well as the resolution, of the psychic stress in these cases is connected with specific culture patterns. It would certainly be difficult to comprehend them except in terms of the particular values and attitudes characteristic of Saulteaux culture. On the other hand, the psychological interpretation in each case is sheer guesswork on my part, for which I crave as much indulgence as seems permissible. I did not make a detailed study of any of these individuals; in fact for the most part, I have depended on hearsay evidence. One of the individuals is dead; another, I never met. The case material suffers accordingly; it can hardly be considered a contribution towards the solution of the problem I have stated, but it does illustrate one angle of attack which a more systematic, detailed investigation might take. Its value can best be judged if this fact is borne in mind.

INSTITUTIONALIZED CONFESSION AS A MEANS OF RELIEVING PSYCHIC STRESS [††]

Back of confession itself lies one facet of the Saulteaux theory of disease. The relief from psychic tension that the confession affords is actually a by-product of the conscious desire on the part of some in-

---

[*] Cf. Herskovits, M. J.: "Freudian mechanisms in primitive Negro psychology." Essays presented to C. G. Seligman, 1934.

[†] These Indians represent a typical segment of the contemporary native population of the woodland region of the Province of Manitoba, Canada. The river on which they live flows into Lake Winnipeg at approximately 52° N. Lat. They speak an Ojibwa dialect, and a portion of those living up the river are still un-Christianized.

[††] Confession in varying culture contexts is very widespread among the so-called primitive peoples, especially in America and Africa. See the survey by R. Pettazzoni, *La Confession des Péchés*. Paris, 1931.

dividual to cure himself or a member of his family of an illness. This follows from the belief held that disease may be the result of some moral transgression such as murder, incest, or deception.

This last-mentioned transgression specifically means the offering of professional services under false pretenses, that is, without supernatural validation. Specialists in certain methods of curing disease, and in clairvoyance and sorcery, for instance, are only able to pursue these vocations because they have been blessed by certain supernatural entities. Their letters patent were obtained in a dream revelation. To practice any special vocation, such as sucking out disease entities or conjuring without supernatural sanction, mediated through dreams, is a form of criminal deception. Sickness is sure to follow. Apparently nervous diseases, no less recalcitrant to Saulteaux pharmacology than to western medicine, are frequently accounted for in this way. One old man, who had a stroke during the summer of 1934, was no sooner stricken than the river began to buzz with gossip to the effect that his illness was due to deception. But retribution, in the form of sickness, may fall not only on oneself; the sins of the fathers are sometimes visited upon the children —to how many generations, I do not know. There is even a native term for sickness attributable to the wrongdoing of parents. Confession of the crime is the only possible method of cure in such cases.

CASE 1

Confession of Deception in the Case of a Man Who Suffered from a Phobia

This Indian was a conjurer. Power to exercise this particular vocation requires not a single dream revelation but four of them. In this way conjuring is supernaturally inspired. The details of the conjuring lodge itself, such as the particular kind of trees to be used, and other matters, are all conveyed to the human individual in these dreams. When the lodge is entered by the conjurer it begins at once to tremble and later sways from side to side while the voices of the conjurer's guardian spirits issue from it. These spirits do not enter his body and speak through him, but sit on the lodge poles and speak to him.* They give information about lost articles, the welfare of people at a distance, and so on. It is equivalent to a mediumistic performance in our culture. To those of us not spiritualistically inclined by faith, it can be assumed that the voices are not actually those of spiritual beings and that the conjurer himself makes

---

* Possession, i.e., the belief that a spirit (evil or otherwise) may enter the body of a human being and control his behavior, is as foreign to the ideology of most New World cultures as it is conspicuous in those of the Old World. Cf. Boas, Franz: "America and the Old World." Göteborg Proceedings, International Congress of Americanists, 1925, p. 27; Oesterreich, T. K.: *Possession, Demoniacal and Other.* New York: R. R. Smith, 1930, pp. 292–293.

the structure move, but even at this late date, the actual technique of the manipulation of the tent is in doubt. The contemporary Saulteaux, moreover, while maintaining, one and all, a vital belief in the essentially supernatural character of conjuring, admit cases of imposture. It was in this connection that I was told about the case of William Goosehead. A few years ago he could not go into the woods alone, not even for 200 yards. One can readily comprehend how abnormal this is for a man brought up in the Canadian wilderness. Finally, Goosehead confessed that he had been shaking the conjuring tent illegitimately. He had been deceiving his public. A short time after this he is said to have completely recovered from his phobia. I do not know whether there was any real connection between his confession and his recovery, but it is apparent on the face of things, that he must have labored under a considerable sense of guilt, else he would not have confessed. From the native viewpoint, confession was a possible remedy and it appears to have worked.

But if tent-shaking is all hocus pocus, why should this man have felt any sense of guilt about doing what other conjurers did? I was told, for instance, that he admitted shaking the lodge with his own hands. Still, I do not believe that this is the core of the matter. I would assume that, in this culture, dream validation of conjuring is not merely a theory, it actually involves real dream experiences of the required pattern, interpreted as divine revelation. The mechanical means employed to shake the tent may then be looked upon as a sort of necessary materialistic evil. Since everyone accepts the supernatural origin of significant dreams, the sincere conjurer is supported by this common tenet of belief, as well as by his private experience. Within such a cultural context, surely this must be convincing enough to make most individuals feel that their efforts are supernaturally inspired. The native charlatan then is a man who has not experienced the stereotyped dreams demanded by the culture pattern, yet, motivated by a desire for prestige or the material compensation involved, undertakes to conjure. I would guess that W. Goosehead was one such man. It is even conceivable that his specific fears were actually connected with some personal version of supernatural retribution that made him dread going into the woods alone on account of some danger from this particular source.

CASE 2

Confession of Some Secret Sin as a
Means of Helping to Cure One's Offspring from an Illness

Sickness due to this cause, as I have said, is designated by a special term. Although I was not able to secure the details of it, one case of this sort did arise in the summer of 1934. In this instance, as in others of its kind, the diagnosis of the illness as due to some moral transgression on the part of a parent was obtained by conjuring. The father of the youth who was taken ill was supposed to have confessed to the conjurer. What his crime had been, I was unable to find out. His son suffered from spells of unconsciousness and whether the boy finally recovered I do not know. But since every one can find some hidden deed that troubles him, the illness of the child furnishes, in Saulteaux culture, the occasion, and the confession the means, for the release of a psychic tension and for the cure of an illness at the same time. Of course the transgression must be a serious one and likewise conform to the panel of Saulteaux crimes.

AN APPEAL TO LOVE MAGIC TO RELIEVE SHAME, EMBARRASS-MENT, AND PERHAPS UNCONSCIOUS GUILT, AS WELL AS TO COMBAT A SOCIAL ATTITUDE OF RIDICULE

CASE 3

A young man was discovered sleeping with an old woman. Everyone teased him about it and made him very much ashamed. No one in his proper senses, according to my informant, would ever have thought of sleeping with the old woman in question. Besides, the young man was in no way cut off from younger women. Consequently, the fact seems established that the old woman was the young man's choice, or, in psychological terms, a genuine compulsion. This was likewise the level on which the young man explained his conduct. He said that he had once insulted the old woman and that, in revenge, she had lured him to her by love medicine. He remembered nothing from leaving his tent until he found himself at the old woman's side at day-break. My informant was convinced by this explanation and offered the anecdote as convincing proof of the effectiveness of love magic. The other Indians were probably as well satisfied with the boy's personal defense; the terms of rationalization chosen by him were effective. Since the belief in love magic is strongly entrenched, even among the contemporary Saulteaux, his psychic stress could be most satisfactorily resolved by this particular explanation. In terms of native belief he became volitionally absolved in the opinion of others and possibly to himself, because it is quite possible that the old woman was actually a mother surrogate. Assuming this to have been the case, and that he actually had insulted her, the act might have been an overt defense reaction to only partially repressed inclinations towards the intimate relations which finally took place. The sexual act itself would then be a symbol of incest, the compulsion towards which he was no longer able to suppress. In these premises, his claim that the old woman had employed love magic was doubly appropriate; it not only protected him from the ridicule of his fellows, but also protected his own ego from knowledge of his unconscious desires.

THE ROLE OF DREAMS IN THE RESOLUTION OF PSYCHIC STRESS

A. Dreams of having one's soul kidnaped and escaping from a conjuring lodge, as symbols of self-punishment and release from some specific guilt and fear.

According to native theory, a conjurer with malevolent intent may abduct the soul of a sleeping victim. To be able to accomplish this, he must have a conjuring lodge set up somewhere, enter it, and summon his spiritual helpers to his aid. With their assistance, the soul of the sleeping individual is brought into the conjuring lodge. It may be killed there, and if this happens, the person from whom it was abducted will be found dead the next morning. On the other hand, the soul may sometimes find a way to escape from the conjuring lodge and return to the body of the sleeper. In this case the victim may suffer illness, but not death. The conjurer has missed his chance.

The testimony of individuals who have interpreted dreams of soul abduction as real experiences is accepted by the Indians as proof of the powers of the conjurers. In each of the two following cases, I wish to emphasize the connection of the dream with a previous experience of the individual which engendered a feeling of guilt and, in the first case, actual fear that a particular conjurer would take some malevolent action.

CASE 4

"I was just about sixteen years old when someone tried to kill me. This is what happened. We boys were playing ball one day and I got one of them mad. I guess it was my fault. He was a 'humpy' and his father was a conjurer. The 'humpy' looked so funny when he ran that I ran the same way to tease him. All the boys laughed but he got mad and said to me, 'You'll remember this.' This happened in the summer and I soon forgot all about it. I was too young to understand what he meant. The next winter, in March (Eagle Moon), we were camped about four miles up the river and all ready to pull out the next day. Everybody was well. That night after I had gone to sleep I saw someone coming from the north directly towards the camp. It was a young man. He came and stood at my feet as I lay sleeping. He spoke to me: 'You are wanted over there,' motioning with his lips towards the north. I got up and started off with him. I found that we were traveling through the air, not along the ground. I looked up and saw a river ahead of us and just one bark-covered tipi. I could see the kind of trees growing there. There were lots of very straight Jack pine on the north side of the river. Now we came down to the ground near another kind of 'tent.' I walked into it. There was humpy's father in the center. I could see no end to the tent, it stretched out as far as I could see and it was full of all kinds of people. I knew then that I was inside a conjuring lodge. 'I'm going out,' I said. But the old man said, 'No. You can't go.' Then I saw my own head rolling about and the 'people' in the lodge were trying to catch it. I thought to myself that if only I could catch my own head everything would be all right. So I tried to grab it when it rolled near me and finally I caught it. As soon as I got hold of it I could see my way out and I left. Then I woke up and I could not move my legs or my arms. Only my fingers I could move. But finally I managed to speak. I called out to my mother to make a light. I told her I was sick. I could not manage to move my head. When morning came I was still sick. I told my father about what had happened. He knew at once that someone had done something to me and that I had really been in a conjuring lodge. All that day and the next I lay sick. Then I got better. It was my soul that the conjurer had drawn away while I was asleep. If it had not found its way back to my body, I would have been found dead in the morning."

That both guilt and fear were involved in this case, is, I think, plain: guilt, because the boy's deliberate mimicry was evidently in disharmony with the demands of his conscience; and fear, because of the implied threat of subsequent harm, coupled with the fact that the hunchback's father was a conjurer. The induction of fear arose from the native belief in the malevolent powers of conjurers, typical of this culture. A similar interpersonal situation, involving individuals of a different cultural context, would not have caused the same emotional precipitate. The striking fact is that the cultural pattern of the society in which this situation seems to have created inner tensions in an individual also provided a means for their resolution. In gross psychological terms, the manifest content of the dream not only met the cultural requirements in regard to a type of vengeance that the conjurer might be expected to take, but also it functioned unconsciously as a means of self-punishment, in this latter respect doubtless meeting what were inner psychic demands. By so doing, it resolved the psychic tensions which had arisen. It may also be surmised in this case that the physical symptoms were also involved. I do not mean that they necessarily were psychogenic; they may have been seized upon, let us say, by the superego and exploited concomitantly with the dream, as a convenient means at hand for ego punishment. Since in the account as given the individual was quite certain that he had successfully escaped the conjurer's clutches, it would seem that an equilibrium was achieved and that his ego had sloughed off both guilt and fear as a result of the dream experience and subsequent illness.

CASE 5

I was told of another Indian who had a similar dream experience, but I was unable to secure his own account of it. Here again it is significant that several months prior to this particular dream he had committed an act of defilement which, if I understand the attitude of these Indians aright, might well have continued to trouble his conscience.

This youth was out hunting with some other young fellows. They came upon some traps belonging to the Indians of an adjoining band. The youth had to defecate. His companions dared him, as we would say, to defecate on one of the traps. He did so and sprung the trap so that a piece of the excrement was left sticking out. Now this sort of defilement was not only an insult to the owner of the trap, it was also a deterrent to any animal that might prowl that way, and worse still, it was an affront to the "spiritual" owner of any animal species. This latter was the worst offense of all. No wonder then, that this youth needed absolution. There came a dream in which his soul was abducted, but managed to escape from a conjuring lodge. I find one detail in my notes which seems to clinch the connection: The young man dreamed that his soul was taken into the lodge of a conjurer of the same band as that of the man whose trap he had defiled.

B. A dream of self-reassurance that a son would recover from an illness that also was a token of semi-emancipation from pagan beliefs.

CASE 6

W. B., who is the Chief of the Berens River Band today, was about ten years old when the first Christian missionary came to live on the Berens River. His father, chief before him, was the first Christian convert on the river and was married to a white woman. The paternal grandfather of W. B., however, was a thorough-going pagan, who lived to be a very old man and seems to have been greatly admired by his grandson. W. B. spent a good deal of time with him and thus was subjected to typical aboriginal beliefs along with the Christian aspirations of his parents. An old man today, W. B. is consequently the product of mixed Saulteaux and Christian traditions.

In order to understand the possible significance of one of the dreams of W. B., one needs information on the native beliefs in regard to *micipijiu* (the Great Lynx),* a semimythical animal, and on the attitude of the Saulteaux towards dream visitations of this creature. It must be understood, of course, that the Great Lynx is held to have a real existence. But unlike almost all other spiritual entities that appear to man in dreams, this *pawagan* † brings misfortune. The Great Lynx will appear to a boy as an attractive woman inviting seduction, and to a girl in a male guise. To become involved in such a relationship provokes the unremitting jealousy of this being. If the individual who experiences such dreams later marries, his or her spouse will die or the children of the marriage will sicken and die. Consequently, it is the native dogma that individuals who have dreamed of the Great Lynx should avoid marriage. If such a person should want to risk it, their prospective spouse, if an inkling of such a dream leaks out, will not go through with it. How potent the belief has been in actually deterring the marriages of thorough-going pagans, I do not know. But there are extremely few unmarried individuals among the Saulteaux. Nevertheless, it may be assumed that the belief is likely to be a source of latent fear in such individuals as do run the risk of marriage subsequent to dreams of the Great Lynx. That this was actually so in the case of W. B., despite the fact that he was a Christian, is proved by a significant coincidence.

W. B. had several such dreams, but he was not inhibited from marrying. A few years after his marriage, one of his sons became critically ill. While the boy was sick, W. B. again had a dream visitation from the Great Lynx. He was thoroughly alarmed, thought his son was going to die, and consulted a conjurer about the matter. (I failed to ask him whether he prayed about

* Conceptually modeled upon the cougar or mountain lion (*Felis couguar*) which was once found practically all over North America as far north as the Great Lakes.

† I.e., dream visitor.

it, too.) The conjurer promised to help overcome the Great Lynx. The next night W. B. received another visit from this *pawagan*. On this occasion they had a terrific fight. W. B. was completely victorious. He escaped without a scratch. This, he said, was because his own guardian spirits came to his aid as well as those of the conjurer. When the latter learned of the outcome, he assured W. B. that everything would be all right. And the sick boy did recover.

This dream exposes another facet of the linkage of theories of disease and its cure in Saulteaux culture patterns. The dream victory of W. B. over the Great Lynx relieved the immediate stress caused by his concern over the son's illness. But I think that it may also have symbolized the inner conflicts of W. B. with respect to the mixed authority of pagan and Christian beliefs which he held simultaneously. Today at least, while outwardly adhering to the Christian faith, W. B. is profoundly convinced of the truth of many pagan beliefs. Yet, he has had more contact with the whites than any man on the river. His conscious aspirations are focused in many respects toward the culture patterns of the white man, but at the level of belief he is much less emancipated from aboriginal patterns than are his wife and children. While his dream is of a culturally stereotyped pattern relevant to the son's illness, it may likewise have symbolized, in a more personal unconscious sense, the desire of W. B. to be still further freed from the influence of native beliefs. Since he was victorious over the Great Lynx and his son recovered, the dream may have given him unconscious assurance that he had at least freed himself from one native belief with impunity.

C. Supernatural dream revelation as a means of validating the gratification of an incestuous desire, tabooed by custom and under a disease sanction.

CASE 7

All the incest taboos among the Saulteaux are upheld by a disease sanction. Marriages of certain classes of near kin are believed to be followed by the sickness and death of offspring. Specific cases are cited to prove the inevitability of these consequences. The genealogical data show that incest taboos are actually in operation. Sib exogamy is sometimes broken, but usually such sib mates are not blood kin, since distinct family lines may have the same totemic name. Marriage of any close blood relative, on the other hand, except a cross-cousin, is extremely rare, although I have recorded a few cases. No case of father-daughter or mother-son marriage has ever been heard of, and the case of full brother-sister marriage I wish to discuss is unique, an outstanding psychological achievement for the man who undertook it. It involves the overcoming of a severe brother-sister taboo which embraces parallel cousins and other individuals to whom the sibling terms are applied in daily life. The taboos between siblings of opposite sex not only forbid sex relations but also restrict their social intercourse. From a psychological point of view, it might well be expected, in view of these systematic repressions, that deviant individuals might appear from time to time to challenge their authority. At any rate it may safely be assumed that there was considerable psychic stress engendered in this individual who did so. Such a man was Sagaski. It is significant that he was no common mortal but a man reputed to possess unusually strong magical powers, and to have many supernatural helpers at his command. On this account, he was in the best strategic position possible to do as he pleased. This is probably an objective judgment rather than one which assumes the point of view of the Saulteaux themselves. For Sagaski did not do simply as he pleased. He did not live with his sister until he let it be known that one of his guardian spirits—the spiritual "owner" of the beaver—commanded him to take his sister as a wife, in short, to follow the beaver mating pattern instead of the human. Now since dreams are believed to be the medium of communication among the Saulteaux between man and the supernatural world, Sagaski did nothing less than invoke the highest authority possible for his marriage—a supernatural one. Furthermore, it is believed to be a sin not to follow the instruction received in dream revelations. In terms of Saulteaux theory, then, Sagaski had a perfect case. And I have no doubt, moreover, that he actually dreamed the dream he reported. Considering the psychological function of a dream theory such as that to which the Saulteaux adhere, it seems to me that their dreams should serve them in this way. At any rate, it is easy to understand how Sagaski's marriage to his sister was validated in the most effective terms which the culture itself, although tabooing incest, could offer. But there is another chapter to the story.

Evidently the guilt feelings experienced by Sagaski were not quelled even by the supernatural sanction he invoked. Perhaps his culture was too elastic, and perhaps there were deeper psychic involvements which only some means of ego punishment, not supplied by the prevalent culture patterns, could balance. At any rate, many years later, after he had had three children, he tried to induce one of them, a son, to marry his sister. But the boy refused. It would seem that this behavior of Sagaski may have represented the still latent need to justify his own previous conduct. It may even have been in response to a need to circumvent incestuous desires for his own daughter. This latter possibility receives some measure of support from a few details about the family. Sagaski's sister-wife died and only one of the children of this incestuous marriage now survives. This daughter never married and neither did two daughters by a second marriage. This is most unusual among the Saulteaux. Moreover, Sagaski trained his daughters to do many of the tasks men usually perform and guarded them much more closely than Saulteaux fathers ordinarily do. In summer, he used to camp with his family on an island and would never let the young men passing up and down the river put up their tents there even for a single night.

It would also be interesting to know how individuals in other societies, with different culture patterns, have managed to win sufficient social approval to enable them to break such a universal incest prohibition. In a recent article, C. M. Garber (4) refers to genealogical data he had collected on an Eskimo family on the Kuskokwim River. He stresses the inbreeding that he found. This includes cousin marriages and he

adds, "it is not extremely rare that brother married sister." He also recorded four cases in which a father married his daughter. One cannot
but wonder what was the attitude towards these marriages. Were they
casually undertaken and socially accepted like other marriages? Were
the individuals concerned subject to no resulting psychic stress, or were
they, like *Sagaski*, forced to resort to some established cultural means
in order to justify and support their conduct?

In human history, supernatural sanctions of various kinds seem to
have been an almost constant factor in the support of established cultural institutions. It is less frequently emphasized that they have been
likewise the court of appeal for the deviant behavior of the individual.
The double role which this sort of authority has played is of very considerable psychological importance. Hallucinations, delusions, visions,
and dreams, as culturally interpreted, have provided the individual with
possible ways of adjustment to psychic stresses and to accepted social
values. These individual adjustments must of necessity depend upon
specific culture patterns. Without the values and the attitudes integrated
with them and shared by one's fellows, one becomes isolated in a subjective world. If one cannot communicate with others through the
medium of common cultural values, it is not possible to make one's deviant behavior plausible to one's fellows. It is quite possible that the
decline of supernaturalism in western civilization has forever under-
mined the status of a generic culture pattern which, in a multitude of
forms, has been an effective, although to us naïve authority, previously
available to the individual as a means of resolving various forms of
psychic stress. At the same time, certainly, one must not forget the
potent role that supernaturalism has played in causing psychic stress.

INTRAPSYCHIC CONFLICT IN THE GUISE OF TRANSFORMA-
TION INTO A WINDIGO (CANNIBAL)

Finally, I should like to draw attention to a brief account by David
Thompson of one of those numerous cases of cannibalistic desires (the
so-called "windigo psychoses"), which occur so typically among Cree
and Ojibwa Indians. Whether all such cases can be regarded as some
form of mental disorder with a culturally patterned symptomatology,
is a question which Cooper and I have discussed elsewhere (2, 3, 5).
Let me quote the case reported by Thompson as an instance in which
cannibalistic desires on the part of a young man may possibly have been

the culturally determined disguise of unconsciously activated incestuous desires. The youth concerned expressed a desire to eat his sister.

The episode took place in an Ojibwa summer encampment on the Lake of the Woods in 1798. Thompson says:

One morning a young man of about 20 years of age on getting up, said he felt a strong inclination to eat his sister; as he was a steady young man, and a promising hunter, no notice was taken of this expression; the next morning he said the same and repeated the same several times in the day for a few days. His parents attempted to reason him out of this horrid inclination; he was silent and gave them no answer; his sister and her husband became alarmed, left the place and went to another camp. He became aware of it, and then said he must have human flesh to eat, and would have it; in other respects, his behavior was cool, calm and quiet. His father and relations were much grieved; argument had no effect on him, and he made them no answer to their questions. The camp became alarmed, for it was doubtful who would be his victim. His father called the men to a council, where the state of the young man was discussed, and their decision was, that an evil spirit had entered into him, and was in full possession of him to make him become a Man Eater (a Weetego). The father was found fault with for not having called to his assistance a Medicine Man, who by sweating and his songs to the tambour and rattle might have driven away the evil spirit, before it was too late. Sentence of death was passed on him, which was to be done by his father. The young man was called . . . [and] . . . informed of the resolution taken, to which he said, "I am willing to die"; the unhappy father arose, and placing a cord about his neck strangled him, to which he was quite passive; after about two hours, the body was carried to a large fire, and burned to ashes, not the least bit of bone remaining. This was carefully done to prevent his soul and evil spirit which possessed him from returning to this world and appearing at his grave; as they believe the souls of those who are buried can, and may do, as having a claim to the bones of their bodies. It may be thought that the council acted a cruel part in ordering the father to put his son to death, when they could have ordered it by the hands of another person. This was done, to prevent the law of retaliation; which had it been done by the hands of another person, might have been made a pretext of revenge by those who were not the friends of the person who put him to death. Such is the state of society where there are no positive laws to direct mankind.*

The other reported cases of the windigo psychoses that have come to my attention are not detailed as to the person or persons towards whom the cannibalistic desires were directed. In those of which I had an opportunity to inquire, I have not succeeded in securing this particular information. The conviction has grown in me, however, that we have a particularly significant field for exploration here. Psychiatrists have

---

* Tyrrell, J. B., ed.: *David Thompson's Narrative of His Explorations in Western America* (*1784–1812*). Champlain Society, 1916, p. 259 *seq.*

reported data suggestive of a relation of the act of eating and the sex act, and have inferred a generalized symbolic relationship. Be this inference warranted or otherwise, it certainly offers an intelligible hypothesis in the case reported by Thompson, which in turn is an illustration how an unconscious symbol may become reified in the terms of a specific culture pattern. I have elsewhere (5) questioned whether the "windigo psychosis" is to be regarded as a unitary type of mental disorder, and have suggested that further investigation will probably reveal that the cannibalistic pattern functions as a cloak for a variety of mental processes. They would seem, however, in every case to be particularly well worth detailed study to elucidate the relation between psychic stresses and culture patterns in the individual.

In conclusion, let me make due apology for the fragmentary nature of my facts, and the extended inferences that I have drawn from them. The purpose of this paper is not the solving of problems, but the pointing out of the relevance of anthropological field data to investigations in the relations of culture and personality. It seems that the anthropologist, if he were aided in formulating his problems by the psychiatrist sensitive to the implications of culture, might well collect data on the behavior of individuals in societies with culture patterns different from our own that would be of real significance to psychiatry. The relation of psychic stresses to the patterns of our own culture may perhaps best be attacked by way of the pseudoexperimental setups that are available for study elsewhere in the world.

BIBLIOGRAPHY

1. Benedict, Ruth: *Patterns of Culture*. New York: Houghton Mifflin Co., 1934.
2. Cooper, J. M.: "Mental disease situations in certain cultures." *Journal of Abnormal and Social Psychology*, 1934, vol. 29, pp. 10–17.
3. Cooper, J. M.: "The Cree witiko psychosis." *Primitive Man*, 1933, vol. VI.
4. Garber, C. M.: "Marriage and sex customs of the Western Eskimo." *Scientific Monthly*, 1935, vol. 41.
5. Hallowell, A. Irving: "Culture and mental disorder." *Journal of Abnormal and Social Psychology*, 1934, vol. XXIX, no. 1, pp. 1–9.
6. White, William A.: *Outlines of Psychiatry*, 10th ed. Washington, D.C.: Nervous and Mental Disease Publishing Co., 1924, pp. 45–46.
7. Winston, Ella: "The alleged lack of mental disease among primitive groups." *American Anthropologist*, 1934, vol. 36.

A. Irving Hallowell
Department of Anthropology
University of Pennsylvania

2

FEAR AND ANXIETY AS CULTURAL AND INDIVIDUAL VARIABLES IN A PRIMITIVE SOCIETY *

A few years ago Dewey pointed out some of the inadequacies of a simple stimulus-response concept in psychology.

That which is, or operates as, a stimulus, turns out to be a function, in a mathematical sense, of behavior in its serial character. Something, not yet a stimulus, breaks in upon an activity already going on and becomes a stimulus in virtue of the relations it sustains to what is going on in this continuing activity. . . . It becomes the stimulus in virtue of what the organism is already preoccupied with. To call it, to think of it, as a stimulus without taking into account the behavior that is already going on is so arbitrary as to be nonsensical. Even in the case of abrupt changes, such as a clap of thunder when one is engrossed in reading, the particular force of that noise, its property as stimulus, is determined by what the organism is already doing in interaction with a particular environment.†

The general principle implied in these remarks suggests a further inference. The effects of stimuli cannot be predicted solely from their intrinsic properties. This conclusion is borne out by some recent experiments (1, 7). These indicate that inferences in regard to the emotional experience of individuals cannot wholly be based upon an account of immediate stimuli and bodily responses. In addition, knowledge is required of what the individual actually experiences. In the experiments referred to,

the stimulus-situation was identical: adrenalin chloride was intra-muscularly injected. The physiological or bodily response was identical: certain phenomena

* This paper was originally published in *The Journal of Social Psychology*, 1938, vol. 9, pp. 25–47. Reprinted by permission.

† Dewey, J.: "Conduct and experience." In *Psychologies of 1930* (C. Murchison, ed.). Worcester: Clark University Press, 1930.

of sweating, shivering, etc., were produced. But the individual mental processes were remarkably different. One person had no emotion—the emotion was "cold" and impersonal; another had a pseudo or quasi emotion, reminiscent of another occasion when he had experienced a similar set of symptoms, but not an emotion in the present; and a third individual really felt the complete emotion of fear.*

The differential factors in these cases must lie, of course, in the constitution or personal history of the individuals concerned. If we seek them in the latter sphere the problem is further complicated by the universal and primary importances of learned or acquired experience in the broadest sense of the term. In life situations in particular, as contrasted with the more highly controlled experimental setup of the laboratory, the relevance of factors of this order, while extremely complex and difficult to evaluate with precision, cannot be ignored. It is hardly surprising then, to find that C. Landis, at the close of a recent survey of experimental data stresses the need for further investigation of the relation between learning processes and affective experience. He writes:

The question of nature *versus* nurture is as marked in emotions as in any other type of human behavior. It is customary to speak of emotion as a natural reaction; one which is little varied by experience. Certainly this is a very inexact concept. What the natural emotional life of an individual might be like is an unknown territory. Emotional life is modified more rigorously in the growth and education of an individual than perhaps any other variety of human experience. The reason for the statement so frequently made that emotion is a natural reaction, unmodified by learning, is that emotional reactions occur in such large units of physiological disturbances that they frequently swamp the mental life of the individual. Consequently, "the most important line of future research is that of the nature of the relation existing between emotion and learning in the broadest sense of each term." †

If we consider this problem not only with respect to the affective experience of individuals in western society, but from the standpoint of humanity as a whole, a fresh angle of attack is indicated. It is possible to investigate, analyze, and compare the factors that influence the typical or commonly experienced affects of individuals in human societies with widely different cultural traditions, as well as the factors that are

* Ruckmick, C. A.: "Psychology tomorrow." *Psychological Review,* 1937, vol. 44, pp. 138–157.

† Landis, C., and Hunt, W. A.: "The expression of the emotions." In *Handbook of General Experimental Psychology* (C. Murchison, ed.). Worcester: Clark University Press, 1934.

involved in the affective experience of individuals who deviate from the collective norms of these societies. Factors of the former order I shall call cultural variables. Their importance as constituents of affective experience emerges from the recognition of the following general considerations:

1. Human behavior, considered as a whole, differs from that of the higher primates and lower mammals in that learned responses, acquired through social interaction with other human beings, predominate over innately determined behavior patterns.

2. These socially transmitted responses are intimately related to a definable body of traditional concepts, beliefs, institutions, etc. that are historic products, transcending the lifetime or experience of the individuals whose lives they mold. A system of religious beliefs and practices, a language, a set of moral standards, are examples of the social heritage we call culture.

3. Since the cultural traditions of mankind are found to vary radically in their pattern as we go from people to people and age to age, it must be recognized that affective experience, in part, is a function of these cultural variables.

Since culture includes the content of socially transmitted experience, to which each new individual born into a society is exposed, it provides the primary frame of reference to which all varieties of learned behavior may be related. With respect to the emotions, culture defines: a) the situations that will arouse certain emotional responses and not others; b) the degree to which the response is supported by custom or inhibitions demanded; c) the particular forms which emotional expression may take (6). It is to these norms that the individual will learn to accommodate his behavior and in terms of which his affective experience will function.

The Indians whom I have been studying and whose fears and anxieties I wish to discuss with reference to their native culture, live on the Berens River in Canada. This river rises in Ontario and flows westward, emptying into eastern Lake Winnipeg at approximately 52° N. Lat. There are nine hundred of these Indians today and they make their living by hunting moose, deer, and caribou, by trapping fur-bearing animals, and by fishing. Except for a few white traders, trappers and missionaries, there are no white people living in the area which they inhabit. It is still undisturbed bush country, of low elevation; a wilderness of rock, muskeg, and labyrinthine streams and lakes. Travel is by canoe in summer, and by dogsled and snowshoes in winter. The Indians living closest to Lake Winnipeg have been Christianized, although they still retain many of their pagan beliefs, while many of those farther inland cling to the old native dogmas with great tenacity. During the course of several summers' field work I have visited all the settlements on the river in order to accumulate as much information as possible on all aspects of their lives.*

I think that the relation between some of the characteristic fears experienced by these people and their traditional system of beliefs will become sufficiently clear if I discuss the former with reference to the situations in which they occur. Some of these situations, such as illness, are common to human life everywhere. Yet they do not give rise to equivalent affects. The psychological differentia, I believe, are to be sought in the content of the beliefs that are part of the cultural heritage of these Indians. These beliefs not only define each situation for the individual in a typical manner, they structuralize it emotionally. But at the same time it is interesting to note that there are usually traditional means available for the alleviation of culturally constituted fears. The individual is not altogether left at loose ends; he may obtain some relief and reassurance through the utilization of institutionalized defenses.

ENCOUNTERS WITH ANIMALS

The traditional attitude of the Berens River Indians toward animal life must be distinguished from our own. Animals, like men, have a body and a soul. Each species is controlled by a spiritual boss or owner that is of the nature of a transcendental being. Guns and traps are of no avail if this spiritual boss of the species is offended and does not wish human beings to obtain his underlings. Consequently, wild animals as a whole must be treated with respect lest their bosses be offended.

While this general attitude is characteristic, the affective responses of the Indians to different animals is not uniform. It would be impossible, however, to make any *a priori* judgment, based upon our attitude toward wild life, as to which animals are feared and which are not. Wolves and bears, for instance, are common in this region, but the Indians are never afraid of them. The creatures they fear most are snakes,

* Investigation of the problem discussed in the present paper was part of a project supported by a grant from the Faculty Research Committee, University of Pennsylvania, May, 1936.

toads, and frogs, animals that are actually among the most harmless in their environment. Indeed, the only species of snake that occurs is a small variety of garter.

The attitude of these Indians toward snakes was brought home to me by a striking occurrence. Once when I was traveling with a small party, one of the Indians sighted a snake, perhaps eight inches long, swimming in the water near the rock where we were eating lunch. This Indian picked up his gun and took a shot at it, missed, and shot again, and missed. The snake started to swim toward the shore, and as it began to wriggle up the rock, another man picked up a paddle and with a few hard strokes managed to kill it. But that was not enough. They built a small fire and burned the harmless creature to a crisp!

While this episode may appear to be a trivial one, it was no trifling matter to the Indians. Even objectively considered it suggests an exaggerated affective response to an animal of this sort. To say the least, there was nothing intrinsic to the situation as such that demanded the immolation of a harmless garter snake on a pyre! It is partially intelligible, however, if reference is made to mythology. Once the earth was inhabited by many monster snakes and some of these persist today. A few individuals claim to have seen them and they are much feared. It is the identification of actual snakes with the mythical variety that accounts in part for the attitude of the Indians toward the former. But on the occasion described there was more involved than this. The snake was burnt because its approach to our camp was interpreted as having a meaning that aroused apprehension and consequently demanded the treatment received.

Wild animals, of course, habitually avoid the dwellings of men so that we might suppose that the Indian would "naturally" be startled to find a bear or snake near his wigwam, or to find a bird or squirrel inside of it. The fear that some people in our society experience when a bat flies in their bedroom at night might be thought to be comparable to the emotions which the Indians experience. But this is not the case. The beliefs of the Indians make the affect a qualitatively different thing. For to them the approach of a wild animal of any sort to their camp or habitation is an ill omen. It is a sign that someone is trying to bewitch them. The animal is thought to be the malevolent agent of the sorcerer.

In one case a man had been ill. He had taken lots of medicine but it seemed to do him no good. Then he noticed that a bear kept coming to his camp almost every night after dark. Once it would have gotten into his wigwam if he had not been warned in a dream. Since an evilly disposed medicine man may sometimes disguise himself as a bear, the sick man's anxiety rapidly increased. He became convinced that a certain man had bewitched him. Finally, when the bear appeared one night he got up, went outdoors and shouted to the animal that he knew what it was trying to do. He also threatened to retaliate, with dire results to the suspected witch, if the bear ever returned. The animal ran off and never came back.

Even if birds alight on a dwelling, it is considered an evil omen. It is still more serious if wild animals actually enter a human habitation. On such occasions, the animal may not only be killed but burnt, as was the snake, since this is the appropriate institutionalized procedure. This act serves to dispel the fear engendered as it is thought to be the safest way of disposing of malevolent agents of this kind.

One night after settling down to sleep in our tent, my traveling companion, an Indian about sixty-five years of age, found a toad hopping toward him. He became so panic-stricken that it was difficult for him to kill it. But he finally managed to do so. Then he went outside the tent with a flashlight in order to discover if there were any more toads about. He killed several with a stone. Then he collected a number of large stones and, after carefully examining all sides of the tent, weighted down the canvas here and there so that there was no possibility of any more of them crawling in. He slept hardly at all the rest of the night. After this experience, W. B. always took special pains to see that the front of the tent was closed at night and weighted snugly to the ground with a line of stones. We jokingly called this our "toad dam." It must be emphasized that this man had spent most of his life in the bush, was an excellent hunter, and accustomed to handling all sorts of animals. What then were the determinants of his phobia? In the first place, toads are not simply "loathsome creatures" to these Indians. They are associated with evil forces, certain parts of the animal being used in malevolent magic. Hence they are to be avoided and even their presence bodes no good for the reason I have stated. But there were more complex determinants in the fear response of W. B. It is said that if the taboo upon narrating myths in summer is broken, toads will come and crawl up one's clothes. Now my friend W. B. had been telling me native stories from time to time so that visits of the toads were good empirical evidence of the truth of the native belief. But since W. B. was a Christian and believed himself to be emancipated from native "superstition," although, of course, this was not actually the case, it may be inferred that the conflict engendered was somewhat disturbing to him. There were then several etiological factors at work: a) the generalized belief in the malevolent attributes of toads; b) the notion that their presence in a dwelling was an ill omen; c) the fact that a taboo had been broken, specifically indicated by the presence of the toads; and d) the conflict engendered by the semiemancipated attitude of W. B. toward these notions.

In addition, however, there was another factor peculiar to the personal history of W. B. When a young boy, a toad had crawled up his pants and he had crushed it against his bare skin. This experience would appear to be an important differential factor which may account to some extent for the exaggerated fear reactions of W. B. to toads as compared with that of the other Indians. This difference was objectively proved on one occasion when I saw another Indian deliberately pick up a toad and put it near W. B. to tease him. Judged by strength of affect, W. B. was abnormal in comparison with the other Indians observed. But etiologically viewed, his phobia cannot be fully explained by reference to his personal history alone. It needs to be related to the native beliefs in regard to toads and the situational factors already mentioned.

The generalized fear of toads and frogs among these Indians is fostered by another fact. Monster species are reputed still to inhabit the country, the tracks of which are sometimes seen.

A few years ago several Indians were traveling across Lake Winnipeg in a sailboat. They pulled in at Birch Island. While a fire was being built and some food cooked, the man who told me this story took his gun and went off to shoot ducks. He came across some fresh tracks near the shore. They were about the size of a man's hand and formed exactly like the tracks of a frog. They indicated a jump of approximately six feet. The Indian who made this discovery hurried back to his companions. They went and examined the tracks, and agreed with him that they were those of the giant frog. The narrator said that he wanted to follow the tracks inland but his companions were so frightened that they insisted upon leaving the island at once.

The psychological significance of this anecdote can best be appreciated by emphasizing two points. First, these Indians are expert hunters and accustomed to recognizing the tracks of all the animals in their environment; second, they were armed. We can only conclude that their misidentification of the tracks was a result of the mental-set which their belief in the reality of monster frogs imposed and that their fears cannot be dissociated from the malevolent attributes reputed to creatures against whom even guns might not be adequate protection. If we take these factors into account, they evidenced a normal response to a danger situation as defined for them in cultural terms.

DISEASE SITUATIONS

Since disease situations occur and recur among all peoples, they provide excellent material for the investigation of the cultural differentia that may influence the individual's attitude toward his own illness and the quality of the anxieties that his relatives and friends may experience. Different human groups have different traditional theories of disease causation and when an individual falls ill, his emotional attitudes and those of his associates are intimately related to the theories held.

Among the Berens River Indians, broken limbs, colds, constipation, toothache, and other minor ailments are considered fortuitous in origin and do not arouse any marked affective states. But a prolonged illness, which has not responded to ordinary methods of treatment, a sudden illness, or one that is characterized by symptoms that are considered in any way peculiar arouses apprehension or even fear. Why? Because of the belief that the person may have been bewitched. The individual believes that some one is trying to kill him. He becomes more and more worried and begins to reflect on his past activities and associations in order to recollect who it is that may wish him out of the way. In such a situation institutionalized means of protection are readily available. A conjurer or seer may be hired to discover the person responsible and measures taken to counteract the evil influence. Jealousy is often the motive attributed to the witch, frequently arising out of rivalry situations.

In 1876 when the Treaty with the Dominion Government was signed and an elective chieftainship first established, J. B. and a powerful medicine man named Sag-*a*-tcïweäs were rivals for the new office; J. B. won. The next day he put on his new uniform and felt fine. But that night he was suddenly taken ill. It was inferred that Sag-*a*-tcïweäs was responsible. Later he developed a recurrent skin disease that did not respond to native drugs. This was likewise attributed to the powerful medicine man he defeated. In this case the usual apprehension typical in such a situation was balanced by the powerful ego of J. B. and the confidence he had in his ability to withstand the malevolent intention of his rival. J. B. asserted more than once that he would outlive Sag-*a*-tcïweäs and he did.

The special form of sorcery that causes the most fear is based on the theory that material objects can be magically projected into the body of the victim. Sebaceous cysts, lumps of any kind, and other symptoms are evidence of the presence of such objects. They are removable by a pseudosurgical technique in which certain medicine men specialize. It involves the withdrawal of the object by sucking. These men, of course, produce actual objects that they claim to have removed from their patients' bodies. This serves to allay the latter's fears and in cases where a recovery is made, empirical support is given to the native theory of disease causation. Examples of such disease-causing objects are magic shells, dogs' teeth, bits of metal, stone, etc. One Indian showed me a series of such projectiles that had been "sent" him. His body was strong enough to resist them and they fell at his side where he found them.

Feelings of guilt for past moral transgressions are also the source of apprehension in a disease situation. This is due to the fact that these Indians believe that sickness may be the result of such transgressions. Again it is the fact that an individual does not respond to the usual drug remedies that precipitates apprehension. The transgressions that fall in the panel of traditional sins are murder, incest, deceit, and sexual practices, such as masturbation, fellatio, the use of parts of animals as artificial phalli, and bestiality. Confession is the necessary preliminary to cure when it is thought that sickness is connected with sin. An interesting aspect of their theory, however, is the belief that such sins on the part of parents may be the source of illness in their children. Consequently the anxieties aroused in disease situations where some transgression is believed to be back of the illness are not confined to the patient. His parents are likewise suspected and they may confess sins committed in childhood or adolescence. In a series of fifteen cases illustrating the transgressions confessed, twelve were those in which sexual sins were involved (3).

ENCOUNTERS WITH CANNIBALS

The most intense fears that Berens River Indians experience are generated in situations that are emotionally structured by their beliefs concerning *windigow-a-k,* cannibals. They believe that human beings may be transformed into cannibals by sorcery, that cannibal monsters can be created "out of a dream" by a sorcerer and sent into the world to perform malevolent acts, and that cannibal giants roam the woods, particularly in the spring. Consequently, when some human individual is reputed to be turning into a cannibal, the Indians become terror-stricken. They are similarly affected when it is reported that a cannibal, created by magic, is approaching their encampment or when some individual traveling in the bush discovers traces of a cannibal or claims that he has seen one.

Gastric symptoms are among those that the Indians interpret as evidence of incipient cannibalism on the part of human beings. When a person refuses to eat ordinary food, or is chronically nauseated, or cannot retain the food he ingests, suspicion is at once aroused. Even the individual so affected will develop anxiety and make the same inference. He may even ask to be killed at once. For this is the inevitable fate of reputed cannibals according to native custom. Usually they are strangled and their bodies burned, not buried.

The last case of this sort to occur on the Berens River was in 1876 when three men killed their mother, built a pyre, and burned her body. Since that time similar cases have occurred farther north. In 1906 two men from Sandy Lake were arrested for murder by the Mounted Police, because they had participated in the disposal of a woman reputed to be a *windigo*. From the standpoint of native customary law, the strangling of a cannibal obviously is not illegal. It is a communally sanctioned defensive act, rationally justified in the premises.

Another type of situation is illustrated by the behavior of the Indians when it is reported that a cannibal monster is headed in their direction. One midwinter night at Poplar River, when a terrific gale was blowing, word got around that a *windigo* would likely pass that way. All the Indians on the north side of the river left their homes at once and congregated in a house across the river. In order to protect themselves they engaged one of the leading shamans to conjure all through the night in order to divert the *windigo* from his reputed path. The Indians firmly believed that the cannibal passed without harming them and part of the evidence they adduced was the fury of the wind, which was interpreted as a sign of his presence. Similar episodes are said to have occurred in the past and mythology recounts terrific fights between strong shamans and cannibal giants in which the former are always successful. To these Indians such monsters are quite as real, quite as much a part of the environment as the giant animals already mentioned, or, in our culture, God, Angels, and the Devil.

It is not surprising then to discover individuals who claim to have seen the kind of cannibal that is reputed to roam the woods, or to have been pursued by one. Such illusions are particularly interesting in view of the fact that these Indians are expert woodsmen, who not only have spent all their lives in the bush, but are familiar with the detailed topography of their country to an amazing degree, as well as with all the various species of fauna and flora. Consequently it might be expected that the whole gamut of possible sights and sounds would be so well known to them that they would be insulated against false perception of any kind. I know from personal experience, at least, that many sounds that have startled me from time to time have always been explained by my Indian companions in the most naturalistic manner. It is all the more significant then to discover cases in which the perceptions of individuals have been so thoroughly molded by traditional dogma that the most intense fears are aroused by objectively innocuous stimuli. It is the culturally derived *Einstellung*, rather than the stimuli themselves, that explains their behavior.

One old man, for instance, narrated the following experience.

Once in the spring of the year I was hunting muskrats. The lake was still frozen, only the river was open, but there was lots of ice along the shore. When it began to get dark I put ashore and made a fire close to the water's edge to cook my supper. While I was sitting there I heard someone passing across the river. I could hear the branches cracking. I went to my canoe and jumped in. I paddled as hard as I could to get away from the noise. Where the river got a little wider I came to a point that has lots of poplars growing on it. I was paddling quite a distance from the shore when I came opposite to this point. Just then I heard a sound as if something were passing through the air. A big stick had been thrown out at me but it did not strike me. I kept on going and paddled toward the opposite side of the river. Before I got to that side he was across the river already and heading me off. I paddled toward the other side again. But he went back and headed me off in that direction. This was in the spring of the year when the nights are not so long. He kept after me all night. I was scared to go ashore. Toward morning I reached a place where there is a high rock. I camped there and when it was light I went to set a bear trap. Later that day I came back to the river again. I started out again in my canoe. Late in the evening, after the sun had set, there was a place where I had to portage my canoe over to a lake. I left my canoe and went to see whether the lake was open. There were some open places so I went back to get my canoe. Then I heard him again. I carried my canoe over to the lake—it was a big one—and paddled off as fast as I could. When I got to the other end of the lake it was almost daylight. I did not hear him while I was traveling. I went ashore and made a fire. After this I heard something again. I was scared. "How am I going to get away from him," I thought. I decided to make for the other side of an island in the lake. I was sitting by my canoe and I heard him coming closer. I was mad now. He had chased me long enough. I said to myself, "the number of my days has been given me already." So I picked up my axe and my gun and went in the direction of the sounds I had heard. As soon as I got closer to him he made a break for it. I could hear him crashing through the trees. Between the shore and the island there was a place where the water was not frozen. He was headed in this direction. I kept after him. I could hear him on the weak ice. Then he fell in and I heard a terrific yell. I turned back then and I can't say whether he managed to get out or not. I killed some ducks and went back to my canoe. I was getting pretty weak by this time so I made for a camp I thought was close by. But the people had left. I found out later that they had heard him and were so scared that they moved away.*

In the situations thus far passed in review I have attempted to indicate the cultural constituents of the fears of individuals and the institutionalized means available for their alleviation. In societies with different culture patterns the same situations would be emotionally structured in a different way, the affects of individuals would be qualitatively, if not quantitatively, different and other traditional defenses would be invoked.

To an outsider the fears of the Berens River Indians, and those of other primitive peoples, appear to be "neurotic," in the sense that they occur in situations where no actual danger threatens and for the reason that the sources of some of these fears are of the nature of fantasies. Can we speak then of "cultural neuroses" that are characteristic of whole populations? I think not. If we do so, as Karen Horney (5) has pointed out, "we should be yielding to an impression based on a lack of understanding" as well as being guilty of a fallacy in reasoning.

---

* So far as tradition is concerned experiences of this sort are not uncommon. But only a relatively few living individuals seem to have undergone them. In the last analysis, of course, selective factors that involve the personal history of such individuals must be taken into account as well as cultural tradition. Personality differences of this order suggest further problems that need detailed investigation. Cf. W. Morgan, *Human-Wolves among the Navaho.* Yale University Publications in Anthropology. No. 11, 1936, p. 3. "But Navaho, even within a family, differ so much as individuals that there is no such thing as a uniform fear of these human-wolves. Many of the stories feature a human-wolf climbing upon the adobe roof of the Navaho hogans and looking down through the smoke hole in order to find his victim. Invariably, he knocks some earth loose and it may be heard by those inside the hogan as it rolls off and drops to the ground. When this occurs, it has twice been my experience that a Navaho who is apprehensive about human-wolves will hurry through the door to look around outside. But the man beside him may show little or no interest. This man may have few fears and few worries; or he may have considerable nervous tension but his anxieties have focussed upon some other cultural pattern such as fears of the spirits of the dead. In either case, he will stay where he is sitting or lying on his sheepskins."

In the first place, the Berens River Indian *is* responding to a *real* danger when he flees from a cannibal monster or murders a human being who is turning into a *windigo*, or when he becomes apprehensive in a certain disease situation. To act or feel otherwise would stamp an individual either as a fool or as a phenomenal example of intellectual emancipation. For, psychologically, the actual order of reality in which human beings live is constituted in a large measure by the traditional concepts and beliefs that are held. Furthermore, the Indians themselves are able to point out plenty of tangible empirical evidence that supports the interpretation of the realities that their culture imposes upon their minds (2). They are naive empiricists but not naively irrational.

Once we relegate commonly motivated fears to their proper frame of reference—cultural tradition—a fundamental etiological distinction can be made between fears of this category and those which arise in individuals from conditions primarily relevant to the circumstances of their own personal history. The genuine neurotic, in addition to sharing the culturally constituted fears of his fellows, "has fears which in quantity or quality deviate from those of the cultural pattern" (5). Any comparison, then, between the fears and defenses of such individuals and the culturally constituted fears and institutionalized defenses of whole human societies is not only superficial, it is actually misleading, since no account is taken of differences in etiological factors. Primitive peoples are sometimes accused of the logical fallacy that results from an inference that two phenomena are identical if one or more elements are shared in common. To maintain seriously that the culturally constituted fears and defenses of primitive peoples are evidence of "cultural neuroses" which are of the same order as the neuroses of individuals in western civilization is just such a fallacy. Manifest surface analogies are compared, whereas the underlying differences in the dynamic factors that produced them are ignored.

A further differentiation between the genuine neurotic and the person experiencing the "normal" fears of his culture is important. The former is inevitably a suffering individual; the latter is not. "Thus the normal person," writes Horney,

though having to undergo the fears and defenses of his culture, will in general be quite capable of living up to his potentialities and of enjoying what life has to offer him. The normal person is capable of making the best of the possibilities given in his culture. Expressing it negatively, he does not suffer more than is unavoidable in his culture. The neurotic person, on the other hand, suffers invariably more than the average person. He invariably has to pay an exorbitant price for his defenses, consisting in an impairment in vitality and expansiveness, or more specifically, in an impairment of his capacities for achievement and enjoyment, resulting in the discrepancy I have mentioned. In fact, the neurotic is invariably a suffering person, . .*

although he may not himself be aware of this fact.

This distinction, so clearly elucidated by Horney, is demonstrable among the Berens River Indians. There are individuals in this society who manifest phobias that are quantitatively or qualitatively deviant from those of the other Indians. These persons are among the genuine neurotics. I have already mentioned W. B., whose toad phobia was quantitatively distinguishable from that of the other natives. Further differential factors in this case, as I have pointed out, have to be sought in his personal history. It is not without interest in the present connection to add that this old man, who is of mixed white and Indian blood and an outstanding leader among his people, also manifests a marked fear of thunder and lightning (which has no cultural sanction), a periodical stutter under emotional stress, a mild echolalia at times, and an identification with his father who was chief before him. He is far less provincial in his general outlook than the other Indians on account of his many intimate contacts with white people over a long period of years and the opportunities he has had to see a little of the "outside" world at firsthand. Besides, he is a man of superior intelligence and mental alertness, with a rich sense of humor and fine physical vitality. Consequently his personality traits, considered as a whole, approach those of the white man more closely than most of the other Indians of the river and to the casual observer present an essentially "normal" picture. Yet were a deeper analysis of his personality possible, I dare say that W. B. would prove to be an example of a neurotic fairly well adapted to the conditions under which his life has been lived. I also suspect, as pointed out above and also in connection with one of his dreams (4), that an etiological factor of importance lies in a deep-seated conflict between W. B.'s ostensible acceptance of Christianity and the very profound importance which many native beliefs have had for him. The cogency of this hypothesis is suggested by the widely different attitudes taken by W. B.'s parents and grandparents toward Christianity during the early

* Horney, K.: *The Neurotic Personality of Our Time.* New York: W. W. Norton & Co., 1937.

decades of missionary effort. For W. B. was only a boy of ten years when the first resident missionary arrived on the Berens River. W. B.'s mother, being white, was a thoroughgoing advocate of Christianity, and his father, with some personal reservations, no doubt, reputedly was instrumental in obtaining a local missionary for his band. On the other hand, W. B.'s paternal grandfather with whom he was very intimately associated in his upbringing immersed him in native beliefs. That W. B. has been exposed to some inner conflict in consequences of these varying attitudes is evidenced by the fact that he has frequently remarked to me that he has grown older, and as a result of the discussion engendered by my ethnologic investigations, during which he has served more as a collaborator than interpreter, the truth of native beliefs has more and more impressed him. He has contrasted this with the more "superior" and critical attitude he assumed when he was a young man. While it is true that all the Indians of his generation were undoubtedly exposed to the same general conflicts in belief, the fact that W. B.'s mother was a white woman presents a unique circumstance which, combined with the extreme pagan views to which W. B. was subjected in the same family circle (household group) may have affected both the quantitative and qualitative aspects of his early identifications.

In contrast with W. B., other Berens River Indians exhibit such marked qualitative deviations from the established culture patterns of their society that there is no obvious connection between certain of their phobias and traditional beliefs. In addition to being afraid of witches, mythical animals, cannibals, etc., these individuals suffer from anxiety as distinguished from fear.* Their phobias are personal and have no culturally phrased causes. Individuals subject to such phobias often rationalize them in terms of whatever beliefs seem appropriate. The most striking fact that characterizes phobias of this category is this: They occur in situations that easily can be distinguished from those that are emotionally structured by common beliefs.

One man, for example, who had hunted and trapped all his life, found himself beset by anxiety whenever he attempted to go any dis-

---

* Cf. Horney, K.: *The Neurotic Personality of Our Time.* New York: W. W. Norton & Co., 1937, pp. 43–44. "Fear and anxiety are both proportionate reactions to danger, but in the case of fear the danger is a transparent, objective one and in the case of anxiety it is a hidden and subjective one. That is, the intensity of the anxiety is proportionate to the meaning of the situation for the person concerned, and the reasons why he is thus anxious are essentially unknown to him."

tance into the woods alone. He happened to be a conjurer and rationalized his anxiety by confessing that he had practiced his profession without the proper supernatural sanction (4).

Another man could go nowhere unaccompanied by one or more companions. When alone he would always keep within sight of human habitations or people. This was the rule even when he had to urinate or defecate. If he had to relieve himself at night his wife would always get up and go with him. Sometimes his companions would tease him by stealing out of sight. As soon as he discovered this he would start to call for them and run frantically in the direction where he thought they were. One winter when he was traveling with a party of men and found himself alone in the woods he threw off his hat and mitts in his frenzy and yelled until his companions came back. Once when he was hired by the Hudson's Bay Company to cut wood he induced some small boys to go along for the ride and walk back with him while he ran ahead of the team of oxen. He rationalized his anxiety by saying that he once dreamed that a jackfish would swallow him, if this creature found him alone.*

A third man, whom I know personally, lives 100 miles up the Berens River at Grand Rapids. The Indians of this band are only superficially Christianized and live much in the purely native fashion. J. D. has spent all his life here. His children are all married and he is now about sixty years of age. He is a tall, sparsely built individual, energetic in speech and movement, and an exceptionally fine singer and drummer. But he has suffered from phobias all his life. Darkness disturbs him profoundly. "Ask J. D. to go and fetch a kettle of water for you some night," one of the Indians said to me, "you'll find that he will refuse, even if you offer to pay him well for it." Once when J. D. was traveling in winter with some other men they were attempting to reach their camp late at night because they had no blankets or bedding with them. Before darkness fell, J. D. insisted that they help him collect birch bark so that they could make torches to carry with them during the rest of their journey. They did this, but every now and then the wind would blow them out. When this happened and they were plunged in darkness J. D. would fall to the ground and writhe and scream like a "crazy" man. The situation described is one which may be contrasted with those referred to earlier

---

* Since dream experiences are believed to be the source of supernatural blessings and esoteric knowledge, such a rationalization is fully acceptable to other members of this society because they share the same views regarding the nature of the universe. Presumably the giant jackfish, not the ordinary variety, is meant.

in this paper. J. D.'s fears are unsupported culturally. They are unique and his behavior sharply deviates from that of other individuals in the same situation. When it is understood, moreover, that the winter months are those in which these Indians are most active, since this is the trapping season, and that at the latitude at which they live the days are shortest then, so that there is constant necessity for moving about when it is dark, the abnormality from which J. D. suffers is thrown into even greater relief.

J. D. also suffers from a kind of agoraphobia. He usually skirts the shore when he goes out alone in his canoe on the lake. In fact, he never will head directly across any extensive body of water if he can avoid doing so.

The case of J. D., however, transcends in interest the fact that he exhibits such obvious neurotic symptoms. He is a well known conjurer (seer),* doctor, and the "owner" of one of the four *wabano* pavilions up the river, in which the most important native ceremony that still survives, is held. According to Indian dogma the "ownership" and hence the leadership in this particular ceremony is a supernatural blessing, mediated in a dream. The details of the structure erected by different leaders thus differs in minor details and so does the procedure followed and the content of the dream validation itself. But superficially there is adherence to a common pattern and the prophylactic and therapeutic purpose of the ceremony is common to all.

Since a man who is both a conjurer and *wabano* leader is reputed to be an extremely powerful individual because he has been "blessed" by many supernatural guardian spirits, it would appear that the exhibition of such deviant fears as J. D. manifests would prove to be not only inconsistent but a definite liability. Consequently it was of some interest to discover that J. D. has long been the subject of comment for just this reason. "If he is such a strong man as he claims to be," one old Indian remarked to me, "and he has so many *pawaganak* (guardian spirits), why is he afraid to do so many things?" This commentator went on to say that while some of the people had faith in J. D. he himself had none. Because these Indians are extremely individualistic and pragmatic a wide range of judgments in respect to the abilities of any person who essays to conjure or cure is possible. Consequently the expression of a skeptical attitude toward J. D. is not in itself significant. These Indians are genuinely tolerant because they are always ready to have an individ-

---

* A professional status acquired through a supernatural blessing.

ual demonstrate his professed abilities, while at the same time they never "pull their punches" if they find some flaws in his claims. In former days it is even possible that any expression of skepticism whatsoever was rarer. For the traditional attitude toward great medicine men was typically one of prodigious respect verging on fear. No one would have dared tease such a person nor challenge his authority unless he considered himself equally powerful.

In view of J. D.'s neurotic traits, which are not, of course, classified as pathological by his fellows, it is all the more interesting to note the expression of skepticism referred to above and also a lack of respect, which I found to be fairly widespread. But even this would be less significant were it not for the fact that no such attitude was manifest toward the three other *wabano* leaders on the river. One of these even shared the distinction accorded the medicine man of a generation ago in being somewhat feared because he was reputed to have done away with several Indians by magical means. So far as J. D. is concerned, I was told that on one occasion when he was conjuring,* members of the audience quietly stole away without his knowledge while the performance was in progress. Since seership is one of the functions of a conjurer this put J. D. on the spot. For as people said, his guardian spirits could not be much good if they did not immediately tell him what had happened right in the neighborhood of the conjuring lodge itself. On two other occasions that I know of, some of the younger men deliberately stimulated J. D.'s fears in order to "tease" him. Once when he was making a speech in his *wabano* pavilion during the course of a ceremony, a toy mechanical snake was released on the earthen path. It was headed for J. D. who stamped around in a panic when he saw it coming and finally ran out. Another time a young fellow obtained a firecracker and set it off at J. D.'s side while he was singing and drumming. On this occasion J. D. was so frightened that he not only ran away, he failed to come back for his drum † until the next day. Amusing as they are, these episodes sufficiently indicate in themselves the profoundly personal character and depth of J. D.'s anxiety. They also document the attitude which many of the Indians hold toward J. D.

Although I know practically nothing about the details of J. D.'s personal life, I suspect that his conjuring, doctoring, and *wabano* leadership

---

* This is done in a specially built structure. The conjurer is concealed within it and those observing the performance sit in a circle surrounding it.

† An extremely sacred article.

are intimately bound up with his neurosis. They probably screen repressed aggression and somewhat compensate his deep feelings of insecurity. There is some evidence, at least, that this may be the case. J. D. assumes a domineering attitude toward others that is frequently a matter of comment. It was J. D., too, who showed me the magically projected objects that symbolized a half dozen futile attempts to kill him. It is possible that the discovery and personal interpretation he attributed to those objects may represent the projection of his own repressed hostility toward others. At any rate, the culture of these Indians, containing as it does a theory of "disease-object" intrusion, provides an institutionalized background against which projective mechanisms in individuals can readily function. J. D.'s propensity to impress others is also so very evident that, together with the other features mentioned, it may be taken as evidence of a fundamental insecurity, connected with his anxiety. In recent years, for example, he has incorporated in his *wabanowiwin* certain features of the defunct *midewiwin,* the curative ceremony that once ranked highest in prestige, not only among the Berens River Indians, but elsewhere among Algonkian peoples. He has even gone so far as to coin a new term, *wabano midewiwin,* for his ceremony. To enhance his prestige further he has also borrowed features originally found in some of the other *wabanowiwin.* Almost every year he makes some new innovation while the other *wabano* leaders do not. He was the only *wabano* owner, moreover, who tried to "sell" me himself as an informant, when I first visited Grand Rapids. This made me mistrustful as I was aware that such information is traditionally sacred and esoteric. In fact previously I had been able to obtain the information I wanted from a *wabano* leader farther up the river only with the greatest difficulty. The last time I was at Grand Rapids J. D. said he had much more to tell me but I soon found out that all he was able to do was to repeat himself with minor variations. One summer he asked me to send him a flag with an eagle * on it from the United States. He wished to fly it over his *wabano* pavilion.† I was told later that upon receiving the flag J. D. called a number of the old men together. Exhibiting it to them, he baldly pointed out that whereas some of the Indians had no faith in him, here was a token of the regard of a white man who had journeyed all the way from the United States to obtain medicine and information. As might be expected J. D. is also extremely sensitive to real

* Associated with the mythical Thunder Bird by these Indians.

† In imitation, no doubt, of another leader in a neighboring settlement.

or fancied slights. Once when he had planned to hold his *wabanowiwin* for three days, I attended the first day but spent the whole of the second day with an informant a couple of miles across the Lake. J. D. was much annoyed, despite the fact that my contribution of tea, flour, and tobacco had practically subsidized his ceremony. On another occasion he got angry because only a few Indians attended the third day and he was forced to close the ceremony earlier than he intended. He once berated his sister, too, when he heard she had been giving me some personal reminiscences that included information about his father. J. D. evidently considered this his prerogative; a fact partially explained by the position of women among these Indians and the marked sexual dichotomy in social, economic, and religious life. But I doubt very much whether any other Indian would have become quite so emotionally upset over a matter of this sort. By and large, it would thus appear that unfortunately for J. D., the institutions of his society that have offered compensatory defenses for his inner conflicts have not been sufficiently adequate to his needs. He remains not only a suffering individual but a deviant one, even from the standpoint of native culture itself.*

It would be highly desirable, of course, to know a great deal more about the four individuals discussed above. In order to demonstrate the actual etiological factors at work a psychiatric or psychoanalytic study of each case would have to be made. I have only attempted to indicate that the manifest behavior of these individuals suggests that the causes of their anxieties are of a different order than the culturally constituted fears of the general run of the population. In contrast with the latter, the situations that provoke the fears of these individuals are emotionally structured by highly subjective meanings that are personal and unconscious.

This differentiation, it seems to me, is of general significance. It indicates that a comprehensive account of the determining factors in the affective experience of individuals must include, on the one hand, an analysis of the influence of cultural patterns and, on the other, an investigation of the factors that determine quantitative or qualitative individual variations from a given cultural norm. In any particular society

---

* In August, 1937, I received a letter from one of my Indian informants. He said that J. D. had been "very sick," that some people said he was crazy and that there was talk of sending him to "the hospital or to the asylum." My correspondent added that he did not believe J. D. was crazy but that some of the people were afraid of him. "I don't think that the poor man was looked after right," he added.

these two aspects of the problem are inseparable. But in western civilization a great deal of attention has been paid to factors thought to be relevant to individual deviation without reference to the influence of the characteristic culture patterns that mold the ideologies and affects of individuals in a common manner.

In clinical practice, cases have turned up more than once that necessitate an evaluation of such factors. Some years ago a Negro committed to a mental hospital and thought to be suffering from private delusions was discovered by a psychiatrist to belong to a local religious cult of which his ideology was characteristic (8). In another case,

an elderly Neapolitan cobbler comes to a hospital clinic with a rambling story told in broken English. His account wanders from headaches and listlessness to an old woman who has made him sick. He is referred to the neuropsychiatric department with the comment: Question of psychosis. Examination brings out little more than irrelevant detail about the enemy and how long she has wished him ill, and why, and how she makes his head hurt. There is all the first indication of a persecutory delusion. The man is told to come back with an interpreter. He returns with a fluent Italian-American who explains apologetically that the old man is illiterate and believes the woman is a witch and has cast the evil eye on him. The apparent delusion dissolves into a bit of superstition typical generally of the lower orders of Neapolitan society. What is a normal belief there is a psychotic symptom in one of our hospitals. If the writer or reader of these lines were to harbor the same conviction as this Neapolitan, it would be prima-facie evidence of mental derangement. The norm of one culture is a sign of nervous pathology in the other.*

Hence the necessity of taking the immediate cultural background of the individual into account as a primary frame of reference.

It is only through the study of affective experience in a number of different human societies that the role of cultural variables can be thoroughly understood. Comparative data of this sort may also indicate that individual deviations themselves take on characteristic forms in different societies. But while the typical conflicts engendered by different cultures may vary and the symptomatology of individuals may reflect the traditions of their society, from an etiological standpoint genuine neurotics will remain comparable insofar as we can account for their behavior in terms of common dynamic processes.

* Kroeber, A. L.: "Cultural anthropology." In *The Problems of Mental Disorder* (M. Bentley, ed.). New York: McGraw-Hill Book Co., 1935.

BIBLIOGRAPHY

1. Cantril, H., and Hunt, W. A.: "Emotional effects produced by the injection of adrenalin." *The American Journal of Psychology*, 1932, vol. 44, pp. 300–307.

2. Hallowell, A. I.: "Some empirical aspects of northern Saulteaux religion." *American Anthropologist*, 1934, vol. 36.

3. ————: "Sin, sex, and sickness in Saulteaux belief." *British Journal of Medical Psychology*, 1939, vol. 18, pp. 191–197.

4. ————: "Psychic stresses and culture patterns." *American Journal of Psychiatry*, 1936, vol. 92, pp. 1304–1305.

5. Horney, K.: *The Neurotic Personality of Our Time*. New York: W. W. Norton & Co., 1937.

6. Klineberg, O.: *Race Differences*. New York: Harper & Brothers, 1935.

7. Landis, C., and Hunt, W. A.: "Adrenalin and emotion." *Psychological Review*, 1932, vol. 39, pp. 467–485.

8. Sullivan, H. S.: Personal communication.

Anthony F. C. Wallace

Eastern Pennsylvania Psychiatric Institute
and
University of Pennsylvania

3

THE INSTITUTIONALIZATION OF CATHARTIC AND

CONTROL STRATEGIES IN IROQUOIS RELIGIOUS

PSYCHOTHERAPY *

INTRODUCTION

Many persons have remarked an apparent shift in the preferred style
of neurosis in western civilization during the past century, from the
classic conversion hysterias, obsessions, and compulsions, to the so-called
character disorders (3). Such a shift (whether it be truly a temporal
change or rather a sociocultural difference between central European
and, say, American patients) poses certain difficult problems for a theory
of psychotherapy. In particular, the question has been raised, and is still
under discussion, of the relative merits of a psychotherapy based on the
therapeutic value of catharsis and a psychotherapy based on the therapeutic value of ego or superego reinforcement (including the reinforcement of defenses). Early orthodox Freudian theory tended to consider the expression and complete, partial, or indirect satisfaction of repressed wishes to be at least symptomatically therapeutic; the position
of some later analytic theory, of combat psychiatry, and of psychologists
like Mowrer, has emphasized the psychological need, not so much for
freer expression, but for more effective repression of irresponsible and
socially disruptive impulses. While most practicing therapists do of
course recognize a time and place both for expression and repression,

* Much of the material for this paper was collected and analyzed while the
writer was a Faculty Research Fellow of the Social Science Research Council (1951–
1954). Sheila C. Steen provided valued research assistance, and W. N. Fenton and
my colleagues in the symposium, useful criticism.

63

there remain important theoretical issues: do the distributions of mental disease types in a society change over time in response to sociocultural changes; and are there corresponding and predictable shifts in the distribution of preferred therapeutic strategies? Consideration of the data from the Iroquois, a nonwestern society, with a different "psychiatric" tradition from our own, may be of help in answering these questions.

Before going on to describe Iroquoian data, however, let us first make explicit the hypothesis that will guide us in the selection and analysis of this data: 1) In most human societies, mental disorders of various kinds, classifiable under western diagnostic labels, do occur; 2) a rational motive for using psychotherapeutic procedures (i.e., procedures for prevention, amelioration, or cure) is given individuals by the discomforts which mental disorders entail for either the victim or his associates or both; 3) the frequency distribution of the types of mental disorder in a given society may vary from time to time, depending on changes in the frequency and intensity of operation of the various etiological factors; 4) the cultural emphasis may shift from one type of psychotherapy to another, as individual sufferers or practitioners perceive the balance of individual and social needs; 5) in particular, a change in the status of the sociocultural system, from a relatively high level of organization to relatively low, will be accompanied by a change from emphasis on cathartic methods to emphasis on control methods. "Level of organization" is a multiplicative function of the complexity and the orderliness (predictability) of the system (25, 26). Acculturation processes, for example, are apt to increase the complexity of native systems but to reduce drastically their orderliness. This paper, however, does not treat primarily the manifold social and cultural functions of various rituals, but their psychological function for individuals. Furthermore, teleological functionalism is eschewed: I shall try not to characterize individual mental conditions as mechanisms by which society or culture accomplishes some "purpose" of its own (like "social integration").

The Iroquois about whom I shall write are a group of linguistically related and geographically contiguous American Indian tribes who in the seventeenth century occupied southern Ontario and western New York. Although their numbers and territory have declined continuously since that time, several Iroquois reservations still exist in Ontario and New York, some of them including the sites of their ancient villages. They were a horticultural people, living in permanent villages during the summer and hunting and trapping, for trade and consumption, during the winter. The tribes with which we shall be particularly concerned are the Huron, the Seneca, the Cayuga, the Onondaga, the Oneida, and the Mohawk, the latter five constituting the nucleus of the so-called League of the Iroquois. Careful descriptions of their language and customs were made by the Jesuits during the seventeenth century; there now exists a set of observations spanning the three hundred odd years between the first Jesuit relations and the field reports of twentieth century anthropologists. Since we are concerned with presenting historically dynamic as well as psychofunctional interpretation, we shall use material from several periods.

MENTAL DISEASES AMONG THE IROQUOIS

The ethnographic and historical literature on the Iroquois contains considerable, if scattered, data describing cases and concepts of mental disorder at various points in their history. This paper is not intended to present and analyze all these data; but a sketch of their range is necessary to give background to the study of the psychotherapeutic strategies. In the *Jesuit Relations* (15) for the seventeenth century, there is described a variety of types of mental disease, for instance: a case of impotence; chronic nightmares of being captured and tortured, among warriors; hallucinations and delusions of grandeur in a woman who had joined her husband in a strange village, accompanied by "a giddiness in the head and a contraction of the muscles." The words of the ancient condolence ritual, recorded in various forms since the early eighteenth century, and most definitively reported by Fenton (12), explicitly invoked concepts of mental disease, describing a state of melancholia or agitated depression in almost clinical detail: the bereaved person was thought of as lying alone in a darkened cabin, weeping and withdrawn from reality, unable to hear "the sounds made by mankind, nothing of what is taking place on earth," unable to speak.

The organs within the breast and the flesh-body are disordered and violently wrenched without ceasing, and so also is the mind. . . . Verily, now, the life forces of the sufferer always become weakened thereby. . . . The disorder now among the organs within (the) breast is such that nothing can be clearly discerned . . . when a direful thing befalls a person, that person is invariably covered with darkness, that person becomes blinded with thick darkness itself. It is always so that the person knows not any more what the daylight is like on the earth, and his mind and life are weakened and depressed . . .

the sky is lost to the senses of that person . . . such a person knows nothing about the movement of the sun [i.e., night and day and the passage of time are not noticed] . . . invariably the mind of that person is simply tossed and turned on the grave of him in whom he fondly trusted. . . . Verily, it is a direful thing for the mind of him who has suffered from a grievous calamity to become insane, [for] the powers causing insanity are immune from everything on this earth, and [insanity] has the power to end the days of man. . . .*

Fenton (5) also discusses a time series of Seneca suicides, some of which indicate pathological depression as a motivation. Less definite as evidence for psychopathology are the familiar themes of alcoholism and witchcraft panic, particularly among eighteenth century Indians. The prophet Handsome Lake refers to an obscene psychotic in his Code (17). And there exists, largely in manuscript form (1), an extensive account of the paranoid delusions of the aged Cornplanter, brother of Handsome Lake, in the early nineteenth century. Speck (22), in a discussion of the "psychiatric causes of illness" for which the medicine societies traditionally provide cures, cites a series of recent cases among the Canadian Cayuga: hysterias in which the victims howled, bellowed, and crawled on the ground like animals; tics and tremors; convulsions; hallucinations; kleptomania; persistent nightmares; impulsive dancing; weakness or paralysis of musculature. Fenton (4) notes in his material on the Midwinter Ceremony that persons who refused to recount their dreams at the longhouse were deemed in danger of having their heads "stuck to the ceremonies"—a phrase denotative of a condition of obsession. In my own notes (1948 and 1949) on late nineteenth and twentieth century Tuscarora, I find cases (some of them treated by physicians, psychiatrists, or social workers) of chronic alcoholism, paranoid and other types of schizophrenia, senile psychosis, epileptiform disorder, and mild depression. Snyderman (21) describes in some detail the case of a young Seneca man who was "cured" of his paranoid delusions by native healers only to fall victim to chronic alcoholism.

It would be hazardous to assert, on such evidence as this, that the Iroquois were at any particular period characteristically prone to any particular type of disorder or to delineate for any period the relative frequencies of various syndromes. Even with these scattered and anecdotal materials, however, two general conclusions do seem to be obvious: First, that Iroquois men and women, from the time of their

* Hewitt, J. N. B.: "The Requickening Address of the Iroquois Condolence Council" (William N. Fenton, ed.). *Journal of the Washington Academy of Sciences,* 1944, vol. 34, pp. 65–85.

earliest historians, have fallen prey to a wide variety of mental disorders, and that these disorders, while they may include culturally specific content, run the gamut of the major diagnostic categories recognized by western psychiatrists; and second, that the prevalence of behavior disorders, such as drunkenness, irresponsibility in kinship and political contexts, and in-group quarreling and bickering, seems to have increased through the eighteenth century to a peak after the end of the Revolutionary War.

The Iroquois furthermore seem to have recognized undesirable mental states by much the same general criteria as we use, although they did not label them uniformly as disease. They did regard severe depression as a pathological state of mind (cf. the words of the Condolence Ritual). They also considered that unsatisfied and unconscious wishes of the soul might lead to physical and mental disorder. They regarded certain other states, which we would classify as psychopathological, as clearly undesirable, even though the etiology given them in native theory did not permit precisely of a concept of psychopathology in our sense. Thus paranoid delusion, obsession, hallucination, hysterical mimicry, and conversion hysteria might all be interpreted as possession by an alien spirit, or as a result of witchcraft by the mechanism of intrusion of foreign matter into the body. But however the phenomena were classified and explained, the Iroquois were in general accord with us in their definition of what constituted an undesirable mental condition: the presence of chronic anxiety, relative inability to perform socially appropriate roles, or a persistent tendency toward actions useless or inconvenient to either the victim or the group. They were even able to make, intuitively, the difficult distinction between normal and abnormal use of culturally accepted beliefs. Thus, although they generally agreed on the effectiveness of witchcraft and the validity of prophetic visions, the Iroquois did on occasion regard individuals as silly or sick whose use of these beliefs passed the bounds of acceptability. Cornplanter's delusions and prophetic speeches were laughed at while those of his brother, Handsome Lake, were taken seriously, because Cornplanter's did not "make sense" and Handsome Lake's did.

CHANGING PRINCIPLES OF IROQUOIS THERAPY

The popular favor of the various items in the repertory of culturally standardized responses to the occurrence of these unwanted mental conditions varied considerably over time. Certain traits were maintained in the repertory from beginning to end, but suffered gradually increasing neglect; others have been either invented or newly introduced in relatively recent times, or have come to occupy greater attention. As the data will show, the major shift occurred in the late eighteenth and early nineteenth centuries, from a predominant reliance on expressive, cathartic procedures, to a heavy if not predominant reliance on repressive,

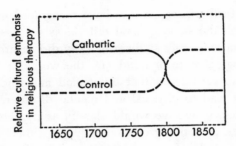

FIG. 3-1. Changing cultural emphases on cathartic and control strategies in Iroquois religious psychotherapy, 1650–1850.

disciplinary measures. The former therapy centers around the cult of dreams, the medicine societies, and the condolence rituals; the latter therapy centers about the Handsome Lake religion, with its public confessions, fear of witchcraft, and authoritarian moral commands. (We neglect here the role of Christian religious beliefs and various western psychiatric procedures.) It is noteworthy that the first tradition flourished in early contact times, when the Iroquois tribes were militarily powerful, politically independent, and culturally intact; the latter tradition flowered following the loss of territory, political and military emasculation, and the development of seriously dysfunctional cultural inconsistencies, such as the continuance of a male prestige system based on hunting, warfare, and political roles, in a situation where game was scarce, war catastrophic, and political independence an empty form. Furthermore, although it is impossible to demonstrate it with quantitative data, it does appear probable that alcoholism and what we would today call "character disorders" became more common toward the end of the eighteenth century.

The changing cultural emphases on the cathartic and control types of therapy are crudely represented by the schematic diagram in Figure 3-1.

THE IROQUOIS EGO-IDEAL

The Iroquois recognized a moral ideal which, in general outline, both men and women expected themselves approximately to realize. This moral ideal was a person who, while he was personally free, autonomous, and emotionally independent, was also careful to conduct himself so as to fulfill the needs of society. Thus a person was, ideally, courageous, indifferent to pain or insult, truthful, generous, meticulous in observing the duties of kinship, and so on: in a word, "inner-directed" to an extraordinary degree and at the same time socially very "responsible."

As a living prototype, we may cite the case of an Onondaga war captive named Aharihon, who in the seventeenth century bore the reputation of being the greatest warrior of the country. Since it is this type of man who was the idol of Iroquois youth, let us note what is told of Aharihon, a realization of this ideal in an almost pathological perfection, in the *Jesuit Relations* (15).

Aharihon was a man of dignified appearance and imposing carriage, grave, polished in manner, and self-contained. His brother had been killed, about 1654, in the wars with the Erie (the Nation of the Cat), a tribe westward of the Iroquois. As clansman and close relative, he was entitled—indeed obligated—either to avenge this brother's death by killing some Cat people, or to adopt a war captive to take his place. Aharihon, within a few years, captured, or had presented to him for adoption, forty men. Each of them he burned to death over a slow fire, because, as he said, "he did not believe that there was any one worthy to occupy his (brother's) place." By 1663, Aharihon had achieved international fame. He was the Captain General of the Iroquois, and was known to the Frenchmen at Montreal as Nero, because of his cruelty. His career of death had, indeed, continued without interruption by them for nearly ten years, and he was said to have killed sixty men with his own hand and to have burned fully eighty men over slow fire. He kept count by tatooing a mark for each successive victim on his thigh.

The French finally captured him near Montreal but his manner was still impressive. "This man," commented Father Lalemant,

commonly had nine slaves with him, five boys and four girls. He is a captain of dignified appearance and imposing carriage, and of such equanimity and presence of mind that, upon seeing himself surrounded by armed men, he showed no more surprise than if he had been alone; and when asked whether he would not like to accompany us to Quebec, he deigned only to answer coldly that that was not a question to ask him, since he was in our power. Accordingly, he was made to come aboard our Vessel, where I took pleasure in studying his disposition as well as that of an Algonquin in our company, who bore the scalp of an Iroquois but recently slain by him in war. These two men, although hostile enough to eat each other, chatted and laughed on board that Vessel with great familiarity, it being very hard to decide which of the two was more skillful in masking his feelings. I had Nero placed near me at table, where he bore himself with a gravity, a self-control, and a propriety, which showed nothing of his Barbarian origin; but during the rest of the time he was constantly eating, so that he fasted only when he was at table.*

This voracious captain was not, however, known to the Onondaga as nothing but a killer. He was, to the contrary, also a trusted ambassador, dispatched on occasion to Montreal on missions of peace. He was, in a word, a noted man. He was a killer, but he was not an indiscriminate killer; he killed only those whom it was his right to kill, tortured only those whom he had the privilege of torturing, always as an expression of brotherly love. And although his kinfolk sometimes felt he was a little extreme in his stern devotion to his brother's memory, they did not feel that he was any the less a fine man or that they had a right to interfere with his impulses; they were willing to entrust the business of peace, as well as war, to his hand.

A similar model of Iroquois manhood is described in the person of one of her husbands by Mary Jemison, a white woman captive who lived among the Seneca in the latter part of the eighteenth century (19). Hiakatoo was kind, generous, considerate, and devoted to the welfare of kin and community; he was an avid killer of tribal enemies and an ingenious torturer of prisoners; and he took pride in his fortitude and indifference in the face of both personal discomfort and the agonies of his victims. Mary Jemison was never able to reconcile entirely her love and admiration for him as a husband and father, and her horror at his cruelties.

THE CATHARTIC STRATEGIES

The presence of a culturally standardized ego-ideal of this kind suggests at once that the content of repressed wishes would in a great many individuals focus on passivity: being given things, being taken care of, being irresponsible and infantile, being assured of warmth, friendship,

* Kenton, Edna, ed.: *The Indians of North America*. New York: Harcourt, Brace & Co., 1927.

and love, being granted oral pleasures. Furthermore, it is reasonable to suspect that an individual's recognition in himself of such strivings toward passivity would arouse anxiety, and a recognition of them in others, contempt or fear. Consequently, one would expect a cathartically oriented therapy to concentrate on offering opportunities, ritually insulated from contact with the sterner business of life, for the gratification of these essentially passive strivings. And this is precisely what one finds in three of the major mechanisms of the early psychotherapy: the cult of dreams, the medicine societies, and condolence. It is noteworthy that Iroquois culture did not employ the institution of *berdache,* so prominent among Plains tribes, as an avenue of escape for the passive male. The reason may perhaps lie in the less thorough identification, among the Iroquois, of passivity with femininity; and this may in turn have depended to a degree on the importance of the female role in agriculture and in public councils. Furthermore, because Iroquois women could not, by virtue of the female roles themselves, enjoy so passive an existence as could the womenfolk of buffalo hunters, the problem of struggling against passivity itself might well not be perceived as significantly sex-linked either.

The cult of dreams, which I have described in some detail in another paper (24), functioned both as a therapeutic measure and as what might be called, metaphorically, a pressure-vent for wishes. (Indeed, much of Iroquois "therapy," being phrased religiously and being open to all members of society, was also "prophylactic" in function.) The Iroquois looked upon dreams as the windows of the soul, and their theory of dreams was remarkably similar to the psychoanalytic theory of dreams developed by Freud and his associates. In brief, the Iroquois believed that the soul had wishes of which the conscious intelligence was unaware, but which expressed themselves in dreams. Furthermore, the wishes of a supernatural being might be expressed in a person's dreams. Unless these wishes, either of the dreamer or of the supernatural, were gratified, the soul (or the supernatural being) would vex the mind or body of the frustrating host, causing illness and even death; and in the case of a supernatural's wish, disaster might fall on the whole community if the wish were not satisfied. Since these wishes were, in dreams, sometimes expressed indirectly by cryptic symbols, and since the distinction of supernatural's wishes from those of the dreamer's soul was very important, special procedures for diagnosis were required. An elaborate repertory of belief, custom, and ritual was available to every person for the diagnosis of his unconscious wishes and for their direct or symbolic gratification. Furthermore, because of the imperative character of dream wishes, dreams were a never-failing fountain of cultural innovations, particularly in regard to matters of ritual and myth. Thus the cult of dreams was not a specific organization of individuals nor a definite set of rituals fixed in tradition; rather, it was a generally accepted body of theory whose applications, partly formalized and traditional, partly derived *ad hoc*, changed constantly and ramified throughout the socio-cultural system.

In general, the less sick the individual and the more evidently the dream wishes were his rather than those of a supernatural, the more the progress of diagnosis and satisfaction was a private matter. Individuals frequently acted in mundane affairs according to their interpretation of their own dream wishes: made trips, obtained articles, performed minor rituals, indulged in sex, set upon the warpath, and so forth. Such compliance was thought to be, and in some cases no doubt was, prophylactic if not therapeutic. Specifically prophylactic was the semiannual telling of one's recent dreams in the longhouse on the occasion of the Midwinter and Green Corn Ceremonies: failure to do this, it was said, would bring about the condition known as having one's head "stuck to the ceremonies."

Dreams of sick persons and dreams which revealed the intentions of supernatural beings were likely to invoke community participation in diagnosis and wish-fulfillment. Soothsayers, using mechanical techniques of divination or depending on their own intuitions, diagnosed wishes of souls and supernaturals, and prescribed the modes of gratification. Where the community was involved by implication, as, for instance, when a warrior dreamt that he was being tortured by tribal enemies, a council of chiefs and leading men might convene to discuss the best way of satisfying the intentions of the supernatural with least inconvenience to dreamer and community. In the case of the warrior with persistent torture nightmares, a routine measure was to put him through a part of the torture cycle, so as to satisfy the dream without killing the dreamer. In certain cases, the whole community would make peace, go to war, offer rich presents, and so forth to satisfy the supernatural's program. Some dreams were diagnosed as indicating the soul's wish for membership in a particular medicine society (about which we shall say more below). Others involved the performance of the *Ononwharoria*, the "brain turning upside down" or feast of fools, in which a dreamer gave cryptic clues to his dream to a series of his fellow citizens, each of whom was obligated to contribute the article which he guessed, until someone hit upon the true wish.

The effectiveness of the Iroquois dream-therapy was admitted, in some cases, even by the Jesuits, who had neither psychological insight into, nor religious sympathy for the primitive dream-theory. Father LeJeune described the case of a woman who had gone to live with her husband in a strange village. One moonlit night, during a feast, she walked out of her cabin with one of her baby daughters in her arms. Suddenly, she saw the moon dip down to earth, and transform itself into a tall, beautiful woman, holding in her arms a little girl like her own. This moon-lady declared herself to be the "immortal seignior" of the Hurons and the several nations allied to them, and announced that it was her wish that from each of the half-dozen or so tribes she named, a present of that tribe's special product—from the Tobacco Nation, some tobacco; from the Neutrals, some robes of black squirrel fur; and so on—should be given to the dreamer. She declared that she liked the feast then being given, and wanted others like it to be held in all the other villages and tribes. "Besides," she said, "I love thee, and on that account I wish that thou shouldst henceforth be like me; and, as I am wholly of fire, I desire that thou be also at least of the color of fire," and so she ordained for her red cap, red plume, red belt, red leggings, red shoes, red all the rest.

The moon-lady then vanished and the mother returned to her cabin, where she collapsed "with a giddiness in the head and a contraction of the muscles." Thereafter she dreamt constantly of "goings and comings and outcries through her cabin."

It was decided by the chiefs that this was an important matter and that every effort should be made to give satisfaction to the sick woman: not only *her* wishes, but those of the moon-lady, were involved. She was dressed in red; the disease was diagnosed (from the symptom of giddiness) as demanding the Dream Feast or *Ononwharoria* ("turning the brain upside down"); and messengers collected for her the articles she required. The Jesuits sounded a sour note, refusing to contribute the blue blanket she wanted from a "Frenchman," but the lady went through the five-day ritual, supported most of the way on the arms of sympathetic friends. She hobbled in her bare feet through over two hundred fires; she received hundreds of gifts; she propounded her last desire in dozens of cabins, relating her troubles "in a plaintive and languishing voice" and giving hints as to the content of her last desire, until it was at last guessed. Then there was a general rejoicing, a public council, a giving of thanks and congratulations, and a public crowning and completing of her last desire (which Father LeJeune, exasperatingly, does not describe or even hint at).

An honest man, the father was compelled to admit that all this worked. "It is to be presumed that the true end of this act, and its catastrophe, will be nothing else but a Tragedy. The devil not being accustomed to behave otherwise. Nevertheless, this poor unhappy creature found herself much better after the feast than before, although she was not entirely free from, or cured of her trouble. This is ordinarily attributed by our Savages to the lack or failure of some detail, or to some imperfection in the ceremony . . ." *

Slightly apart from all these procedures was the guardian spirit quest, which received somewhat less emphasis among the Iroquois than among their Algonkian neighbors. Many youths did fast in solitude, and achieved visions in which a supernatural patron promised his aid and protection; *Adonwa* songs in honor of these patrons were sung at Midwinter and Green Corn.

The medicine societies, as I have intimated, were linked to the dream cult, both because (if one may judge from origin legends) they were instituted in accordance with dream commands, and because the need for their services was indicated in the dreams of sick persons. The medicine societies were numerous; some of them were masked; some were more secret and exclusive than others. Each tended to assume responsibility for particular areas of symptomatology, although these areas overlapped; an individual might belong to a number of them, for receipt of the ministrations of the society conveyed membership, and in the course of a lifetime, or even of a single illness, a series of treatments might be tried. In general, the diagnosis of a dream, or the nature of the patient's symptoms, indicated both a therapeutic need for the ritual treatment by a specific group, and a wish of the soul for membership in the group.

In his discussion of the medicine societies among the Cayuga, Speck (22) stressed the peculiarly "psychiatric" orientation of the societies,

---

* Kenton, Edna, ed.: *The Indians of North America.* New York: Harcourt, Brace & Co., 1927.

although they treated both physical and mental afflictions. It will be simplest to quote Speck's data directly:

Bear Society Rite: relief from howling hysteria and attacks of dementia in which the victim "crawls on the ground in the manner of a bear"—Will and Tama Porter, brother and sister (about 35 years ago); Ernest Davis (about 5 years ago).

Otter Society Rite: relief from nervous tremors and associated afflictions (not dementia)—Jim Miller (about 15 years ago).

White Buffalo Society Dance: relief from dementia, convulsions, bellowing hysteria—an Oneida woman (about 35 years ago). At the first diagnosis of this case a medicine man prescribed the Bear Society Rite, but the patient had a relapse during the performance. Another suggested the White Buffalo Society Dance. They tried it and it worked a cure.

Wooden False Face Society Rite: relief from hemorrhages of the nose, facial paralysis, mouth drawn to one side, dream persecution by visions, and annoyance by False Face spirits and frights in the bush—most recent cure, Augustus Hill's daughter (1 year ago).

Corn-Husk Mask Society Rite: relief from afflicting dreams or hallucinations.

Medicine Men's (Big Rattle) Society Rite and the Pig Mask Rite: cures bodily injury, wounds, and incurable diseases and immunizes against the coming of sickness foretold by a dream or vision—Mrs. Chauncey Powless (15 years ago); Ernest Davis (15 years ago).

Little Water, or Dark Dance, Society Rite: relief from general sickness, called for when a person has a vision of the dwarf spirits—Melinda General (convulsions) (15 or 20 years ago); Mrs. F. Martin (2 years ago).

Eagle Society Dance Rite: relief from nervous debility (St. Vitus' dance)— Mary General (5 years ago).*

Speck adds a list of particular ritual games and dances, some of which may have been associated with particular societies. He emphasizes dream-prescription as the major occasion for their use, and notes the specificity of some of them to particular disease categories. For kleptomania, for instance, there was the Chipmunk Rite, described by Speck as "specific for compulsion to steal and hide objects. No cases remembered at Sour Springs; a very rare dance" (22).

There is no need to enter here into detailed description of these and other medicine societies among the Iroquois. It is worth remarking,

* Speck, Frank G.: *Midwinter Rites of the Cayuga Long House*. Philadelphia: University of Pennsylvania Press, 1949.

however, on certain aspects of the Society of Faces, because of the many ramifications of its rituals and mythology.

Without the ministrations of the Society, a Seneca community would (in theory) face early extinction. In the spring and in the fall the Company of Faces conduct a public exorcism of disease, tornadoes and high winds, malevolent witches, and ill luck of all kinds from the entire community. At Coldspring, in recent years, the Company of Faces has divided in two groups, starting at opposite ends of the settlement. Preceded by heralds wearing masks of braided cornhusks, and from time to time augmented by recruits, the Faces visit every house. Stripped to the waist, masked, bearing rattles, the young men shout terrifying cries as they move along. At last the company assembles at the longhouse, where the faces rub their rattles on the windows, bang on the doors, and finally burst into the room and crawl toward the fire. Now the Faces are to be paid for their work; and they must be paid quickly, lest they assault the stoves and scatter hot coals about the room. A speaker thanks all the spirit forces, and burns tobacco (collected at the houses just visited), imploring the Faces to protect the people against epidemics and tornadoes.

Partake of this sacred tobacco, O mighty Shagodyoweh, you who live at the rim of the earth, who stand towering, you who travel everywhere on the earth caring for the people.
And you, too, whose faces are against the trees in the forests, whom we call the company of faces; you also receive tobacco.
And you Husk Faces partake of the tobacco. For you have been continually associated with the False-Faces. You too have done your duty.
Partake of this tobacco together. Everyone here believes that you have chosen him for your society.
So now your mud-turtle rattle receives tobacco.

Here the Faces scrape their rattles on the floor in delight.

And now another thing receives tobacco, your staff, a tall pine with the branches lopped off at the top.
So presently you will stand up and help your grandchildren, since they have fulfilled your desires. Fittingly, they have set down a full kettle of mush for you. It is greased with bear fat. Now another thing is fulfilled: on top there are strips of fried meat as large as your feet.

At this, "the Faces roll in ecstasy on their backs, grasping their feet, peering at them, and trying to put them in their mouths."

Besides, a brimming kettle of hulled-corn soup rests here.
Now it is up to you. Arise and help your grandchildren. They have fulfilled
everything that you requested should be done here. In my opinion we have
these ashes here for you to use. Arise and make medicine.*

Now those sick persons who have dreamt of a False-Face, or whose
illness has been diagnosed by a clairvoyant shaman as produced by the
Faces, come forward and stand by the fire, or if they are not well enough
for that, sit on the bench in the middle of the floor. The Faces swarm
over them, blowing ashes on their heads, rubbing ashes in their hair,
manhandling them with roughly tender, kindly hands, and dance around
the longhouse to the music of a turtle rattle and a singer singing for the
Common Faces. The Doorkeeper's Dance which follows is for the Great
World-Rim Being (Shagodyoweh). And finally, all persons within the
longhouse join in a round dance. Dancing is compulsory. Those who resist become possessed by the Faces and fall to the floor, crawl toward
the fire, and shuffle the hot coals.

The Faces treat the sick in public rituals in the longhouse at Midwinter. But most of their curing rituals are not public at all, but private
affairs, conducted in the home of the sick person by the Order of Common Faces. These ceremonies are performed, on a request being made
to a leader, whenever they are needed, in response to a patient's dream,
or the diagnosis of False-Face sickness made by a clairvoyant. The
masked beings bang on the house with their rattles and rub their staves
up and down the door frames, burst in, howling and babbling incoher-
ently, dance, blow ashes and lay on hands, receive hot mush and tobacco,
and depart.

Probably the most widely noticed occasions of the appearance of the
Faces is on the fifth and sixth nights of the Midwinter Ceremony, when
the Faces (the same masks who on other occasions are Common Faces,
or World-Rim Faces) are known as Beggars and Thieves, and, worn by
little boys and youths, go about from house to house begging for tobacco and stealing food if not given tobacco, and then repair to the
longhouse to beg again for tobacco from the people congregated there.
There are the usual rattling, bumping, and scraping noises outside the
building; then the door bangs open, and in crawls a ragged company of
men wearing Faces, but dressed in ragged, patched, torn clothes. Some
carry the big turtle rattles, some horn rattles, some staves, with which

* Speck, Frank G.: *Midwinter Rites of the Cayuga Long House.* Philadelphia:
University of Pennsylvania Press, 1949.

they hammer incessantly on the resonant floor. A ripple of delighted laughter goes around the congregation; here and there one hears an exclamation of mock terror as a Face thrusts its leering visage close to a pretty woman. A few pirouette clumsily; one rolls around hugging its knees; a third walks up and down the rows of benches, peering hopefully into each face, and cooing like a mourning dove. At last some young man hands over a handful of Indian tobacco; this is what the Face was waiting for; and he immediately begins his dance, solo, with the tobacco giver beating out the tempo with the sharp edge of the rattle on the scarred floor. Soon all the Faces have found kindred spirits with tobacco to exchange for a dance, and the floor is creaking under the clumsy boots of the capering Faces, until at last all suddenly depart, their appetite for tobacco satiated.

Just as the roles which these Faces perform are various and apparently none-too-well assorted, so are the myths and legends which explain and identify the Beggars and Thieves, the Common Faces, and the Great World-Rim Dweller. Surprisingly enough, however, the identities of these alternately comical and awful Faces merge, through a series of transitional states, with the Evil Twin, the brother of the Creator, and thus involve the Faces with the inmost secrets of the cosmos. The Faces represent a being, the powerful giant Shagodyoweh, who dwells on the rocky rim of the world, who was defeated by the creator in a contest to decide who had created the world. The twisted nose of many of the masks is a memento of the event. But behind the bent-nosed giant stand, in shadowy file, other beings who can be alternately (or simultaneously) invoked by the same masks: Tawiskaron, the Evil Twin; the father of the twins; the Four Brothers (the "Mystery Masks") who control the winds; the Whirlwind Spirit; and He-Whose-Body-Is-Riven-in-Twain (the spirit, half Tawiskaron and half his good brother, who is half winter and half summer). And also represented by the masks are a whole legion of forest spirits—huge, shy, featureless heads who flit from tree to tree on spindly legs, with their long hair snapping in the wind, and who sometimes visit lonely hunters, begging for food and tobacco. Shy and querulous as these forest faces are, they are also powerful: the unexpected sight of them can cause paralysis, or nose bleed, or possession, but properly fed and placated, they bring luck to the hunter. Logically, the same mask could hardly be embodiment of all these beings; but this is not a matter for logic. The Faces are the faces of many gods.

The triangular interaction between the maskers and the masks and the audience, on the various occasions when men wear these Faces, runs through the gamut of human feelings. The adult masker, wearing the face and impersonating the Great World Rim-Dweller or the Forest Faces, may vent attitudes and feelings which are not permitted him in sober social life. He may gurgle and coo like a baby, crawl on the floor, suck his toes, and beg for things to eat. He may thump with sticks on walls and windows, bang open doors, throw fire and ashes around, dance uninhibitedly. He may throw people out of bed, smear them with human excrement, upset the furniture, and frighten the timid with wild cries. And at the same time, he controls mighty matters, with the power to cure incurable disease, avert deadly tornadoes, cast out malevolent old witches, and bring order to a whole community. The Seneca, as masker, can recapture the fancied omnipotence of infancy, doing the impossible with impunity, even with the applause of spectators. The beings whom he represents are the very prototype of the infant: ambitious beyond their years, desirous of emulating their betters, mischievous and destructive, quickly enraged at neglect or frustration, careless of their parents' welfare, yet hopeful of forgiveness if these dreams of stolen glory are discovered.

It is hardly to be wondered at, then, that not infrequently Seneca men and women—normally so reserved, so self-sufficient, so hardy and independent—are seized with an irresistible and terrifying urge to be like the Faces. Some resist it, refuse to join the dance, try to get out of the longhouse, but once touched by the doorkeeper in a great "doctor" mask, they may fall to the floor in a fit. As far back as 1616, Champlain saw women possessed, walking "on all fours like beasts," and cured at length by the masked company who blew ashes on them and pounded out raucous music with turtle rattles. Sometimes people are obsessed by the idea of the masks: they experience repetitive nightmares in which they see faces peering out of bushes in the twilight and hear the long-drawn "Hoo-oo-oo!" Such disorders are specifically cured by the Society of Faces, which manhandles the victim, blows ashes, and inducts him into the Society so that he too comes to possess and recognize a Face, feeds and anoints it, and wears it to cure others. The ministrations of the Faces also cure a wide variety of difficulties, many of them, in the language of a later day, hysterical or "psychosomatic" in large part, such as intractable aches and pains, paralysis and tics, and nose bleeds. Induction into the Society of Faces, identification with one or another of the legendary figures represented by the masks, and the acting-out of infantile roles (modified by good taste, and in the name of socially desirable goals like the curing of disease, the averting of witchcraft, and the like) logically should, and indeed often does, produce a cure or at least give benefit.

The Faces of the gods, then, are really the faces of the Seneca themselves. They represent that strange and forgotten part of the self where repressed and disallowed desires of various sorts, but usually childish or infantile in form and content, normally subsist in silent turmoil. Rage and fear, lust and hate, boundless ambition and abject passivity, cold cruelty and noble altruism, are all forever ready to emerge; and, depending on time and place and person, they emerge in various ways. With unconscious wisdom, the primitive Society of Faces found a means of venting these emotions, of bleeding them off harmlessly, and without too much frightening the patient. Membership in the Society made it possible for the poised, independent, self-controlled, self-sacrificing Seneca to express what he did not allow himself to feel: a longing to be passive, to beg, to be an irresponsible, demanding, rowdy infant, and to compete with the Creator himself; and to express it all in the name of the public good (4, 6, 22, 23, 24).

The Iroquois recognition of the disorganizing consequences of grief has already been noted in the quotation from the condolence ritual. Death of kinfolk was, in general, a theme which received heavy, if ambivalent, emphasis in the culture. A panicky fear of separation is expressed in burial customs, in the capture, adoption, torture, and eating of captives, in the presenting of condolences from the "clear-minded" to the "dark-minded" moiety in the condolence ceremony; while fear and resentment at the dead and those who represented him is also expressed in mourning and in the torture themes. Such a conjunction of extreme love and extreme hate toward the dead is not uncommon in the mourning process as observed in western mental patients; among the Iroquois, however, the elaborate ritual provision for overt expression of these twin themes may have partially averted their manifestation in idiosyncratic individual pathologies.

"There is something peculiarly pathetic," wrote missionary Asher Wright, "in the attachment which these interesting people (the Seneca) cherish for their patriarchal sepulchres. The feeling of reverence for the graves of their ancestors is universal among them. 'Tis a national trait." He described affecting instances. "Bury me by my grandmother," said a little boy of seven a few minutes before he died; "she used to be kind to me." And, "Lay me by our mother," said a little orphan girl, under the missionaries' care, when she knew she would not get well. An old woman of eighty, speaking of a planned tribal migration, lamented, "I am sorry for I had hoped to be laid by Mother in yonder graveyard." A chief complained also of the same removal: "We can not go to the west and leave the graves of our fathers to the care of strangers. The clods would lie heavily on our bosoms in that distant country should we do it." Wright spoke of seeing middle-aged men and women "weep like children" when the least allusion was made to dead loved ones, and he wrote of the solicitude with which the grave goods were placed beside the bodies: a chief's best clothes, guns, traps, and knives; almost the whole of an infant's wardrobe; even the poorest people would scrimp and borrow to buy for departed friends a respectable robe. Others often visited the graves of their children and noticed the least change in the appearance of the enshrouding earth; sometimes they identified the spot of an unmarked grave after years of absence (28).

In Iroquois metaphor, The Being That Is Faceless, the Great Destroyer, roams night and day with its club uplifted over the peoples' heads, waiting to strike down all men, and boasting, "It is I, I will destroy all things. . . ." But death can come in many forms: by violence, in war at the hands of an enemy, in peace at the hands of a drunken friend; by stealth, at the wishing of a witch; by accident or disease. Death comes to the mighty, the chiefs, upon whom the people lean; death comes to the weak and insignificant; death comes to the proud captive. And what the people do in the face of death depends both upon who died and upon how he died.

The death of a League chief, one of the forty-nine *royaner,* was ritually defined as an international calamity. When a League chief died, it was as if the Great Faceless had kicked apart the burning brands and, exulting in destruction, stamped out the Council fire with dancing feet. No business could be done; the people were (at least metaphorically) dismayed and appalled at the havoc. The universe itself seemed to be shaking.

The psychological significance of this ritual does not lie in the possibility of mass psychosis whenever a chief died, but in the explicitness of the psychological theory which rationalized the ritual. This implies an intimate acquaintance of the Iroquois with the phenomena of reactive depression. The death of a chief was considered to be serious, not only because it formally interrupted council procedure, but also because of the disorganizing consequences of grief. Grief over the death of any loved one was traditionally conceived by the Iroquois as being capable of practically pulverizing the personality. A woman, for instance, was formally regarded as likely to disintegrate if one of her family died, casting herself onto the cold earth over the grave, where ashes were thrown over her head and shoulders mixing "with tears and drivel from the mouth and with blood oozing from many lacerations on the body." (Actually, such scenes—repugnant to the sensitivities of the restrained Iroquois—are rare. Condolence and other mourning rituals were intended to forestall them.) The death of a League chief, bereaving the entire moiety of the departed (i.e., roughly half of the Five Nation's population), was expected to produce catastrophic grief-symptoms in whole nations. It was a "calamity . . . hopeless and dreadful." The nations, personified as individuals, were thought of as lying alone in a darkened house, weeping and withdrawn from reality, unable to hear "the sounds made by mankind, nothing of what is taking place on earth," and unable to speak. The description of the melancholia of bereavement is almost clinical in its detail and insight, as it is recited in the monotonous intonations of the Requickening Address of the Condolence Council.

In order (theoretically) to prevent the consequences of such extreme grief, when a League chief died a Condolence Council was held at an early opportunity and before the chiefs undertook any new business. At this Council the mourners were cleansed of their despair, and a new chief installed to replace the old. Little, indeed, was said about the departed: it was the survivor, not the dead, who was the object of compassion.

The Condolence Council was "given" by the "clear-minded" moiety to the mourning moiety. The clear-minded ones came through the forest to the village of the dead chief, singing the Hai Hai or Role Call of Founders of the League as they walked along. It is a mournful song, recounting the glorious names of the original founding fathers, still preserved as titles of office, but lamenting that their work has grown old and that their successors are a weaker race. Then at the wood's edge, where the cleared fields began, the clear-minded and the mourners met and sat down together across a fire, to exchange greetings and the Three Rare Words of Requickening. The Three Rare Words are: Eyes, Ears, and Throat. The clear-minded, perceiving that the mourners' eyes are blinded with tears, their ears clogged and unable to hear, and their throats choked with sadness so they cannot speak and can breathe only with difficulty, wiped away the tears with the white fawn-skin of pity, cleaned out the ears, and removed the throttling obstructions from the throat. Then the mourners reciprocated, and took the clear-minded by the arm and conducted them to the longhouse, where the Thirteen Matters were dealt with, one by one, by the clear-minded on behalf of the mourners.

The Thirteen Matters—each but the last endorsed by a string of wampum passed across the fire—were the therapeutic or "requickening" ritual which delivered the melancholic mourner from the toils of his depression. The first matter rearranged the wrenched internal organs by pouring in the water of pity. The second wiped clean the bloody husk-mat bed where the wretched one sat cross-legged. The third let daylight into the darkened house of grief. The fourth pointed out that the sky is beautiful; the fifth that the sun still rises and sets. The sixth leveled the rough ground over the grave, and placed a little roof of wood and thatch over it, so that the heat of the sun and the wet of the rain will not disturb the corpse. The seventh reminded the mourners that if their kin had died by murder, they were not to seek blood revenge, but to accept the traditional twenty strings of wampum as wergild. The eighth gathered together the scattered brands of the council fire and convened the council to do business again. The ninth exhorted the warriors and the women to be of strong heart, to help one another to do the work of life, and not to be listless and indifferent—for that mood of mind should properly prevail only when the earth is split asunder and the doom of all things impends. The tenth matter forbade the chiefs to neglect the mourning people, lest their minds become insane from grief. The eleventh instructed the people of the League, in case of another death, always to run with the Torch of Notification through all the villages of the League. The twelfth was the request of the clear-minded that the mourners point out the man who was their candidate to be the new chief.

After a return of condolence by the mourners to the clear-minded (who also were grieving, although less wretchedly), the new chief's face was shown and he was examined, and, if the condoling moiety accepted him, the antlers of office were placed on his head, and he was charged to show henceforth the proper qualities of a chief: to have a skin seven spans thick, immune to malicious gossip and cantankerous criticism; to act always in the best interests of the people, not only those living now, but the generations to come; and to lead a good, clean personal life.

Then there was a feast for all in the longhouse, and finally an evening of dancing in which the chiefs were to "rub antlers," and the crowd of common people were to have a good time in a series of social dances. The clear-minded visitors were granted access to the mourners' women, with humorous appeals for self-restraint. "I now let escape from my hands our womenfolk. Accordingly you shall use them properly. Don't anyone treat them too roughly!" announced the master of ceremonies.

And he added, "So now another thing. Time may also be devoted to something else. Perhaps one of you may have had a dream. Then in that event let us amuse our minds with dreams."

And so, with clear minds, the erstwhile mourners began life anew, feasting, dancing, flirting, and telling one another their dreams of the previous year (12).

The deaths of ordinary people did not require such elaborate condolence procedures as those described above, but burial and mourning rites were similarly calculated to relieve the mind of melancholy. The dead were buried in graves, frequently seated with knees drawn up under the chin, and surrounded by the goods they would need in the next world. The graves were lined with boards or bark. Because, in Seneca belief, the soul remained close to the body for some time after death, and from time to time even re-entered it, a hole was cut in the tomb lining, in order to give it easier access to the head. The funerals themselves were under the charge of the women, who during the procession to the cemetery near the village, and again on their return to the feast at the house of the deceased, wept and tore their hair and rolled on the ground. The female relatives and neighbors of the dead one, for nine more days, every morning gathered at the house of mourning, to weep and lament. At last, on the evening of the tenth day after death, there was held the "ten-days feast," at which the hungry soul of the departed was fed and sent on its way, and the mourners were constrained to dry up their tears and become clear-minded.

The soul (ghost) might, however, be reluctant to leave the neighborhood, and so occasionally for the next year, food might be laid out for him. Furthermore, these haunting souls, frustrated in their longings for food and companionship, were apt to bother people in their dreams, or even to plague survivors with sickness and misfortune. Such persecution by the spirits of the dead was countered by the *Ohgiwe* ceremony: a nighttime occasion, at which a feast was held for the ghost and the living together, and certain chants for the dead were sung. These *Ohgiwe* songs were not to be profaned by being sung for no reason; if they were sung for amusement, some misfortune was bound to afflict the singer (14, 21).

For the dead were dangerous. The negative side of the passionate mourning for the lost loved one was an elaboration of gruesome fantasies about the cannibalistic appetites and sadistic humor of the dead. A particularly common legend was that of the vampire skeleton. Once upon a time, a man and his wife went out to hunt. The hunting ground was a two days' journey away, and on their way home, heavily laden with meat, they came to a cabin where the owner, a famous medicine man, was dead. Because it was already dark, the husband decided that they should spend the night there, in spite of the fact that the dead man's body lay on a shelf in a bark coffin. The husband gathered wood and lit a fire and then lay down to rest while his wife cooked meat and corn meal cakes. After a while he fell asleep. The wife went about her work. Suddenly the woman heard a noise behind her, near where her husband lay; it was like the sound of someone chewing meat. She thought about the corpse on the shelf and remembered that the dead man was a witch, so she put more wood on the fire and made it blaze up, and then she looked again. She saw a stream of blood trickling out from the bunk. At once she knew that her husband had been killed by the dead man.

But she pretended that she did not notice. She said, as if speaking to her husband, "I must make a torch and bring some water." She made a torch of hickory bark, long enough to last until she could run home. Then she took the pail and went out; but as soon as she was outside the door, she dropped the pail and ran through the woods as fast as she could. She had gotten halfway home before the vampire realized that she had gone. He ran after her, whooping. She heard him behind her; the whooping came nearer and nearer. She was so scared she almost fell, but she ran on until, her torch almost out, she reached the lodge in her village where the people were dancing. She burst into the lodge and fainted.

When she revived, she told the story of what had happened to her and her husband. In the morning, a party of men went to the cabin, where they found the bones of her husband, from which all the flesh had been eaten. The face and hands of the skeleton in the bark box were found to be bloody. Thereupon the chief said that it was not right to leave dead people above ground in that way. They took the bones of the vampire and buried them in a hole which they dug in the ground, and they brought the bones of the husband back to his village and buried them there also. And thereafter the dead were no longer placed on scaffolds or in shelves in bark lodges, but were buried in the ground (2).

Even more dangerous than vampire skeletons, however, were the souls of murdered kinsmen. Those who had been murdered by men of other nations could find no haven in the next world until their lust for vengeance had been appeased. Generally speaking, whatever economic or political considerations might be involved in the tensions that led to war, the actual formation of war parties was either inspired or rationalized by the obligation to avenge dead relatives. Women whose kinfolk had been killed would appear at public dances and feasts, weeping inconsolably; if this display did not succeed in arousing the warriors, the women might offer payments or accuse the lagging warriors of cowardice (18). Men might dream of their murdered kin and interpret the dream as the lost soul's desire for revenge: such a dream could compel the dreamer to organize a war party. Until the bereaved had "gotten even," until there had been retaliatory killings and tortures, it was as if the blood of the murdered one had not been wiped away, and his corpse not covered. War-caused bereavement was a state of unavenged insult and shame (and, indeed, war parties might be organized to avenge mere verbal insults as well as killings). One might, indeed, regard the Iroquois war complex as being, psychologically, a part of the mourning process.

With some nations, usually distant, like the Catawba and Cherokee of the Carolinas, the Iroquois remained on terms of chronic warfare for generations. Neither side intended to exterminate or dispossess the other; the "war" consisted of occasional raids by revenge squads of ten to fifty men who, at the most, would burn a small camp, kill a few people, and bring back a dozen or so prisoners to be tortured or adopted. At any point in time, some family on either the Iroquois or the Catawba or Cherokee side had a score to settle, and young men seeking to validate their adult masculinity, led by the males of mourning families, sooner or later would take to the trail.

Such chronic wars, if they involved close neighbors, however, quickly reached a point of critical involvement. Separated by five hundred miles, the Seneca and the Cherokee probably were sufficiently insulated by distance for an equilibrium to be reached, such that there was no cumulation of unavenged killings over the years; a stable equilibrium, involving at any one time only a few families on either side, was maintained. But with a neighboring tribe, physical proximity multiplied the opportunities for incidents, as well as for more diffuse economic and political tensions over such matters of competition as the fur trade. Thus feud wars with neighboring tribes, like the Huron, the Erie, and the Susquehannocks, annually dragged more and more families into the revenge process, and increased the opportunity and motivation for non-mourners to take part in a raid. Feud wars with neighbors developed into total wars, which had eventually to be settled either by peace-making diplomacy or by major campaigns involving hundreds of warriors. The process of involvement of a tribe in a war was like the building up of a nuclear explosion: as long as the two social masses were a long distance apart, their mutual bombardment by war parties remained in equilibrium without any cumulative increase in the rate of emission; but as the two masses were brought closer together, they stimulated each other to more and more activity, and when two sufficiently large masses were adjacent, the rate of mutual bombardment accelerated until the explosion of war occurred.

The common aim of all war parties was to bring back persons to replace the mourned-for dead. This could be done in three ways: by bringing back the scalp of a dead enemy (this scalp might even be put through an adoption ceremony); by bringing back a live prisoner (to be adopted, tortured, and killed); and by bringing back a live person (to be allowed to live and even to replace in social role the one whose death had called for this "revenge"). One death might be avenged several times over, in different ways; and the sentiments of the nearest (or loudest) mourner determined what disposition was to be made of a given case. Earlier we described the insatiable desire of Aharihon to kill and torture in honor of his departed brother. Other, less morbid mourners were more humane: a woman who had lost her son might "cast her girdle" about a likely looking prisoner and adopt him as her son; a man might take a new brother; and henceforth these adopted kinfolk were regarded and treated almost as if they were the reincarnation of the dead. Whole villages might even be adopted; at times during the seventeenth century, when war casualties were heavy, as many as two-thirds of the population of the Oneida nation were adoptees, and the other nations, including the Seneca, similarly depended heavily on adopted manpower. White prisoners thus adopted, as well as prisoners of other Indian tribes, apparently in many cases identified themselves thoroughly with their new roles and, in the case of white prisoners, objected vigorously to being repatriated when prisoners were exchanged. Many of the cases of reported mistreatment by returned "prisoners" (aside from deliberate torture) probably reflect either the adoptee's refusal to learn the language and accept normal native standards of living or the misfortune of being adopted by personally disagreeable relatives (a misfortune not unknown to adopted children in our own society).

Many prisoners were, however, consigned to torture, particularly during the seventeenth century. (The manifest horror of Europeans at the sight of tortures was doubtless responsible in part for the lapsing of the torture complex during the eighteenth century.) Torture was a ritual and followed a formal, predictable course, in which the victim and his tormentors were expected to play traditionally respectable roles. The victim (usually a man, occasionally a woman, rarely a child) was expected to show composure and hardihood: weaklings who were unable to perform the role, who broke down, wept, and cried for mercy, were sometimes dispatched in disgust with a quick hatchet blow. While undoubtedly unconscious meanings, various according to the participant and spectator, attached to the torture ritual, many of the tormentors consciously were not anxious to see transports of agony and emotional collapse, but rather the reverse: they wanted to see a stout-hearted man with unconquerable self-control, maintaining defiance and self-respect to the bitter end, and the torture was a test of these qualities. Since the victim was afterward, in many cases, eaten and had in some cases been previously adopted, he was in a very real sense being incorporated by a family and a community. (Here again Iroquois cathartic ritual acts out fantasies—in this case, the cannibalistic fantasies of the sufferer from melancholia—which the psychoanalytic method aims to recover from the "unconscious.")

THE CONTROL STRATEGIES

The two hundred years between 1650, which has been the date of reference for the early, expression-oriented, cathartic system, and 1850 were years of cumulative disaster for the Iroquois. Wars, cultural invasion, the arrival of contemptuous settlers on their doorsteps, military subordination, loss of land—all had produced, by 1850, a situation of relatively high disorganization of the sociocultural system. By system disorganization in this case I do not mean merely that current economic hardship or culture change had produced differences between recollection and perception, or that traditional and new elements of culture existed side by side, but also that the current instrumentalities did not lead reliably to the realization of current goals. Thus, in 1850, it was still a goal of the Iroquois male to perceive himself as courageous, self-reliant, respected by friends and enemies alike. But the instrumentalities for realizing this goal were no longer efficient. A man might be a clever and persistent hunter, but he could not easily be a successful one, because the game was thin and the Iroquois had lost most of their lands in a series of treaties from 1768 to 1797. The dwindling of the hunt in economic importance meant both a reduction of the supply of meat for food, and of the trade goods—hardware and dry goods —on which the Iroquois family now traditionally depended. A man might be a brave warrior, but native enemies were now protected by the United States, and the whites were willing and able to destroy not only the warrior but his village and his women and children if he tried to avenge personal insult or the murder of a relative by taking a scalp or burning a farm. A chief might be a wise statesman and an adroit diplomat, but his efforts to negotiate advantages to his people were now made meaningless by the contempt of his listeners, who smiled at his quaint metaphors, deprecated his logic, and used the threat of force to silence his protests at chicanery and injustice. If he drank, seeking relief from tension in alcoholic brawls, the damaging consequences of this form of catharsis remained for him to see when he sobered up: murdered friends, mutilated relatives, lost and stolen money, documents, horses, and peltries. If he sought, with tolerance for the fact of cultural differences, to discuss religion with a white friend, he was likely to discover a scornful Christian impatient of his stupid heathen superstitions. He learned that white men deemed his women to be fit only for pleasure, not for marriage, and that white women were prohibited to him; that his families were not good enough for white prisoners to be adopted into; furthermore, he learned that he was, in white men's eyes, dirty, ragged, ignorant, doomed to extinction, and damned to eternal hell-fire.

It is impossible, from this distance, to estimate the pathogenic force of such a situation, but, to this writer at least, it would seem intuitively to be very great. The Iroquois male, in particular, must have suffered bitterly, seeing himself a failure by the standards of his own people, and an object of contempt (expressed either by pity or by rejection) to the whites with whom he was constantly forced into association. He must furthermore have perceived the world about him as a bewildering, confused maze of blind alleys and uncertain choices, with the expected rewards rarely in their proper places. In such a setting, he needed not so much the opportunity to act out, under ritual safeguards, his repressed wishes; indeed, the combination of existing cathartic rituals, and the real passivity and dependence enjoined by economic and political disaster, gave ample scope for acting out. What he needed was control, order, organization: the image of a coherent, predictable world, and of himself as a self-controlled, responsible, respected actor in it.

The so-called New Religion of Handsome Lake satisfied this need. Above all else, Handsome Lake inveighed against disorganized and irresponsible self-indulgence. Alcohol, he preached, was the gift of the devil. People were to be loyal to one another, kindly, helpful; husbands and wives must be faithful; parents must love and protect their children; orphans must be adopted; chiefs must protect the interests of the tribe and not sell its resources, like land, for private gain. Dancing and card-playing, like alcohol, led to infidelities and quarreling; gossip, wife-beating, sexual promiscuity, witchcraft, greed and envy eroded the foundations of the community. Men and women *must* live self-controlled, cooperative lives: those who sinned would burn in hell, and if sin remained rampant, the world would be destroyed. Sinners *must* confess their sins and change their ways. Even the old cathartic rituals were dangerous, for they led to the very excesses of self-indulgence which were destroying the nation, and so the old medicine societies would have to be disbanded, and most of the old cathartic rituals abandoned. Only the four sacred rites might remain: the Great Feather Dance, the *Adonwa* (which is a modification of the guardian spirit chants and includes Handsome Lake's *Adonwa* to the Great Spirit), the Worship or Skin Dance (a thanksgiving rite, modified from the old dance in which warriors boasted of their cruel exploits), and the Bowl Game. (And, of course, a certain secondary gratification of passive strivings was provided many by submission to Handsome Lake's authoritarian personal leadership.)

These puritanical injunctions were supported by threats of devilish persecution, hell-fire, and damnation which suggest both Protestant revival preaching and also ancient traditions of torture now serving a new function. Thus, for instance, those who sinned by fiddling, dancing, and playing cards were tortured by fire.

Now the punisher called out in a loud voice saying, "My nephew, come hither," and the man stood before him. "Now, nephew, play your violin as was once your delight." The punisher handed the man a bar of hot iron and forced him to rub it upon his arm. So he played and the cords of his arms were the strings of the instrument and made the music. So in great agony he cried and screamed until he fell.

Then said the four messengers, "You have seen the punishment of the man who failed to repent."

So they said. Eniaiehuk.

Now they revealed another.

Now the punisher called out in a loud voice and commanded two persons to appear before him. Now when they stood before him he handed them what seemed a pack of red hot iron cards. Then he forced the two to sit down facing each other and compelled them to shuffle the cards and as they did flames spurted out from between them. So they cried out in great agony, sucked their fingers in their mouths, handled the cards again until their flesh was eaten away and the meat fell off. So this is what he saw.

Then the messengers said, "This is the punishment meted out to those who handle cards and repent not."

So they said. Eniaiehuk.*

The first therapeutic success of the New Religion was Handsome Lake himself. In 1799 he had been a bedridden alcoholic, supported by his brother Cornplanter, irresponsible and depressed, and expecting to die. After his first visions in that year, he rose from his bed to undertake the mission which the Great Spirit had given him, and he lived for fifteen active years. His preaching was phenomenally successful and white men in association with the Iroquois soon remarked with amazement on the great reduction in drunkenness, the new seriousness about religion, the new industriousness to be seen in their villages. Since Handsome Lake also acted as a shaman for curing disease, and as a censor, condemning witches and judging the behavior of the nation, he was able to exert much authority, and was able to combine specific treatments of disease with general prescriptions to society at large.

It is difficult to estimate precisely the therapeutic impact of the new religion under Handsome Lake's guidance. From its effectiveness in reducing the prevalence of drunkenness, this writer at least would con-

---

* Parker, Arthur C.: *The Code of Handsome Lake, The Seneca Prophet*. Albany: New York State Museum, Bulletin 163, November, 1912. Courtesy of New York State Museum and Science Service.

clude that it did tend to organize the individual's perception of the world and instill confidence in his ability to accomplish his purposes; that it significantly dispelled the demoralizing miasma of uncertainty and irresponsibility; that it crystallized the sense of guilt at failure to achieve the ego-ideal, and provided, or widened the channels for obtaining absolution by emphasizing the ritual of confession (which in itself may have been older than Handsome Lake).

Literate observers in contact with the Iroquois testified to remarkable changes in behavior, which they often ascribed to the effect of the prophet's teaching or to this in combination with the missionary efforts of the Quakers. Thus, in September, 1806, Halliday Jackson and some friends from Philadelphia visited two Seneca reservations, at Allegheny and Cattaraugus, and observed (13):

That in the course of our travels among all the Indians on the Allegheny River, or either of the Villages at Cattaraugus, we have not Seen a Single Individual the least intoxicated with Liquor—which perhaps would be a Singular Circumstance to Observe in traveling among the same number of White Inhabitants.

The speaker for the Allegheny Seneca informed Jackson's party, in a council on the sixteenth of September:

All the Indians and white people know that the Great Spirit talks with our Prophet. It is now seven years since he began first to talk with him, and he tells the Indians they must leave of drinking whisky, and they have declin'd the use of it—

Brothers, you must tell your friends, when you go home to make their minds easy, for we are determined never to let the Whisky rise again and also to pursue habits of industry and never decline it—

The redoubtable Samuel Kirkland, missionary to the Oneida, also in 1806 gave an account of the prophet, and he admitted that the prophet's opposition to the demon rum was having success (16):

Many among the Senekas and more among the Onondagoes in proportion to their numbers strictly adhere to the prophetic injunction. . . . The prophet insists upon oral confession and when it is entire, gives absolution, insisting at the same time upon their preserving in reformation.

Confession, at least as I have seen it in recent years at Coldspring longhouse (Seneca), is not a perfunctory matter to many of Handsome Lake's followers. The men, one after the other, begin to confess in loud, almost defiant voices, then their voices die down until they are inaudible; and then they start off again after a deep breath. They are deeply moved. They sigh spasmodically; cheek muscles twitch; they wheeze; they cough; they rub their eyes; in one man, tremors course through his arms and legs, as if he were shivering with cold. They have publicly confessed their sins: one, drunkenness; another, quarreling with his wife; a third, the least upset, apparently, merely announces that he is sorry for the evil things he has done and is resolved to do them no more. They sit down, looking sheepish and relieved.

The women confess—most of them—more demurely, simply repeating the formula of admitting to sin without specification, repentance, and resolution to sin no more. One woman, however, is in the grips of a severe struggle. She waits until the longhouse matrons have all confessed, and then climbs down from the spectator's seats and sits with shoulders bowed on the confessional bench. She is a stolid-looking woman, but her face is flushed and has a turgid, swollen, almost bluish color. She looks at the floor; her face twitches, and she seems to be deeply depressed. When at last she takes hold of the strings of white wampum handed to her by the confessor, her whole body quivers. She speaks slowly, almost inaudibly, and her fingers stroke and caress the wampum as if it were her sole support. Her confession is that she had left the longhouse and become a Catholic; now she repents and wishes to come back to the longhouse. Tears roll down her cheeks; from time to time she dabs at her eyes with a handkerchief. The spectators listen very quietly. After she stops speaking, the confessor, who has been standing in front of her, leaves and goes to the visitors' benches. She sits shaking all over. A preacher from another reserve gets up and stands in front of her and harangues her for ten minutes. She looks exhausted and slumps on the bench, shoulders sagging. Then all the officials, local and visiting, and many of the congregation come up and shake hands with her. She goes back to her seat, and two more preachers speak, and the meeting is closed for the afternoon.

The puritanical severity of Handsome Lake's original doctrine was not maintained throughout his life and has not become a part of the religion as institutionalized between 1800 and 1850. The people refused to abandon the medicine societies, or their associated curing rituals; and, after experience of the evil consequences (including a near-war with a nearby reservation) of witch-hunting, abandoned that preoccupation. Thus, even at the height of Handsome Lake's evangelical success, the old cathartic rituals were partially being kept up. It was not so much a matter of replacement as of addition and shift of emphases. Today, both traditions form major elements of the religious repertory of the so-called "longhouse people," to whom both the sober Code of Handsome Lake, and the noisy antics of the False Faces, are equally valuable to the searcher for salvation.

CONCLUSION

We have reviewed briefly the procedures which the culturally intact Iroquois of the seventeenth century employed in the treatment and prophylaxis of mental disturbances, and have pointed out their reliance on providing safe, ritual opportunities for the expression of wishes, particularly those involving passivity and dependence. To this early cathartic pattern were added, in the early nineteenth century, the religious teachings of Handsome Lake, the Seneca prophet, who aimed to combat the demoralization, and particularly the rampant alcoholism, of many Seneca in the early reservation period. Handsome Lake opposed irresponsible wish-indulgence, even in ritual, exhorting the people to rigid self-control, and offering a clear dogma explaining the problems, responsibilities, and opportunities of the Iroquois in the acculturation situation.

The observed shift in emphasis from catharsis to control as the primary psychotherapeutic strategy, as the Iroquois moved from an organized to a disorganized sociocultural situation, is congruent with a general hypothesis: that in a highly organized sociocultural system, the psychotherapeutic needs of individuals will tend to center in catharsis (the expression of suppressed or repressed wishes in a socially nondisturbing ritual situation); and that in a relatively poorly organized system, the psychotherapeutic needs will tend to center in control (the development of a coherent image of self-and-world and the repression of incongruent motives and beliefs). Because of the difficulties in making valid cross-cultural comparisons on such dimensions as catharsis, control, and organization, it is likely that the hypothesis will prove to be more useful in primarily cross-temporal (diachronic) than primarily cross-cultural (synchronic) types of application. This hypothesis may help to explain the oft-remarked circumstance that psychoanalytic theory, as applied to the socially secure upper middle class of central Europe at the turn of the century, in the treatment of the "classic" neuroses, emphasized the value of catharsis, while in melting pot America, with a greater prevalence of so-called "character disorders," emphasis has tended to fall on the concept of ego-strength. If such a relationship among level of sociocultural organization, relative prevalence of disease type, and preferred strategy in psychotherapy does exist, then it may be suggested that the optimal therapeutic strategy for a given individual be chosen with both the psychodynamics of the individual case and the level of sociocultural organization in his social context taken as guides.

BIBLIOGRAPHY

1. "Cornplanter's Talk," February, 1821. Draper Collection 16F 227, State Historical Society of Wisconsin (Princeton Microfilm).

2. Curtin, Jeremiah, and Hewitt, J. N. B.: *Seneca Fiction, Legends, and Myths*. Washington, D.C.: Bureau of American Ethnology, 32nd Annual Report (1911–1912), 1918.

3. Fenichel, Otto: *The Psychoanalytic Theory of Neurosis*. New York: W. W. Norton & Co., 1945, pp. 463–464.

4. Fenton, William N.: *An Outline of Seneca Ceremonies at Coldspring Longhouse*. New Haven: Yale University Publications in Anthropology, no. 9, 1936.

5. ———: *Iroquois Suicide: A Study in the Stability of a Culture Pattern*. Washington, D.C.: Bureau of American Ethnology, Anthropological Papers, no. 14, 1941.

6. ———: *Masked Medicine Societies of the Iroquois*. Washington, D.C., Smithsonian Institute, 1941.

7. ———: "An Iroquois Condolence Council for installing Cayuga Chiefs in 1945." *Journal of the Washington Academy of Sciences*, 1946, vol. 34, pp. 110–127.

8. Fenton, William N., and Kurath, Gertrude P.: *The Iroquois Eagle Dance, an Offshoot of the Calumet Dance*. Washington, D.C.: Bureau of American Ethnology, Bulletin 156, 1953.

9. Hewitt, J. N. B.: "Tawiskaron" and "Teharonhiawagon." In *Handbook of American Indians* (F. W. Hodge, ed.). Washington, D.C.: Bureau of American Ethnology, Bulletin 30, 1907.

10. ———: *Iroquoian Cosmology*. Washington, D.C.: Bureau of American Ethnology, 21st Annual Report (1900), 1903.

11. ———: *Iroquoian Cosmology, Second Part*. Washington, D.C.: Bureau of American Ethnology, 43rd Annual Report (1925–1926), 1928.

12. ———: "The Requickening Address of the Iroquois Condolence Council" (William N. Fenton, ed.). *Journal of the Washington Academy of Sciences*, 1944, vol. 34, pp. 65–85.

13. Jackson, Halliday: *Journal to the Allegany and Cattaraugus Seneca in 1806.* West Chester, Pa.: Chester County Historical Society. Unpublished manuscript.

14. ———: *Sketch of the Manners, Customs, Religion and Government of the Seneca Indians in 1800.* Philadelphia: Marcus T. C. Gould; New York: Isaac T. Hopper, 1830.

15. Kenton, Edna, ed.: *The Indians of North America.* New York: Harcourt Brace & Co., 1927.

16. Kirkland, Samuel: *Journal of Samuel Kirkland* (1806). Clinton, N.Y.: Hamilton College. Unpublished manuscript.

17. Parker, Arthur C.: *The Code of Handsome Lake, The Seneca Prophet.* Albany: New York State Museum, Bulletin 163, November, 1912.

18. Raudot, Antonne D.: "Memoirs concerning the different Indian Nations of North America." In *Shawnese Traditions, C. C. Trowbridge's Account* (Vernon Kinietz and Erminie W. Voegelin, eds.). Ann Arbor: University of Michigan Press, 1939, pp. 339–410.

19. Seaver, J. E.: *A Narrative of the Life of Mary Jemison.* New York: American Scenic and Historic Preservation Society, 1856.

20. Skinner, Dorothy P.: *Seneca Notes,* 1928–1929. Harrisburg: Pennsylvania State Historical Museum Commission. Unpublished manuscript.

21. Snyderman, George S.: "The case of Daniel P.: An example of Seneca healing." *Journal of the Washington Academy of Sciences,* 1949, vol. 39, pp. 217–220.

22. Speck, Frank G.: *Midwinter Rites of the Cayuga Long House.* Philadelphia: University of Pennsylvania Press, 1949.

23. Wallace, Anthony F. C.: Field Notes, Grand River Reservations. December, 1946.

24. ———: "Dreams and the wishes of the soul: A type of psychoanalytic theory among the seventeenth century Iroquois." *American Anthropologist,* 1958, vol. 60, pp. 234–248.

25. ———: "Study of processes of organization and revitalization of psychological and socio-cultural systems, based on a study of nativistic religious revivals." Philadelphia: *Yearbook* (1957) of the American Philosophical Society, in press.

26. ———: "The quantity of organization in stochastic systems." Unpublished manuscript, 1957.

27. Williams, Seneca Benjamin: *Notes Recorded about 1843* (probably from words of Blacksnake or Brooks Redeye). Draper Collection, 22F 23–44, State Historical Society of Wisconsin (Princeton Microfilm).

28. Wright, Asher: *Pencil Notes on Box "Indians."* Buffalo, N.Y.: Historical Society, Parker Gift.

Marvin K. Opler

Department of Psychiatry
University of Buffalo School of Medicine
and
Department of Sociology
University of Buffalo

4

DREAM ANALYSIS IN UTE INDIAN THERAPY

From 1936 to 1938, the author conducted field studies among the Ute and Southern Paiute Indians of Colorado and Utah (13–21). In 1937, following ceremonial adoption and induction into the Ute tribe during the annual Sun Dance, he promptly underwent shamanistic treatment for a feigned illness. Studies of the Ute shaman or "doctor" and particularly of the shaman's use of dream analysis in therapy continued throughout two consecutive field trips. Both the Sun Dance and Bear Dance afforded special occasions for all such inquiries (15, 16). Participation in Peyote Cult or mescal-button-eating rituals gave further opportunities (14, 17). These ceremonies and systematic studies of Ute Indian practitioners, their own families and relatives, the performance of unusual "cures," their patients' families, and connected dream materials of the patients themselves formed a coherent body of data. We first published on this under the title, "Psychoanalytic Techniques in Social Analysis" (18). For it was obvious that Ute shamans employed quasi-psychoanalytic techniques, independently invented in their culture and that of the Paiute, but found vestigially with less emphasis among such linguistically cognate people as their Hopi "neighbors" and the Western Shoshoni to the north (4). D. Eggan, particularly, has discussed these customs and beliefs for the Hopi agriculturalists (5).

Although we have, in our earlier paper on psychoanalytic techniques, sketched the general nature of the shaman and his dream analysis, we intend here to go beyond this first extended but preliminary account. We will here consider the place and function of the Indian practitioner in his society, the cultural values of a hunting and gathering milieu, and

97

the role of dream analysis in maintaining not only health, but cultural continuity.

DREAM AS DELUSION AND REACTION TO CULTURALLY INDUCED STRESS

The stuff that dreams are made of in Ute culture is the very material that Indian shamans constantly analyze. The Indian shaman is a man or woman, ordinarily not only adult chronologically, but mature, poised, and serious in personality. As a practitioner, it is his duty to cure and comfort all manner of ailing persons, young and old. Throughout the bands aboriginally, the shaman's seasonal haunts and his family circuit were generally well known; and there were formal modes of approaching him and offering payment in advance which were widely recognized by custom and reputation. In his hands, as with the medical practitioner in our society, lay an enormous responsibility for maintaining the health and vigor necessary in the culture. However, the Ute added to health and vigor—values in most cultures—the absolute necessity for maintaining mobility in essential seasonal movements consistent with their hunting and gathering way of life and seasonal circuits of small family groupings. In this highly mobile setting of small and scattered family groups, the shaman was called upon not only to counteract the illness which was patent and visible, but to treat any avowed incapacities, transient hysteriform complaints, allegedly growing impairments, sudden paralyses which came and went, and perceptual and locomotor inadequacies.

Although only one band of Southern Ute, the *Weminutc*, was in any sense mobile in the recent period referred to, this dominant theme in religion was sufficiently well integrated so that by actual count the vast majority of "marvelous cures" fell within the area of restoring vigor, mobility, and more optimal functioning to persons beset with temporary impediments. Hysterical blindness, paralyses, and incapacitating *malaise* constantly came within the purview of shamanistic intervention. The shaman, now as earlier, loomed large in all functions safeguarding the spatial movements of society and the temporal continuity of culture. His role, depending on his prowess, became in most instances a crucial and respected one, not merely medical but ethicoreligious in essence.

There are confusions in our own cultural ideology, and possibly in early forms of Freudian doctrine as well, in regard to the place of the individual *within* the context of cultural process. Even an anthropologist like Sapir stated categorically: "It is always the individual that really thinks and acts and dreams and revolts" (22). However, this is an individual whose cognitive, action, fantasy, and emotive processes never take place *in vacuo.* They are influenced profoundly, not merely by the learned behaviors strongly sanctioned in the culture, but by common stress points or inadequacies in the cultural pattern itself. As White has stated this: "Relative to the culture process the individual is neither creator nor determinant; he is merely a catalyst and a vehicle of expression" (23). Even this puts the matter weakly, for individual behavior is a function of family, community, and cultural dynamics, destroying the abstracted distances between individual and culture. Religious and healing activities among the Ute are both cultural and individual events and are so categorized by the Indian practitioners. Again with the Ute, if not always in our individualistically competitive ideology, the nature of healing and of religious or ethical activity is socially, not idiosyncratically, defined. Religion and curing are social and cultural institutions. Consequently, there is a socially significant systematization about dreams which in our culture took centuries of philosophical and psychiatric inquiry—plus the genius of Freud—to adumbrate.

The chief and constant instrument of therapy, and the basis for ethicoreligious instruction among the Ute is a nonindividualistic theory of dreams. Realizing that dreams may be condensed, sudden, bizarre and dramatic, and hinge upon events half-real or half-imagined, the dream is seen as emotionalized striving, or in illness as containing components of reaction to stress. Wishes, culturally geared motivations, and typical attitudes are dissected by shamans in dealing with the thematic material in dreams. The continuity of this process is assured by the shaman himself having motivations, problems, and character structure explored by techniques of apprenticing, by his own exposures to illness, and by a clearly organized body of lore concerning dream phenomena.

As with dreams in our society, the dreams of Utes abound with the mythology of animals, ghosts, and monsters. In the folklore, these configure side by side, but are distinguished from "historically true stories." The latter comprise remembered incidents from historical accounts of real ancestors, passed on in family lines sometimes long after the individuals' deaths, and some gaining currency throughout band and tribal groups. The true story of real ancestors is often traced back genealogically and will contain battles or heroic exploits which are both memorable and told with the skill of raconteurs who lack a written language (20). The true story, in Ute classification, has less religious and consequently less health connotations than the animal or ghostly tale of religious mythology. These last, or the dreams inhabited by unusual figures and punctuated by more frightening or bizarre events, are believed to be diagnostic or prognostic indicators in illnesses, fraught with special meanings. Such symbolic meanings are open to shamanistic interpretation. Dreams of departed relatives or even their animal-namesake surrogates are especially significant. The strange dream of living relatives, among which resented parents, grandparents, or sibling rivals commonly appear, are recognized as having exactly these psychological and health connotations. Because of such clear formulations, the delicate unraveling of the dream in therapy is a prime task of the practitioner.

Among the Ute, as with us on occasion, the repetitive dream is likewise believed to be highly meaningful. Recognition of this point throughout the society means that much more simply or more readily repetitive dreams are recalled and reported to the shaman. Here there is overlapping with the above categories, since dreams classified as obvious nightmares or those disguised by recondite religious symbolic formalisms are classified as the more important. Anderson and Foster report for our culture that the earliest unpleasant dreams in childhood are centered in animals, which is expectable in terms of our children's lore, or domesticated animals and zoological gardens (6). For the Ute, however, animal dreams are found more consistently throughout the life cycle. While these authors further report for our children that frightening dreams involving people or endangering situations occur later in life, the Ute merge such elements with the animal content we have noted. In general, the Ute do not regard animals as being "wholly different" from man and their anthropomorphic animal mythology further blurs the distinction. The Anderson-Foster finding that dreams involving the torment of the dreamer and his friends occur in our culture, usually after the tenth year, seems consistent with the Ute data only if we make the above modifications.

Kimmins, who found wish-fulfillment the leading characteristic of over 5,000 children's dreams from our society, also finds corroboration in the smaller population of Ute but always on any age level (9). Blanchard's study of 300 child guidance clinic cases, in which parental and animal figures were chief actors and wish and fear motivations the chief themes is again repeated in Ute data for all ages (1). One may add that the shaman, in selecting the wishful or fear-laden themes, is at an advantage not afforded in our culture in that he may promptly blame these as intrusions, point to their unrealistic features without blaming the patient, and merely require the patient's assistance in exorcising the evil.

The Ute shaman, however, is not only a careful observer of people in his culture, but he is in the best instances an acute analyst of the cultural stresses. On one occasion, when priding myself on the insight that shamanistic cures fall into such categories as restoring individual mobility and family balances, my informant, who was the most outstanding Southern Ute shaman and a recognized Sun Dance leader, informed me bluntly: "You should notice that Indian doctor or *pöŕat* cures people who in the old days were the very ones who would slow down camp movements with their sickness or, in time, cause family quarrels." Most discussions of the shaman state in terms as clear as this that his functions also relate to the maintenance of cultural continuity.

The question arises whether the shaman himself is in some way trained to overcome his personal problems. The repeated charge that curing shamans or healing practitioners among nonliterate peoples are compensated neurotics or psychotics deserves careful scrutiny. There are, of course, societies like the Chukchi of Siberia, reported by Bogoras, where this appears notably to be the case (2). But most such claims have been distinctly more moderate, since fieldworkers constantly encounter shamans who appear more balanced. Kroeber and Devereux may be cited as two outstanding exceptions (11, 3). In Kroeber's account, he speaks of psychotic factors in shamanism, and after discussing the well-known data from Siberian tribes, he refers to many Californian peoples for whom he describes some of his own fieldwork experiences with shamanism. There are, of course, societies like the Chukchi where cultural dislocations are described apart from the body of materials on shamanism. When we put the two discrepancies together, we notice several factors which may be specially responsible among the Chukchi for the high rate of aberrancy among their shamans. Bogoras describes the floating population of chronically unemployed and perennially single laborers, who take care of reindeer herds. Like the Biblical figures who worked long years to achieve a bride-price, they often faced the necessity of work periods, such as seven years, during which they attempted to build up a part of the herd belonging to themselves. Both they and sons living with property-owning fathers faced the often quite arbitrary paternal authority, which is reflected in rigid patriarchal controls over property inheritance. In this way, they encountered barriers to their plans, and throughout youth and early adulthood there were the frustrations of delayed marriage. Bogoras describes the shamanistic outlet for this period as a kind of escapism, and the pathology he reports is often associated with the attainment of this form of escape.

When we turn to Kroeber's paper on "Psychosis or Social Sanction," written in 1940 and reprinted a dozen years later in *The Nature of Culture* (11), we can see that the reference to Californian tribes with problems of cultural dislocation, not unlike the Chukchi, is to a parallel situation. California is one of the states most famous for violent attacks on aboriginal populations. The hunting down of human beings from Indian tribes often followed prayer meetings devoted fanatically to eradication of the "heathens." These movements had a kind of thoroughgoing success which led in many areas to the entire destruction of whole tribes down to the last man, woman, or child. Kroeber, himself, worked with one of these last survivors of a group which had been wiped out. When, therefore, reiterations of the Chukchi and California cases from Kroeber's early paper are adduced by Devereux, we should look carefully at the examples being added to his own Mohave material (3). With slight encouragement from Kroeber and from Linton, Devereux is willing to generalize in a sweeping way upon *the* shaman's psychological problems, using his Mohave data which is geographically close to the areas Kroeber describes. In both 1956 and 1957, Devereux stated that the shaman is a neurotic using socially sanctioned symptomatic defenses which differ from those of psychotics in our society only in the absence of socially deviant symptoms.

It is hard to reconcile this last sweeping assertion with data on Eastern Apache tribes, where the author participated in fieldwork (1932–1933). Among Mescalero, Chiricahua, and Lipan Apaches, practically every adult person possessed supernatural shamanistic power. In subsequent field research among Ute and Southern Paiute of Colorado and Utah, a shamanism, almost as widespread as the Apache form, could not be correlated significantly with any rates of deviant behavior. To the contrary, both the Eastern Apache and Southern Ute had shamanism widespread for sociocultural reasons, relating to their scattered population and needs for mobility and vigor. As we have suggested, the shaman is responsible for all the healing and curing techniques developed in the culture, the setting of broken bones, the herbal *materia medica,* the prescribing of such common "cures" as powdered sage-brush inhalants for upper respiratory congestion, all coming within his purview. He may even become famous for certain specialties. In fact, much of the shaman's functioning mediated between the healing of obvious ailments and the treatment of psychological problems we have discussed above.

The dream and its psychological relationships are experiences open to all Ute, whether they are shamans or not. At about seven or eight years of age, a Ute child may begin to take note of his dreams and report them to adult family members. We have implied that the ordinary dream embodying a commonplace event is taken simply as a dream among these people without special connotations. But the unusual dream which may involve animals and birds behaving like humans or which may include heavenly bodies (sun, moon, and stars)—these things mean nothing less than nightly visitations of supernatural power. The dream, however, overlaps significantly with religious life among the Ute and usually is dated for most informants at the latency period.

The attention paid dreams in Ute society, beginning in the latency period, is, therefore, part of the introduction into religious life in general. Supernatural power among the Ute is, of course, a matter of immense personal importance, as it is among most peoples of the world. We are confronted here with the important question of the function, not only of dream analysis, but of religion generally among these people. For the Ute, religion is not separated out in Sunday observances from the conduct and explanations of the commonplace events of the week. With less secularism in their society, persons having supernatural power are found in each family group and could be called "family shamans." Further, the supernatural realm is a reflection of the needs and urgencies of the everyday world. In the animal mythology, for example, these mythological beings live in families and conduct their lives in a manner remarkably like the Ute. The central purpose of crisis ceremonialism at birth and puberty is to attain such desirable and mundane things as a long life, good health, and economic skills in the various tasks assigned to men and women. Illness and similar threats to mobility threaten the delicate economic balance in a hunting and gathering scene of scattered extended family "communities," narrowing the margin between the survival and the extinction of such family groupings. The family shaman, or in times of more extreme need, the more noted practitioner called in from afar would, therefore, specialize in ceremonies that were curing rites designed to safeguard such vigor and mobility.

Having noted that religious life subserves everyday needs and that the shaman or *pörat* represents a considerable cross section of Ute population, we may add that the power to cure resident in a shaman's songs, rituals, and paraphernalia are unique endowments offered to the doctor alone in his own previous encounters between himself and the supernatural. The shaman's power, like his own significant dreams analyzed by an older shaman, bears the stamp of his particular individuality. This is called his secret or personal way, and no shaman divulges more of his own nature than is actually necessary in ceremonial practice. His neutrality and religious importance is parallel, perhaps, to the efforts of the analyst in evoking free associations and self-expressions from the patient before becoming involved in counter-transference functions. The Ute recognize that such supernatural power or insight is not something easy to obtain, and that this possession is potent and dangerous to hold, for both the practitioner and his relatives and patients. As with a medical function, it is viewed as a trust granted those who have proven their serious intentions, their abilities, and their above-average character. Unlike the adult Apache, where practically all persons have some gift of power, the Ute individual will sometimes not handle his encounters with the supernatural in such a way as to ensure shamanistic power to himself. He may, in their phrasing, draw back as if overwhelmed by the experience. In parallel, again, to analytic thinking, power is not, therefore, granted persons easily angered or prone to despair. Since power is a trust to help in the curing of others or to "do good," the basically hostile or depressed individuals are forewarned, as it were, that they are not suitable candidates for analytic training.

A fountainhead of supernatural power is conceived of being a kind of trinity composed of a supreme God called Creator-of-Humans, or as Sunavawi, the Wolf of mythological times (part culture-hero and part mischievous trickster), or as the Sun. To these generalized deities, the Ute, whether shaman or not, address their prayers and present their most pressing needs. But it is recognized that in addition to these powerful creative forces, there operates in nature a wide variety of lesser supernatural agencies, including animals, plants, and such natural phenomena as Ute in aboriginal life were forced to contend with constantly. These last entities which stand closer to man in Ute cosmology transmit the high voltages of supernatural power to more humble human practitioners or doctors. During puberty, when the shaman is maturing, such reservoirs of power as the moon and stars, or various animals, or elements like lightning and wind may transmit the power along with the rules and paraphernalia governing its use. The chief indicators of this supernatural visitation are the insistent dreams which the young man or woman often faces fearfully; before acceptance he may enlist the help of an older shaman whose strength and experience already are greater. As we have suggested, there are ways of interpreting these visitations as signs of illness itself, and if one dependently requires the shaman's total intervention and withdraws, only the practitioner can ward off illness. Acceptance, however, entails coping with one's own problems in such a way during a dream-analytic procedure that one ensures both future responsibility and prowess as a shaman.

Obviously, both the widespread channels for obtaining supernatural power and the systems of apprenticeship and training are guided to fruition with safeguards against what Kroeber and Devereux have reported as the general introduction of neuroticism into the shamanistic sphere in a few scattered societies. The Ute organization of curing practices is geared in tightly with the fundamental economic and social needs of the cultural system. Consequently, a doctor whose superior abilities become famous is expected as a medical-religious leader in the society to answer any family's call for help from no matter what distance. The sick person's relative will approach him, being advised in advance of the proper ritual procedures for the summons. The most famous shamans require a formal present of some symbol of their office, such as a painted stick or eagle feathers, along with an advance gift or a token of what payment is later to come. Following the introduction of the horse among the Ute, this became the standard payment for ceremonial services. Since the shaman was himself a representative of the supernatural, any laxity in delivering such a gift later would signify duplicity or a lack of sincerity which often led to a recurrence of the supernatural attack in illness.

A consideration of dream analysis involves not only the shaman and his functions, but it must also include the dreamer and his unique problems. While we may say that the therapeutic analysis of dreams among the Ute was aimed at restoration of mobility and health in the cultural system, the actual problems in illness often depended upon family tensions of which the dreamer was a party. The Ute shamans or the ailing persons themselves who confided to the author usually explained that analysis proved to them that dreaming often reflected life problems in a distorted or delusional way. The dreams when stripped of such disguises show evidence of dominant drives and motivation of personality. In the dream world, the individual mind was free to roam or imagine, and its fantasies revealed tendencies toward the disguised expression of unconscious wishes. Many times, the shaman's interpretation was a translation from the overt story to that which expressed less manifest urges. The repressed portion of dreams or their disguised content was important in divulging tendencies in the individual which the cultural system stamped as socially reprehensible. Therefore, in Ute society, the dream was looked upon as an indication of mental and physical integration or its opposite.

Since dreams were also the agency through which shamans obtained individual supernatural curing power, the shaman in his own development learned much about his own past unconscious motivations. Much of this was defined as learning one's religious place in the spiritual world; or it was looked upon, on the other hand, as the medium through which the powers of evil producing witchcraft, illness, or death could be coped with in the shaman's own process of attaining power. By his encounters with the supernatural, the shaman not only learned much about the rituals of driving out evil spirits in patients, but he came to understand himself better. Ute ideology makes no simple distinction between mental and physical disturbance, so that it becomes natural for the practitioner to feel that he is learning about the control of patently physical ailments at the same time he learns to counteract psychological disabilities.

Widespread in nonliterate societies is the belief that soul-loss or loss of spirit or "breath" is a potent cause for death. Among the Ute, loss of breath may lead to death, but it may also be connected with chills, fevers, and convulsions associated with serious illness. The harmful dream may spell such impending disaster, and the rationale of this belief is that the person in dreaming seems to travel, so far as spirit or soul is concerned, into a kind of spirit world. Where one goes and whom one encounters is, therefore, of interest to the shaman. His diagnosis may include items that to us would be listed as hysterical paralysis, the temporary loss of sight or hearing, or some other functional disorder. If, for instance, one dreams of close relatives who have died, this may be interpreted as a visitation to the land of the dead. It might be interpreted as guilt or boundless worry over the death of a close relative. Relatives thus can figure in Ute dreams in ways as destructive to health as the eating of a poisonous plant. The shaman's view of health includes mental and physical well-being, and his injunction to anyone who thinks too much about dead relatives is ordinarily that if one continued such dreams, one would become sick and perhaps die.

In respect to illnesses which are impairments to mobility and vigor, we can hypothesize that aboriginal life imposed upon these people heavy burdens of being industrious and more or less constant in their movements throughout the rugged Ute terrain. For this reason, the one large category of hysterical impairments may be posited as a widespread reaction of people who must be constantly on the move. Ute mythology is full of amusing sequences concerning the rapid travels of Sunavawi the Wolf, who rushes along accomplishing tasks typical for Utes. In the Sunavawi stories, the various antics of the wolf allow the Ute to sit back and laugh at the impositions and rules of their own culture. In actual life, however, there is no such opportunity afforded to reflect upon the necessities for mobility and vigor in one's own case. We, therefore, view the high incidence of hysterical impairments as personal reactions to typical stresses produced by this way of life.

But the necessity for movement, vigor, and industry does not act alone in producing disabilities. The overwhelming social stress among the Ute, if we may categorize mobility as an economic stress, is the necessity in each extended family grouping for the younger family members to pay heed to the riper wisdom and experience of older relatives. The Ute kinship system carefully formalizes this age distinction on all generation levels other than the grandparent-grandchild one. For example, while siblings and cousins are grouped together, the older brothers and male cousins are distinguished from younger ones, as are the older and younger sisters and female cousins. The same age and sex distinctions operate to define uncles and aunts related through a father or mother. Such a system, primarily differentiating relatives according to sex and age, is a reflection of customs and practices operative throughout the society by which conduct is determined through the age and sex principles. Ute Indians are, as a consequence, often resentful of the principle of authority in every camp defined by virtue of age rulings. While it is true that an older sibling, cousin, or uncle and aunt may represent a diffusion of authority beyond a simple pattern of the authority vested in one's own parents, nevertheless it is also true that the Ute rankle against this ubiquitous system which forces the individual to show constant respect toward older relatives. The scattering of extended family groupings means, further, that the pressures of older authoritarians, male and female, may be felt by the individual Ute all the more intensively since the diffusion of social controls in this sense extends beyond single family boundaries.

While resentments, fears, and hostilities may be felt especially in regard to authoritarian pressures toward industriousness and mobility, the Ute necessarily disguise these facts of cultural stress in a complex series of beliefs. Only a few may be indicated here. There is the idea that dreams of dead relatives are a potent source of danger to the living, and there is much evidence that such dreams, both guilty and wishful in character, occur frequently. The Ute call these ghost dreams. Interestingly, the typically shamanistic procedure blames the ghost for "returning and troubling" the dreamer. The shaman strongly advises the individual to cease worrying about the person as a way of preventing these trips to the land of the dead. One is expected to forget dead relatives immediately, and all the weight of curative social sanctions are placed behind the living and their more realistic tasks. Dreams about relatives who bear the same name as an animal and who actually appear in the form of their animal namesakes are readily interpreted as referring to the real person, whether alive or dead. There is a second possible case of this typical form of animal disguise for people in an extension of ghost dreams to troubled dream experiences concerning living relatives. The spirit world of ghosts, which is ancestral, is but a less realistic and sharper warning to the dreamer than a dream populated with troubled events concerning living relatives in animal disguise.

Related to this concept of power in a dream is the belief that the delusional structure of the dream is supernatural and, therefore, potentially dangerous. A shaman, because he is constantly involved with the supernatural, requires his own personal dream analysis and various ritual procedures for his own protection. When a shaman is lax about his powers, he may be instrumental in bringing harm upon himself or to younger members of his own family. For example, most shamans whose efforts are crowned with success are said to have within themselves a kind of spirit mannikin who swallows down and destroys evil internally. Many shamanistic ceremonies locate an evil within a patient, which is not only described psychologically and socially but objectified physically as well. These sharp objects causing pain or curious objects producing discomfort are ritually swallowed at the peak of most ceremonies by clever sleight-of-hand tricks. Obviously, one may function as a shaman too actively. Whereas a functional statement of this overactivity might point to the shaman's desire for gain or prestige, the Ute simply formalize their objections to such aggrandizement by stating flatly that the mannikin may be overfed with evil or surfeited.

At such a point, a shaman's real power to cure becomes attenuated by overuse. He has too many patients, or even more tellingly, his curative power has become weakened by long years of service, so that it retaliates by becoming dangerous to himself. Should he, in turn, ward off the bad effect of his power's vengeance, the power can strike again at younger relatives using the dream contacts as the main avenues of approach. For this reason, supernatural power should not be used after it shows signs of temporary weakness or long overuse, and the shaman's loss of a patient should be followed by a rest period lest the process be repeated. A shaman also owes obligation not only to the members of society, but he must wisely conduct the affairs of his own family. By beliefs culturally sanctioned, younger relatives may express in supernatural terms the fears and resentments they feel toward the strict authority of shamanistic elders in Ute society. They do so by stating such fears.

Mourning customs reflect these same fears. At death, family camps are moved, and the relatives take care always to avoid that specific locality in the future. They cut their hair, wear old or borrowed garments, and attempt to make themselves as little noticed and unrecognizable as possible. For a period of four days and nights before the time of "forgetting" is invoked, they maintain strict quiet in the camp and restrain any noises such as singing or laughter. This is a fearful time, rather than one of commemoration. If there is grief, it must not be commented upon, and tear-stained faces are left unwashed, while dirt and grease are rubbed over the body to make it further unrecognizable. The fear is again fear of the dead and hope that the deceased relative will not recognize his kin. Or if he does, he sees them in circumstances so dull and uneventful that he will prefer to leave them alone forever more. It is particularly significant that the greatest fear and almost hostile resentment of the ancestor is aimed at an old relative who had long life or at the deceased shaman who dominated a family scene. When an infant or child dies, it is phrased that the "young ghost" or "child ghost" cannot possibly travel very far because of its tender years and will not be expected to exert spectral visitations on the living. While one should not worry and dwell upon reminiscences of a younger dead relative, these are always less dangerous than the ones who in real life exercised more authority.

Finally, the ghost frequently plays the disliked role of failing the shaman in his effort to cure. If an ill person is steadily sinking, the shaman often says his heart and spirit are wandering from his body. Shamans will send a light pinfeather to catch the wayward heart; some may in addition to the sleight-of-hand plead with the power to return the heart. In curing ceremonies, attending relatives are requested not only to join in the chants of the shaman but to express their solidarity with the sick person. Heart or breath departed through soul-loss in extreme illness is returned not only through the shaman's own powers, but by enlisting the further entreaties of living relatives. The painting of faces during shamanistic ceremonies is likewise intended to fool the ghost. It also adds to the participant functions of the whole family to be involved in curing, and the shaman often explains that with many ghosts and problematic tendencies on the part of the patient, he requires family allies in waging his fight on the sickness.

The fear of older relatives and of ghosts among the Ute is second only to the respect they must lavish upon them while they are living. Ambivalent fear and respect is the product of some extended family groupings, which are poorly structured in an emotional sense, although outwardly cohesive and cooperative. In families where boundless authority is exercised over the younger members, and the young bow readily to the authority of age, the temporary impairments we have listed occur most frequently. For example, with the leading shaman and Sun Dance leader among the Southern Ute, his own son became hysterically blinded during one of the rest periods in the Sun Dance (15). The young man, whose own family was beset by certain tensions during this period, was himself anxious to obtain supernatural power, such as his father possessed in abundance. In the dreaming and reverie period of the Sun Dance, he became aware that he was (hysterically) blinded. His father's total explanations in curing sessions left little doubt that a prime motivation was his overly strong wish to be sightless as in a dream and to obtain quickly all the benefits of supernatural power. It was indicated that the patient was not yet in a position to assume such power through his father's help, but must work toward it gradually. A thorough ventilation of his own family problems and current tensions seemed miraculously to restore his sight, and he continued in subsequent Sun Dance rituals to obtain power (18).

THE ROLE OF THERAPY IN UTE RELIGION

Having seen how dream and delusion are products of the economic stresses of mobility and the social pressures of an authority vested in age, we may now consider how the therapist figures in Ute religion more generally. D. Eggan, in an article on the manifest content of dreams, has pointed out that the frequency elements in dreams may be charted statistically in order to throw light on social and religious patterns in the culture (4). In this point of view, dreams are treated as one of the varieties of meaning to persons in the culture. Dream experiences are, therefore, seen as links in a chain of behavioral events in which kinds of cultural stimuli are reflected into the dream world much as in other symbols utilized by the individual. A summary of element frequencies would show that the Ute's concerns depend upon social tensions in such a way that an atomistic treatment of the elements might lose sight of these larger patterns. If, for instance, we listed such headings as Eggan uses for our data, we would detach dreams about specific physical hazards or elements of persecution and conflict, such as she uses, from their individual and social contexts. It is worthwhile to note, however, how the Ute persecutions and conflicts figure in dreams which relate to the authoritarian structure; or how physical hazards occur to the dreamer primarily where an authoritarian figure is urging him to be more industrious.

Ute dreams ordinarily occur in a context of events which are vivid in having the elements of the physical environment, animals, and situational features very much in evidence. Ute thinking, itself, is not abstracted out of environment and situational contexts. There is, indeed, very little necessity for abstract thinking or hypothetical futures, which are not at once strongly contaminated by the conditions of the present. In other words, Ute dreams, however much they might reflect wishes, unreal motivations, and distortions of possible events, nevertheless were devoted to the work of "problem-solving" according to the situations confronting an individual and a family in a social milieu. Since these problems are individualistic variations on common stress features in the culture, it is not surprising that the shamanistic religious form handles these as individual and family problems under some general rule of analysis.

We have already seen how the features of age and individual experience operate both on the side of stress-producing factors and on the side of shamanistic controls. In most societies beyond this shamanistic level in evolution, the religious organization is less centered in the individual or family and centers less in the typical demands society makes upon these two related systems than is the case with the Ute. Their religion is, therefore, therapy; whereas, in most nonshamanistic societies, group and cult activities will reflect more of the schematic segmentation of social groups. Ute ceremonies are, therefore, crisis ceremonials concerned with long life, health, and vigor (13), or where the larger band group in society becomes involved, they are vehicles for obtaining and dispensing such therapeutic power (14–16). The three Ute ceremonies which may involve the total band or large band segments are the Sun Dance, the Bear Dance, and the Peyote Rite. In all of these, individual curing is a special part of the ceremonial. In the Bear Dance period, for example, the springtime camps of the Ute not only convene for this ritual, but provide the setting for other individual and family ceremonies (16). The chief feature of the Sun Dance is the attainment of power and the adjunctive curing by those who are noted for their curing powers (15). The Peyote Rite, most recent of all, was frankly used by parts of band groupings in a revitalization of shamanistic practices (14). Even minor dances which recurred in the spring and summer period of band group consolidation had connections with shamanism as attached or coexistent features (21). While the seasonal character of Ute ceremonies was heightened in the spring period as the bands convened, one can note that both individual and family problems and tensions which had grown up in scattered family camps were dealt with at such times. Shamans were more accessible and their individuality merged also according to principles of maintaining social continuity.

Kluckhohn has also listed ways by which myths and rituals protect "cultural continuity" through the stabilization periodically of social functions (10). He has also asked how ritual and myth become rewarding enough in individual daily lives so that they continue "to prevail at the expense of more rational responses" (10, pp. 55–70). Among the Ute, where the family and individual emerge as the most important units in the society and where the band is almost temporary and seasonal in character, the whole emphasis in religion is to achieve more rational responses or realistic activities on the part of family and individual. In Kluckhohn's terms, the emotional life of the Ute, requiring discharge, seizes upon culturally sanctioned forms in the society as the individual copes with his typical problems in the economic and social scene. Kluckhohn's further suggestion, that these cultural forms are used by the individual as "mechanisms of defense," is overtly recognized by the Ute in accordance with quasi-psychoanalytic principles.

Therapy is central in Ute religion because the economic life and social pattern make unusual demands upon two areas, the individual and the family. The social pattern is such that larger groups are not often involved. There is, further, no concern about crops, domesticated animals, a future life, or a notion of good conduct leading to inevitable rewards. Among the Ute, the purpose of life is living in a highly dynamic present, and in keeping with this, the individual and family must remain ready to cope with current and immediate emergencies.

Ute Rorschachs in a limited series that were studied by Hauck are consistent with these observations (8). Hauck claims that the Ute in Rorschach performance see "the forest and not the trees." Environmental changes are seen under gross categories, the large headings being used, no doubt, because of the unreality of the Rorschach blot to a naturalistically inclined people. This tendency to be concrete-minded and to fit things into neat pigeonholes is consistent with the experience of people who do not use general abstractions, but instead are constantly pitted against nature. As Hauck notes, the Ute prefer to classify each new experience in a contextual or established framework rather than to generalize upon something so impressionistic as an inkblot. In actual life, Ute are more willing to pay attention to the details of the situation since these are realistically presented in nature and have not become an abstraction on cardboard. Hauck tellingly states that, generally speaking, most of the Utes look upon the inkblots as if they were actually supposed to represent something. Consequently, their questions, as to whether some portion of a blot may be a particular object or the whole thing represents a "bear rug," were typical of their general awareness of contexts, and their interest in concrete aspects of nature (8).

Beyond the therapy with which Ute religion is primarily connected, all other ceremonies are family and individual rituals concerned with the life cycle. In most of these, the family shaman officiates. Because shamanism is so uniquely designated as the religious organization in the society, the theory of shamanistic power also contains, besides power for good, its counterpart in power for evil. If, for example, one promises a shaman a certain payment and then fails to produce it, the power may fall into a rage and call for its victim. Witchcraft or sorcery, once started, keeps calling for blood. There are recorded cases where a shaman himself pleads with his power, but to no avail. Since the outcome of sorcery is to cause illness, misfortune, and death, the social sanctions against it are severe. When death from witchcraft was established in former days by the diagnosis of another medicine man, the outcome would be a feud, in which the Ute family angrily attempted to wipe out its loss by killing the sorcerer. Thus, the toll paid for this highly realistic therapy procedure is its equally individualistic interpretation in the society at large. In one famous myth, when Sunavawi the Wolf, acting as a trickster, attempts to cure White-Crown Sparrow and is actually practicing sorcery, the sick person's relatives call upon Wild Duck, the first shaman, for another diagnosis. The outcome of this story is that Sunavawi is killed on the spot.

The role of therapy in Ute religion is, therefore, premised upon the structure and functioning of this particular society. From the point of view of epidemiology, the chief disturbances in the culture to mobility and family harmony are reflections of the particular stress system (18). The time is long past when one approached the therapeutic and research tasks of psychiatry with the naive belief that man is everywhere the same. As we have seen from the Rorschach differentials on the Ute, as well as from allusions to abundant case material, Ute processes in cognition, perception, and emotional tension varied from those of other peoples in a manner consistent with their cultural differences.

Hallowell, in his lifelong study of a Northeastern Indian tribe, the Ojibwa, has documented such differences in case materials, Rorschach performances, and cognitive processes in another culture (7). Particularly noteworthy have been Hallowell's discussions of cultural factors affecting not only the values orientation in this culture, but perceptual processes in space or time orientation as well. Hallowell has stated in his valuable book that "a human level of existence implies much more than existence conceived in purely organic terms." In areas of perception and cognition, the Utes similarly show variations that are built upon their unique cultural experience. Their individual adjustments are, as the dream material particularly points up, reactions to family and situational context.

It may be asked then, since the mobility factor has diminished in the lives of modern Utes, whether the dream materials should not reflect this change as well. However, at the time we were studying the Southern Ute, the westernmost band, the *Weminutc*, was still living in tents and moving throughout their terrain. This band even preserved to some extent the pattern of families moving up into the hills or mountains in the warmer seasons of the year. Ute Mountain on their reservation was such a retreat. For the two eastern bands, a limited mobility occurred in travel between two reservations, at Ignacio and at Ute Mountain. In the main, however, the substitution for mobility demands was upon industriousness and proper adherence to the Ute way of life. In this last area, on both southern reservations, the conflicts between older and younger generations, in respect to such values, were heightened by acculturation rather than diminished. As a matter of fact, most dream materials were collected on the more acculturated Ignacio side of the picture, where the intergeneration conflict or pace of acculturation was most intensified, and where dream phenomena reflected this rapid change (13). The Southern Paiute, ranging in the general vicinity of Allen Canyon, Utah, were extremely mobile and would most resemble the *Weminutc* band in respect to the mobility factor.

To a large extent, our materials on dream analysis, gathered in a changing society, continued to reflect the strains and stresses of authority conflicts within the family, as well as pressures toward industriousness and cultural conformity in this changing scene. While no dream materials were gathered among Northern Ute, their pace of acculturation would appear to be still more rapid than that of the *Weminutc* and Allen Canyon Paiute (12). A comparison of the dream materials from these various levels of acculturation would be instructive in denoting whether the faster pace of acculturation is always accompanied by greater intergeneration conflict.

The whole discovery of anthropology has been that the element of culturally symbolized experience produces not a uniformity, but a diversity in human existence. Given the basic differences in their economic way of life, the Ute have fashioned a system in religion which emphasizes their necessary values. In viewing their dreams from a psychological and social point of view, one recognizes the impact of family members upon the individual, as well as the larger context affecting family life in general. While the principles of dream analysis in Ute therapy may not be universally applicable to all societies, they are remarkably well suited to Ute cultural experience. This is why Ute shamans, to this very day, exercise an enormous influence upon their tribesmen, and, far from being assessed as the compensated neurotics of their culture, they are widely regarded as the pillars of society. Subsumed under their functions in social leadership and ethical-religious thinking, comes their constant functioning in relation to the psychological and social health of their community. Every Ute informant who knew anything about this community could provide the author with an extensive list of actual cures that shamans had accomplished. This total integration of the cultural values, the religious system, and the active meeting of the needs of people living this way of life cannot be expected to withstand the increasing tempo of change among the Southern Ute.

In the future transitions from shamanism to modern medicine, it is hoped that the values of psychological care will not be lost from the Ute scene. Every Ute lives out his life in a constant homeostatic relationship with his total social environment. His unique individuality is matched by variations, often subtle, in the structure and functioning of his family. But just as his own life has its cycle, so cycles may be discerned in the families composing such cultural communities. In order to understand dream, delusion, and cultural stress systems, obviously the culture itself must be understood in addition to the family and the individual. Ute religion, basically therapeutic in character, will only be supplanted by current modern science if its function of producing health and some modicum of cultural continuity are preserved. In this transition, it is hoped that some essential values of the older culture will play a role.

BIBLIOGRAPHY

1. Blanchard, P.: "A study of subject matter and motivation of children's dreams." *Journal of Abnormal and Social Psychology*, 1926, vol. 21, pp. 24–37.

2. Bogoras, W.: *The Chukchee*. Jesup Expedition Report (7), 1904–1909, Memoir XI. New York: American Museum of Natural History.

3. Devereux, G.: "Dream learning and individual ritual differences in Mohave shamanism." *American Anthropologist*, 1957, vol. 59, pp. 1036–1045.

4. Eggan, D.: "The manifest content of dreams: A challenge to social science." *American Anthropologist*, 1952, vol. 54, pp. 469–484.

5. ———: "The personal use of myth in dreams." *Journal of American Folklore*, 1955, vol. 68, pp. 445–453.

6. Foster, J. C., and Anderson, J. E.: "Unpleasant dreams in childhood." *Child Development*, 1936, vol. 7, pp. 77–84.

7. Hallowell, A. I.: *Culture and Experience*. Philadelphia: University of Pennsylvania Press, 1955.

8. Hauck, P. A.: *Ute Rorschach Performances and Some Notes on Field*

Problems and Methods. Salt Lake City: University of Utah Anthropological Papers, 23, 1955.

9. Kimmins, C. W.: "Children's dreams." In *Handbook of Child Psychology* (C. Murchison, ed.). Worcester: Clark University Press, 1931, pp. 533–536.

10. Kluckhohn, C.: "Myth and rituals: A general theory." *Harvard Theological Review,* 1942, vol. 35, pp. 45–79.

11. Kroeber, A. L.: "Psychosis or social sanction." In *The Nature of Culture.* Chicago: University of Chicago Press, 1952, chap. 39, pp. 310–319.

12. Lang, G. O.: *A Study in Culture Contact and Culture Changes: The White-rocks Utes in Transition.* Salt Lake City: University of Utah Anthropological Papers, 15, 1953.

13. Opler, Marvin K.: "The Southern Ute of Colorado." *In Acculturation in Seven American Indian Tribes* (R. Linton, ed.). New York: Appleton-Century-Crofts, 1940.

14. ———: "The character and history of the Southern Ute Peyote Rite." *American Anthropologist,* 1940, vol. 42, pp. 463–478.

15. ———: "The integration of the Sun Dance in Ute religion." *American Anthropologist,* 1941, vol. 43, pp. 550–572.

16. ———: "Colorado Ute Indian Bear Dance." *Southwestern Lore,* Sept., 1941, pp. 21–30.

17. ———: "Fact and fancy in Ute peyotism." *American Anthropologist,* 1942, vol. 44, pp. 151–159.

18. ———: "Psychoanalytic techniques in social analysis." *Journal of Social Psychology,* 1942, vol. 15, pp. 91–127.

19. ———: "The origins of Comanche and Ute." *American Anthropologist,* 1943, vol. 45, pp. 155–158.

20. ———: "The Ute Indian War of 1879." *El Palacio,* 1939, vol. 46, pp. 255–262.

21. ———: "The Southern Ute Dog-Dance and its reported transmission to Taos." *New Mexico Anthropologist,* Sept., 1939, pp. 1–7.

22. Sapir, E.: "Do we need a superorganic?" *American Anthropologist,* 1917, vol. 19, pp. 441–447.

23. White, L. A.: "The individual and the culture process." *Centennial, American Association for the Advancement of Science,* New York, 1948, pp. 74–81.

Jacob Fried

Department of Sociology and Anthropology
McGill University

5

ACCULTURATION AND MENTAL HEALTH
AMONG INDIAN MIGRANTS IN PERU *

This paper is concerned with the problems of Andean Indians, who, in very large numbers, are migrating from their native highland communities to coastal urban centers. The migration has assumed such proportions that it has become a serious economic, social, medical, and psychiatric problem; *economic* in that the food-producing populations are leaving the land and not being successfully absorbed in the urban work setting; *social* in that the large numbers of Indians, culturally distinct in their language, dress, work habits, and skills, are unable to engage in social and economic activities on the same footing as non-Indian coastal or urban populations, and thus become a large minority in need of special governmental care and protection; *medical* in that the changes in altitude, climate, and diet affect the migrants, putting them under a grave physiological strain in adapting to the new physical and social environment; and finally, *psychiatric* in that the combination of these features suggests that these Indians are under severe handicaps in their struggle to adapt, and as a result may well be responding by a high rate of illness, both physical and mental.

* The research was undertaken as part of a program in *Transcultural Mental Health Studies* developed jointly by the Department of Psychiatry and the Department of Sociology and Anthropology of McGill University. The writer is indebted to Mr. A. L. Lawes (Montreal) and the McGill University Faculty of Graduate Studies for travel grants, and to Dr. E. Wittkower (Department of Psychiatry, McGill), Dr. A. Seguin and Dr. S. Zapata (Department of Psychiatry, Hospital Obrero of Lima), Dr. J. Matos, Mr. A. Montalvo, Mr. E. Flores (Department of Anthropology, University of San Marcos, Lima) and Dr. W. Blanchard (Cornell University Peru Project, Vicos) for invaluable assistance in organizing and carrying out field work in Peru.

BASIC THEORETICAL FORMULATIONS

In the summer of 1956 the writer joined Dr. C. Alberto Seguin, head of the Department of Psychiatry of the Hospital Obrero, Lima, in the task of organizing a research project to study the effects of migration on the mental health of Andean Indians. The point of departure for this study was Seguin's experience over a period of several years with hundreds of Indians who were referred to his psychiatric section after having passed through a series of other hospital departments. They displayed an astonishing range of physical symptoms which could not be successfully treated, and in addition showed anxiety and depression as part of the clinical picture. Three significant facts appeared in case histories of such patients: they were Indians and hence culturally distinct from the rest of the hospital admissions; they had recently migrated from the Andean highlands; and they were experiencing grave difficulties in their attempt to adjust to city life.

From all over the world psychiatrists are reporting similar findings. Migration is a factor in the etiology of mental ill health, and very specifically of psychosomatic disorders.

Dr. Eng Kung Yeh (Formosa): "The outstanding characteristic of the clinical picture of both neurotics and psychotics among the group of migrated patients [i.e., Mainland Chinese] as compared with the group of Formosan born [is the] . . . great tendency to utilize somatic symptoms in neurotic patients of the migrated group."

Dr. Abraham Weinberg (Israel): "There are indications of psychosomatic diseases among certain groups of the population; for instance: bronchial asthma among immigrants from Iraq."

Dr. D. C. Maddison (Australia): "There is a substantially higher percentage of Polish migrants in mental hospitals than would be expected from the incidence rate for the country as a whole." *

Thus, it is not only exotic tribal or technologically backward Indians or Africans who suffer from the transition to new surroundings.

In a carefully controlled study of hospital admissions for the period 1939–1941 in New York State, Malzberg and Lee (9) concluded that "the rates of first admission to hospital for mental disease were markedly higher for migrants than for non-migrants, regardless of sex or color.

---

* These statements were taken from answers to a questionnaire sent to psychiatrists in thirty-eight different countries concerning incidence and frequency of mental disorders.

. . . Our second conclusion is that the rates of first admission for total psychoses were much higher for recent than for earlier migrants."

Having established the fact that mental ill health is statistically correlated with migration, we must ask what factors attending the migration are actively direct or contributory agents. The concept of sociocultural "stress" endured by migrants is one of the most prominent explanations offered by both anthropologists (11, 12) and psychiatrists. The migrant enters a new social environment where he must learn new skills, attitudes, and values. The old and the new clash. Tyhurst (22, p. 209) explains that the migrant, moving from one culture to another, may also try to move from one social class to another so that it is not only a matter of learning new customs or skills, which might be relatively easy, but changing deeply held attitudes or values, which is a more dangerous process. Ruesch (17) also emphasizes the great importance of the transitional period in which the older responses are not appropriate to deal effectively with present realities of daily life, and the task of changing values and rearranging behavior can be disastrous. Overwhelmed by some immediate problem, the migrant experiences frustration and responds with anger; this makes him hostile and impedes his further acculturation, leading to further frustration, etc.

From a psychodynamic point of view, the consequences of this period of cultural transition is a growing isolation, insecurity and helplessness. Tyhurst (22, p. 209) states that ". . . [the migrant] tries to find an absolute answer either with an obsessional preoccupation with self leading to somatic symptoms, or with the environment."

The migrant, who is a culturally disoriented person, is subject to special strains which exacerbate the tensions within the personality and he is at the same time bereft of the culturally useful means of reducing these tensions (11, p. 73). He may make use of his body, then, to express resultant psychic conflicts, and the choice of organs expressing the conflict will depend either on accidental or constitutional weakness, or as some psychiatrists believe, on psychosexual developmental factors and character type (2).

In the case of Peruvian Indian migrants there exists an additional and direct physiological factor which produces somatic disturbances. This was investigated thoroughly by the Peruvian physiologist, Carlos Monge, and his associates of the Instituto de Biología Andina, who demonstrated that migrants from altitudes of over 10,000 feet suffer a considerable physiological trauma in adapting to life at sea level. Monge (15) has shown how the physiology of maintaining life on an active basis in the rarified air of the Andean highlands requires an unusually high lung capacity, and a blood chemistry in which the numbers of oxygen-bearing red blood corpuscles must be double that needed at sea level. Thus the *normal* Indian who is born, works, and reproduces at high altitudes is different in significant physiological and morphological criteria from the normal coastal or sea-level inhabitant. This research amply documents the severely traumatic stress that is put upon the migrating high-altitude man, and often results in serious impairment of ability to work. It also lowers resistance to disease, especially of the respiratory tract. Even after three or four months on the coast, subjects still showed chemical, physiological, and morphological deviations very different from those considered normal for coastal inhabitants (14). This clinical picture is now generally known as Monge's "adaption syndrome."

Seguin, while not denying the physiological trauma experienced by Indians on their translation to sea level, suggested that this did not explain the wide range of observed phenomena. The type of breakdown among hundreds of Indians observed by Seguin seemed to conform to a special pattern, and going beyond Monge he labeled it the "psycho-somatic disadaption syndrome" (20).

The clinical picture of Seguin's syndrome included the following categories of symptoms: *1*) *circulatory:* cardiovascular failures, arrhythmias; *2*) *gastrointestinal:* gastritis, peptic ulcer, colitis, hemorrhoids, etc.; *3*) *respiratory:* bronchitis, pulmonary tuberculosis, etc.; *4*) *rheumatic;* *5*) *neurologic:* neuritic neuralgias, headaches, migraines, etc. All these somatic reactions were accompanied by *depression and anxiety.* Seguin observed that by focusing attention upon the purely physiological processes of adaption and attempting to relieve these physical symptoms, one may overlook the very significant aspect of maladaption of Indians to their sociocultural environment. Indian patients arrived with physical complaints, but significantly enough the illnesses seemed to coincide with crises in the social sphere of adaption, e.g., death or illness, bad news from home, loss of job, difficulties with fellow workers, unhappy love affairs, etc.

The syndrome appears, according to Seguin, generally in young men or women, age fifteen to twenty-five, of Indian or Mestizo extraction who come from small agricultural communities of the Sierras. The time elapsing between arrival in Lima and the appearance of the symptom varies; sometimes it is short, one or two weeks, or sometimes it may be a year.

It seems clear that there are at least two pathogenic sets of forces at work among Indians: *1*) Monge's "adaption syndrome" that no migrant can escape the difficult period of transition in which his body must fight to establish a new physiological equilibrium; *2*) Seguin's formulation that at this critical period migrants also have to overcome severe problems in social, economic, and cultural adjustment to the city.

Since immigrants in Europe and America are reported as having excessively high rates of physical and mental illnesses, Indian migrants who come from Andean regions and must endure special physiological stress must be even more susceptible to illness. If urban European immigrants in urban American centers can experience rejection and social isolation, then the rural, very backward, illiterate Indian coming to Lima must overcome even greater cultural barriers.

HISTORICAL AND CULTURAL BACKGROUND

This section traces the history of population shifts and seasonal migration patterns. The modern scene represents but another chapter in a story that stretches back into prehistoric times. The Inca Empire as part of its military and political strategy shifted whole tribes about the Sierras. Later the establishment of Spanish colonial rule seriously disrupted many Indian communities, causing tens of thousands to flee into remote regions still free from Spanish domination.

Soon after the conquest the Indian agricultural communities again stabilized themselves. They remained firmly rooted to the soil and effectively maintained the essential organization and ethos of traditional culture. Spanish technique of economic exploitation left native life relatively free of destructive prohibition. After an initial period in which Indian culture absorbed much of Spanish material culture, as well as certain social and religious elements, a resilient community emerged, preserving its own integrity while acquiescing to the economic demands of the Spaniard (8).

A castelike system arose. Indians were in a separate category, sharply differentiated from Spaniards; from *Mestizos* (Hispanicized mixed bloods, or *Cholos* as the Sierran variant is called); and *Criollos* (Peruvian born, but of Spanish antecedents).

One of the demands Indian communities had to meet was to supply manpower for the rich mines and vast haciendas.

Autonomous Indian agricultural communities were threatened by economic pressures resulting from bad harvests and droughts. Continual subdivision of land by inheritance practices and loss to haciendas made their situation precarious. Many Indians, poverty stricken and landless, became peons on haciendas where they were given parcels of land to till in exchange for their labor. Neither mode of economic adjustment was adequate to provide economic security and migratory wage labor was often needed as a supplement.

Today, of approximately 3,000,000 Indians of Sierra Peru, some hundreds of thousands work annually in the Andean mines, on the great coastal plantations of cotton and sugar cane, or on road construction and other public works. Uncounted hundreds of thousands seek temporary agricultural employment in their local Sierra region from Mestizo land owners, and provide occasional unskilled labor in small towns and hamlets.

During World War II new economic developments started another type of migration, this time from the Sierras to industrial zones that were urban. In postwar Peru modern technological innovations in transportation make possible fast and cheap mobility between regions formerly virtually isolated. The economic upsurge due to heavy internal demands for Peruvian minerals and agricultural products is expanding the labor market, affecting and attracting Andean labor. While in the Sierras droughts and land shortages, disease and overpopulation, and chronic unemployment still typify the problems facing the Indians, the coastal centers with their expanding economic horizons offer attractive alternatives. Postwar salaries for unskilled labor are about ten times as high on the coast as in the Andes. [See Almenara (3) for a review of the social and economic problems created by the modern rural exodus.]

A summary of the cultural position of modern Indian communities is necessary to establish the intensity and direction of culture change. First we will outline the principal features of culture in the recent historical past, and then give an example of a present-day hacienda community to show the increasing failure of the traditional order to maintain itself.

The most profound sentiments of Indians revolved about their dedication to home and soil. Despite pressures from the outside world that threatened to destroy the community by expropriating its lands, by forcing its members to make seasonal migrations, a powerful community spirit was maintained. Native forms of land distribution and use, as well as communal work aid patterns formed the basis of economic organization. Community social and political integration was maintained by a series of native officials, and expressed in participation in elaborately organized ceremonial *fiestas*. Native officials were at once respected members of the community, religious officers, and agents of social control empowered to exercise authority over the behavior of members of the community. Psychologically, the community provided security for the individual, giving him a strong focus of identification. He did not resent or struggle against his inferior status or his social isolation from the Mestizo world. He adopted a submissive and dependent attitude toward the powerful Mestizo and in return received the benefits of political nonresponsibility and paternalistic protection. He clung tenaciously to a distinctive costume and language (*Quechua*) and was unaffected by the Mestizos' ridicule of his social customs which involved extended drinking fests and a fondness for chewing coca leaves.

Now we turn to an account of the state and quality of community organization in a modern hacienda community, that of Vicos, located in the Callejon de Haylas, province of Ancash (5).

The methodological device used to determine the effectiveness of the social and economic organization of this Indian community focused upon the study of families undergoing some crisis serious enough to force a mobilization of family and extrafamily assistance. In the context of an actual stress situation it was possible to see how social forces were operating, and to compare expectations with actual performance. Among the stress-producing situations chosen for special attention was that of an incapacitating illness. Since the obligation to work three days for the hacienda underpins the economic security of the peon, he must react strongly to this threat.

First it was necessary to identify all the social structures that exist in the community and then determine how they in fact contributed or did not contribute to assisting or resolving the problems of such individuals. We find in Vicos the structural outlines of a complete social organization. It includes sets of native officials with traditional powers to adjudicate disputes between families and among spouses, settle inheritance wrangles, and uphold the values and ideal norms of the culture. The rich *fiesta* complex provides a basis for the display of a prestige hierarchy through organized and elaborate religio-recreational events. There is discernible the outlines of a kinship organization based on the patrilineal *sib* (*casta*) which functions as a local grouping with corporate functions such as social and economic reciprocity; in times of illness work aid is provided, and widowers and orphans are incorporated into other households. Bilateral kin also provide work aid and emotional support in times of need. A network of spiritual kinsmen (*compadrazco*) provides for the broadening of interpersonal relations beyond the kin group. Godparents can intervene in inner family disputes, lend money, or offer work aid. The household, which is most typically of a nuclear family composition, is the true core of deepest security, for it is a socioeconomic unit almost autonomous in its functioning.

In Vicos, then, a traditional social organization and way of life persists, but how effectively does it in fact function? The first striking conclusion resulting from analysis of case histories of illnesses is that households are so jealously inner directed that extended social obligations of any kind do not have any priority. In case after case a picture of woeful neglect, refusal to aid or even visit the seriously ill by brothers, sisters, or *compadres* emerged; this despite ideal patterns in which support and aid could be expected from members of one's kin group or *compadrazco* relations. What has priority in Vicosino life is the constant struggle to maintain and extend security through acquiring and exploiting land and animals by means of the effective manpower of the household.

Despite the existence of some form of unity in the community as a whole, symbolized in the person of the native official, there is a marked lack of actual social structural bonds that unite families who must rely on their own immediate resources for security. Interfamily strife based on jealous economic rivalry over land is common.

Native officials readily concede that their traditional powers are weakening and that in actual cases of intra- and interfamily disputes, godparents or hacienda officials are called upon to intervene. If we exempt the well-organized fiesta complex, then no strong mechanisms for mutual cooperation function effectively. Communal work aid (*minka*) is avoided as being too expensive, since payment in food and drink is necessary. The Vicosino who is not a member of a large and healthy household is indeed in a seriously vulnerable position. The case histories of ill widowers and widows, that is, members of fragmented households, clearly showed the tragic fate of persons bereft of security-providing family members, for some were utterly neglected by kinsmen or neighbors and directly threatened with starvation.

Having discussed the cultural situation of Sierran Indian communities, we can now concern ourselves with the sociocultural adjustments of migrants in Lima. The nature of the migration is a complex one. Single men and women as well as whole family units are involved. While the great bulk of these migrants find residence in the incredibly squalid squatter settlements that have mushroomed among the arid hills on the outskirts of the city, many live in private homes as servants, or have settled in the slums of working-class districts. Although the most powerful motive for migration is an economic one, a whole complex of factors usually accompanies this central theme—such as the need to escape intra- or interfamily conflicts, unhappy love affairs, the escape from responsibilities or unwanted spouses, the desire for adventure or education.

In order to study the urban Indian, research was carried out by the writer in the squatter settlement of San Cosme, located just above the main market of Lima, the *Mercado Mayorista*. It produced the following picture: The earning power of married Indian men is so meager and uncertain that in most cases it must be supplemented by the efforts of their wives. Typically the Indian male is an unskilled laborer, a porter, a watchman, or engaged in construction work, while his wife, if he is married, very often sells fruit or vegetables in a market. Some enterprising women sell lottery tickets in the center city. The work history patterns of all men interviewed showed periodic unemployment.

From the subjective viewpoint of many informants, it was clear that many felt depressed and disillusioned by their mode of life. They expressed this in terms of anxiety and concern over their inability to buy sufficient food or clothing or save any money. An investigation of housing showed that Indians in this squatter settlement often live in more wretched and crowded quarters than they occupied in the Sierras. Many families share single rooms with either married children or relatives; the renting of a half room is common.

Apart from economically generated anxieties, the problem of health features most prominently in the consciously expressed problems of migrants. Health and ability to work are the front lines of objectively and subjectively felt security, for to become ill means to slip behind in the daily battle to earn enough to survive. In the cloudy and chill winter of Lima, where the sun is shut out by clouds that rarely dissipate from June through September, colds and influenza often lead to pneumonia. In crowded quarters without sanitation facilities, with a diet almost devoid of vitamins and vital food elements, illness is almost unavoidable. At one time or another all persons interviewed had been ill, and chronic aches and pains are recognized as accompanying hazards of life on the coast.

The immediate social environment surrounding the Indian families in San Cosme is limited to a few immediate family members resident nearby, or in some cases to acquaintances from the same Andean community. A squatter settlement is a chance conglomeration of Indians and Mestizos from every poverty-stricken zone of the coast and the Andes. Neighbors are typically treated by recent migrants with suspicion and apprehension. Some of their fears have an objective basis, such as fear of robbery, and others are projections of their inability to relate to an unfamiliar and chaotic environment. Indians isolate themselves from any contacts with Mestizo neighbors and show a similar lack of interest in cultivating friendships among Indian migrants not members of their own home communities.

Despite residence in the city the Indian's primary focus of emotion, loyalty and concern remain rooted in his family in the Sierras. In the city he has left behind the majority of security-providing social figures, his parents, kinsmen, and *compadres,* and is unable or unwilling to form new useful social bonds, i.e., friendships, memberships in clubs or societies. Thus, the impoverishment of social relations is most marked.

In terms of recreational patterns, the Indian both cannot and will not take advantage of the rich resources of urban life—movies, museums, carnivals, sport events—but maintains in abbreviated form Sierran patterns which include heavy drinking of *chicha* (corn beer) and cane alcohol, and coca leaf chewing. The serious consequences of this partial maintenance of Sierran cultural features in an urban setting will be reviewed in a following section.

The foregoing studies have established that the social and economic order of the Sierran Indian communities is giving way to extensive changes and therefore producing more and more dilemmas and difficulties for its members. Both Indian migrants who go to the coast to overcome a financial crisis but fully expect to return to an Indian existence, and those who have abandoned the Indian community as a place of residence and a way of life are reacting to an increasingly unviable situation. In certain Sierran communities one can already note the change from a castelike status to that of Mestizo (1). Neither the Sierran Indian nor the urban migrant can escape severe cultural strains. Sayres (18, 19) shows how Indian communities in the process of abandoning their traditional culture and struggling toward the Mestizo's individualized economic and social order produce high rates of severe psychological upsets, known locally as *trastornos* [this is a "magic fright" type of manifestation of the sort described by Gillin (6)].

On the other hand, the adjustments made by Indians to the city are so precarious and marginal that these Indians are especially vulnerable to physical and mental breakdown. They come from one situation that does not fulfill their now subjectively felt need to another in which they fail to gain a really improved standard of living or a socially meaningful participation in the urban setting.

MENTAL HEALTH AND ACCULTURATION

The foregoing cultural summary gives sufficient background material to broaden the analysis of the nature of the sociocultural stresses that are contributing to ill health among urban Indians.

Murphy (16, p. 192) concluded in his study of mental ill health among refugees in England that the rates of mental breakdown are highest when the local population is definitely unfriendly, and mixing is not attempted. In Lima, the Indian experiences an even more striking isolation because of his inferior caste position and the even more extreme differences in culture. The Indian is considered as "primitive" and any kind of social commingling is ruled out. Since the Indian joins no clubs, attends no churches, and participates in no political activities, he has too few points of contact with non-Indians.

The Indians interviewed in San Cosme made no attempt to "assimilate," yet they nevertheless are being exposed to conditions to which they cannot hope to adjust without making changes. They are maintaining a strong "cultural distance." However, many of their children are now attending schools. Can we predict greater difficulties for this next generation? Initial impressions indicate that the more conservatively "Indian" type of migrant, unable to respond to the new environment with changes in his functional mode of life, responds to outstanding difficulties by direct and simple somatization of his struggles and failures.

Another factor which is retarding culture change is the absence of an effective ethnic community. The well-integrated ethnic community has long been recognized as a powerful aid to the recent migrant in overcoming the first shocks of change. It provides him with orientation and a sense of security within a familiar world of countrymen. Later it may retard further acculturation, as can be noted among the ghetto type of ethnic communities in large cities in North America. In Lima, the Indian has no such effective community within which he might secure guidance and aid. True, some associations of "progressive" Indians have been organized, but the majority of migrants neither belong to such societies nor get vital aid from them. The squatter settlements may contain large numbers of Indians but they are not organized into an ethnic community. The only effective source of aid and security for the Indian remains his family. On the other hand, some Mestizos in squatter settlements are showing signs of interest in organizing for some collective action. The difference, again, is a matter of culture; the Sierra Mestizo is a variant, albeit backward, of Western European culture, and the Indian is not.

Indians maintain powerful emotional ties with their Sierran families. Many migrants are deeply disturbed by the poverty and life crises their home families must endure and send packages of food and other gifts frequently. When serious illness or a death occurs, they will allow no consideration to deter them from returning home. As a result there is a continual shunting back and forth from city to the Sierras by persons who can ill afford the expense. In some cases an Indian will give up his job—suddenly, without notice—to disappear mysteriously for months. This older pattern of mobility can be tolerated as part of the rural agricultural complex, but in wage labor such "capriciousness" is undesirable. Thus, the Indian does not seem disciplined or dependable as a worker.

A further complication is that the Indian husband or wife will leave his spouse unattended in Lima for months while he or she returns to settle some family business, such as inheritance disputes or a marriage. Such temporary family instability is tolerable in extended households in the Sierras, or in situations where the spouse can take the children to the home of a parent or sibling; this is a common occurrence in the culture of the Sierras. Its effect on urban Indians can be devastating. It is not uncommon to find a woman living alone for months with several children, completely dependent upon her own economic activities to provide food and shelter. To work she must either take her children with her or leave them behind without care.

Another culture pattern concerns savings. Traditionally the Indian migrated for economic motives. Since he earned very little, it was necessary to be exceedingly careful of expenditures for basic necessities. Often, the Indian endangered his health, and tragically many failed to survive to return to the Sierras. This pattern is apparent still among recent Indian migrants. In the attempt to save money they give up foods necessary for an adequate diet. To combat the terrible effects of the altitude, the harsh climate, and the crowded and unsanitary conditions of their dwellings, they should enrich their diet, but on the contrary, they further impoverish it. This can become a vicious circle. To save money the Indian lives in wretched quarters on an inadequate diet. This makes him ill so he cannot work, and thus has less money.

Another feature of the life of the Sierras is the extensive use of alcoholic beverages and coca leaves as the very cornerstone of all social life. No social occasion, secular or religious, can take place without drinking. All births, deaths, marriages, and funerals involve social drinking, and the religious *fiesta* complex results in organized drinking that is carried on for days. Such drinking actually occurs under conditions where strong social controls are operative so that aggression and antisocial behavior are kept within certain confines rather successfully (10). But it must be recognized that the expense involved in buying alcohol and coca leaves is a heavy burden on the economic potentialities of an agricultural people living at subsistence or near subsistence levels (4, pp. 5–10). Caravedo and other Peruvian health experts believe that the Indian's ceremonial and social involvement with drinking seriously prevents his using his economic resources to raise his standard of living, and is therefore a powerful cause of his backward condition. Sierran Indians, for example, were found by medical experts to suffer from a protein and vitamin deficiency, although they consume an enormous quantity of expensive alcoholic beverages. Further, the type of liquor favored is a crude cane alcohol which contains a very high percentage of near toxic impurities (4, p. 11).

There is strong evidence that the drinking pattern of Indians, culturally prescribed and socially well-controlled in the Sierran environment, becomes an area of serious danger for large numbers of Indians in Lima. If Mangin (10, p. 58) is correct in his observation that the Sierra Indian, despite his enormous alcoholic intake, shows a remarkable "dearth of alcohol-related pathology," then the astonishingly high figures of alcohol psychosis among Indians in the mental hospital, Victor L. Herrara, must be related to acculturation and migration.

In a study of total hospital admissions in the Lima mental hospital, Victor Larco Herrara, between 1938 and 1949, 772 cases were recorded under the category of alcoholic psychosis (4, pp. 30–31). Out of these,

100 or 12.9 per cent of the cases were Indians. (In the 1940 census, Indians were stated as forming 45.86 per cent of the total population). Another suggestive statistic shows that the highest percentage of alcohol psychosis was found among the group labeled Mestizo (68.7 per cent). Since in Peru this category of Mestizo must include many persons on the borderline of racial categories, the figure of 12.9 per cent for "Indians" is misleading. With the problem of *meztizaje* among Indians becoming increasingly important, this category must be carefully studied.

If we accept Mangin's formulation that a strong sense of social solidarity enhanced by ritual and convivial drinking, and combined with lack of conflict, guilt, or ambivalence connected with the overt act of drinking itself, accounts for a lack of alcohol-related psychosis in the Sierras, then the extremely high rate among Lima Indians must represent a new kind of situation in which drinking behavior now out of cultural context has disastrous consequences.

A useful preliminary hypothesis is that migrants will continue to respond to problem situations in the city with the psychological and cultural modes that they learned in childhood in their home communities as long as they do not have to face insurmountable problems. Previously effective patterns of behavior when applied out of context may be entirely dysfunctional. Because under distressing conditions his behavior patterns, attitudes, values, and skills are not effective, the migrant has at least four possible alternatives: 1) He can try to master new skills and attitudes and develop new sets of social contacts; 2) He can so restrict, narrow, or distort his contacts with the alien environment that he can get along with what he already has—the families studied in San Cosme represent this kind of adjustment; 3) He can give up and go home, which thousands in fact do without waiting long enough to experience acute mental or physical breakdown leading to hospitalization; 4) He can escape into illness. Seguin makes a strong case for this latter motive.

PSYCHIATRIC CONSIDERATIONS

Seguin (21, p. 408), reporting on the psychological significance of psychosomatic disturbances among his Indian patients, states:

In reality, the psychosomatic syndrome of disadaption is only a particular and quite exaggerated case of the very common picture of homesickness or nostalgia, the *morrina* of the Spaniards or the *saudade* of the Portuguese. Its importance rests on its not being a very frequently found reaction in Lima and its not being understood *because attention is focused on the examination of organs, disregarding the person,* (author's emphasis) a point of view causing a complete diagnostic and therapeutic disorientation (for migrants) . . . Superficially, the syndrome is a case of "flight into illness." [*]

Tyhurst's (22, pp. 205–208) study of forty-eight immigrants in the Montreal area is of special interest here since her sample concerns a group of patients all of whom are either domestics or laborers and so can be compared with Seguin's migrants. She distinguishes two psychological stages following arrival: *1)* a period lasting about two months characterized by a subjective sense of well-being, with increased psychomotor activities as a primitive way of getting rid of tension and anxiety concomitant with the strains of migration; *2)* a period in which the appreciation of the current social situation gradually forms and the individual becomes increasingly aware of language difficulties and differences in customs and values. As difficulties arise, there is a tendency to escape into fantasies of the happy past (nostalgia).

In the second period the psychiatric reactions tend to become obvious and reach their peak about six months after arrival. She notes the diagnostic categories and character of symptoms exhibit almost daily variability, and she distinguishes three main trends:

1. Suspiciousness and paranoid trends.
2. The presence of anxiety and depression.
3. Somatic complaints: (a) fatigue weakness, muscular or joint pains, insomnia, loss of appetite, nausea, trembling, shaky feelings; (b) peptic ulcer, ulcerative or mucous colitis, asthma; (c) tendency to change somatic symptoms from one system to another.

Thus, there seems to be a most remarkable parallel between Tyhurst's material and that reported by Seguin. Seguin reports the same psychological reactions of nostalgia, and his list of categories of somatic symptoms includes most of Tyhurst's category "somatic complaints," along with the appearance of depression and anxiety.

In fact, the only contrasts between the two sets of physical symptoms lie in the richer variety among the Indians. Seguin's list includes: *1) circulatory:* palpitations, tachycardia, extrasystole, pain in the precordial region, several chest paresthesias, dyspnea: *2) respiratory:* cough, dyspnea, difficulty in breathing, chest pains and aches; *3)* headaches.

[*] Seguin, C. Alberto: "Migration and psychosomatic disadaption." *Psychosomatic Medicine,* 1956, vol. 18, no. 5, pp. 404–409.

The most obvious explanation for this difference can be Monge's adaption syndrome. The Indian who migrates from altitudes above 10,000 feet has special problems not faced by European migrants. The difficulties with the circulatory and respiratory tracts are clearly a "normal" health hazard for anyone who is adapted to life at rarified altitudes. Even Indians who do not display the psychosomatic type of disorder may yet experience many of the above difficulties. Thus, to understand the psychosomatic syndrome of disadaption one must incorporate "Monge's disease" with heightened sociocultural stress concepts. Certainly all of the features shown by Indian patients cannot be ascribed solely to the physiological stress.

In order to understand the differences between reactions of Peruvian Indian patients as opposed to other migrants, we must inquire whether psychosomatic reactions are necessarily something novel, and appear in such a form only among migrating Indians as a result of the stress of coastal urban life.

Since Seguin specifically mentions that his "syndrome" appears among young men and women fifteen to twenty-five years old, we offer two parallel cases from the highland community of Vicos.

CASE 1

M.E., female, age approximately 20 years: Her physical complaints included severe diarrhea and heavy bodily swelling. She had suffered since early childhood from diarrheal attacks, but never so severe as the present instance. She was obsessed with the fear of dying, expressing great fear and anxiety. What preceded the attack, and indeed probably precipitated the illness, was a violent assault upon her by the parents of her sweetheart, who had received a letter from their son in which he appeared more concerned for M.E. than for their welfare. The parents reacted with jealous rage, calling M.E. an *objecto piojoso* (verminous), which caused her so much resentment and anger (*colera*) that its effect did not wear off for days. Finally, while herding cattle on a *puna* (high plain) she suddenly had a severe attack of diarrhea. In Indian concepts, she was seized by the Earth (*patza*) and was "frightened."

CASE 2

M.T., male, age 16 years: His physical complaints included diarrhea, bloody stools, pains in the stomach and small of the back, and swellings all over the body. He suffered from insomnia. He felt anxiety and depression (*locura*) and was subject to crying spells. During the night, unable to sleep, he paced about the house naked without feeling cold. He lacked appetite and could only eat meat. His first attack came when he fell out of a tree a year ago (the "Earth" seized him). His family history is a disturbed and unhappy one. His mother suffered a series of unhappy marital experiences, beginning when her husband died, and again when a second trial marriage had to be terminated due to the excessive cruelty of the man. M.E. was born out of wedlock. The mother had reacted to misfortunes with crying spells.

In both these cases there is no doubt a strong physical or medical reality factor. Many Indians suffer from diarrhea and internal parasites. Yet the psychological background is clearly important as a precipitating element, and fully satisfies the criteria of a psychosomatic reaction.

Until we have from combined psychiatric-medical-anthropological research a good knowledge of the types and patterns of illness, *and of reactions to illness* among Sierran Indians, we will not know how much of the psychosomatic syndrome displayed by migrating Indians appears as a result of the novel stress features of migration and culture change, or is merely an extension of pre-existing trends. Many of the Sierran Indians have, or have been exposed to, internal parasites and diseases of the respiratory tract, and suffer from dietary deficiencies, the effects of which may be masked or kept in check in their home environments. A precarious equilibrium which is maintained at home can be destroyed by the shocks of migration. Indians may well carry certain predisposing factors within them, which in combination with outside stresses overwhelm them.

Such materials concerning illness patterns of Sierra Indians are also extremely important because many of the reported symptoms of patients in Lima, containing references to seizure by the "Earth" or "Lake being," or to witchcraft, must not be considered as clear evidence of disturbed mental processes. A psychiatrist or physician unaware of the cultural conceptions concerning illness might well assign an Indian to psychiatric treatment when it is not really indicated. However, some mentally ill migrants will use such cultural expressions in a truly paranoid sense. Thus, both normal and abnormal Indians must be studied against the background of their culture. Mestizo or *costeño* cultural norms cannot be used in interpreting the meaning of the projective fantasies of Indian patients.

CONCLUSIONS

In the light of evidence assembled on migration and the impact of culture change on the mental health of Indian migrants to Lima, the following conclusions seem justified. The psychodynamic and sociocultural theoretical frameworks useful in analyzing the behavior of immigrants in Europe and America can be applied to the Peruvian scene, but there are at least two special features which must be considered: *1*) the physiological stress attendant upon descending from altitudes above 10,000 feet; *2*) the extreme differences between the cultures of the Sierran Indians and the coastal urban populations which magnify the dimensions of change required of the Indian.

Another complicating factor is that Indians come from the Sierras where increasing cultural change is producing many conflicts and dilemmas. In the city this situation is further aggravated as even more radical changes are introduced.

In this time of transition the Indian will maintain for many years a strong residue of deeply held values and attitudes which will impede assimilation of coastal cultural forms.

BIBLIOGRAPHY

1. Adams, Richard: "From caste to class in a Peruvian Sierra town." *Social Forces*, 1953, vol. 31, pp. 238–244.

2. Alexander, Franz, and Szasz, Thomas S.: "The psychosomatic approach in medicine." In *Dynamic Psychiatry* (Franz Alexander and Helen Ross, eds.). Chicago: University of Chicago Press, 1952, pp. 369–400.

3. Almenara, Guillermo: "Causas y efectos del exodo rural." *Informes sociales,* organo de la caja nacional de seguro social, April–June, 1954, no. 2, pp. 3–18.

4. Caravedo, Baltazar, and Vargas, Manuel Almeida: *El alcoholismo, problemo de salud publica.* Lima, Peru: Ministerio de salud publica y asistenci social, departamento de higiene mental, 1956.

5. Fried, Jacob: *The Social Organization and Value System of a Peruvian Hacienda Community: Vicos.* Unpublished manuscript, 1957.

6. Gillin, John: "Magic fright." *Psychiatry*, 1948, vol. 11, pp. 387–400.

7. ———: "Mestizo America." In *Most of the World* (R. Linton ed.) New York: Columbia University Press, 1949, pp. 156–211.

8. Kubler, George: "The Quechua in the colonial world." In *Handbook of South American Indians* (J. Steward, ed.). Washington, D.C.: Bureau of American Ethnology, Bulletin 143, 1946, pp. 331–410.

9. Malzberg, Benjamin, and Lee, Everett S.: *Migration and Mental Disease.* New York: Social Science Research Council, 1956.

10. Mangin, William: "Drinking among Andean Indians." *Quarterly Journal*

of *Studies on Alcohol* (Laboratory of Applied Biodynamics, Yale University), 1957, vol. 18, no. 1, pp. 55–66.

11. Mead, Margaret: "The concept of culture and the psychosomatic approach." *Psychiatry*, 1947, vol. 10, pp. 57–76.

12. ———: "The implications of culture change for personality development." *American Journal of Orthopsychiatry*, 1947, vol. 17, no. 4, pp. 663–645.

13. Mishkin, Bernard: "The contemporary Quechua." *Handbook of South American Indians* (J. Steward, ed.). Washington, D.C.: Bureau of American Ethnology, Bulletin 143, 1946, pp. 411–470.

14. Monge, Casinell C.: "Glucosa, acido lactido y acido piruvico al nivel del mar y en la altura." *Annales, facultad de medicine*, (Lima, Peru), 1949, vol. 32.

15. Monge, Carlos C.: *Acclimatization in the Andes*. Baltimore: Johns Hopkins Press, 1948.

16. Murphy, H. B. M.: "Refugee psychoses in Great Britain: Admissions to mental hospitals." In *Flight and Resettlement* (H. B. M. Murphy ed.; UNESCO series on Population and Culture). Paris: UNESCO, 1955, pp. 173–201.

17. Ruesch, J., et al: "Acculturation and illness." *Psychological Monographs*, 1948, vol. 62.

18. Sayres, William C.: "Status and magic fright." *America indigena*, 1955, vol. 15, no. 4, pp. 292–300.

19. ———: "Disorientation and status change." *Southwestern Journal of Anthropology*, 1956, vol. 12, no. 1, pp. 79–86.

20. Seguin, C. Alberto: "On the concept of psychosomatic medicine." *Acta Psychotherapeutica*, 1955, vol. 3, no. 4, pp. 304–312.

21. ———: "Migration and psychosomatic disadaption." *Psychosomatic Medicine*, 1956, vol. 18, no. 5, pp. 404–409.

22. Tyhurst, Libuse: "Psychosomatic and allied disorders." In *Flight and Resettlement* (H. B. M. Murphy, ed.; UNESCO series on Population and Culture). Paris: UNESCO, 1955, pp. 202–213.

Section II

PEOPLE OF THE
SOUTH PACIFIC
—WELL AND ILL

Melford E. Spiro

Department of Anthropology
University of Washington

6

CULTURAL HERITAGE, PERSONAL TENSIONS,
AND MENTAL ILLNESS IN A SOUTH SEA CULTURE

Although the literature on mental illness in primitive societies is by no means scanty, reliable knowledge concerning the types and incidence of psychopathology in these societies remains a scientific desideratum. Nor is this surprising. Specialists in primitive societies, the cultural anthropologists, are often either disinterested or untrained in psychiatry, and psychiatric specialists rarely conduct anthropological field work. This gap in our knowledge is regrettable on two counts. Students of culture remain ignorant of the range of psychobiological variability within which cultures can function, and psychiatrists remain fairly culture bound in their theorizing about psychopathology.

That culture and personality are interdependent variables is a proposition that today evokes almost universal assent. It is generally assumed, moreover, that some cultures are more pathogenic than others. Simple cultures, for example, are thought by some writers to produce less emotional strain than more complex cultures. It is frequently noted in support of this view that contact between aboriginal and European peoples is a pathogenic situation par excellence. The (emotionally) crucial variable in societies with simple cultures may not, however, be cultural simplicity, but some other associated characteristic, such as relative isolation, a high degree of cultural integration, relative social and cultural homogeneity, etc. Available data seem to indicate that, instead of being correlated with a simple-complex cultural dichotomy, both the incidence and types of psychopathology exhibit marked variability. Although this simple typology is useful and sometimes crucial for certain types of institutional analyses, its explanatory value for personality analysis would seem to be meager unless it be demonstrated

141

that the configuration of cultural stimuli impinging on the individual are more complex (or are perceived by him to be more complex) in the one than in the other society. (Indeed, since cultural complexity is associated with individual specialization, it might even be argued that to some extent and for certain activities the individual in societies whose cultures are simple must cope with the greater degree of complex stimuli.) But again the paucity of systematic research prevents us from passing sound judgments in these matters. At the best our judgments, when they are not wild speculations, are but educated guesses. The materials to be presented in this chapter would seem to suggest that variables other than simplicity account for the low incidence of mental illness to be found in at least one society with a simple culture.

It is my guess—hopefully, educated—that each culture creates stresses and strains—some of them universal, some unique—with which the personality must cope; that the cultural heritage provides, to a greater or lesser degree, institutional techniques for their reduction, if not resolution; that the incidence of psychopathology in any society is a function, not merely of the strains produced by its culture, but also of the institutional means which its cultural heritage provides for the resolution of strain; that those individuals who, for whatever the reasons, cannot resolve the culturally created strains by means of the culturally provided instruments of resolution resolve them in idiosyncratic ways (neuroses and psychoses); and that to the extent that different cultures create different types of strain, idiosyncratic resolutions of strain (neuroses and psychoses) will reveal cultural variability. This general theory, it need not be emphasized, does not deny the importance of idiosyncratic experiences in the development of mental illness. Indeed the importance of such experiences is documented in the cases to be presented below. In general, however, these experiences, though pathogenic, contribute to psychopathology because of the absence of institutionalized means for tension reduction.

The first four of these points will be tested against the materials collected in one South Sea society. It should be observed, however, that since these points were first suggested (in part) by the materials to be presented in this paper, it is not surprising that these materials support the four theses.

SOCIAL STRUCTURE AND PERSONAL TENSIONS IN IFALUK

Ifaluk is a tiny atoll, inhabited by 250 people, in the Central Caro-lines of Micronesia. Although the Carolines have had contact with the West for three centuries, Ifaluk has had only slight contact—its remote-ness and small population probably served to deter governments, traders, and missionaries alike. Hence until the end of the Second World War —and except for a ten-day visit by Sarfert (a member of the Thilenius expedition) in 1909, and irregular visits by Japanese trading ships be-tween the two world wars—foreign travelers to Ifaluk were restricted almost exclusively to other peoples within the Central Carolines. Cer-tainly Dr. E. G. Burrows and I were the first foreigners to live on this atoll for an extensive period when we arrived in 1947. (Since the Ifaluk have had continuous contact with various types of American govern-mental personnel since then, almost all my statements refer to the period, 1947–1948, during which our study was conducted. Field work was made possible through the C.I.M.A. project of the Pacific Science Board of the National Research Council, in cooperation with the Office of Naval Research.)

Although few foreigners had visited Ifaluk prior to 1947, some of the Ifaluk had been exposed to foreign, and particularly to Japanese, culture before that date. The Japanese had set up a native school in Yap which was attended by a few Ifaluk boys, and some of the Ifaluk men had been inducted by the Japanese to work in the phosphate mines in Angaur. Despite the opportunities for borrowing arising from these experiences, the Ifaluk were singularly unacculturated when we con-ducted our study. Material objects such as pots or adzes had superseded their aboriginal equivalents, but in the main the traditional culture was intact and functioning.

The Ifaluk live in coconut-thatched dwellings, on the lagoon side of the two inhabited islands of the atoll (1). The typical residential group, as well as the primary economic and socializing unit, is the matri-local extended family. Kinship ties are extended unilaterally through matrilineages and matrisibs, as well as bilaterally through a recognized kindred. Marriage is monogamous, but premarital sexual intercourse is both practiced and sanctioned. Extramarital affairs, too, although not formally sanctioned, are practiced with impunity as long as they are con-ducted privately and with propriety. The subsistence economy is based on fishing and horticulture, the former being men's, and the latter women's, work. Although there is some economic specialization—carpenters, shipwrights, and navigators are the chief specialists—true division of labor does not exist. Leadership in all group activities and formal social control are exercised by five hereditary chiefs. Except for the annual three-month deep-sea fishing, life is leisurely and placid. The ordinary routine is punctuated by religious ritual, feasting, and dancing.

A notable feature of Ifaluk culture, as well as of the ecological setting of Ifaluk society, is the paucity of anxiety-producing or conflict-provoking stimuli. The climate is pleasant, and although typhoons occur, they are only infrequently destructive. The Ifaluk diet is somewhat limited in variety, but ocean and land produce an abundance of food; and although the exploitation of these resources demands skill and diligence, few occasions call for long or strenuous work.

Ifaluk social structure seems to evoke as little conflict or anxiety as its physical setting. Absent from its economic system are important inequalities in, and social classes based on, wealth. Real property and capital goods are either publicly owned or are held by corporate kinship groups; and although the holdings of the latter groups—taro patches or coconut groves, for example—are not of equal size or value, they are sufficiently extensive that differences in quantity are of no functional significance. Absent too is economic competition, either for subsistence or for prestige goals. Finally, distribution patterns preclude the possibility of economic want as a result of old age, illness, or death. The distribution of fish according to the needs of the participating families, the network of economic obligations within lineage and clan, and the functioning of the extended (rather than the nuclear) family as the primary economic unit—all serve to eliminate the threat of economic deprivation. In short there is little if anything in the Ifaluk economic system to evoke feelings of hostility, insecurity, or anxiety.

This conclusion applies to its political system as well. Ifaluk is governed by five hereditary chiefs who initiate and direct all important group activities—economic, social, and religious—and who, at public meetings, exhort the people to conform to the traditional values of Ifaluk culture. Although their responsibilities are heavy, the chiefs enjoy few privileges; and although their authority is great, they uniformly exercise it benevolently and informally. Respect and love are the typical attitudes of the people toward these unusual leaders.

Analysis of the Ifaluk kinship system similarly reveals few points of potential tension or conflict. Reciprocity and cooperation characterize the various kinship relationships. Joking relationships, avoidance taboos, etc., which serve to engender, as well as to express tension, are absent.

It should be mentioned, finally, that there is no discordance between sanctioned goals and sanctioned means. [Merton, in an incisive analysis, convincingly argues that much deviance in our society results from the disjunction between cultural means and cultural ends (5).] All important and rewarding goals are open to all, and the sanctioned culture patterns are efficient instruments for their attainment. Any normal Ifaluk can, by performing his various social roles, attain those cultural goals which confer esteem and respect—from others and from self.

That the Ifaluk social structure evokes little tension is not only a theoretical expectation, but it is a conclusion supported by empirical findings as well. The Stewart Emotional Response Test reveals that hostility is rarely evoked by features of the social structure or within the context of interpersonal relations.

Within this context it is interesting, and important, to note that the Ifaluk ethos stresses kindliness, cooperation, and nonaggression as paramount values. But what is striking about Ifaluk is not the content, but rather the implementation, of its ethos. Not one individual could remember a single instance of murder, rape, robbery, or fighting (with the exception to be noted below); nor did we witness such behavior in the course of our study. Whereas aggression is almost entirely absent from interpersonal relations, cooperation and sharing are characteristic features of social life. People are generous with food, property, and assistance. It is as unthinkable for a woman not to offer a passerby some of the food she is cooking, as it is for a man not to assist a fellow in the construction of a canoe (7).

These characteristics of Ifaluk social behavior seem to be rooted in Ifaluk personality—at least in those conscious aspects of the personality that are tapped by the Stewart Emotional Response Test, and the Bavelas Moral Ideology Test. Thus, 48 per cent of the subjects claim to find happiness in knowing that others are happy, while 31 per cent are saddened by the sadness of others. Sixty-three per cent of the subjects stated that the possession of property was the "best thing" that could happen to them—so that they could have gifts to offer to visitors or to the chiefs who would offer these gifts to strangers. Finally, the overwhelming majority of praiseworthy acts concern generosity, while most of the blameworthy acts concern aggression. It is hardly accidental that, with one unimportant exception, all the activities for which the children reported being punished were concerned with aggression.

Despite minimal instigations of conflict and tension in Ifaluk social structure and their absence in most interpersonal relations, Ifaluk personality is not without hostility and anxiety. Hostility is revealed most clearly in individual and cultural fantasy. Since the people as a whole have only a superficial acquaintance with their oral literature, folklore cannot be used diagnostically for the entire group. The chiefs, however, know the folklore, and their reactions are both interesting and significant, for they are not only the symbols and the guarantors of the Ifaluk ethic of nonaggression, but they practice it most conscientiously. In discussions of theology, the chiefs displayed only meager interest. But when they recounted the legends of the early history and colonization of Ifaluk, according to which Ifaluk conquered and completely wiped out the populations of other islands, they became animated and enthusiastic, detailing these acts of aggression with relish. We may infer that the aggressive content of Ifaluk legends represents repressed and projected hostility.

Religion offers a second cultural clue to the existence of hostility. Although Ifaluk religion postulates the existence of a pantheon of high gods, the functionally important supernaturals are the ghosts—souls of departed ancestors. There are two types of ghosts (alus), malevolent and benevolent. The character of an Ifaluk ghost is a persistence of its terrestrial character. Hence, the soul of a good person becomes a benevolent ghost, while the soul of an evil person becomes a malevolent ghost. Since there are very few "evil" people in Ifaluk—almost everyone conforms to the cultural ideals of kindliness, generosity, nonaggression, etc.—the fact that evil ghosts not only exist but that they are more numerous than good ghosts suggests that the evil ghosts represent a symbolic projection of repressed hostility. (Whether they are direct projections of the believer's hostility, or whether they are projections of the hostility which he attributes to others is irrelevant since the latter is also a projection. Perhaps both processes are operative. That hostility is projected onto others may be inferred from the findings of the Emotional Response Test. The majority of responses to the question concerning the "worst thing" that can happen comprise various types of aggression perpetrated by others against the self. Since these activities are, in fact, almost nonexistent, it is hard to escape the conclusion that these responses are projections.)

There is evidence of repressed hostility on the individual level as well. Almost seventy per cent of the dreams collected from over fifty persons were of an aggressive nature. The dreamer was either attacking or being attacked—by humans, animals, or malevolent ghosts. Similarly, almost 50 per cent of the themes in the adult T.A.T. records are "aggressive" in character—quarreling, fighting, physical conflict, and murder are the contents of this category.

The T.A.T. also yields indirect evidence for the hypothesis of repressed hostility. If hostility is a personality drive, and if it is repressed, we would expect some of the hostility to be inverted and to be experienced as inner tension. Moreover, because of the character of the Ifaluk ethos, we would expect the people to experience inner tension as a function of the discrepancy between the real (hostility) and the ideal (the taboo on hostility). This expectation is borne out by the T.A.T. More than one-third of the themes expressed in this test fall into the category of "internalized emotional strain." Although not all their "internalized emotional strain" is a function of repressed hostility, it seems safe to say that at least some of it is.

This brings us to Ifaluk anxiety, whose existence (in addition to the T.A.T. findings) is inferred from clinically derived interpretations of Ifaluk group behavior. In the first place, the Ifaluk spend much time during the day in sleep and rest which, together with a listlessness which is perceptible on many occasions, is quite striking. Since the climate is not debilitating, since food is plentiful, and since physical labor—with seasonal exceptions—is not strenuous, it is difficult to attribute these characteristics to physical, climatic, or dietary causes. But if this general picture reflects excessive expenditure of, and the consequent need to recoup, energy, and if it cannot be explained in physical terms, it would not seem inappropriate to explain it in emotional terms. Since we know that emotional energy is required to "handle" inner tensions (a process which can sometimes result in extreme enervation), it might be suggested that this syndrome, together with other kinds of behavior to be discussed below, is a sign of anxiety. (It is possible, of course, that this condition is produced by some type of disease or some dietary deficiency of which I am unaware or for which I have no data.)

Other "clinical" observations support the anxiety hypothesis. The Ifaluk, for example, have a compulsive need to be with others. A solitary Ifaluk is almost unknown—at least, I never observed one. Regardless of what they may be doing, the Ifaluk insist on doing it in a group—or rather, on being in a group. The latter qualification is important, for the significant thing about Ifaluk gregariousness—and the reason I term it "compulsive" rather than merely "frequent"—is its apparently noninstrumental nature. People insist on being in groups although no apparent end, personal or social, is thereby served or satisfied, not even social intercourse; sometimes an entire afternoon can elapse without a word being exchanged among the men in a canoe house. If compulsive behavior is interpreted as defensive behavior, a possible explanation of Ifaluk compulsive gregariousness is that it is a defense against inner anxiety. Through experience with persons and events outside themselves —a "flight to reality"—the people are assured that whatever the basis for their anxiety (the basis will be examined below), it has no substance in reality.

If a "flight to reality" is both an indication of and an attempt to deal with anxiety, an inordinate emphasis on food is still another; and an extreme emphasis on food is one of the first aspects of Ifaluk culture with which the observer is impressed. Preoccupation with food is expressed in a number of diverse ways (7, pp. 138 ff.). It is a favorite and almost ubiquitous topic of conversation. Its distribution is an invariable part of every secular and religious meeting. The opportunity for eating motivates people to stop any other activity, however important. The presence or absence of food is a basis for linguistic expressions of emotional states. Thus the Ifaluk word for "happiness" is *eratu-dipei*, literally a "good belly"—which is to say, a full stomach; the word for "sadness" is *engau-dipei*, literally a "bad belly"—which is to say, an empty stomach.

Preoccupation with food is reflected in the psychological tests as well. Food, according to the Emotional Response Test, is the most important source of happiness. Its consumption is the second "best thing" that can happen; its absence is both an important source of sadness and a serious provocation to anger. The perception of food is marked in the T.A.T. as well, so much so that I included it as a separate scoring category. Finally, food is an important subject for the free drawings of the children.

Since this overevaluation of food cannot be explained as a response to food deprivation—for, as we have observed, food is plentiful—and since clinically, food consumption may be interpreted as a replenishment of "ego supplies," it is not improbable that the Ifaluk emphasis on food reflects rather an emotional condition (anxiety) and an attempt to reduce anxiety. Moreover, since in Ifaluk the breast is used in infancy to reduce presumed anxiety or insecurity, it would not be surprising for food to serve the same emotional function in adulthood.

The same interpretation may be offered for the people's compulsive need for coconut toddy—a whitish, sappy liquid obtained by tapping the flower stalk of the coconut tree. Toddy is consumed every morning and evening. The diurnal collection of toddy is one of the important responsibilities of all men. When, due to excessive rain, toddy cannot be collected, the people become moody and morose; so that the very first activity to be performed following a storm is the collection and consumption of toddy. If the primary function of alcohol, as Horton's cross-cultural findings seem to indicate, is "the reduction of anxiety," the Ifaluk compulsive need for toddy is still another indication of anxiety (4).

CULTURAL INSTIGATIONS OF TENSION IN IFALUK

If the Ifaluk are characterized (among other things) by hostility and anxiety, and if Ifaluk social structure does not appear to be responsible for the evocation of these drives, we must assume that they are characterological dispositions rather than situational responses. We must therefore look for their origin in Ifaluk personality development and in the socialization system that importantly influences it. This theoretical assumption derives from my agreement with Dollard that aggression, in the mature person, appears to stem from at least two sources: "First, through continuing demands for satisfaction which had to be tabooed in the course of socialization. . . . Second, aggression is aroused through rivalry over the securing of desired goals or values such as high status, sex partners, or satisfactions incident to a standard of living" (2, p. 17). Since the second source of aggression is relatively unimportant in Ifaluk, it is the former source with which we are primarily concerned. In addition to those universal characteristics of socialization which inevitably frustrate the child, there appear to be two crucial experiences in Ifaluk socialization which are sufficiently threatening to contribute to the development of hostility and anxiety.

The first threatening experience, which begins at birth and continues for the duration of infancy, is the daily washing of the infant at dawn in the cold water of the lagoon. That this immersion is painful and threatening is an inference drawn from three considerations. First, the

water at dawn is sufficiently cold that even adults do not enter the
lagoon until after sunrise. In addition, the contrast between the infant's previous activity—sleeping, wrapped warmly in a blanket, between its parents—and the sudden wakening and immersion in the cold
water must be particularly painful. That this is so is indicated by the
crying and wailing of the infants during the entire bathing, and continuing unabated as the months pass. Finally, this is the one activity over
which the infant has no control. An Ifaluk infant, with this one exception, is the master of his environment. His slightest cry elicits attention
and care, the Ifaluk believing that the infant's every whim must be satisfied and that he must never suffer pain. Thus the experience of the morning bath stands in sharp contrast to the typical experience of the infant.
Not only does he suffer pain in the bathing experience, but all his cries,
which are so remarkably efficacious in achieving his ends in other situations, are of no avail in this one.

These, then, are the reasons why we term this experience "threatening." And this threatening experience, I would suggest, contributes to
the development of both hostility and anxiety in the Ifaluk personality:
hostility, because like any infantile impulse which cannot be effectively
reduced or expressed—in this case the infant can merely express his
hostility in cries of rage—it persists as a personality drive; anxiety, because the infant is the object of "an attack" which he cannot understand
and with which he is powerless to cope. Ifaluk mothers are quite aware
of the pain which the infant suffers from this bathing ritual. They explain the practice by the ubiquitous refrain of *musuwe, musuwe*—"this
is our custom" (literally, "before, before"). [In his brilliant analysis
of Sioux character, Erikson suggests that much of Sioux hostility may
derive from the inability of the infant in the cradleboard to "abreact"
his rage (3).]

The hostility and anxiety produced by this infantile experience are
reinforced by a later, even more highly threatening, experience. The
Ifaluk infant is ordinarily showered with love and attention. Except for
the bathing experience, he is never handled roughly or spoken to sharply,
and he is never left alone. His mother remains by his side for the first
three months after his birth. The moment he cries or shows signs of dis-
comfiture, he is attended to—picked up, fondled, fed, consoled. Even
after her three-month post-partum confinement the mother may not
leave the house unless she finds someone else to take her place by the
infant's side.

As the infant grows older, he is constantly handled, loved, played with, fondled—not only by his parents, but by all the adult members of his household (all of whom are classificatory parents) as well as by other adults. Moreover, the infant is the center of attention wherever he may be taken. Needless to say, and consistent with the above description, all disciplines are instituted both late and gradually.

But this highly indulgent treatment is transitory. Adult eyes remain focused on infancy, so that as infants become children they become, as it were, out of focus, and new infants take their place as the foci of adult attention. Overt signs of affection are rarely displayed. Children beyond the age of four or five are only infrequently held in an adult's arms, kissed, or fondled. Adults not only *ignore* the child's emotional needs, but they sometimes quite consciously *reject* his solicitation of love and affection; and his frustrations may even provoke in them mild amusement.

This rejection—both witting and unwitting—of the Ifaluk child is his second threatening experience. Apparent loss of parental love is probably threatening to a child in any society; it is doubly threatening to the Ifaluk child whose previous experience was one of overindulgence. Thus it is not surprising that Ifaluk parents report that shortly after the birth of a sibling—real or classificatory—the older sibling becomes "ill," refusing to eat or sleep. They report, too, that although he does not like his younger sibling and may even attack him, after his parents explain that he should love his sibling, he has a change of heart and—in the words of our interpreter—"he savvy, he like." But the actual facts are not so simple; it is rare that "he savvy, he like."

After this sibling "illness" was called to my attention, I interviewed all mothers of children who had young siblings. Of twenty-four children whose favorable positions had been recently "usurped" by younger siblings, no fewer than 58 per cent and as many as 96 per cent *chronically* displayed the following characteristics: fighting and attacking, willful disobedience, destruction of property, temper tantrums, difficult eating, night terrors, thumb-sucking, crying and whining, shyness, and "negativism." I did not personally observe all twenty-four children, but I did observe a sufficiently large sample to be able to confirm the reports of the mothers.

If the clinical interpretations of these symptoms are as valid for the Ifaluk as they are for Americans—and I believe they are—we are surely justified in characterizing this rejection experience as "threatening"; and like the earlier threatening experience, I would suggest that it contributes importantly to Ifaluk hostility and anxiety. Since the hostility which results from the frustration (of dependency needs) cannot be expressed against either parents or siblings, it persists because it has little effective release. And the anxiety attendant upon the feeling of parental rejection persists for the simple reason that the rejection persists. Hence the Ifaluk child learns to perceive his world as potentially threatening and attacking, a perceptual set which is reflected culturally in the threatening, attacking, malevolent ghosts [For an analysis of the psychodynamics of Ifaluk ghost belief, and for a detailed description of the impressive isomorphism between ghosts and parents, see (9).]

CULTURALLY INDUCED STRAINS AND MENTAL ILLNESS IN IFALUK

In the first section of this chapter it was suggested that the culture of any society produces strains in its members which, if not resolved by cultural means, are resolved idiosyncratically. It was suggested, moreover, that different cultures may produce different types of tensions, so that the emotional problems with which human personalities must cope may differ from society to society. If our analysis of Ifaluk tensions is valid, we may conclude that the Ifaluk must cope with the twin problem of anxiety and hostility.

Ifaluk anxiety seems to derive from the experience of rejection and the consequent feeling of not being loved, as well as from early "attack" and the resultant perception of the world as threatening. Some of the anxiety may also stem from the repression of hostility and its consequent inversion, as well as from their awareness of their own hostility and the moral anxiety induced by such an awareness in a society in which hostility, as well as aggression, is taboo. Ifaluk hostility seems to derive from and be a response to those early experiences which give rise to a perception of others as (among other things) hostile; and it seems also to be a persistence of the hostility which is evoked by these early frustrating experiences, and for which there is no adequate release. This hostility constitutes a grave problem in Ifaluk since its ethos prohibits the expression of aggression in interpersonal relations. Hence, if mental illness is found in Ifaluk, it should reflect (among other things) these two foci of tension.

Most illness in Ifaluk is interpreted as possession by a malevolent ghost. This interpretation applies to mental illness and to mental deficiency, as well, which are lumped together under the common term, *malebush*. Since the *malebush* are singularly resistant to therapy, it is believed that they are possessed by especially powerful ghosts.

In a population of approximately 250 people, the Ifaluk considered eight persons to be *malebush,* and the anthropologist would probably add two more. Of these ten, six seemed to be mental defectives—an idiot girl, about six or seven years old, who was in the constant care of her mother; three teen-age siblings, one boy and two girls, who appeared to be low-grade morons; a female moron or near-moron, about forty-five years old, the only woman in the atoll who had never been married; a very old demented woman—and one (approximately) four-year old girl who appeared to be an epileptic. This discussion is restricted to the remaining three cases of apparent psychogenic mental illness. Of these three, two were probably psychotic and one probably neurotic.

Vegoilep, a male of approximately forty years, is the only bachelor in Ifaluk. For a number of years (I could not discover how many) he has remained confined to his home, leaving only at night to wash and excrete in the lagoon. People who know Vegoilep well say that his voluntary confinement is motivated by a generalized fear of others. Vegoilep himself, when I propounded the question to him directly, said that he remains in his house because of his diseased legs which cause him great pain. His legs, covered with scabs and open sores, are indeed a horrible sight, and may well cause him pain. But if the motivation for his confinement is pain, why should he remain inside the house? Why does he not sit outside in the fresh air, or with the other men in the canoe houses?

Since Vegoilep leaves his house only at night, many adults and almost all the children rarely see him. When he agreed to talk to me, his arrival in the canoe house for the interview caused a minor sensation. Children came from all parts of the island to see him.

Vegoilep is the eldest child of the deceased paramount chief. He has sorrowful eyes and long slender fingers. His features are very feminine, and his body is soft and flabby. His long hair is tied in back. His face has a haunted, tragic look, and he gives the impression of great suffering. Prior to his confinement Vegoilep was, according to those who knew him, an able, energetic, and capable man. He was an excellent fisherman, a stimulating conversationalist, and—in the words of the interpreter—he "savvy everything." No one was able to volunteer an explanation for the dramatic change in his behavior.

During the testing session and the interview, Vegoilep was cooperative. He seemed to be concerned with two dominant themes: fear of malevolent ghosts and an eagerness to do the will of the chiefs. Although he rejected three cards, his Rorschach responses were "normal," and his T.A.T. stories, although exclusively descriptive, were perceptually accurate. In short, although Vegoilep gave the impression of suffering from depression and anxiety, he gave no indication of bizarre intellectual functioning.

Aneitin, a male in his early forties, shows many symptoms of schizophrenia. Aneitin is "in" the society, but not "of" it. He lives alone in a small hut which is physically isolated from other houses. When we took a population census, the chiefs, who guided us from house to house, excluded his house from our itinerary; and since he is an isolate, it was not till some months had elapsed that I became aware of his existence.

Aneitin not only lives alone, but he takes no part in Ifaluk social life. He makes no attempt to contribute to his own economic support and is sustained by his sisters who bring his food. He participates in none of the numerous communal activities, either secular or religious. When he is not in his hut or alone on the beach, he sits in the canoe house apart from the other men, neither talking nor talked to. A short time before our arrival his isolation was even more extreme: he moved to the uninhabited islet across the lagoon, where he lived for one year. He seems to like to be in or near water, for he can frequently be observed to fish from the shore or to sail model canoes made from strips of coconut branches.

Unlike Vegoilep, Aneitin had in the past been dangerous. Periodically he became violent, shouted and screamed at people, and physically attacked them if they came near him. He is still liable to outbreaks of shouting, but he has not attacked anyone for some time. Nevertheless, women are still afraid of him and tend to avoid him.

Aneitin is the second of three children. As a young man he participated fully in Ifaluk social life, and he was married to a very attractive woman. His difficulties are traced by the people to his induction by the Japanese to work in Angaur. Only after his return did he display the aggressive behavior noted above.

Although it is almost impossible to conduct an intelligible conversation with Aneitin, I interviewed him on at least two occasions. In the interviews he seemed obsessively concerned with "good talk" and "bad talk." It was difficult to understand what he meant by "good talk," although it seemed to be related to kindly and considerate speech. "Bad talk" quite clearly meant malicious gossip directed against him.

Unlike Vegoilep, who never referred either to his deviance (which he denied) or to his lack of social participation, Aneitin expressed dismay and "shame," at his inability, for example, to work. When asked why he did not work, he said he was ashamed to be with people because he had "something" on top of his head. When asked to identify that "something" he said he did not know what it was. Later he said it was rather in his "mouth and stomach." Still later he characterized it as something very sharp which stung him. When asked how he responded to it, he replied:

A. It goes inside me; it's painful.
Q. What do you do then?
A. In a little while, it's gone. . . . It's very painful; it comes out through

my mouth and eyes. Then I'm better. When it comes out, I talk all the time. When it stops coming out, I stop talking.

Q. What is it that comes out of your eyes and mouth?

A. It has a foul smell, like feces.

Q. Where does it go when it comes out?

A. It's like the breath; it goes inside the mouth. . . . It's like rope. Some man put a rope inside my mouth and my nose. Later he took it out.

Q. Who did that?

A. I don't know.

The theme of "something" on top of the head is picked up later in the T.A.T. In five of the twelve T.A.T. pictures he perceived something on top of, or coming out of a subject's head—the "something" being smoke. And in the Rorschach all the above themes are repeated. Of his ten responses, five were concerned with smoke—smoke by itself, smoke coming out of people's mouths, smoke being inside their bodies, smoke coming out of their bodies. Two responses were "feces," and in one the feces were in people's eyes. His last response was also concerned with "something" inside the body, although in this instance it was blood—blood ("or paint") inside a person's stomach.

Many of the themes that emerged from the earlier interviews and tests were repeated in a later interview:

Q. Are you happy today?

A. A little (Note: He seems depressed today).

Q. Is there anything you would like?

A. No.

Q. Why don't you work today with the other men?

A. I would like to, but my arm is very bad.

Q. What's the matter with your arm?

A. I have a bad arm and a bad stomach. The inside of my body is always moving, moving.

Q. What do you mean?

A. When I work, I can't see anything. It's like smoke in my eyes.

Q. How does the smoke get there?

A. I don't know. It comes from far away. Then it goes away. If I sit down it goes away.

Q. Why do you live alone? Wouldn't you like to live with other people?

A. I like to live alone; I don't like to live with people.

Q. Why?

A. I like to be with people, but then something inside my stomach is very bad. It moves a lot.

Q. What?

A. I don't know.

Q. Are you afraid of people?

A. No.

Q. Then why don't you participate in the feasts, dances, etc.?

A. I don't know; I want to go, but an *alus* comes to me and says he doesn't want me to go.

Q. Do you know who the *alus* is?

A. No.

Q. Does he come often?

A. Sometimes I am happy, sometimes I am sad. I don't like people.

Q. What do you do when you are alone in your house?

A. I just sit, because I don't like to be with people. I don't like their conversation. If I'm with them I want to talk about other things.

Q. Why don't you like their conversation?

A. Some people talk bad—too loud. I don't like it.

Q. What do they say that is bad?

A. They talk too loud.

Q. What do you think about in your house?

A. I only look at things. I don't think about anything.

Q. Why do you shout when you are alone? (Note: At times, especially at night, Aneitin—for no apparent reason—shouts and screams.)

A. I shout when I am very sad.

Q. What makes you sad?

A. I think people are coming, and they talk bad. If I lie down, I think I am moving, moving. I think people are moving me, but there are no people.

Q. What is their "bad talk"?

A. It's as if people come and shake me; then I shout. I see them coming to my house, and I shout. Then I look, and nobody is there.

Q. Do you recognize the people who come?

A. Some are from here, and some from other places. Sometimes they are boys. They scratch my body. I don't like it.

Q. When do they come?

A. At night. If I sleep during the day, they come in the day.

Q. Why do they come to you?

A. I don't know. They come, and scratch and pull me. Also when I walk around, something goes into my anus. I try to pull it out, but nothing is there.

Q. What is it that goes into your anus?

A. It's like a vein. Once a man pulled out my vein, and I pulled it back.

Q. Did you know the man?

A. He was like a New Guinea man. If I sleep I dream that I go to another place. After a time I go to another place.

Q. Where do you go?

A. I go to a mountainous country, where there is sand. Then I come back.

Q. What do you do in that land?

A. I am afraid when I go there, for someone tried to catch me. Someone said, "Go away to another place."

Q. What do you do in that land?

A. I went to the canoe house. There were many people there. They said, "Go away to some other house." So I went, but I did not go inside.

At this point I was called away by the announcement of a death. As a parting question, I asked whether I could do anything for him. He replied, "No, I'm *malebush*. If you can remove my *malebush*, I would like that."

The third case, like the other two, is a male in his early forties.* Tarev is an only child. His parents are dead. As far as I was able to learn, Tarev had a normal childhood, and led a most exemplary life as a young man. He was a good husband and father, industrious in his work, and generous and cooperative. He was, moreover, recognized as a skilled carpenter and had been acclaimed as an expert fisherman. In short, before the onset of his illness he had enjoyed the respect and esteem of his fellows.

Shortly before World War II Tarev, like Aneitin, had been inducted by the Japanese for work in a labor gang on Angaur, and—again like Aneitin—it was only after his return that the people became aware of drastic changes in his behavior. Instead of working, he remained by himself, engaging in seemingly meaningless conversations with unseen persons, performing apparently meaningless dances, and singing incomprehensible songs. At other times, and without apparent provocation, he became violent, accusing others of wishing to kill him, and aggressively defending himself against these putative attackers. As these outbursts became more frequent, his wife and her family were afraid to live with him; and Tarev was moved to his parental house where, it was thought, his family could perhaps control him. This, roughly, was the situation when we arrived in 1947.

Though we reached Ifaluk in July, I did not encounter Tarev until September. I do not know if he had been quiescent during that period or if I had merely not been informed of any violent or untoward behavior on his part. Later, when it became apparent that, for some obscure reason, I had some measurable success in subduing him, the people would inform me of his outbreaks. Thus from the end of September until our departure, I was able to observe many of his "psychotic" episodes and, frequently, to interview him soon after. These episodes, and the subsequent interviews, have been published elsewhere (6). Here a synoptic chronological account of his behavior, as well as some brief extracts from interviews, will suffice:

SEPTEMBER 24. Tarev insists on visiting his wife, but is physically restrained by the other men.

OCTOBER 15. Tarev attempts to commit suicide by drowning (a few days after the death of his wife), but is saved by three other men. He does not sleep that night, shouts vituperations at everyone, insists that he is superior to everyone in Ifaluk and that he is really an American.

OCTOBER 19. Tarev finds a long, heavy pole, which the people thought he would use to attack them.

OCTOBER 22. Tarev comes to tell me that "people" had attempted to kill

* Field notes which follow on the case of Tarev originally appeared in *Psychiatry,* 1950, vol. 13, pp. 189–204, in my article, "A Psychotic Personality in the South Seas." We gratefully acknowledge permission to quote from this article in *Psychiatry,* copyright by the William Alanson White Psychiatric Foundation, Inc.

him the previous night. He also says that he has not eaten for two days, because an *alus* "on his head" had ordered him not to.

NOVEMBER 4. Tarev tries to escape to Falalap (one of the two inhabited islands in the atoll), is pursued by the other men, and returns when, at the request of his pursuers, I asked him to.

NOVEMBER 7. Tarev again tries to commit suicide by drowning, and is persuaded to return to land. He returns reluctantly, charging one of the chiefs with plotting to kill him.

NOVEMBER 14. Tarev dances in his house throughout the night, and disturbs others by his shouting. Later he becomes aggressive, throwing rocks at his (classificatory) mother. When I interview him he is very depressed.

NOVEMBER 23. Tarev attempts to burn down his house. He is more agitated than I have yet seen him, claiming that people are talking "bad" to him and are plotting to kill him.

NOVEMBER 25. Tarev performs a dance inside his house, singing in tongues, in a trancelike state.

NOVEMBER 27. Tarev attempts to attack a chief (Maroligar) with a pole. Later he tries to burn down his house and is subdued only after physical struggle. Men decide to tie him up for the night. He shouts imprecations at Maroligar.

NOVEMBER 28. Tarev escapes to our tent. Insists that Maroligar (a chief) and others wish to kill him. I persuade him to return. He performs his dance and sings in tongues.

DECEMBER 6. Tarev is violent, attempts to beat his sister. Later he steals a basket, gets into intense argument with people, accusing them of wishing to harm him.

JANUARY 4. Tarev has been behaving very well. He has moved to a house in an uninhabited part of the island, remains isolated for long periods, performing his dances, and singing in tongues. He comes frequently to our camp site, cleans up around it, brings us fish and coconuts, asks my permission to go places or to do things. He continues—what he had started from our first encounter—to seize my hands and smell them deeply when he sees me. Suddenly everything changes. He beats a youth for fishing in the lagoon in front of his house and engages in a violent argument with those who subdued him. Again the men decide to tie him.

JANUARY 5. In the night Tarev comes, sobbing, to our tent, asking that I untie his hands. He is returned to his house, and his feet (as well as his hands) are tied. The next morning, feet and hands still tied, he crawls to our tent, and I take him back to his house. In the afternoon, unknown to us, he comes to our tent, takes a hunting knife, and cuts three clusters of coconuts for our use.

JANUARY 16. Tarev comes daily, smells my neck, body, and legs, as well as my hands, and returns. Today he comes, in a trancelike state, and performs a bizarre dance in front of our tent while holding our typing chair to his nose.

JANUARY 21. Tarev, intrigued with our calendar, takes it to his house. At night he goes to a public meeting house, and, while singing, alternately bows before and spits upon the wooden phallus attached to the front pillar.

January 27. Tarev has been in a trancelike state, impossible to get through to him. But today—for the first time—he joins a cooperative group hauling in seines.

February 6. Tarev attempts to drown himself when he learns that we are leaving on the ship that has arrived. He claims that when I leave, the people will again attempt to kill him.

Since our departure from Ifaluk Tarev has, if anything, become worse. The anthropologist for the Trust Territory reports that he has been kept in a hut, from which the people do not permit him to leave. His conversation is "partly unintelligible, partly incoherent."

Tarev's thinking (or, at least, his speech) was "partly unintelligible, partly incoherent," in most of the interviews I had with him. The following excerpts from three of the interviews are fairly typical. It will be noted that some of his thoughts and fantasies are similar to those of Aneitin—smoke, objects intruding into his body, attack by others, "bad" talk, journey to foreign lands, characterization of much of behavior as ego-alien (attributed to an *alus*).

Q. Is it true, as people have told me, that an *alus* has possessed you?

A. Yes, the *alus* in the moon has entered my head and my stomach. (This convinced Tom and Maroligar that he was lying, because there is no *alus* in the moon.)

Q. How do you know that he has possessed you?

A. He came to my father. He lives in another place. When he possessed my father, he possessed me.

Q. Where is your father?

A. Those pictures you showed me (the Rorschach cards), I liked them very much. The place in the North, that's the place I see now.

Q. What place?

A. There's another one in the Northeast. This place in the North is very light. When I sit in my house, it's very dark; then, that North place, the one I like very much, comes on top of my head.

Q. How does it feel when it comes on top of your head?

A. I like it very much. When I pull up the blanket, I look underneath the sleeping mat, and smoke comes out. I then lower the mat and look underneath another one, and smoke comes out from it, too.

Q. What happens to you when the *alus* of the moon possesses you?

A. That man inside that padre book (the Bible that a missionary had shown him) and his mother come inside me.

Q. What does it feel like when they come inside you?

A. I don't know.

Q. Did they come inside you this morning, when you tried to commit suicide?

A. No.

Q. Did they come inside you last night?
A. The *alus* gave me something—something very fine.
Q. What did he give you?
A. Smoke. He put smoke inside my mouth, but it did not enter my stomach.
Q. You like that smoke?
A. I like it very much.
Q. Why?
A. (No answer.)

. . . .

Q. Why did you go to the public meeting hall yesterday?
A. I was in my house and somebody told me to go there, because the chiefs are there holding a meeting.
Q. Where were you going when I saw you later?
A. I was afraid that a small *alus* was hiding near my house, so I left.
Q. Did you see the *alus?*
A. No, but I heard it moving inside the house.
Q. How are you feeling today?
A. My arm is very tired. When I walk, I feel that I am not walking on the ground. I feel as if my feet are walking on air.
Q. Why is that?
A. I don't know. When I attempt to walk, I fall down.
Q. Is anything bothering you today?
A. Wotrilitu (a relative by marriage) stole my wife.
Q. How do you know?
A. He stole her from me a long time ago.
Q. Are you angry with him for that?
A. I took care of his children, but he stole my wife.
Q. Are you feeling better today than the last time we spoke?
A. I feel happier. But I can't stay in my sleeping mat because it is always moving.

. . . .

Q. Is there anything you would like, now?
A. I thought I was happy. And then I heard many voices, and I became unhappy. Yesterday I wanted to go to the ocean and swim away, for I can't stand all that talk.
Q. What talk?
A. That someone stole my wife from me.
Q. Did you dream last night?
A. No.
Q. Has the *alus* come to you lately?
A. He comes very often, day and night.
Q. What does he do?
A. (He said nothing, but clasped his hands together, as in Christian prayer, and pointed them at me. He then put his hand on my head and

rumpled my hair. He then put his finger on my head, then my stomach, and finally on my leg. Apparently he was demonstrating to me what the *alus* does to him.)

Q. Are you afraid of the *alus?*

A. No.

Q. Is it a male or female *alus?*

A. It dances. It bends and sways. I like to see it. I see the *alus* dance. Then I imitate the *alus,* I dance too.

· · · · · · · · · · · ·

Q. Why did you do that dance?

A. The Americans danced in those clothes.

Q. What clothes?

A. People walked in those clothes.

Q. What kind of clothes were they? Like my clothes?

A. They were soldier clothes (uniforms). What the soldiers did, I did.

Q. Were you afraid of the soldiers?

A. I fought with one of the soldiers. He knifed me in my stomach and my head. I removed the knife. He gave me much money, but I did not keep it. I threw it away.

Q. But I don't see any wounds on you.

A. The knife came through my head and back. I pulled it through, rubbed the wound, and it disappeared.

Q. Where did the soldiers go?

A. The knife came through my head and back, so I pulled it out, rubbed the place, and the wound disappeared. Then another one came to fight me.

Q. Why did the soldiers want to fight you?

A. Because I was very bad. I drank wine, and then I began to shout and break things. So they came to fight me.

Q. Why did you drink so much and break things?

A. Those men did not like it. Four men came to fight me. They threw me to the ground and I began to bleed. Then they began to fight with me. They gave me money.

Q. What kind of soldiers were they?

A. American soldiers. I did an American dance.

Q. How do you feel now?

A. I am always happy, for a dance comes to me, just like the wind.

Q. Do you like the dance?

A. I like.

Q. Has the *alus* come to you lately?

A. He is in me now. He never goes away.

Q. Where is he in you?

A. In my stomach.

Q. Is it a male or female *alus?*

A. Male. Last night I dance. Last night I danced, and there was a typhoon, and a tidal wave. I wanted my mother to see.

Q. Really?

A. I was at the land of the *alus* when it came.

Q. Where is that place?

A. The ocean came on top of me in huge waves.

Q. Where is the land of the *alus*?

A. I saw that paper, and I understood. A man came to me; he did not talk bad to me, he talked good. So I did not go to the land of the *alus*.

Q. Where is the land of the *alus*?

A. It is like the movies. An American man came to me. He said, "Do you have any copra?" "I have no more." "Why?" "We need the coconuts to eat here." "Then I'll kill you." "No, don't kill me." "I'm going to kill all the people here." "No, don't kill them." "I'll kill you," So he killed me.

Q. Are you dead now?

A. No, he killed me, but I was revived. Four American men gave me some whiskey. I drank one glass, and then threw away the bottle. I finished four bottles. The men gave me money, but I told my children, "You take the money."

MENTAL ILLNESS AND CULTURAL RESOLUTION OF TENSION IN IFALUK

In addition to their frequently bizarre thought processes, the salient feature in the behavior of both Aneitin and Tarev is aggression. Aneitin (in the past) and Tarev (today) commit unprovoked acts of aggression, and both claim that others either attack or wish to attack them; hence their own aggression is justified as self-defense. Vegoilep's difficulties may also be interpreted as stemming from his concern with aggression—if the people are right, his self-imposed confinement stems from his fear of others (That this fear is a projection of his hostility to them is, in my opinion, a strong possibility, but there is no evidence to support it). This fear has led him, like Aneitin to a lesser extent, to isolate himself from others. Tarev and Vegoilep share another characteristic: their obsession with the chiefs. In Tarev, the obsession takes the form of aggression against them; in Vegoilep, the obsession takes the form of an excessive desire to comply with their requests. As in their relationships with people in general, Tarev attacks chiefs while Vegoilep fears them. His fear of the chiefs is revealed not only in his interview responses, but in a telling incident that occurred in the course of the interview. Vegoilep did not seem much disturbed by the arrival of the numerous people who came to look at him; but when one of the chiefs arrived, he became agitated and the color drained from his face.

In short, the three individuals who comprise the total number of (observable) psychopathological individuals in Ifaluk share a basic syndrome—anxiety concerning, and lack of trust in, people; fear of their aggression; and (in two of the three) aggression against them. Since anxiety and hostility are predicted consequences of Ifaluk socialization, and since typically the Ifaluk are characterized by (among other things) anxiety and hostility, each of these three would seem to possess the Ifaluk personality *in extremis*. They are not only hostile; but, in a society that interdicts all forms of aggression, they are aggressive. They are not only apprehensive concerning, and insecure in their relations with, others—but, in a society in which great store is placed on group experience, they avoid them. They not only perceive others as hostile—but, in a society in which "kindliness" is taken for granted, they accuse them of aggression.

This raises at least two questions: Why did these three alone develop normal Ifaluk characteristics into such exaggerated forms? And how do the vast majority of the Ifaluk manage to escape a similar fate? The first question can best be answered only after we answer the second.

Ifaluk culture, as we have seen, produces feelings of insecurity (dependency anxiety and a generalized perception of the world as threatening) and hostility. If these tensions were not resolved, they could well result in serious personality disturbance. The relative absence of such disturbance leads one to suspect that the cultural heritage provides institutional means for their resolution. The institutions which serve this function seem to be religion and chieftainship.

Although there are some few noninstitutional ways of expressing hostility, it is in religion that Ifaluk hostility finds a prescribed and sanctioned outlet. Aggression is displaced onto the *alus*, the malevolent ghosts. These malevolent beings motivate so much of Ifaluk behavior that we may truly say with E. G. Burrows that "they haunt their minds." Malevolent ghosts, we have already noted, are primarily concerned with causing illness. This they do from sheer delight in perpetrating evil. Hence, although they possess members of their own lineage exclusively, they do so indiscriminately—attacking the good and the bad alike. Although the causing of illness is their main activity, the ghosts are also responsible for Ifaluk antisocial behavior. People, according to the Ifaluk, are intrinsically good; hence, lying, stealing, fighting, etc. are performed only when one is possessed by an *alus*, a malevolent ghost.

Fear and hatred of the *alus* are deep-seated Ifaluk drives, both conscious and unconscious, and they are found in all age groups. Thus no one will venture alone into the bush at night, because it is in the night that the *alus* attack. If they must leave their courtyards at night, the people carry torches because *alus* fear the light. Similarly, doorways are covered at night to prevent the *alus* from entering the house. Formerly the young men slept in the men's clubhouse; they no longer do so, for their number is few and they fear attack by the *alus*. It is no wonder that the *alus* lead the list of fear-inspiring stimuli mentioned in the Emotional Response Test by a wide margin.

The *alus* also figure prominently in the fantasy life of the people. The percentage of *alus* figures in the children's free-drawings is high. More than one-quarter of the collected dreams of adults are nightmares induced by perception of the *alus*. Almost 60 per cent of identified figures in the T.A.T. are *alus*. *Alus* are frequently "perceived," always at night, in ordinary life. A boy sees an *alus* while walking home in the evening; an *alus* throws a stone at a woman as she is bathing at dusk in the lagoon; two young men hear an *alus* walking on the roof of their house; a young woman sees an *alus* as she waits for her lover in the bush; and so on. In all these cases the persons involved are greatly frightened.

The primary concern of religion in Ifaluk is with therapeutic and preventive medicine—in effect, with the *alus*. Great amounts of time and energy are spent in preventing the *alus* from attacking or in exorcising the *alus* once they have attacked. In short, much of the people's repressed hostility can be expressed with impunity against the *alus*, since the aggression taboo does not apply to aggression against them. This argument is valid even if it be argued that aggression against the *alus* is a response to their evil image. For in that case repressed hostility may still be displaced onto the *alus* simultaneously with the conscious hostility which they themselves evoke. As Dollard (2, p. 19) writes, "there is always some displaced aggression accompanying it (i.e., direct aggression), and adding additional force to the rational attack. . . . The image of the incredibly hostile and amoral out-grouper is built up out of our own real antagonism plus our displaced aggression against him . . ."

Thus although Ifaluk socialization provokes a potentially explosive problem by stimulating hostility in a people whose ethos prohibits the expression of hostility, Ifaluk religion serves to resolve the problem by providing the people with malevolent ghosts against whom their hostility can be released with impunity. In short, and consistent with our thesis, we see how culture resolves the tension which it has itself instigated.

And in this case the resolution is particularly to be admired because the *alus* are peculiarly suited to play this role: as deceased members of the lineage, they are almost identical with the persons whose behavior evoked the hostility, which is now reduced in aggression against them. [For other latent functions, social and psychological, served by the *alus*, see (8).]

But the Ifaluk have still another problem. They must not only find some sanctioned means for the release of hostility, but they must also find some means for satisfying their need of nurture (thus reducing their anxiety). In this case, it is the institution of chieftainship that serves this function. Ifaluk chiefs are not, in the narrow sense of "political," merely political leaders. They are, as our interpreter so aptly put it, "all same papa this place." Their approval is one of the wellsprings of Ifaluk behavior. When asked why they conform to some taboo or why they do not violate some other taboo, the invariable answer given by the Ifaluk is that the chiefs would approve or would disapprove of their behavior. The desire to retain the love of the chiefs is a most important— probably *the* most important—motive for conformity to Ifaluk values— the values of the chiefs.

The role played by the chiefs in motivating conformity with Ifaluk values was expressed very ably by the paramount chief:

The chiefs are like fathers here. Just as an empty canoe is tossed about by the waves and finally sinks, so, too, a society without chiefs is tossed about by conflict and strife and is destroyed. If a father asks his son not to behave badly, the latter may not obey him since he may not respect him highly. But all people obey the words of the chiefs, since they are feared and respected by all. The chiefs' duty is to see that the people behave well. The chiefs must constantly tell the people to be good, or else the society, like the canoe, would be destroyed.

The people "fear and respect" the chiefs and therefore conform to Ifaluk values, despite the fact that the latter have neither punitive sanctions nor, even if they did, the power to execute them. But then what is it about the chiefs that the people fear, and which therefore motivates them to behave in conformity with Ifaluk values? It is, as the people themselves say, the fear of their disapproval, of losing their love. Thus it is not the chiefs themselves whom the people fear, but rather the loss of their love. And if the fear of losing their love is great enough to provide a firm basis for social conformity—they conform in order not to lose their love—may we not conclude that the emotional security of the people is, to a great extent, contingent upon the continuing love of the chiefs? What I am saying, in short, is that one of the functions of the chiefs is to satisfy the people's need for nurture, the need for kindly parental figures.

The chiefs are uniquely qualified to play this role. Like the ideal parent, the important psychological characteristic of the chiefs is kindliness. If almost all the Ifaluk conform to the ethic of nonaggression, the chiefs are the personifications of this ethic. They are warm, nurturant parental figures. Like the ideal parent they talk kindly—there is a folk saying in Ifaluk that if the chiefs talk kindly the people will live long, but if they speak harshly the people will perish. Like the ideal parent, the chiefs, whose love the people desire, provide love and approval continuously upon good behavior. And this is where they differ from the real parent. The latter ultimately rejects the child regardless of the child's behavior. But the chiefs will never reject so long as their demands —conformity to the Ifaluk ethos—are complied with. Thus the love and praise of the chiefs provide that emotional security of which the people were deprived when rejected by their parents.

This need (as well as the role of the chiefs in meeting the need) is dramatically symbolized and satisfied in the Ifaluk food-distribution ritual. All group events, secular and religious, are terminated with the distribution of food and tobacco by the chiefs. Since the people bring the food and tobacco to be distributed, and since they receive food and tobacco of approximately the same quantity and quality which they had contributed, the eagerness with which they await the few ounces of tobacco and the handful of coconuts appears to be most irrational. But if our hypothesis about the psychodynamics of chieftainship is valid, this behavior is only *apparently* inexplicable. If the people desire the love of the chiefs, how better can this love be expressed (symbolized) than by the distribution of food and tobacco? Symbols of oral satisfaction and— in this culture—of love are distributed by those kindly parental figures whose love is necessary for emotional security.

It is our contention, then, that, in confirmation of our original thesis, the tensions produced by certain features of Ifaluk culture are resolved by still other features of the culture, and that despite the potential pathogenic characteristics of Ifaluk socialization, there is little pathology in Ifaluk because of the prophylactic-therapeutic characteristics of Ifaluk religion and chieftainship. But if the analysis is sound, how are the three cases of Ifaluk psychopathology to be explained?

Turning first to Tarev and Aneitin, it is obvious that the cultural canalization of aggression was ineffective for them. But, in view of our theoretical assumptions, this is hardly surprising. The cultural resolution of tension is effective for those whose tensions are culturally induced. Thus, in Ifaluk, the displacement of aggression onto the *alus* is an effective release of hostility evoked by Ifaluk childhood traumata. Aggressive experiences in childhood are the only ones for which institutional responses have been developed. But since Ifaluk social structure does not evoke, and Ifaluk ethos does not permit, aggressive behavior in adults, the Ifaluk cultural heritage provides no techniques by which an individual exposed to direct aggression in adulthood can handle it. In the absence of such institutionalized responses the individual is, so to speak, on his own.

This is what happened to Tarev and Aneitin. Both, it will be recalled, were model citizens until their experience in Japanese labor gangs. Although we possess little reliable data about these labor gangs, one fact emerges in bold relief. Japanese treatment of native labor was often harsh and brutal. Ifaluk men tell of the Japanese use of whips in order to ensure compliance with their demands. These inductees, moreover, were exposed to arrogance, if not brutality, even prior to their formal induction. When a Japanese patrol arrived on the atoll, they would demand that the chiefs fill their quota of men. Their arrogance toward the chiefs was expressed in unheard-of (for the Ifaluk) behavior. They would stand on raised platforms (thus violating the taboo on standing over the head of a chief), shout orders at them, and even beat them if they did not immediately comply with their orders. This evoked great hatred and anxiety in the people—a hatred which persisted at least as late as 1947–1948. The men inducted to work in the labor gangs continued to experience this treatment for the duration of their service.

For a people who, like the Ifaluk, live in a society in which non-aggression is the supreme value, and in which great emphasis is placed on kindly speech, the contrasting behavior of the Japanese must have left a deep impression. For such a people Japanese arrogance and brutality could easily have been traumatic. It is probably safe to assume, moreover, that this experience was not only intrinsically painful, but that it was symbolically painful as well, serving to remobilize their painful childhood frustrations with their attendant feelings of hostility and anxiety. Their fantasies of cruel, attacking beings were painfully objectified. Thus, for Tarev and Aneitin, at least, the situation became overwhelmingly traumatic. Provided with no cultural techniques for handling their powerful hostility, they now expressed it in direct and overt aggression. And in the absence of traditional interpretations (cultural fantasies) for their experiences, these men developed their own —idiosyncratic—fantasies. Since they could no longer live, as Hallowell puts it, by means of a "culturally constituted world," each developed a privately constituted world of his own.

Although the details of this interpretation are speculative, the general outline seems to be firmly supported by all the known facts. The Ifaluk could recall no other cases of *malebush* of this type before the Japanese contact; subsequent to contact only Tarev and Aneitin developed this type of *malebush;* and their difficulties began only after their induction into the Japanese work gangs. That other inductees did not break under the strain does not invalidate this interpretation. There are obviously marked individual differences in thresholds of frustration-tolerance— differences which, theoretically, may be traced to biogenic, psychogenic, and sociogenic variables. Since the differences operative in the cases under review are unknown, we can merely say that for those with low tolerance for aggression, the Japanese experience was sufficient to trigger the aggression.

For Tarev (but not for Aneitin) still another factor must be taken into account. We have indicated that one of the motivations for conformity in Ifaluk is the desire to retain the approval of the chiefs. Tarev does not want their approval: indeed, he has committed the extreme act of attacking the chiefs. Perhaps the logic should be reversed. He attacks the chiefs because, for him, they are not father-figures who love him, but enemies who attack him—it is one of the chiefs, Maroligar, whom he consistently charges with wishing to kill him. Hence, since the chiefs do not play a nurturant role in his life—either because he does not want their love, or because he believes that they are his attackers— he is not motivated, as are the other Ifaluk, to comply with their wishes. Moreover, his perception of the chiefs as attackers renders inoperative another prophylactic function of chieftainship. While for others the image of kindly chiefs reduces their rejection anxieties, for Tarev the chiefs only exacerbate this anxiety. For him the chiefs play a complex and ambivalent role. On the one hand, he accuses one of the chiefs of wanting to kill him, and, in return, he attacks the chief; on the other hand, he makes humble obeisance to the symbol of the chiefs—the phallus on the public meeting house. At the same time, he claims that he, Tarev, is a chief. I would interpret his "positive transference" toward me as an indication of his need to replace parent and/or chief with still another "good" parent figure.

It is this second feature of Tarev's behavior that provides the transition to Vegoilep. Vegoilep is in most respects quite different from Tarev and Aneitin; if the latter manifest "psychotic" symptoms, Vegoilep's seem to be "neurotic" in character. So far as I could ascertain, Vegoilep did not share with Tarev and Aneitin the experience of working in, and exposure to the brutality of, a Japanese work gang. And, indeed, his problem seems to be related to, and to be an exaggeration of, the generalized Ifaluk problem of insecurity, rather than that of hostility. Instead of acting aggressively against others, Vegoilep has chosen to retreat from them. He is anxious about others, but he has no (conscious) fantasies of being attacked by them. Since there is no specific precipitating factor to which the onset of his "illness" can be traced, the following explanation for his difficulty is highly speculative.

Why should Vegoilep's insecurity be so intense as to lead to voluntary confinement? The one clue we have is his fear of the chiefs—a fear which is reflected in his obsession to comply with their demands and in his perceptible fright at seeing a chief during the interview. In the typical situation, we have argued, the Ifaluk feel insecure because they perceive the world as threatening and because they feel themselves to have been rejected. This insecurity, however, is considerably mitigated by the role of the chiefs who, as kindly and loving parent-figures, assure them of continuous love and affection (contingent upon good behavior).

Vegoilep is the son of the former (now deceased) paramount chief. If typically the kindly chiefs, perceived as good parent-figures, serve to reduce insecurity, the probability of their serving this function for their own offspring is somewhat lessened. For it is the chief, *qua* parent, who is primarily responsible for the insecurity which he, *qua* chief, typically reduces. In short, it is difficult for the source of the insecurity to become the source of security. Since, from the child's perspective, his parent *qua* parent is a "bad" figure, it is only with difficulty that he, *qua* chief, can be perceived as a "good" figure. If in general the chiefs serve to reduce the Ifaluk anxiety about not being loved, then where the chiefs are effectively precluded from serving that function, insecurity remains a prevailing attitude. Thus Vegoilep's exaggerated insecurity may be explained by the fact that, for him, the culturally provided means for reducing insecurity do not function. Therefore, since he continues to perceive his world as threatening, his one effective response is withdrawal from the source of the threat. And his obsession with complying with the demands of the chiefs may then be interpreted as a defense against his hostility to his parents (just as his isolation may be interpreted, not only as a defense against the hostility of others, but against his own hostility toward them).

CONCLUSION

The analysis of Ifaluk culture and of the cases of mental illness among the Ifaluk would seem to support the several theses proposed at the beginning of the chapter. Features of Ifaluk culture create tensions which are, in turn, reduced by still other features of the culture. Individuals whose life experiences were idiosyncratic developed mental illness either because extant cultural means for tension reduction were ineffective (Vegoilep), or because these experiences gave rise to tensions for which cultural means for reducing tension were nonexistent (Tarev and Aneitin). That other individuals, with similar idiosyncratic experiences, did not develop mental illness indicates that molar cultural investigation must be supplemented by molecular clinical investigations if a comprehensive explanation of psychopathology is to be developed. Nevertheless, the cultural analysis is sufficiently powerful to indicate that mental illness and mental health are intimately related to cultural institutions as tension-producing and tension-reducing variables.

BIBLIOGRAPHY

1. Burrows, Edwin G., and Spiro, Melford E.: *An Atoll Culture*. New Haven: Human Relations Area Files, 1953.
2. Dollard, John: "Hostility and fear in social life." *Social Forces*, 1938, vol. 17, pp. 15–25.
3. Erikson, Erik Homburger: "Observations on Sioux education." *Journal of Psychology*, 1939, vol. 7, pp. 101–156.
4. Horton, Donald: "The functions of alcohol in primitive societies: A cross-cultural study." *Quarterly Journal of Studies on Alcohol*, 1943, vol. 4, pp. 199–320.
5. Merton, Robert K.: "Social structure and anomie." *American Sociological Review*, 1938, vol. 3, pp. 672–682.

6. Spiro, Melford E.: "A psychotic personality in the South Seas." *Psychiatry,* 1950, vol. 13, pp. 189–204.

7. ———: *The Problem of Aggression in a South Sea Culture.* Ph.D. thesis, on file in Northwestern University Library, 1950.

8. ———: "Ghosts, Ifaluk, and teleological functionalism." *American Anthropologist,* 1952, vol. 54, pp. 497–503.

9. ———: "Ghosts: An anthropological inquiry into learning and perception." *Journal of Abnormal and Social Psychology,* 1953, vol. 48, pp. 376–382.

Thomas Gladwin

Social Science Consultant
National Institute of Mental Health

and

Seymour B. Sarason

Department of Psychology
Yale University

7

CULTURE AND INDIVIDUAL PERSONALITY

INTEGRATION ON TRUK *

Studies of culture and personality in non-European societies provide a natural laboratory for testing and expanding our understanding of personality dynamics. It is by now well established that the majority of persons reared and living in a cultural environment different from our own exhibit patterns of behavior consistently variant in some respects from the behaviors upon which existing personality theory has been predicated. These variant patterns, as they arise from and integrate with differing cultural contexts, reveal a range of nonpathological behavior not otherwise observable.

Attempts to apply existing personality theory in non-European settings can thus provide a series of crucial tests of its validity as a statement of human behavior, rather than of European-American behavior alone. Ultimately it can be expected also to contribute new dimensions and concepts to this body of theory, although serious endeavors in this direction have yet to be made by any responsible investigators in the field.

Although studies in culture and personality have been used for the purposes described, they have in general failed to take systematic ad-

* This paper is based on the monograph by Thomas Gladwin and Seymour B. Sarason: *Truk: Man in Paradise.* New York: Viking Fund Publications in Anthropology, no. 20, 1953. Copyright by the Wenner-Gren Foundation for Anthropological Research. Reprinted by permission.

173

vantage of the range of behaviors available. More explicitly, little more than anecdotal attention has been paid to behaviors and modes of integration of individuals in the various cultural settings examined. Such data can greatly expand the available range of variant cases and provide insight into mechanisms of adjustment and personality development at a fairly concrete level of case study. In contrast, the more usual analysis, statistical in method or philosophy, creates an abstract synthesis of basic or modal personality which submerges within itself all individual variation. A number of possible cases of personality-in-culture becomes for comparative purposes a single case.

The present authors therefore undertook to explore methodological procedures which would permit of systematic studies of individual cases, representative of the range of types of adjustment and personality integration within a single cultural context, in this case Truk, a Micronesian island group in the Western Pacific.* The results of this undertaking have been published, and the reader is referred to the original monograph for details (1).

Briefly, twenty-three cases were selected from the adolescent and adult population of the small island of Romonum in the Truk group in such a fashion that they represented both modal and variant personality types. This was accomplished through polling ten randomly selected adults on their like and dislike for each resident of the island. The presumption here was not that the results reflected true "popularity," but rather that a person consistently liked (or disliked) by ten people was probably in some way atypical. Subjects were then selected by chance from the extremes and the middle range of men and women separately.

The Rorschach and the Thematic Apperception Test (using Micronesian pictures adapted under the direction of William A. Lessa) were administered to each subject, and the subject solicited for his life history and any current or remembered dreams, which were translated during transcription. The projective tests were analyzed blind by Dr. Sarason before he had any knowledge of the culture, being given only the sex, age, and pseudonym of the subject. He prepared a summary of each subject's test, and a synthesis of the entire series. His analytic approach was essentially clinical and relied little upon interpretive techniques utilizing scoring categories.

We have reproduced here with a minimum of change four of these

---

* The methodology for this study was a development of that used by Cora DuBois in *The People of Alor*. Minneapolis: University of Minnesota Press, 1944.

case studies, three men and a woman. They were selected because the fullness of the record or other factors made them more useful than others as examples of method. They are not intended in themselves to provide a complete or even adequate picture of Trukese personality, and should not be read for this purpose. Justification for their republication in the present volume lies simply in the fact that studies which would refine and carry forward this or other systematic methods of case analysis have not been forthcoming. We believe that valuable comparative data are thereby being lost and frankly hope that we can entice others to pick up this line of endeavor.

The Trukese economy is typical of small Pacific islands in subsistence patterns, deriving carbohydrates from the land and protein from the sea. The relatively small cash economy is based primarily on the export of copra and wage work at the administrative center; most of the proceeds are spent on imported clothing, household items, and luxury foods. Socially the individual is placed within a household, which may change, permanently within a localized matrilineal lineage which is of great importance to him, and within a clan which extends to other islands within the Truk atoll and beyond to islands further away. These relationships are supplemented by artificial ties to "siblings" of the same sex stemming initially from friendships, but involving other members of the "sibling's" kin group.

Strong, but largely unrealistic, anxieties are associated with the possibility of food deprivation. Since the lineage is the vehicle of production and distribution of food, the possibility of rejection by one's kinsmen can create formidable concern. Restraint and the suppression of overt aggression—or even of undue initiative or personal ambition—therefore characterizes most interpersonal relationships. This, and patterns of child-rearing, undoubtedly contribute heavily to a general psychological constriction and emotional shallowness.

Children from infancy onward are responded to with great inconsistency by all adults, including parents. The same act may be met by the same adult at one time with warmth and approval and at another by hostility and impatience, depending on the adult's inclination and preoccupation at the moment. Children are on their own most of the time, playing or fighting with their age mates, and supported only by their older siblings, real or artificial—an early introduction to dependence on relatives. A childhood of this sort is not conducive to the development of well-integrated expectancies and perceptions of the self or others, nor of flexible and adequate modes of coping with the environment. The individual learns to respond in a minimal, "safe," and concrete way to all situations.

Boys and girls are treated very similarly through childhood. At puberty, however, the boy has to leave home. In the past he went to a men's house. This institution has disappeared, and he must now find a place in the household of any kinsman who will accept him. At marriage he moves into his wife's household, as an outsider dependent upon maintaining good relations with his in-laws. Meanwhile the girl remains at home at puberty, and at marriage controls an increased share of the household's food supplies through the contribution of her husband and his lineage. The status of the husband is severely threatened if he becomes incapacitated and therefore not a food-producer. This situation produces, in adulthood, far greater insecurity in men than in women.

Adulterous sexual relationships provide a primary source of emotional and ego satisfaction. Although one has to be cautious and restrained with all relatives, the incest taboo forbids sexual relationship with any kinsman and thus defines any sexual partner as standing outside of the group with whom one must be careful. Therefore it is only here that free emotional self-expression, within the limitations of possible discovery, is fully possible. Adultery in fact provides not merely self-expression but also self-validation, especially for a man. After the age of perhaps forty he is no longer expected to continue demonstrating his charms and prowess with women and will often thereafter confine his attentions to his wife. Some men, of course, become involved in few or no adulterous liaisons, but they are a definite minority. Out of twelve men we found only one in which this was apparently the case.

The four cases follow. The life histories are largely summarized, as they were in the original publication. Where the subject was questioned or prompted this is indicated. Of the islands within Truk which are mentioned, Romonum is the one on which the study was conducted, Moen houses the present American administration, and Dublon was the Japanese administrative center until 1945. Under the Japanese, Romonum fell within a subdistrict with its center on the nearby island of Udot. All children on Romonum were expected to go to Udot for up to three years of compulsory schooling.

ANDY, Age 19

Shortly before Andy's birth on the island of Moen his mother divorced her husband and married another man who acts in every respect as Andy's own father. After Andy his mother had seven other children as follows: a boy who died at an age of seven or eight, a boy who died at four or five, a girl now thirteen, a girl now nine, a girl who died at two or three, a boy now five, and a girl now two. The lineage to which Andy belongs is among the smallest on Romonum, and Andy is the oldest male in it. Andy's "brothers" are thus mostly artificial.

Andy's father is the Catholic catechist on Romonum and likes to consider himself an entrepreneur, a desire which increases both his importance on the island and his debts. Andy was my principal assistant and companion, and therefore my "brother," during our stay on Romonum. At the time of recording his life history he was pining for a girl to whom he had been betrothed some two years before; her parents broke the betrothal and married her to another man. A few months later he became disillusioned in this girl and began an intensive affair with his "brother's" wife. In the crisis precipitated by this affair he was maneuvered into marrying his former betrothed after her hasty divorce; this marriage was seldom satisfactory to Andy, but four years later he had not yet succeeded in realizing his often stated determination to terminate the relationship.

Rorschach. Andy is probably the most complex and un-Trukese person in the group. He is much more adaptable, spontaneous, and outward-going than the others and can express his feelings and needs in a more direct fashion. He is self-confident and probably is overtly more aggressive (in the positive sense) than the others. He lacks the strong inhibitory tendencies which the others tend to share. He is able to act on the basis of his feelings and is not as afraid to express them. He also lacks the concreteness of thinking of so many of the others. He is flexible in his approach to problem-solving tasks and can use his imagination—he probably is not as afraid of fantasy as so many of the others. He is sufficiently different from others that one might wonder whether this culture permits him to carry out or satisfy many of his inner needs and fantasies. There is some indication that Andy's internal needs, desires, and fantasies may be stronger or more fully developed than his ability to give them satisfying expression. In a sense he is like the child (a smart one) who feels much more and wants to do more than he can say or do. One would also conclude that he feels more aggressive tendencies than he allows himself to express.

So far, emphasis has been given to the non-Trukese aspects of Andy's make-up. He is like the Trukese in that he inhibits, or tries to inhibit, in his case, the expression of strong or conflictful feelings. What one feels strongly one should not express. His initial response tendency is to avoid expression of feeling, but it should be emphasized that Andy overcomes this better than the others. Andy also shows conflict or anxiety in the sexual area. In this sphere strong inhibitory tendencies have a constricting effect. It is interesting that in Andy's record women are described as aggressive and such aggressiveness seems to be associated in his mind with sexuality. Whatever the explanation of the hypothesized sexual problem, in this and in other cases, it would appear that fulfilling the male sexual role is not without its problems.

T.A.T. What is perhaps most distinctive about Andy's stories is that they reveal him to have unusually strong needs for intellectual achievement and personal prowess. He is the one in the series who has most closely identified himself with the Western examiner, whom he regards to be a "thinker" and whom he wishes to emulate. One might put it this way: Andy has an unusually high level of aspiration. He not only wants to be a "thinker" but he wants in general to excel, to be in a position of eminence and power. Although he possesses a degree of self-confidence which is unusual for the Trukese, he is plagued by self-doubts and feelings of inadequacy in regard to the fulfillment of his goals. Given his high level of aspiration, and the contents of it, it would be expected that he would be quite aware of the discrepancy between what he would like to be and what he is or might be. The important point to stress is that Andy not only wants to be a "thinker" and a man of great personal and physical prowess, but he wants to be "on top." It should be emphasized that his achievement strivings are intimately related to very strong aggressive and hostile feelings. From his stories one might conclude that his achievement fantasies and assertive tendencies are sublimated expressions of extremely strong hostile tendencies. This should not be taken to mean that Andy does not consciously experience strong hostile feelings, because the strength of these feelings as reflected in his stories is too great to assume that it is completely or even largely sublimated. The fact that in his stories the aggressive actions of some of the figures are either seen as a "battle of minds," or are connected with guilt, or serve to protect a weaker person, or are punished, or have "accidental" effects, or in some way are associated with feelings of inadequacy—it is on the basis of such factors that it is concluded that much of Andy's hostility is inhibited. One would expect that it would be expressed indirectly or through his excelling in some kind of activity. Andy is a "bright" boy and one would expect that he is able to satisfy, at least partially, his need to excel and achieve. However, the discrepancy between what he would like to do and what he can do is probably a source of concern and frustration.

The question as to why Andy should possess the need to achieve and his relatively good degree of self-confidence seems to receive an answer in the nature of his parent-child relationships. Apparently Andy has or had been able to identify himself with supportive and dominant parental figures. But the stories reveal a difference in his attitude toward mother and father figures. Again it is the mother who is more ambivalently described. What the stories suggest is that Andy's mother, although supportive and protective, was a more threatening and perhaps aggressive person than the father. In fact, Andy appears to react with feelings of inadequacy and submission to adult females. It is as if toward men he feels more secure or self-confident than he does toward women. He feels that women are powerful, undependable, and threatening. However, he is attracted to people, male or female, whom he regards in one way or other as exceptional.

There is evidence in his stories that Andy, like another of our subjects,

Roger, did not have an uneventful oedipal stage. The remnants of the conflict are not nearly as strong as in the case of Roger. It is as if Andy resolved the conflict by identifying with the power of the father whereas Roger was only partially successful in doing so. It would be expected that Andy would be a more mature person than Roger.

There is good evidence in the stories that Andy tends to identify with the underdog who is weak, helpless, or unaggressive. Although he tends to depreciate such people, he nevertheless takes a protective attitude toward them. If one assumes that Andy himself feels like an underdog, the possibility arises that his relationship with one or both of his parents is responsible. It is difficult to be more specific on this point. The fact that fear of "being alone" recurs in the stories in relation to loss of a parent—usually the father—suggests that the family constellation might in some way be responsible for this feeling of being the underdog against which Andy reacted aggressively and assertively. In short, it may be that Andy's strong needs for assertion and achievement are a form of compensation for opposing feelings of inadequacy and some kind of personal loss. Whether this stems from the oedipal conflict or some nonsexual social factors or both cannot be answered in any detail.

What perhaps deserves elaboration here is Andy's sexual attitudes toward women. Although he has strong sexual drives and interests, he seems to have some guilt about their expression. When this is taken together with the typically Trukese attitude that women are sexually not dependable and are threatening to a man's esteem, it would seem that Andy has his problems in this area. It may be that a person with strong needs for assertion and dominance is particularly vulnerable in his relations with Trukese women.

Life History. Although Andy's life history provides us with abundant evidence that he is quite as exceptional among Trukese as his test results would indicate, he tells us little that would provide a reliable basis for determining why he developed in this direction. His account is shorter than the average, and almost a third of what he tells consists in a review of his present status in response to the usual questions in this regard.

Andy's early childhood was spent with his parents on Moen, interrupted by several months on an island on the barrier reef where his parents were cutting copra, and then later on Romonum. His recollections of this early period consist in accounts of no less than four adult feasts at which he was present—during one of which an older man gave him some *sake* and he got drunk—catching some crabs and roasting them, and being accidentally bitten on the finger by a big coconut crab he had been given. He mentions his parents only in passing. He conveys the impression of an assured and anxiety-free period after he arrived as a small child on Romonum: "I don't remember coming here. I liked it much better here than on Moen. [Why?] Because I was bigger and knew what was going on. I used to sing songs and go from house to house getting little presents. There was lots of food . . ."

The only beatings he mentions were administered by his father when Andy was about six in punishment for the common misdeed of swimming when he was told not to. He says, "I was unhappy and cried and cried. My mother was angry at my father and cried too because he was treating me like an animal." This is a most unusual reaction for a Trukese parent and, if true, indicates a greater appreciation of Andy's status as a personality to be reckoned with in the family group than we find in the accounts of others. He never mentions being told to stay around the house or having food refused him for his misdeeds.

By the time Andy was eight he was playing a ghost game very popular with children on the Winisi sand spit, participating with young adults in canoe races, and fishing with a slightly older "brother" (Andy's father's brother's son). From this time onward Andy mentions with pride his skill in fishing, compounded in his opinion of luck and his enjoyment of the sport. He identifies with his father in this regard and yet has anxieties: "My father is the same way: he is number one with the thrown spear while I am number one with the small rubber-propelled spear. I don't know why I can get fish so easily. I have an idea that one day I will be sorry for it, for we Trukese are a little scared of people who are so unusually apt in some form of work. If someone is very lucky in fishing every time he goes out he is not quite the same as other people—perhaps he will soon die for the ghosts will come and get him." This passage spells out the dilemma noted in his T.A.T.: he seeks and enjoys personal achievement, but shares with other Trukese the anxiety which comes with being outstanding and surpassing one's fellows, an anxiety he typically ascribes to the relatively impersonal ghosts rather than to the hostility of actual people.

At about twelve or thirteen Andy spent two months visiting on the reef island of Pis, where he again distinguished himself as a fisherman and began to make advances toward girls: "I used to wear a lot of flowers in my hair and give them to girls; I used to tickle their legs with a coconut leaf rib, up their legs as far as I could go." He did not have any intentions really of starting an affair, however, for he had the opportunity and did not take it. A girl approached a "brother" Andy had acquired on Pis and asked him to arrange that the three of them get together so she could hear Andy talk. "I wondered about this, but we went out to the beach. We sat leaning against a boat with the girl beside me. Later she asked me for my flowers and gave me hers. I did not understand all this and asked my 'brother' about it; he said she liked me very much. I said, 'Really, is that true?' and he said 'Yes.' But there was nothing I could do about it because she was older than I— I was just young."

Andy describes two narrow escapes during the bombing of Truk, one on Dublon during the first raids and a second when a boat was strafed and sunk. The boat was based on Romonum and several people from the island (including a "brother" of Andy's) were killed; this episode is mentioned in several of the life histories. Andy found his father in the water and helped him to land (on Romonum's reef island of Yawata, where they had been fishing). Andy ascribes his escape in each case to his presence of mind, although he adds in recounting the bombing episode on Dublon that he prayed and Jesus cared for him. Those who were killed on the boat "did not dive under the water; they did not observe as I did that the bullets ricocheted off the surface."

In discussing his present status Andy shows clearly his dependence on his parents and the degree to which this centers about food:

"Every day I think of my father and mother and what I would do if they should sicken and die. I am frightened. I don't know what I would do. I would just have to go into some relative's house, although not a real 'mother' or 'father,' and take some food—I would be embarrassed, very embarrassed. I hope they do not die first; I would rather I died first. I would hate to see them die; I love them. If they died I would be hungry and embarrassed. There would be no food, no money, no clothes; there would be, but if they were dead it would not be the same as now. Every day I would go to the house —not of my real mother and father but of others—and just sit down and wait until they asked me if I wanted to eat, if they did at all. Now I just go up and ask if there is any food; I am not embarrassed. If my parents should die I think I would have to go and live with my father's sister. Whenever I go there to eat I notice that her son always is given a bigger share than I —she is not a very good sort of person. On the other hand when he or my father's brothers' other children come to our house everybody gets the same amount of food: it is just as if they were all my parents' own children. That is why I keep thinking how sorry I would be if my parents were to die: if I lived in my father's sister's house I would be embarrassed every day."

In another passage Andy shows his strong identification of himself with his father, protecting and watching over his younger sisters; then in response to a question he shows his anxiety over his adequacy in the event that this protection should involve fighting.

"I also think of my sisters and when they will be married. I am very anxious that they marry, but not to men who will beat them every day. If their husbands beat them all the time I will not know what to do for I will not want to fight them, and yet I will be angry for I love them most of all. I think that finally one day I would get mad enough to fight them. [Why would you not want to fight them—frightened?] No! Not I. I just don't like to fight. When I was small and other boys beat me I could not fight, for I was frightened and small. But now I think I am big enough to fight, and I think that if I were to meet any of those boys I would fight them. Since the time I left the Japanese school where those boys used to beat me I have gotten bigger and if I go far away and meet them I will fight them. I used to feel that I could not fight them when they ganged together against me; I wanted to fight them one at a time but that was not possible. But now I feel I would just do it."

It is evident that Andy's anxiety over fighting is a blend of his common Trukese feeling that he should not be directly aggressive (it would be all right to fight the boys if he met them "far away") and actual timidity in facing a fight (he could have fought as a child if the boys had not "ganged together"). Although he now envisions himself as not afraid, we should note that he does not permit himself the degree of fantasy another subject, Roger, showed in stating as fact his heroic emergence from a fight against overwhelming odds.

In continuing the discussion of his present status Andy tells how much he would like to marry his former betrothed, and what an ideal husband he would be (a hope not entirely realized when the marriage became a fact). He says he likes being a young man, and does not want to grow old. "I am afraid of dying early. Every time I have intercourse or something of the sort I am a little afraid of dying. I am afraid I will die because of doing something bad. [?] I really don't know why I am scared—that is just the way it is. I am a little afraid because I have intercourse with girls and also go to church; that is why I am scared."

Dreams. Four current dreams were recorded in the weeks which followed the life history sessions, the first occurring the night following the conclusion of Andy's interviews. He met his love and she told him angrily to go away, followed by a curse. As he and others were trying to placate her Andy awoke. Andy's interpretation of this dream follows a standard line of reasoning, a device which permits the Trukese to deflect the aggressive implications of their often hostile dream-situations: although his love rejected him, and this meant only that she was thinking of someone else. People are never said really to be angry at the persons toward whom they express hostility in their dreams.

The second dream occurred five days later. Andy simply dreamed a tooth had fallen out, woke, and found all his teeth there. This is interpreted as signifying the imminent death of a relative.

Two months later Andy dreamed he and three companions were by a beautiful mountain covered with soft grass. He saw a magnificent red chicken. They chased it up on the mountain and one of Andy's companions caught the chicken; he gave it to Andy, but it got away. They were off the mountain by then so they again chased it up the mountain, the same man caught it, and gave it to Andy who did not let it go again. Everyone admired it. The interpretation was in terms of chicken medicine, a type of curing magic.

The last dream was ten days later, involving Andy and me, and later the other two anthropologists then still on Romonum. A powerful older man on the island threatened and then attacked me; Andy almost cried, then used a powerful curse to stop the man, but in vain. I defended myself successfully, and then many people closed in on the four of us with knives. We fended them off and then the people drew back, walking around angrily. Andy awoke, but adds that before he woke it occurred to him that he must not walk around at night lest someone knife him. Andy could offer no interpretation. It should be noted that Andy did not enter the fight until he had three companions.

Discussion. As we noted in the beginning of the summary of Andy's life history, he is an unusual boy to find on Truk; his desire for, and pride in, achievement is marked—he is a skilled fisherman, and wants to be a good fighter, a protecting father, and ideal husband. But, as noted from his tests, he finds his path blocked by his anxieties; even his skill at fishing, a culturally approved and essentially noncompetitive activity, gives him pause. We should also note that his goals involve doing things for other people to a degree most Trukese do not show: he wants to be able to fight to protect his sisters, and as an ideal husband he will be kind and tolerant toward his wife. He thus shows the capability for more satisfying and sensitive interpersonal relationships noted in his Rorschach, a characteristic even more evident to one who knows him and has an opportunity to compare him with other Trukese. He can introspect: whereas other Trukese respond to a battery of questions as to their present status with only a few sentences, Andy takes off on a long discussion of his personal problems. It is evident that a person of this sort would have difficulty in finding the sort of relationships he seeks among other Trukese. It is probably this which led him to form a strong attachment to me, an American and therefore less constricted than the average Trukese (and by the same token led me to select him as my companion and assistant). If we remember that his strivings for achievement as expressed in his life history are toward goals within the Trukese framework, it appears likely that his identification with me as a "thinker" in the T.A.T. is an identification with my responsiveness rather than with my superior status as an American. Although not mentioned in the life history, he noted in another context that his closest friend to date had been an unusually kindly Japanese man, "different from the other Japanese." Thus although he knows how to behave in the Trukese society, and accepts its stated goals as his own, he is in important respects unfitted to make a satisfying adjustment to his life there. But by accepting his version of Trukese life goals as the measure of his own success he introspectively examines himself against this yardstick and finds himself wanting; thus to the frustration of his inability to find responsive companionship is added the frustration of his failure to be a successful Trukese.

In seeking an explanation for Andy's atypical development we find in his life history two clues: his seemingly carefree childhood and his mother's sympathy with him when his father was beating him "like an animal." As we noted above, this shows a sympathy and understanding on his mother's part which is unusual. She shows this same attitude toward his younger siblings— observed especially during the latter part of my stay on Romonum when I was living in their house. His father is more neutral, but did not show toward his young children the occasionally vindictive behavior noted in other fathers. It would thus appear that Andy had an exceptionally supportive mother who treated him more as a person, and a father who was at least less punitive than most and with whom Andy succeeded in establishing a strong identification. With the greater responsiveness he thus acquired he undoubtedly became a more amusing "plaything" to older people than most children (as is his five-year-old brother now) and for this reason received more positive attention from other adults as a child—as he himself notes when he describes his unusual activity of singing songs and collecting little presents around the islands.

If Andy had such a "loving" mother (by Trukese standards) on whom he remains very dependent, one wonders why he does not show with any clarity the oedipal conflicts revealed in Roger's T.A.T. The answer very possibly lies in the number of times his mother was pregnant and cared for the resulting small babies: she had seven children after Andy, all of whom survived at least well into childhood. Thus whereas Roger's childless mother could always be available to him, Andy's support and attention from his mother was repeatedly broken by long intervals when she was more or less incapacitated by pregnancy or preoccupied with a baby. It would thus have been difficult for Andy even in fantasy to have believed that he could command his mother's exclusive attention. At the same time the negative component of the oedipus (hostility toward the father) would have been less likely to develop in Andy whose father was only occasionally punitive than in Roger whose father broke him of crying by beating him every time.

Tony, Age 23

Both of Tony's parents are living. He is the oldest of their five living children, although five others died. His older brother died at the age of twenty-three, seven years prior to the recording of Tony's life history; Tony then married his brother's wife. Tony's younger siblings are as follows: a boy who died at four or five, a girl now nineteen and married, a boy who died at eight, a boy now fourteen, a girl now ten, a boy now eight, a boy who died at two, and a girl who died at one. Tony's wife is Roger's older sister; she has a boy of seven fathered by Tony's older brother and two children by Tony, a boy of four and a girl almost one year old. Tony's own lineage (that of his mother) is small, but that of his father is the largest on Romonum.

Rorschach. This appears to be a person whose anxiety level is higher than in most other individuals. By this is meant that he probably experiences anxiety somewhat more frequently than others. He differs from Mike, a constricted, inflexible, and over-controlled youth, in that his anxieties will be somewhat more manifest. But Tony defends himself against them by a suppressive mechanism which, however, impoverishes his adequacy and has a rather constricting effect on him. From the record, one would conclude that there will be times when his defenses do not work satisfactorily. His reality-testing is not consistently good. His conflicts seem to center around the presence of a strong need for expression which he cannot achieve in any kind of direct or satisfactory manner. Whereas with Mike we found personal expression almost completely inhibited, with Tony we found these personal needs nearer the surface. While one may have doubted that Mike would attempt in other than a superficial way to adjust to people and situations, this is not the case with Tony. He tries but he is not very successful. He lacks the assertiveness or self-confidence that is found in Andy and some others. It does not take much to force him to withdraw and pull in his horns.

It follows from the above that Tony responds subjectively to his environment. By this is meant that he responds in terms of his motivational structure, unlike Mike who inhibits such a tendency. One might expect therefore that Tony would experience conflict where Mike would not. Tony would appear to experience more ups and downs than Mike. It would be surprising if Tony's relationship to his environment were as effective or smooth as Andy's. He is not as well-organized or sure of himself.

The fact that Tony is described as a person with personal problems should not be taken to mean they will be blatantly apparent. He does try to avoid their being expressed and frequently succeeds in doing so at the expense of his spontaneity. In a sense this seems to typify the Trukese: in the face of conflict or of an anxiety-arousing situation their behavior loses flexibility, their adequacy is reduced, they become anxious, and inhibit personal expression. They probably become dependent rather than aggressive or assertive. While this description holds in general for the Trukese, it is given here because it fits Tony in all particulars.

T.A.T. Tony's stories are short and superficial and the content distinctive for the relative absence of hostility. Many of his stories deal with people "relaxing," "playing," "dancing," or "eating." Practically none of his stories contains figures who are really active or assertive or who interact with each other on a personal basis. In the only story in which some kind of feeling is exchanged between adult figures, it is the woman who is assertive over the man. Although parental figures are described as frustrating, the degree and strength of their frustrating behavior is much less than is found in the stories of many other males. Similarly, the reaction of the children is only minimally aggressive. When one takes the above, together with the fact that Tony's stories contain little active-conflict themes, one may conclude that Tony is the kind of individual who avoids self-expression or personal involvement and raises the possibility that he was being evasive in the situation. There is some evidence for this conclusion: in one story he describes a young woman as "pretty sexy." In another story he ends with the unexplained and somewhat inappropriate remark: "These two know about the old dances." It is quite clear from his stories that Tony is much interested in dancing. If one assumes that dancing is in some way or other a sexualized activity, it not only indicates where Tony's interests are but also that he was inhibiting or avoiding sexual themes in his responses to the pictures. The nearest he comes to the expression of such a theme is a story in which two men are relaxing in the coolness of a tree's shade and practicing love songs.

There is one comment or sentence made by Tony which deserves brief discussion. In one story he says of a child: "He has no food because he has no one to love him: he has no mother or father." Not only does this comment underline the importance which the Trukese attach to food but also indicates how the association "food-security" is part of Trukese thinking. One might also speculate that to the Trukese giving food is symbolically like giving love and taking away food is equivalent to taking away love. From this and other protocols the possibility can be raised that maternal rejection by refusing or begrudging or withholding food may be something which more than a few Trukese children experience. It should also be pointed out that thus far it appears that it is the men who show more concern and responsibility for the child's food supply than the women.

Life History. Tony's is the only really long life history given by a man; it is about three times as long as the average and includes a report on twelve dreams. It is of particular interest to us (although much of it is concerned with his time in school on Udot and working for a Japanese on Dublon, neither of which is particularly germane to our present interests) because his projective test results indicate that he feels in marked degree the "typical" Trukese conflict between a need for expressing his feelings and the suppression of this expression due to his anxiety in interpersonal relations.

Tony begins his account with a long description of children's play activities —games, make-believe, teasing, fights, and disasters, by day and by night —most of them seemingly applying to the kinds of play groups characteristic of somewhat later childhood. Several of the games are quite aggressive, such as this one: "We had a battle with little fruits, pelting each other with them; if we put sand in they were heavy and really hurt. We knew they hurt but we were just as if we were crazy when we were small. We cried but kept on fighting." Later he mentions again the craziness of children when he describes fighting with firebrands. Discussing his play he says, "We played this way day after day for years because when we were small we had no work to do." Although he describes several fights, he does not mention any "brothers" either helping or opposing him; on the other hand he does not mention that he was beaten very often by his age-mates. He mentions his parents bandaging his shoulder when he cut it with a piece of glass, and his father caring for him when he was bitten on the beach by a "scorpion fish" (presumably a Portuguese man-of-war). Other than this his account is just of an endless round of relatively carefree play with other children, mostly boys when their sex is mentioned.

After spending over a day recording these play activities I asked him to talk about something other than just games, perhaps his relations with his parents. The change in tenor of his account was striking:

"When I went home my parents used to tell me I should not play so much, for when I was out playing all the time if something happened to them I would never know anything about it. They just wanted me to stay in the house until I was grown up. When I came home and asked for food they would tell me there was none for me. They said if I was disobedient and played all the time I could not eat, but if I stayed home I would eat. Later they would feel sorry for me and give me something to eat.

"If I was home and they told me to get a coal from someone's fire to light ours with and I was disobedient and did not go, they would beat me or tell me I could not eat. But then they relented and gave me food after all.

"When I was out playing and came home to find they were not there, having gone inland or somewhere, I would cry, realizing that this was why they told me not to play all the time for now I did not know where they were. When they came home and saw I had been crying they would ask me why and I would tell them; then they would tell me that was why I should not play all the time. They also pointed out that if I was far away playing and was beaten I would be in trouble without anyone to help me.

"When my father used to go out fishing I would meet him when he came in. He would give me the fish to take home but I would just go off and give them to my playmates to eat. Then I would go home and my parents would ask me about the fish; when I told them they beat me.

"When there was no food and I came home hungry I would cry. My parents would point out to me that if I had stayed home I could have eaten what food there was, but by then they had eaten it all.

"When my father used to go to prepare breadfruit he would tell me to come along later to bring him some cigarettes or the like, but I would just go off playing and not worry about him any more. Then when I came home, there he would be, angry at me. He would ask me why I had not brought his cigarettes, and I would tell him I had been playing. Then he would beat me and tell me how naughty I was, and that if I liked playing so much I could eat it too, because I was not going to get any food.

"There was a little baby brother of mine in the house and I used to beat him. They used to tell me not to, for if I beat him and he died when they [his parents] died I would be all alone; but if there were lots of us we would be better off. But I was just naughty and went on beating him, and later they would beat me.

"Several times my older brother, who is dead now, came home and asked me if there was any food. Although there was, I told him to go back out and play because there was none. Later when my parents came home and he returned, he asked them for food and they gave it to him. Then he asked me why I had said there was none and said I probably had wanted to eat it all myself. Then he beat me.

"I used to take my little brother outside to play, and pretty soon start beating him. He would cry, and my mother would come and ask me why. I would tell her I had beaten him and then she would beat me."

The dangers of sorcery were also invoked to keep Tony in line: "My parents used to tell me not to tease older men or be fresh to them for if I did I would not grow up to be big. [?] I could not grow big if I did because the older men would curse me and I would be sick."

In view of the life he describes at home it is small wonder that Tony constantly sought to escape into the children's society. In the above passage Tony spells out with unusual clarity the conflict between his desire to play and his parents' attempts to force him to stay home with threats, beatings, and the withdrawal of food, at the same time keeping his own dependency upon them forcibly in his mind by emphasizing the fact that he might come home some day and find them gone for good. Tony also makes more explicit than most his hostility toward his own brothers. In considering both the unsatisfactory nature of his time spent at home and his aggression toward his brothers we should remember that Tony's mother bore and raised at least into childhood eight children after him, an average of one at least every two and a half years, so that she at almost all times was either pregnant or caring for an infant and thus had an excuse for telling Tony not to bother her.

When he was fourteen, Tony attended school briefly on Romonum, first with a Protestant and then a Catholic native preacher, the former on Tony's own initiative. Then he went to Udot to the Japanese school, thus avoiding the frequent trauma of being ejected from his home at puberty. However, he did not want to go to Udot and when the Japanese teacher came over Tony

hid. But his name had been written on the list of those who were to go and he
finally consented after the teacher threatened to throw Tony's parents in the
calaboose if he did not.

The teacher found a place for Tony to stay with a local chief and Tony
started school. With the chief and in school Tony began almost at once to be
disobedient and uncooperative. He resented being told by the chief to do his
share of the household food production; it is interesting that Tony had to admit
he did not know many of the routine aspects of this work which one would expect a boy of his age to have learned from his father. Tony was very inadequate
in his school work and made little effort to apply himself; he was beaten many
times by the teacher and frequently lied or simply ran away to get out of
school and return to Romonum. After several months of this, however, Tony
and two other Romonum boys ran away again and after they had been forced
to return . . .

"The Trukese teacher lectured us, telling us we should learn Japanese so
that we would be able to talk to them. I felt I did not care a bit whether I
knew Japanese or not. But then he went on to point out that now *he* had an
easy job because he had studied hard night and day when he went to school,
and now he was our master. I realized then that maybe he was right. When I
went to the chief and apologized for running off without telling him he said
it did not matter about him but that I should not run away from the teacher.
Because, he said, the only way I could make life easy for myself later was to
study hard at that time. Everybody—he, my parents, and the teachers—had
all said the same thing and I finally decided they must be right and I should
work hard. So after that I worked hard until I knew a little Japanese and arith-
metic and went into the second grade. By that time the teacher liked me and I
realized I had been right in believing them. When I wanted to go back to
Romonum, if someone was sick or the like, he let me and I always came back
the day he told me to."

This change in Tony's attitude toward school (which is reflected in the
account of his remaining two years on Udot) we should note was a result of
what we may suspect was the first positive instruction he had received in how
to deal effectively with important people. In fact, if we are correct in believing
that he had less than the usual amount of training in food-producing tasks,
this may well have been practically the first purposeful guidance he had received in regard to any sort of behavior outside of the (until then) meaningless instruction in Japanese words and numbers. We should also note that although he was in essence advised simply to submit to authority—the same thing
his parents had been trying to get him to do for years—in this instance he
was told to submit not merely to avoid punishment but rather in order later
to be able to deal effectively with people in authority. It was probably this
reasoning which appealed to Tony. Thereafter he still did not do very well
in school and occasionally rebelled and was beaten, but he learned enough to
maintain the proper rate of advancement through his three years of schooling.

His reform in school did not extend to his behavior in the home of the
chief, and he was finally asked to leave. An Udot boy who had become his

friend in school asked him to stay at his house and Tony moved over there; later he moved again, spending the rest of his time on Udot with his father's "sister." We need not concern ourselves with the many episodes Tony recounts from this period—a typhoon, a woman who was possessed by a sea spirit, a man who fell out of a tree, and so on—because they tell us little of importance regarding Tony's development. He became increasingly competent and willing in undertaking the work of a man and consequently had little difficulty in living with his friend and later his father's "sister." He got in a fight with an Udot boy who was thereafter beaten by Tony's older "brother" (of Tony's father's lineage). It would appear that Tony had no sexual experiences on Udot; he was, however, acutely aware that the girls were better than he in school, a fact brought to everyone's attention repeatedly by the teacher. It was after his first experience of a recitation in which the girls won that Tony became so disobedient with the chief that he was told to leave his house. Tony stayed in school, with occasional visits to Romonum or visits by his father to Udot, for three years and "then the final day came and they gave out the prizes. They gave out prizes for all sorts of things but all I got was a prize for working hard in the outside tasks [cutting copra, gardening, etc.]."

Then they all returned to Romonum and soon the others received letters advising them they were to go to the advanced school on Dublon, but the school authorities "forgot" Tony. "Then later they sent for me and the teacher told me I was going too but I would not be going to school; I would just be a houseboy for a Japanese who was looking for one. But he told me it was just like school for I would be learning things and had a chance to reflect with credit on my island and on him." With his feelings thus salved Tony left for Dublon and started working. We may again omit discussion of most of the episodes which Tony describes during the two years or so he worked as a houseboy on Dublon and later on Romonum, as most of these are concerned with his relations with various Japanese who apparently found him a reliable servant. He was, however, beaten several times by some of the military personnel on Romonum, once very severely.

While on Dublon Tony had an affair with a Trukese woman from Fefan who worked for another Japanese next door; this is the first such experience he mentions. It ended when his master told him to go out fishing with him one night and Tony thus failed to keep a rendezvous he had made with the woman. Later Tony had an affair with a Romonum girl while he was home on a week's vacation; although she went over thereafter to Dublon to be with Tony his father would not permit them to marry. Tony's older brother became very ill and Tony had to spend more and more time on Romonum to be with his brother. Then Tony was himself sick; after two months a Japanese doctor on Romonum cured him and engaged him as cook in the military dispensary on the island so he no longer returned to Dublon. After describing his vicissitudes with the Japanese, Tony said he could remember nothing else, without having said anything more about his affair with the Romonum girl or his sick older brother. I asked him about these and he said, "That was why my father would not let me marry that girl I wanted to marry. He said that if my brother died I should marry his wife, but if he got better I could marry the one I wanted to. But my brother died so I married his wife and I am still married to her." This is all he had to offer on the subject of his marriage and his life thereafter. When asked for more he described several adulterous escapades wherein he made fools of his male companions (one of them a "brother") by having greater success than they in gaining access to women and by ridiculing his friends afterwards. He concludes by saying, "That is all, for my parents told me I should not go to a lot of women. They told me if my wife was very forward with men it would be all right for me to be forward with women; since she is not I should not be either, and I am not."

Asked about his present status he said, "I am pretty happy now for I do not have any more troubles. A while ago when I had so much trouble [during the war] I was not happy but now I have little to worry about. I am happy with my wife because she is humble and gentle; if she were not I would not be satisfied with her. [P] I have no special wishes for the future; I like to go to women but that is about all." Thus Tony submitted to his father's authority and is married peacefully to a "humble" wife; this relationship is apparently not of sufficient interest to him to be worth recounting for he says nothing about it nor about his children. He has found he can express himself and be successful in his adulterous liaisons; the importance of this activity to him is shown in his statement that this is "about all" he likes.

Dreams. It is interesting in view of Tony's life history that six of his twelve dreams involve his being away from Romonum. All but one of these found him on another island in the Truk group and in trouble: he was sick on Tol and the Romonum boat went off and left him there; he gambled on Moen but when he won the Moen men threatened him and he woke up frightened; he capsized in a canoe on the way back from Falabeguets and would have drowned if a U.S. Navy motor launch had not rescued him; he played baseball on Dublon and was hit on the arm (after which a Romonum man gave him a coconut to drink); and when on Dublon he was chased by a policeman and almost missed the boat back while hiding under a bed in a house. His only favorable experience was in a dream about going to Japan, where he bought some bread and the storekeeper accidentally gave him too much change; Tony pocketed this and was very pleased. Thus although he fairly consistently suffers at the hands of his fellow Trukese, when he is away from home foreigners give him money and rescue him from drowning. This and his lengthy description in his life history of his life on Dublon would suggest that Tony found this period in his life the most secure and rewarding of any that had gone before or came after. Although most Trukese do not appear to have any clearly formulated impression of foreigners in general other than as rather authoritarian figures, to Tony they apparently mean support and security.

It is difficult to determine the significance of most of his other dreams; his own interpretations are stereotyped in those cases where he was able to give any. He was chased by a ghost but was able to rout it by lighting a palm frond torch. He lost his shirt and trousers but later found the shirt in his house, and with it five fish and two bundles of breadfruit. The storekeeper and his men came up while Tony was fishing with some boys; the men spread the seine net and caught a lot of fish but a shark came and ripped open the net, eating all the fish. He then reports two complex dreams, one of which is definitely a Japanese folktale; the other has elements which make one suspect a similar origin. In his final dream Tony and some other men got drunk in the island meeting house; the women present were going to leave but Tony persuaded them they would not be molested because there was an order from the "office" saying men should not approach women while they are drunk. The women stayed for some time and Tony got so drunk he could not walk; he asked the women to carry him home but they would not and left him to sober up. We may conjecture that this last dream reflects something of Tony's attitude toward women; he submits to authority and does not antagonize the women, but even then they abandon him in his distress. Any attempt to interpret the symbolism of the other dreams would be too speculative to be warranted in this context.

Discussion. Little need be added to what has already been said in the course of the summary of Tony's life history presented above. Although his recollections do not extend back into early childhood there is no reason to suppose that his relations with his parents were any more rewarding during his first years than they were later. From about the age of five or six onward, if we may assume that is when his account begins, Tony suffered to an unusual degree the restrictions shared by all Trukese children. His parents made great efforts, including frequent withholding of food, to keep him home and away from the play groups where he could express himself and feel more free. His only means of responding which would avoid parental wrath was to be submissive, and submission meant not playing. Tony could not long withstand this restriction and, leaving home, exposed himself time and again to punishment. It is not surprising, then, that in common with Mike, Tony shows in his projective tests a high degree of anxiety in interpersonal relations and inadequacy when faced with conflictful situations. On the other hand it was noted in the tests that Tony's need for self-expression is stronger and "nearer the surface" than Mike's. It is probable that this is to be attributed to the experience of the mutually satisfactory and perhaps even warm relationship which obtained between Tony and his master during the years on Dublon. It should be noted that it was during these years that Tony apparently was first able to initiate a sexual liaison (rather later in his adolescence than most—he must have been eighteen at the time) and thus begin the activity which now provides him with his only satisfactory emotional outlet. As an outlet, however, even this is not without anxiety, an anxiety noted in the T.A.T. and made explicit by Tony when he points out that his father disapproves. Thus although he was able through the security of his life on Dublon to undertake sexual activity and find it rewarding, the shadow of the losing battles of his childhood falls across it and leaves him in conflict.

Tony's sexual conflicts are thus but one aspect of his basic dilemma—having a strongly felt need for self-expression and at the same time strong anxieties about such expression, a dilemma which was crystallized by the years on Dublon. Tony brought to school on Udot an almost random and certainly ineffective mode of behavior; he modified this in favor of more consistent compliance and submission when presented with the prospect of the rewards ultimately to be derived in learning Japanese. These promised rewards became fact on Dublon, and to the submissiveness and inhibition which was as far as Mike could develop Tony added (in the Dublon environment) an element of secure self-expression. When he returned to Romonum, however, he re-entered the environment of his childhood and, although he continued to feel the need for the outlet he had found so rewarding on Dublon, was less able to satisfy this need without anxiety. It is apparently for this reason that Tony shows in almost exaggerated form the Trukese conflict over the expression of strong feeling; from his unusually restricted and unrewarding childhood he derived his strong inhibition and social inadequacy, and from Dublon the almost equally strong need for self-expression—he has tasted of the joys of assurance and response from another person and is not willing entirely to forgo them. It would probably be safe to predict that had Tony not gone to Dublon he would almost have been another Mike.

In regard to anxiety over food it is again not surprising that it should be Tony, for whom the withholding of food was a constant threat, who makes almost explicit the equation between food and security in his T.A.T. The equation had, in fact, been phrased for him more than once by his parents, who told him if he stayed home he could be assured of both food and their support (if not companionship), but if he went out and played he would have neither.

Because it is evident that in many respects Tony is not very effective in expressing himself we may wonder why it should have been he who produced a life history so very much more extensive than any of the other men. Again it is likely that the explanation is to be found in his Dublon experience. We have noted, particularly from his dreams, that it is probable that Tony generalized this experience into a belief that all foreigners (at least of the administrative caste) are essentially supportive and to be trusted. I was of course a foreigner and, while he could not be very productive when faced with the strange problems of the projective tests, he could let himself go and also spin out the time when reminiscing to me about his past.

WARREN, Age 56

Warren's mother and father died when he was adult; he had only one younger sister who grew to adulthood but she is now also dead. The lineages of both of Warren's parents are fairly small. Warren has two children; his wife died when his son was seven and his daughter fully grown. Warren did not remarry. His son is in his thirties and married, but has no children. His daughter is in her forties and has had four children, only one of whom survives. It is more than probable that Warren is appreciably older than his listed age of fifty-six but no more accurate estimate is possible. Warren has a lonely life, spent largely by himself in a house separated from the rest of his village by a taro swamp.

Rorschach. That he is the oldest male in this series is not Warren's sole claim to fame because he is also in certain respects the most responsive and least inhibited. At the same time Warren is one of the most uncritical and unrealistic thinkers in the group. His thinking suffers not only from concreteness but from the relative absence of the Trukese habit of delaying and reflecting about the adequacy of one's response. His initial tendency is not to respond in terms of the objective or external stimulus situation but rather in terms of personal history and of storytelling. To a certain extent Warren fits our stereotype of the aged person in that he is prone to respond to the situation by launching into long and irrelevant discourses. He is like so many Trukese in that, despite his relatively easy and uninhibited way of responding, he reveals little of what is truly personal or private. He gives a lot but tells little. There is little doubt that fantasy, revealed in his storytelling, plays an important role in his adjustment but there is little evidence that this tendency is a reflection of some pathological process.

But Warren is more complicated than the above would indicate. He is capable of an adequate, realistic, and even original way of responding at those times when he has become accustomed to a situation and when his aspirations are modest. There appears to be in Warren a strong need to be liked and recognized; when he attempts to gratify these needs the adequacy of his responsiveness is lowered. It is as if he bites off more than he can chew and is unaware of the unrealistic nature of his responses. But as the strength of these tendencies is reduced the quality of his adjustment increases while the quantity decreases. One might deduce from this that Warren is or was capable of a better quality of adjustment than he now shows.

Warren certainly would fit in with the hypothesis that the older Trukese are not as inhibited or constricted as some of the younger ones. Such a hypothesis, however, is hazardous because of the small number of cases available for study and the selective manner in which they were chosen. In any event, it is doubtful whether the variable of advanced age can in itself be a convincing explanation for the degree of difference between Warren and others. It is inconceivable to think of Warren in his youth as being like Mike or Tony.

T.A.T. As one might expect from the stories of the oldest male, he appears to be much concerned about death and physical disability. What is perhaps most distinctive about the stories is that they reveal Warren to be an extremely concrete individual who found it difficult to tell a story without bringing in or paying attention to irrelevant aspects of the stimulus pictures. Although he was apparently trying to meet the requirements of the situation, he found it difficult to do so. It is probably revealing of Warren that he apparently did not try to be evasive and retreat, but was motivated to respond.

Warren obviously has no pleasant association or anticipations about death for it is always associated with sickness and pain. If one makes the somewhat dubious assumption that Warren's attitudes toward death are probably representative of the society, then one might say that Truk is not one of those societies in which death is welcomed or stoically approached as a means of entering an all-satisfying heaven. From one of his stories one might speculate that aged Truk individuals are dependent on the younger folk for security and the one who does not have children to fall back on is in an extremely precarious position. Such a possibility is in line with the hypothesis that the Trukese develop in the course of their lives a separation anxiety. If they learn to fear isolation and separation from, and loss of, close kin, then one would expect old age and approaching death to accentuate the anxiety. When one adds to this the Trukese concern about an adequate food supply, then the hazards of old age are indeed severe.

As with so many of the other males, aggression is present in many of his stories. In two stories, aggression is a reaction to someone who is stealing; in another, it is to men who try to woo his wife away from him; in another, it is toward naughty children. The interesting thing is that there is little evidence that aggression can be overtly expressed by Warren. For example, in one story one man is *set* to strike another but the story ends without any actual aggressive display. In another story a woman is angry with her husband and the latter "is not saying anything because he is very fond of her." In still another story three men are fighting "in a war" but again the story ends without any "development" of the aggression. In only one story is aggression carried out, but even here the story does not represent his spontaneous reaction to the picture but the examiner's prodding. One may conclude from this that Warren is like most of the other Trukese males in that aggressive display is not characteristic although aggressive feeling is.

The story in which parents kill bad children should be compared to several stories in which parents take a protective and somewhat sympathetic attitude toward their offspring. It is this kind of ambivalent attitude which seems characteristic of the Trukese.

Life History. Warren's life history is somewhat shorter than the average and tends to ramble off on a variety of tangents. He gives long discourses on technology, although there is no indication that this is a means of avoiding more "difficult" topics of discussion.

Warren begins his account with a rather long and highly favorable description of his treatment by his parents who cared lovingly for his every need; it is remarkable, however, in that it clearly pertains to his early infancy when he was being fed at the breast or given premasticated foods and could not yet walk! It is, in other words, a description of an ideal childhood in Trukese terms and Warren's application of this to his own case must be viewed as pure fantasy, although this is not to say it may not be true in whole or in part.

Warren also says he can remember the birth of his younger sister, which took place when Warren could walk but not yet talk. He says he was very happy that there were then two children in the family, although he and his father then had to leave the house and stay in a men's house. He notes that his father returned to sleep at home at night after the birth of the baby, but Warren spent four months in the men's house. As there is no cultural requirement that the other children leave the house after a birth (and we should also question in this case Warren's ability to remember the event) it is possible that this stay in the men's house occurred somewhat later and was unrelated to his sister's birth. Certainly Warren did not wait until his adolescence to enter the society of the men's houses; he says that when he was seven or eight he used to spend most of every day with a "brother" in the "brother's" men's house, going home only at night to sleep. The availability of food was evidently a major inducement to Warren to remain in the men's house: "They prepared breadfruit and other sorts of food and sometimes went out to the barrier reef on a paddling canoe and brought back fish. The women, their wives, used to come and leave fish they had caught and take away starch food to eat. I ate there and stayed around most of the day; in the evening they would tell me to go off and sleep at home."

Thus Warren, by going to the men's house, was able to escape such frustrations as he might have experienced at home in regard to food and was also to identify with the group upon whom the women (their wives, but Warren's "mothers") were dependent for *their* food. He was able not only to be independent of his mother for food but even feel that she was in some measure dependent on him (through the group of men with whom he was associated) for her own food. He also mentions another "brother's" men's house where he stayed and on one occasion ate so much that he developed a stomach-ache and could eat no more.

Warren says (in reply to a question) that he was beaten when he was naughty "until I learned to do what they told me and do it quickly. [?] Only my own parents beat me; if anyone else had my father would have beaten them." Thus although Warren did not of his own accord mention being beaten he is able to give even these beatings a somewhat positive flavor: it was the right of his parents alone which his father would defend. One gets the feeling that Warren achieved a rather strong identification with his father.

Warren says little about his play with other children of his age, but the one activity he mentions specifically is a far cry from playing alone with a little canoe, an activity mentioned by some of the other subjects: "We boys used to fight, throwing rocks at each other. The Winisi and Chorong boys used to fight against each other—sometimes one side won and chased the other, and sometimes it went the other way. On occasion our fathers would be angry because they were afraid we would cut each other with the rocks; then they blew the conch and we all stopped." We should note that Warren pictures the two groups as fairly evenly matched; in contrast, a younger man describes such fighting between villages as episodes in which his group (also Winisi) was always beaten, chased, and stoned by the others.

Warren's entry into adolescence was marked by his having his ears cut to make loops for attaching ornaments; all older men still show this mutilation. His rather detailed account, which was offered spontaneously, emphasizes the pain involved, but also stresses how handsome he looked afterward. Warren was hesitant at first but then acquiesced and the operation was done by a "father" of his who was a specialist while his own father held his head. Five days later his hair was done up in a knot as a sign of manhood and "after my ears were healed I put ornaments in them that hung down to my chest and the effect was very striking."

"My father took me to his men's house and I stayed there. One day we picked some breadfruit and cooked it and pounded it, and then went out fishing with spears. We speared a great many fish, including some big ones.

We brought them back to the men's house and my father told me to take one to his wife. So I went there, carrying it on my shoulder; when I went to the house they were amazed at the fish for it was enormous, as long as my arms. They scraped it and cut it up into pieces and put it on the fire to broil. There was breadfruit, too, so when the fish was cooked they said we should eat. So we started eating and ate and ate; when we were full we slept. Then we woke and ate again, and slept, and ate. My mother did too. Finally my father came and told me not to gorge myself or I would be sick, so I stopped. I went back to the men's house to sleep. The men's house belonged to the oldest man in my father's lineage; he and nine other men, including my father, lived there."

During his adolescence Warren made a number of trips to various islands to cut copra, get food, and the like, always visiting a "brother" on one island or another. Asked about his relations with women during this period Warren said, "I did not go to any women before my ears had been cut because my father did not want me to; he felt I would have been sick because I was too small. But when I started I went to lots of women. Some liked me and when I came in they would let me sleep with them; the ones that did not like me I did not stay with." He also describes the handsome figure he cut when he was all decked out with a comb and coconut oil in his hair and spondylus shell ornaments on his legs, neck, and waist.

Warren says he told his father that he was going to look for a wife for himself but his father told him to wait because he was going to arrange a marriage for him. Warren does not indicate that he either resented or resisted his father's decision. The account of his marriage and married life is very perfunctory, but he describes extreme grief at the death of his wife (at a rather early age), a grief considerably more severe than he reports he experienced when his parents died later. He says, "I did not marry again because I loved my children; if I had taken another wife they would no longer have stayed with me. I am staying with them still for I love them." As we have noted, Warren actually lives alone, although his children do support him fairly well.

Asked about the disciplining of his children, he said that he and his wife beat and lectured them when they were naughty and did not obey at once, but as in his own case no one else was permitted to beat them. He also mentions threatening not to feed them if they were naughty, although he did not refer to this sort of discipline by his parents.

Warren describes making a trip after he was married with his father to Udot where his father had some business with a "brother." After they had been there ten days Warren became impatient to return; when his father did not leave right away Warren was quite angry with him. His father's "brother" suggested that they return to Romonum and his father come back to Udot after a while. His father, however, accompanied Warren to Romonum and then went back immediately to stay for some time on Udot. When his father finally returned Warren was still angry and did not visit him until his father had come and apologized and promised he would not take Warren on any more long trips. This episode is rather odd as Warren gives no explanation for his wanting to leave Udot except his homesickness for Romonum, and yet he describes his own rather more extended trips in which he was seemingly not accompanied by a relative at all. One suspects that there was more involved here than Warren has told us.

Although in his life history Warren tended to skip around and give an episodic account (which has been somewhat rearranged above) he told most of his story without being prodded or directed by any questions. It was near the end that he began to lean more heavily on accounts of food production, fishing, thatching houses, etc., and he was then asked the questions which are noted above. In regard to his present status he said:

"I am happy now because I will soon die. I look forward to dying for I no longer enjoy my life. I am weak and can no longer do any work; I am just like a little child. There is no point in my being alive any more for I cannot climb a coconut tree; I cannot pick breadfruit. If I am dead I will lie under the ground; now I lie on the ground, but there is little difference. Little of my life is left, for I am weak; if I were strong a lot would remain.

"Now I am afraid of my son and can no longer tell him to do things and demand that he do them, for if he were to beat me I would be dead. However, he feels sorry for me and does not talk harshly to me either, for I am weak and I cannot do much work anyway."

Dreams. Warren reports ten dreams, all but one of them current, and all involving him in some sort of a disaster. His interpretation in each case is that he will be killed or hurt or else that he does not know its meaning although in one (in which he drifted away and was rescued) he felt that God had helped him. In one dream he was alone in a canoe and capsized; he tried to swim to land but could not reach it and drowned. In another he climbed a coconut tree, fell, and was injured. He was accused by a man of stealing his breadfruit; the man cut off Warren's head, beat on it, and cut it up. In his only dream reported as having occurred in the past Warren was bitten by a dog; he hit the dog but its owner came up and made the dog bite him again because he felt Warren should not have hit it. In discussing this dream Warren said, "I think that one day I will die. I think that having my head cut off and my body bitten and the like means that if I get in a fight with someone I will be killed. Therefore I do not think it is wise for me to speak forcefully to anyone. I will just say 'yes' to anything anyone tells me so that I will not get in a fight."

Continuing with his dreams Warren told of falling out of a breadfruit tree and being cut and injured when he landed. He was on a large boat and an American aboard thought he was stealing things; he shot Warren and threw his body overboard where it was bitten in two by a shark. He was again beaten, this time by a relative, for stealing breadfruit and although some relatives came and stopped the beating he says in conclusion "If I don't die from falling from a tree I will die from someone beating or cutting me." In another dream a tree fell on his house and pinned him in the wreckage. Later that night a ghost threw a rock against the house but did not answer when Warren called; Warren fanned the fire and did not sleep the rest of the night after he awoke.

In his last dream Warren drifted away with two other men on a canoe; this time, however, they reached a little island (which God had put there for them) and were later brought home by some men on a sailing canoe.

These dreams show clearly Warren's anxiety over his weakness and imminent death, a theme which was also apparent in his T.A.T. It is notable also that in four of the ten dreams his injury was the result of his trying to get food—either falling out of a tree or being accused of stealing food and beaten.

Discussion. It is evident that the weakness of Warren's old age has affected his entire approach to life: he is hesitant in his social relations and unable to get his own food. It is interesting in regard to the fantasy of a well-nurtured infancy with which he began his account that in describing his present debility he said "I am just like a little child." We can readily see how Warren in his helpless old age could view as highly desirable the feeding and physical support received by a similarly helpless infant. By describing his own infancy in these terms he not only in effect negated any unpleasant memories he may have had of his childhood relations with his parents, but also was able in fantasy to create for himself something of the feeling of support he describes. It is as if in fantasy he views himself literally as an infant enjoying the parental care to be expected in this state.

Despite his present difficulties it would appear that Warren's childhood left him if anything better prepared than most to deal with his problems as a younger adult. His childhood was (as far as we can tell) in most respects a usual one for a Trukese. Although he does not directly mention any difficulties over food, the fact that he used this means to discipline his own children, and that he showed the usual concern about food, would lead us to believe that he also experienced deprivation and frustration in eating; in all probability his relations with his parents at home were of the sort we have described previously. Unlike the other men we have discussed, however, Warren was not tied in exclusive dependency upon his home and his parents for food or even a place to stay. He could and did find both in the men's houses, even in his childhood. By staying there he was able not only to reduce the effectiveness of his parents' strongest sanction—food—but even to feel that in some respects he was turning the tables by identifying with the group who were supplying his parents. With this already rather positive association with the men's house it is safe to conclude that his banishment from home at puberty, while not necessarily to be welcomed, must at least have been far less damaging to his sense of security and belonging than it is for young men today. One wonders of course to what degree Warren's experience was typical of the children of his time. The men's house is not stated as having been the place young boys typically spent their time and it is possible that Warren (perhaps like Andy) was a "cute" child who appealed more than most to his elders and was thus taken in by the men for the amusement he was able to provide them. This is at least suggested by the statement that Warren at a very early age (even if not on the birth of his sister) slept in a men's house while his father returned home at night. If he slept there it can only have been because some older man was willing to take care of him. On the other hand, all boys may have spent more time in the men's houses than our informants have indicated and the benefits Warren derived from this experience may thus have been shared by most of his contemporaries. This is a question we cannot answer. It is, however, an important point, for it implies that the elimination of the men's houses may have had an even more important effect on the personality and security of Trukese men than we have indicated.

In any event in Warren's case it would appear that the lessened dependence upon his home and particularly his mother which Warren felt as a result of being able to escape to the men's house would have permitted him to form a picture of his mother and hence of women in general as rather less domineering and unpredictable than would otherwise have been the case. It was probably for this reason that he was able to undertake rather early a fully active sexual role. Since he did not find women in other respects as threatening, he was able to approach them sexually without as much anxiety as others experience. This must not, however, be taken to mean that Warren was without anxiety in a sexual or any other context. We should remember that even as a child he was presumably as dependent as most Trukese upon his "brothers" and other relatives, and even his escape from the inconsistency and frustration which he presumably experienced at the hands of his mother could only have taken place after the crucial years of infancy.

Warren's ability to find a place other than home where he could stay and be fed does not by any means imply that he was thus able to be really independent of his parents, for it is evident that his departure from home was only to stay with male relatives and therefore presumably required his parents' permission. We also note that as a child he was punished not only if he disobeyed but even if he did not obey quickly. His submissiveness is apparent in the seeming meekness with which he accepted his father's decision to arrange his marriage for him. On the other hand, his father's selection cannot have been too unacceptable since there is reason to believe that Warren became very dependent upon and presumably somewhat devoted to his wife, if we may judge from his despair at her death.

In sum, then, we may say that although Warren's present effectiveness is severely limited by his physical weakness and his consequent desire to please and not offend (as we saw in his Rorschach performance) his adequacy in the past was not only better than it is now but may well have been in some respects rather above average.

It should be added that in one respect the interpretation of Warren's Rorschach, as well as those of other older persons, suffered from the fact that the interpretations were done "blind." It was concluded from his protocol that Warren was among the "least uninhibited" of all subjects, whereas he was actually very inhibited, a characteristic of highly dependent older Trukese people too weak to produce their own food. The explanation appears to lie in the high degree of anxiety created by sexual content perceived by younger people in the Rorschach cards. After the age of about forty an active sexual role is no longer culturally demanded, and with the lifting of this demand sex no longer appears so anxiety-producing.

SARAH, Age 21

Sarah's parents are both dead; they died recently, her father before her marriage and her mother after. Sarah has one living older sister; we do not know if any other siblings have died. The lineages of both her parents are comparatively small. Sarah has not been married long and has no children.

Rorschach. The distinctive feature of Sarah's record is that it indicates that, unlike many of the others, she can respond to her environment in a rather sensitive and differentiated way. One would expect her to be aware of, and respond to, situations in other than a concrete, superficial manner. Like so many of the others, however, the subjective or personal aspects of her reactions or thoughts would not too easily reach overt expression. Sarah is able to keep her feelings under control. Whereas in the face of uncertainty, conflict, or strong feeling others have the initial tendency to inhibit and retreat, Sarah is able to continue to respond; although the adequacy and quality of her responsiveness will be reduced somewhat, the important point is that she does not passively retreat. One might say that Sarah's defenses against strong or unacceptable feeling are more adequate than most. Sarah appears to be comparatively self-confident and resourceful. It might be better to say that Sarah is capable of a direct and somewhat productive relationship with her environment.

Although there are elements of concreteness in Sarah's thinking they are not as pronounced as in some of the others. In fact, her ability to analyze and integrate seems to be of good quality. That she is able to function in this manner is probably a function of the fact that she is able to handle strong feeling (uncertainty, conflict) better than many. Put in another way, in terms of overt behavior Sarah would be expected to be more than usually calm and less tempermental.

T.A.T. Sarah's stories reveal her to be an individual who is essentially conforming. Although she harbors aggressive and hostile feelings, her tendencies to conform to her cultural role appear adequate to avoid any particular conflict about such feelings. It is as if she has learned to receive satisfaction from conforming. Although she is ambivalent toward authority and parental figures, the positive feelings seem to be the stronger. The hostility which Sarah does feel seems at present to be directed toward men, although it should be emphasized that Sarah would not be expected to be overtly aggressive. For example, in one picture where the woman is usually described as assertive over the man, Sarah also tells of an assertive woman but in the end it is the man's will which prevails.

It appears that she feels envious of the greater freedom which boys enjoy. In one story, the father advises his son to take care of his sister, not to beat her, for when she grows up a little she will do his work for him. What may be deduced from such a story is that rather early in their lives restrictions are placed on girls, and they are not always treated kindly by brothers for whom they are expected to work. It should also be pointed out that, in the one story in which a girl is clearly the chief character, she is prevented by her mother from watching men who are playing.

There is also evidence in these stories that men are considered "lazy" by the women. In one story a man decides not to work the next day but changes his mind when his wife says: "You may be tired, but what are we going to eat?" In another story, a "popular" for both men and women, it is the man who wants the wife to carry the child and the food, and he presumably would carry nothing. In still another story a father is described as happy that his boys were no longer playing but were thinking about work. That Trukese men may be on the lazy side would fit in with the fact that more than a few of the males gave stories in which people were relatively passive: playing, relaxing, eating, etc.

It is probably because Sarah's conformity is greater than her hostility that she had no difficulty adjusting to the requirements of the test situation. There is, among other things, no indication of evasiveness in her record.

Life History. Sarah's life history is considerably above the average in length and, while episodic, reveals a good deal about her childhood relationships with her parents, sister, and others.

Sarah begins her account, "When I was small I used to go out playing and then come back home to eat. My mother would tell me to go out and bathe; I would, and then come back and eat again. I used to eat many times a day when I was small." The remainder of her life history appears to bear out the observation that Sarah ate freely and usually whenever she wanted. Although she mentions being beaten several times, she only describes one episode in which food was withheld; this occurred in her late childhood and was the result of Sarah's refusing to help her father as much as he wished in the preparation of some breadfruit—it was this particular batch of breadfruit, rather than food in general, which he refused to let her eat. The withholding of food we have noted is most commonly used as a sanction to keep the child from spending too much time away from home playing. It would appear that Sarah experienced a minimum of this sort of restriction. She tells of many occasions on which she played for extended periods of time both in the daytime and at night and does not once indicate that she incurred any parental displeasure as a result of these long absences. When questioned after recounting one episode in which she and a close friend of hers had gone out to play at night after Sarah's mother had refused her permission, Sarah denied that her mother was angry on her return.

Sarah says that she was sick many times in her childhood with a variety of illnesses. "My parents would pick me up and hold me because I could not sleep night or day." As most children have a number of illnesses we cannot tell whether Sarah had more than most or just places more emphasis than others on a normal amount of sickness.

Whether she was sickly or not it is apparent that Sarah had some difficulty in holding her own among her playmates. "I used to go out playing and lots of boys and girls would beat me, and I would cry because I was afraid of them." While the specific episodes she relates do not indicate that she got the worst of all her fights, we must remember that having only her older sister and a rather small number of other close relatives to call upon for help, Sarah was at a disadvantage. As a matter of fact Sarah does not mention being supported in a fight at any time by an older "brother" or "sister"; she did, however, once come to the aid of her older sister when her sister was fighting another girl and was bitten on the shoulder. Sarah beat the other girl across the legs with a stick and broke up the fight. The girl's father came up at this point and after seeing Sarah's sister's wound beat his daughter. On another occasion she was beaten by a boy but then hit him over the head with a bowl and made his nose bleed; Sarah was beaten by her father for this, although, at least by her account, it was not she who started the fight. It appears that a child who draws blood on another is usually in the wrong, regardless of the circumstances. On the other hand, Sarah had another fight with a girl and cut her with a knife; the girl's father intervened and chased Sarah in order to beat her, at which point Sarah's father came up and almost had a fight with the girl's father. That evening the girl's father came and apologized to Sarah while she in turn apologized to him. It would appear that in this case Sarah's guilt in wounding the girl was less than the girl's father in attempting to beat someone else's child. Sarah even had a fight with her girl friend, a result of her friend's eating all the meat out of a coconut they were sharing; this time her friend's father intervened and beat his daughter for not sharing the meat also.

There is some suggestion of rivalry and hostility between Sarah and her sister. This is most evident in the following episode, in which we should also note the stress Sarah puts on the rewarding nature of her relationship with her mother. Sarah and her sister decided to join their mother who was fishing on the reefs offshore. "We found her and walked out to her on the reef. She told us to go back lest we fall in the water and drown but I told her I knew how to swim. She told me to show her, so I did. We stayed out with her until she was through fishing and then we all went in. I took out a big fish for myself but my mother told me I could not have it; she said my sister should have it because she was older. I cried at this so my mother got out another fish for me and we went home. I broiled my fish and asked my mother for some breadfruit to go with it; she gave some to me and I ate. I went to sleep where I was and after a while my mother woke me and told me she was going to fix my sleeping mat and the mosquito netting. She did and then I went back to sleep again. Later when my sister came in under the netting she stepped on my leg and I cried. My mother asked me why I was crying and I told her my sister had stepped on my leg; my mother took a stick and beat her. I went to sleep again, but later woke and cried because I was thirsty. My mother asked me what was the matter and I said I wanted some water; she got me some and I went to sleep again."

There is a suggestion that Sarah actually enjoyed a closer relationship with her mother than did her sister: Sarah tells of her mother's grief over the death of Sarah's grandmother (Sarah's mother's mother) who lived with them. When they returned home after the funeral Sarah's mother suggested that they both slash themselves with a knife as women occasionally did in the past. Sarah said she could not do it, but her sister overheard the conversation. Her sister asked what they were going to do but her mother would not tell her, insisting that she and Sarah had not been talking about anything of importance.

Whether or not Sarah was actually closer than her sister to her mother, it appears that she and her mother had a rather warm relationship. The night following her grandmother's funeral Sarah awoke after dreaming of a ghost; her mother tried to persuade her that it had just been a cat but when this was not successful, "She just held me in her arms until I fell asleep. Later she fell asleep and we slept until the morning." Sarah mentions several episodes similar to the one above in which she woke during the night and her mother brought her some water or some food if she was hungry. On the other hand, once in her later childhood Sarah had been playing all day and in the evening felt like singing; her mother wanted to sleep and told Sarah to stop. Sarah kept on singing until her mother hit her with a fan. "I was angry and told her she should just go to sleep and let me sing, but I did not sing any more because I was afraid of her."

Sarah's father could also be kindly and protective. We have already mentioned his threatening to fight the man who had chased Sarah. Even on the occasion when Sarah's father beat her for making a boy's nose bleed, later the same day she accompanied him inland, where he picked some coconuts and oranges for her and later carried her around on his shoulders, something which all Trukese children appear especially to enjoy. However, Sarah's father appears more often in her account in a hostile or punitive role toward Sarah, and her mother aligned more or less defensively against him. This was the case in the episode we have already mentioned in which Sarah's father refused to let her eat breadfruit; she had at first helped him prepare the breadfruit but then had grown tired and gone away to play. When she returned her father beat her and was apparently very angry indeed, at which time he told her she could eat none of the breadfruit. He later told her mother Sarah was not to have any because she was lazy. Her mother asked if he had not told Sarah to do a number of things at first which she had done. He said he had, so she upbraided him for making Sarah work all the time. He replied that he had no one else to help him, but his wife was not satisfied with this. When he conceded the point, however, Sarah would not eat until her father had left.

It is interesting that her father later that day told Sarah's mother to take some cigarettes to a "mother" of his (Andy's mother). Sarah went with her and while they were talking her father's "mother" asked Sarah to play more often in her house. Sarah went home and then returned the same day; while she was playing at her father's "mother's" her father came up and told her "that from then on I was not to live in our house but just stay with his 'mother.'" Sarah remained there for some time until one day in rapid succession she was bitten on the leg by Andy (who resented her taking him home from swimming) and stepped on a broken bottle, cutting her foot. These calamities made her "homesick" and she returned home. Although it is considered gratifying when children stay for long periods with various relatives of their parents, we may wonder whether, coming as this did right after a family crisis involving Sarah as the central character, her visit was not a means of resolving the tensions created by the dispute.

Sarah does not indicate that any steps were taken to resolve another family crisis which apparently took place when she was younger (although Sarah rarely differentiates between events which took place in early or late childhood or sometimes even adolescence). "I remember one day when my mother and father had a fight. I cried too [i.e., with her mother], because I felt sorry for my mother whose arm was bleeding. My mother picked me up and we went over to the other side of the island. We had been there for some time when I began to cry because I was hungry. My mother found a ripe coconut, cut it open, and gave me the meat to eat. But I still cried because I wanted to eat breadfruit. But she said she was too afraid of her husband to go home. That night we returned and my father called me. But I did not go to him because I was frightened of him. He told me he did not want to beat me but only to pick me up—he said I was very bad because I just paid attention to what my mother told me and ignored what he said."

In contrast to the episode previously described, this time Sarah's mother was routed but Sarah makes it very clear that her identification was strongly with her mother. On another occasion (perhaps in Sarah's early adolescence) she again shows her mother and herself acting together, this time to shame her father. They were supposed to go to a meeting and feast but Sarah's father left without taking any of the household's contribution of breadfruit. Sarah at first refused to carry any herself but then agreed to take half. They arrived late and were scolded mildly by the chief. Sarah's mother said they were slow because the breadfruit was so heavy (although each carried two packages totaling probably not over fifteen pounds). The chief asked why her husband did not help and Sarah's mother said, "He was very bad because he just wanted to walk along without carrying anything." If she really said this it must have been a cause of acute embarrassment not only to her husband but to all present.

When she was nine Sarah began attending a school conducted by the Protestant teacher on Romonum, who taught the children religion, writing, and food preparation. Sarah says little about the actual school work but mentions a number of the children's work activities—planting manioc, cutting copra, preserving breadfruit, and the like. Sarah apparently found these tasks arduous and on one occasion her mother took her place while Sarah played. The teacher saw Sarah playing and discovered that her mother was substituting for her; he disapproved and her mother left. Asked about this Sarah said, "She helped me because she felt sorry for me getting worn out making the preserved breadfruit."

While Sarah was in school her parents made a three-day trip to Uman. They asked to have Sarah excused from school to accompany them but the teacher would not permit it. They left her behind and Sarah says she "missed them terribly." She refused to eat the night they left and could not concentrate on her school work. When her parents returned laden with food, "I asked them why they had not tried harder to have me go with them because I wanted to very much, but they said it would not have been a good idea because I was in school. They did not say anything more about it." As an incidental note Sarah mentions that the night their parents left she and her sister went to bathe "and a man spoke to my sister. I told her not to say anything more to him so she would not get in trouble and go to the calaboose, so she just went on and did not speak to him any more."

After the Protestant school on Romonum Sarah went to the Japanese school on Udot. Her parents did not accompany her; she hated it because the Japanese teacher beat her all the time and she was terrified of him. After three months she went home to Romonum. Only one letter was sent over telling her to return; she ignored this and simply stayed at home.

Sarah worked for a while for the Protestant teacher cooking and keeping house for him but after two weeks she tired of the work and quit. After this she just helped her mother fishing and doing household tasks. One night when Sarah had been fishing she was too sleepy to eat on her return; her mother cooked Sarah's fish and put them away for her, but not in a high place. A pig came and ate the fish and in the morning Sarah was angry, but her parents said to forget it because it could not be helped. That night Sarah again went fishing and, having caught only a few fish, returned and ate them all herself. She refused to give her mother any and her mother admitted this was justified. This is a rather neat example of the use of food as a means of expressing aggression.

Sarah did not yet help her parents with the heavy work in the gardens; while they were inland she played. Her parents would not let her stay with them inland because they felt she should stay home to see that no one stole anything from the house; Sarah did not like this for she was thus alone in the house. On one occasion she mentions going out to play in spite of her parents' instructions to watch their house, but her parents were apparently not angry when she told them. Although Sarah did not work in the gardens she did a lot of fishing on the reefs; on one occasion when she had caught only one octopus she was obviously reluctant to part with it but took it to her mother's "brother" when her mother told her to. "So he ate it and we did not."

When Sarah was about eighteen a man came to her and wanted to marry her. Her mother chased him out of the house two nights in a row; he was discouraged and did not return. He tried to persuade Sarah to intervene on his behalf with her mother, but she said she could not for her mother would beat her. After the second time, "I asked her why she made him leave and she just said it was a bad thing for him to come to me." Sarah offered no comment on this episode and we cannot know what either her or her mother's reactions were to the situation.

Later her parents attempted to force her to marry another man who was partially paralyzed and also somewhat older than Sarah. "They told me I was to marry this man. I said I did not want to; they insisted and I cried. They asked me why I did not want to. I said I hated him because he was an old man. [Actually he is not old, but merely weak and ill.] My brother beat me and I cried some more. They said they could not see why I should dislike him when they liked him so much. My mother told me that if I did not marry him I could not marry my lover nor anyone else. I said that was all right with me because I certainly did not want to marry that man. Later they told me again I had to marry him and he came to our house; I cried again. But I did not marry him, for I left the house. I went to a 'mother' of my father's. She asked me why I left my 'husband' and I told her I refused to marry him, so she told me to stay with her. Later, the man left my house and I went home again."

Some time later Sarah went to stay with a "sister" on Dublon for six months. On her return another man came and asked to marry her. This time her mother approved and they have been married since. He beat her once and Sarah ran home to her mother. They were living at her house and when her husband came home late and embarrassed, "She asked him why he beat me. He said because I was disobedient and did not come when he called. I said I had not heard him. He said that was a lie and then my mother just told me not to be disobedient any more. [?] He has not beaten me since because I obey him when he calls me. He obeys me too. He told me that if I disobeyed him just once more he would beat me again but I have not been disobedient."

In reply to a question Sarah described the death of her parents: "My parents are both dead. My father died first, before I was married. He got sick, with pain in his back and legs, and went to his 'sister's' house. He stayed there, very ill, for some time, and finally one night at about eight o'clock he died. We all cried because we loved him. The next morning they wanted to bury him right away but I did not want them to. I told them to wait a little while. Then at about ten o'clock they went off inland and buried him. I did not go with them because I had a headache from crying. I did not cry any more after this.

"My mother died quite recently. When she got sick she had a terrible pain in her head; she could not sleep and neither did I, for she cried out all night with the pain. After a while we went to stay with a 'brother' of hers, but she kept on crying out. She was close to death and they brought her medicine; they heated a rock and put it in a bowl and put it under a sheet with her. Later they removed the sheet. But it was clear that she was about to die and my younger sister and I began to cry. At seven o'clock that night she died, and we cried more. My sister began to have pain too from her unhappiness and I held her. My mother's 'brother' came up and hit me twice on the head, saying that if I held her she would die from the same illness. They brought her some of the same medicine and her illness was gone. They all slept that night, except me and my husband, for my head hurt from the blows my mother's 'brother' had given me.

"The next morning a great many people came bringing presents, and my sister told me to put them on the body and I did. Then they all left again and my mother's 'brother' came in and suggested we bury her. So we did, as it was about three o'clock and getting late. We put her in a coffin and lowered it into the grave. We stayed there by the grave for we were very unhappy. At about nine o'clock we went home and slept."

We should note that although Sarah speaks of her unhappiness she did not stay by the grave, a function not reserved culturally to men, and she did not even attend her father's burial because of a headache.

Questioned about her present status Sarah said, "Some days I am happy and some days I am not. If there is something to be happy about I am happy, but if there is not I am not. I am happy over goods, clothes, and the like. I am happy with my husband. I have no lover—I have never slept with anyone but my husband. . . . For the future I only want people to like me, to give me things, and to talk to me. I just want to be able to do my own work."

Dreams. Sarah's only current dream was as follows: "A big dog chased me and I ran away. I tried to run fast but I could not; I would start running and fall, then run, get up and fall again. I tried to shout or cry out but I could not do that either. That is all, for I woke up in a fright. [?] The dog did not reach me." Sarah said the old people had told her that dreaming about a dog meant she would be sick or in trouble.

Discussion. Although Sarah's failure to make clear the chronology of events does not permit us to define any sequence of changes from early childhood onward, we are at least able to see rather clearly the structuring of her relationships with her parents. Both could on occasion mete out fairly arbitrary punishment and at other times be kindly and supportive. However, at least in her account, Sarah's mother tended as far toward the positive side as her father did toward the negative. It was only her father who precipitated real crises by his anger, and on these occasions Sarah and her mother presented a united (if not always successful) front against him. It is apparent that Sarah had a very strong identification with her mother, who not only sided with Sarah against her father but herself seldom became angry over what would for other children probably have been considered serious misdeeds. It is to be presumed that it was this essentially rewarding and responsive relationship which laid the foundation for the sensitive, productive, and adequate approach to her problems seen in her Rorschach.

With her contemporaries, on the other hand, Sarah had less happy relationships. It appears that she felt some rivalry with her sister and, although Sarah may have enjoyed an advantage here as far as her mother was concerned, her sister was one of the few people upon whom Sarah could rely when playing with other children. She does not mention her sister helping her, but it appears to be characteristic of most of the life histories that the informants prefer to recount episodes in which they were undefended in their fights or else were helping someone else—although if they defended others they almost certainly must in turn have been defended themselves. From her account it appears that Sarah was at least on occasion able to acquit herself successfully in a fight, but at the same time she must also have had to rely as others do upon her "brothers" and "sisters" as well as her own sister for support. Because she had so relatively few of these "siblings" it is reasonable to suppose that she felt rather more than most the necessity of retaining their allegiance. If this is true, presumably she was even more careful than most not to offend them and hence became rather unusually conformist in her relations with her peers. This was perhaps easier for her than for others because of the peaceful and secure relations between her and her mother—not coming from a frustrated and restricted life at home she did not have to "blow off steam" among her playmates. If she was attacked she defended herself but otherwise she created few disturbances.

She tells us little of her married life, but it appears that she has applied the same technique of complacent conformity described above to her relations with her husband and, so far as we can tell, it has been successful. While her sex activity may have been limited, as she says, to relations with her husband, we should note that her father was of the same lineage as Andy. Andy's "brother" relationship with me thus made her my "daughter" and precluded her telling me of any other sexual activities if such did exist.

These case studies have been cited at some length to suggest the variations in modes of adjustment which persons within even a small and fairly homogeneous society may adopt, and some of the reasons for the development of these individual modes. The discussion of each case intentionally highlights factors of this order. A review of the entire twenty-three cases can show the significance of such differences even more clearly.

For example, this is not a society whose members characteristically reveal an oedipal conflict of any consequence. Yet in one case, that of Roger (referred to above, but not cited) oedipal conflicts are striking. It was possible in analyzing his life experiences to understand why he developed such conflicts, and thereby gain valuable perspective on the more usual nonoedipal personality.

At a somewhat different level of analysis, we may note that the extensive intervention of parental surrogates (usually other adults within the lineage), the large amount of time spent by children in the company only of other children, and the inconsistency of all adults in responding to children—all combine to reduce the impact on the child of his own parents. Many consequences of this reduced impact can be discovered, probably including the lack of oedipal conflicts, and the question has sometimes been raised whether in societies of this sort the true parents do not blend sufficiently with other adult relatives in the child's perception to blur or eliminate the key role which we assume the parents play. A partial answer to this question was possible through examination of those cases in which adequate relationships were not possible with one or both parents. Inadequacies were due either to early death of the parent or to unusually punitive and inconsistent treatment of the child with corresponding unpredictability of support in times of distress or crisis. Comparisons of the various combinations of inadequate and adequate parental relationships in the twenty-three cases permitted us to conclude that despite the weakness (in our terms) of parent-child ties on Truk, a satisfactory relationship with the parent *of the same sex* was of primary importance in personality development. Regardless of the availability of supportive adult kinsmen or consistently satisfactory status within the children's play groups, every individual who failed of a good relationship with the parent of the same sex proved to be constricted and inadequate, even by Trukese standards. Conversely, several subjects who were born into small lineages had very few adult relatives and, in some cases, in addition could not find much satisfaction within the society of their peers; yet despite these handicaps and sometimes even a hostile parent of the opposite sex, all such persons who enjoyed consistently good support from the parent of the same sex grew up able to meet the challenges set by their culture and society. Evidence of this sort, available only from the examination of individual experiences and development within a single society, provides strong support for believing that the process of identification with a single parent is of crucial importance even in a society which appears poorly suited to such identification.

This conclusion regarding identification is of considerable significance. It focuses our attention on a key process in learning how to operate within a culture, and therefore, on an essential ingredient of successful transmission of the cultural heritage from one generation to the next. It also suggests a comparison with one of the major ills of our own society, juvenile delinquency. The very brief synthesis of Trukese personality outlined at the beginning of this chapter bears more than a little resemblance to the attributes usually ascribed by us to socially inadequate persons or even psychopaths—shallow emotions, little or no conscience (superego), inability to introspect, limited goals or expectancies for the self, diffuse hostility, etc. In Trukese society, dependence upon the kin group reinforced by food anxieties keeps the individual in line through external sanctions and control, and it is doubtful that a tight-knit social fabric such as found on Truk could be maintained without the suppression of individual initiative, which is an ingredient of this personality structure. In our society, however, we place primary reliance on controls *internal* to the individual. For a person to be effectively self-regulating requires not only that he be motivated to exercise restraint, but also that he learn what his society expects of him and how to obtain satisfaction within the limits of these expectancies.

We would not be stating a very startling conclusion if we observed that a person is more likely to be an adequate participant in our culture if he has been able to identify successfully with a parent of the same sex. However, it is customary to view the process of identification in terms of love of the parent for the child, while we despair of the futility of urging a nonloving parent to start loving his offspring. We would not want to say that Trukese parents are totally lacking in love for their children, but certainly the parent-child relationships described and exemplified above would seldom, even in such a favorable case as that of Andy, meet our criteria for adequate and consistently warm love. The general lack of emotional depth and of sensitivity to the feelings of others which characterizes Trukese personal interaction practically precludes a real love relationship as we understand it. Yet within this social context, wherein love is generally inconsequential, identification with a parent of the same sex is of primary importance in successful socialization of the individual. This forces us to view identification as a mechanism for the learning of culturally prescribed role behavior rather than as a source of emotional strength. In this connection it is also interesting to note that those men who were most preoccupied with the need to validate themselves through a succession of adulterous liaisons— a widespread but highly disruptive activity on Truk—were regularly found among those whose opportunity for identification with their fathers was most limited or lacking.

It is not possible here to explore the implications of personality development and of the contribution of identification to this process when viewed as cultural learning rather than emotional integration, although this is a highly important subject which anthropologists in particular have been remiss in neglecting. It has been discussed briefly here only to provide an illustration of one of the several kinds of insight which can be derived from the study of personality in other cultures if one focuses on individuals as well as on group modalities. We cannot speak of mental illness or health in terms only of statistical sorts of abstractions without understanding what these concepts imply with reference to individual social adequacy and individual personality and cultural learning.

BIBLIOGRAPHY

1. Gladwin, Thomas, and Sarason, Seymour B.: *Truk: Man in Paradise.* New York: Viking Fund Publications in Anthropology, 1953, no. 20.

Section III

ASIAN
CONTRASTS

William Caudill

Department of Social Relations
Harvard University

8

OBSERVATIONS ON THE CULTURAL CONTEXT
OF JAPANESE PSYCHIATRY *

During 1954–1955 I had the opportunity to devote several months of a year in Japan to an exploratory study of Japanese psychiatry. As a part of this study, I visited fifteen Japanese psychiatric hospitals in order to obtain an impression of the range of public and private care, the most frequent kinds of patients, and the types of therapy being used. Following these visits I worked more intensively in two hospitals in Tokyo— one of which was a 1,000-bed public hospital, while the other was a 50-bed private hospital. My interest in this study was stimulated by previous research I had done both among Japanese-Americans (3, 10) and on the social structure of a psychiatric hospital in the United States (8).

What is said here about the context of Japanese psychiatry is offered very humbly and is subject to revision through further research I hope to do in Japan during the next few years. As such the remarks in this paper are descriptive and tentative, and the main justification for them is that there is as yet so little on the subject in English—probably not many more than a dozen titles. What follows is divided into three parts: *1*) the general problem, *2*) some questions concerning Japanese culture and personality, and *3*) a discussion of some historical and contemporary aspects of psychiatric illness and its treatment in Japan.

* The research assistance of Mr. Ezra Vogel and Miss Mieko Imagi in the preparation of this paper is gratefully acknowledged. The material presented here represents part of the research which was carried out under contract number DA-49-007-MD-685 with the Office of the Surgeon General. The opinions expressed herein are, of course, solely those of the writer.

THE PROBLEM

Despite a good deal of work that has been done over the years on the general influence of culture in psychiatric illnesses (34, 44), it is still not possible to chart very accurately the detailed processes going on in the family or hospital which have a bearing on the course of the illness. With regard to the latter, a number of hospital studies have been carried out in the United States and Europe (4, 8, 17, 21, 39), but as yet thorough studies of psychiatric hospitals in non-Western cultures have not been done.

In thinking about such work it is legitimate to raise the question of why one should initiate a study of Japanese psychiatry at all. There would seem to be several reasons: First, such a study is intrinsically interesting in a humanistic sense; second, it helps to provide a meaningful perspective on one's own life and culture; third, Japanese psychiatry provides a case, an instance, for cross-cultural comparison in the search to find out more about human similarities and differences. This cannot be done, or can be done only with considerable effort, in a single culture—the variations are not extreme enough, and moreover the variations that do exist are set within a single dominant matrix of values concerning what is proper or allowable, good or bad. Freud (14, 15), and later writers in the field of psychodynamics, have taught us much about the vicissitudes of the instincts—of the many and varied ways they can be expressed and reworked—and in clinical cases from any culture it is possible to see a wide variety of defenses and solutions. If the defenses and solutions are not in line with the values of the particular culture in which the doctor and patient are living, then the expression of these defenses and solutions by the patient takes place within a context which, outside of the psychotherapeutic relationship, is disapproving. Without cross-cultural comparison there is no way of knowing the extent of influence this context of values has—whether approving or disapproving—on the underlying dynamics of the individual's personality.

It is now possible to state the basic question of this paper in a more specific form. The question is just how deep into the structuring and reworking of the instincts does the influence of culture go? Obviously, this is not solely a matter of symptomatic differences which lie relatively close to the surface of the personality and which certainly are influenced by the preferred patterns of behavior in a culture. It is more a concern with the anthropological problem of cultural universals (23), and with such questions as whether there is always, at bottom, rivalry between a parent (or parental surrogate) and a child of the same sex as part of the process leading to the emotional maturation of the child. Or variously, do certain feelings of love and aggression necessarily have to undergo the process of repression in the development of an adult personality? To make any sense of these questions it would seem necessary to be clear whether one is thinking of culture in the generic sense as a property of being human, or is thinking of culture in a particular sense. This distinction is the usual one made by anthropologists between "culture" and "a culture."

This paper will not attempt to direct its attention to the influence of "culture" on personality in a generic sense. In passing, however, the question certainly would seem to be related to what Huxley (20) has referred to as a shift in the emphasis in evolutionary processes so far as man is concerned from biological to cultural and psychological areas. Beyond this it is important to consider, as Freud (15) did earlier, and as Redfield (36) and Marcuse (27) in a somewhat different vein have more recently, the question of the handling of aggression among men at a simple hunting and gathering stage as contrasted with life in an agricultural community, and later in an urban world. It is not possible here, however, to pursue these matters further.

In the following pages this paper will be concerned with the question of the influence of "a culture" on the personalities of its members, and particularly with the sort of questions that frequently arise in the discussion of psychiatric symptoms. In exploring such questions it is useful to look at the context within which certain activities which are close to the instinctual level—for example, drinking and sexual behavior—are handled from one culture to another.

It is striking that there is much drinking by men in Japan, and a great deal of male dependency and passivity, but there is little alcoholism as this would be defined in the United States. Some aspects of this question may be illustrated by a simple thing like a whisky advertisement in *Bungeishunjū* (a popular monthly magazine) which says a great deal about attitudes in Japanese culture when it shows a pleasant old gentleman smilingly anticipating the pleasure of drinking the six bottles of whisky he has saved up, while his gray-haired elderly wife kneels on the floor and counts her money. The caption reads, "To each his own happiness." Further understanding is provided by the fact that the wife in the Japanese family manages the money and, circumstances permitting, gives her husband an allowance on which to go out and do his drinking. It is not likely that such an ad, nor the cultural circumstances represented in it, would occur in the United States, and from this example it is possible to gain some appreciation of the influence of the cultural context on the patterning of instinctual gratification.

One might say reasonably enough of the above example that it is merely an ad in a popular magazine, although the ad gains a certain validity from the fact that it would not be likely to appear unless it were acceptable in the culture and useful in selling whisky. That such an ad, however, had its counterpart in behavior was brought home to me in the experiences of several of my friends in Japan. I had one friend with whom I spent many evenings drinking and talking. He had a habit on one night each week of taking the allowance provided for the purpose by his wife in the family budget and going out to drink with his cronies. When he arrived home late in the evening his wife would meet him at the door, help him off with his shoes, prepare a snack for him in the kitchen, and then assist him to bed. Equally, I had another friend whose job entailed great responsibility and power. He liked to drink American whisky, and I would occasionally bring him a bottle as a gift. He saved these bottles and others, until his store amounted to several dozen. His plan was to wait until a suitable vacation period permitted him the leisure to drink them up. This vacation became a reality in the interim between one important job and another, and he was able to put his plan into effect.

These examples would seem to indicate that the Japanese man does not anticipate rejection from others because of his drinking and is less likely, at least through stimulation from this outside source, to feel guilty about his drinking. Similarly, such examples indicate the way in which the Japanese woman takes on the role of ministering and caring for the man. This is in line with the behavior of Issei women in the United States, as evident from research on the acculturation of Japanese-Americans (7). Such an analysis could be extended further but it would begin to appear that drinking occurs in a somewhat different context for men in Japan than in the United States, and that the instinctual components of the motivation to drink are handled somewhat differently in the two cultures. This is equally true for sexual behavior, and the attitudes toward sex in Japan are fairly well known and discussed in the literature. At this point the sort of examples that have been given are useful merely in that they stimulate hypotheses which must be tested by systematic work in the future.

The above examples have stressed the influence of the cultural context in the satisfaction of certain instinctual desires. The other side of the coin, the restraint exercised in foregoing such satisfaction, is equally important in Japan and, as Benedict (5) and others have said, a Japanese man would not allow himself to drink if this activity interfered with the fulfilling of his obligations to his family, to his job, and so forth. This raises the issue of the "contrasts" or "dualities" in Japanese culture that have been commented upon so often by Western observers. Whether such contrasts are perceived as sharply by the Japanese as by Western observers is another question. In any case the discussion in this paper will be furthered if it turns more specifically to certain aspects of Japanese culture. Such cultural background is essential for the understanding of psychiatric illnesses and their treatment in Japanese psychiatric hospitals.

SOME QUESTIONS CONCERNING JAPANESE CULTURE AND PERSONALITY

Upon arrival in Japan I was struck, as have been many others, with the contrasts in Japanese culture. There are many ways of stating these seeming contrasts, but one of the best known is contained in the title of Ruth Benedict's book, *The Chrysanthemum and the Sword*. About her title Benedict (5) says: "When a serious observer is writing . . . a book on a nation with a popular cult of aestheticism which gives high honor to actors and to artists and lavishes art upon the cultivation of chrysanthemums, that book does not ordinarily have to be supplemented by another which is devoted to the cult of the sword and the top prestige of the warrior." Thus, Benedict would seem to be setting up a contrast between a peaceful and controlled way of life on the one hand, and a life frequently punctuated by violence on the other. This sort of contrast did seem evident to me in my observations in Japan, and yet, it was with a flash of further insight that I examined a pocket knife I had purchased and found that the manufacturer's name was *Kikuhide*. The word *kiku* (and the Chinese character which represents it) in this knife maker's name is the same word (and character) as that for chrysanthemum. It seems to me that there is a suggestion in this that things which we in the West tend to pull apart are combined more within a single frame of reference by the Japanese. Thus, for example, love and hate, and control and release are perhaps more easily seen as being intimately connected in Japanese culture than in Western cultures.

When I began to ask questions about the manufacturer of my knife, I found that this particular company had a long tradition of making swords during the Tokugawa period, and had turned its attention to the more mundane business of making knives after the Meiji restoration. It also seemed of interest that, in another area of activity, some brands of *sake* (Japanese rice wine) included the word *kiku* in their trade name. It is true that the term for chrysanthemum may be applied as a symbol of superlativeness to many things, but when it is used symbolically for swords and wine, the contrast implied in the opposition of the chrysanthemum and the sword tends to lose its sharpness, and control and release become two closely related aspects of a single process.

In thinking about contrasts, if such they are, in Japanese culture, several ways of approaching the question have been useful: *1*) personally, in terms of my experiences in the culture as indicated in some of the examples that have been given; *2*) historically, in terms of what life was probably like in pre-Tokugawa times as contrasted with life during the Tokugawa regime and in the period from the Meiji restoration to the present; and *3*) developmentally, in terms of the balance between human feeling and obligation at different periods in the life of the Japanese person from childhood through old age.

In my own experience I was struck with the orderliness of interpersonal relations in Japan, but I also quickly became aware of the way in which Japanese life contained periods of freedom and recreation where there was little emphasis on formality. This latter aspect of life is heightened during the frenzy that often accompanies a festival, or *matsuri*, which forms part of the yearly cycle in any Japanese village or urban neighborhood. For example, I remember with great vividness the fire festival at Kuramayama, a small mountain village near Kyoto. The village is set in a cut in the mountains, and a narrow path leads through it. During the festival there was a large bonfire in front of each house, and masses of people were pushing their way along the path through the village while trying to avoid the fires. This was made more difficult because the young sons of families, stripped to a minimum of clothing, were wildly carrying burning torches from one end of the village to the other. In transit, the sons would swing the torches at the crowd jammed into the narrow path. The torches varied in length from about 4 feet for those carried by the youngest children to about 14 feet for those carried by adolescents. One way to decrease the apprehension aroused by all this was to drink, and most of the crowd had decided on this course of action. About two o'clock in the morning the men of the village took smaller torches and made their way up a steep mountain to the shrine located on the top. Here they picked up the *mikoshi,* or portable shrine, and started to carry it, swinging it in every direction, down the mountain side. A long rope extended from the back of the shrine and the women of the village hung onto this in order to prevent the men from tumbling precipitously into the center of the village. Such activity went on until dawn, and certainly provided a contrast in release of emotion with the everyday formality of Japanese life.

From such examples one has the impression that a great deal of emotion is readily available under the tightly controlled surface of Japanese interpersonal relations. This seemed evident in the printed statement made by the Japanese employees of a British bank in Tokyo who were striking for higher wages. They had set up a picket line outside the bank, and, in order to enlist the sympathy of both Japanese and foreigners, they had placed a statement of their position in both Japanese and English on the wall of the bank. The statement indicates much about the nature of Japanese personality, and was as follows:

Please listen to our voice! We know too well that this kind of action is not decent at all. However, we cannot help doing so, as our salary is not good as you can easily understand from our clothing, etc. About two months ago we demanded the back payment to us of the summer season allowance for the first time since the bank was reopened. It is only for one-month salary and we have reasoned the bank over and over again the necessity of this allowance with a polite and humble attitude and hoping to receive a satisfactory answer from the bank. In spite of the above, the bank has firmly rejected our humble demand. Upon this, our anger has burst out: we cannot stand this kind of treatment any more. In the long course of our life, if there exists a time to get angry from the bottom of our hearts, such a time has now come. We believe that our demand is quite reasonable and we will surely get your assistance and encouragement. We sincerely request you to assist us and lend us your sympathy. We will surely win in this struggle.

One can see in this statement the formality and control in Japanese interpersonal relations which is maintained until a certain point is reached. After this point, the anger, as the strikers said, "bursts out." This sequence of events is similar in many ways to my observations in Japanese psychiatric hospitals where, in line with the observations of other Westerners, I noted a relative lack of violence on the wards. It was not so much that occasional violence did not occur, as it did at one point when one patient kicked another to death, but rather that life in the hospital went along on an even keel for a long time until there would be a short outburst of violence, after which things would quickly subside again. This is in contrast to observations in psychiatric hospitals in the United States where, particularly on so-called violent wards, there is usually a fairly sustained high level of tension in the air. This rhythm of life in Japan, whether in the general culture or on hospital wards, is somewhat different from the rhythm of life in the United States.

One line of thought which might help to explain such a rhythm is related to the differences to be found in various periods in Japanese history. For example, Reischauer says:

The Japanese . . . seem to have been an openly emotional and unrepressed people during much of their history, perhaps until as late as the sixteenth century. . . . The two centuries of stability and peace of the Tokugawa period, however, seem to have brought a great change in Japanese society. The land was filled up by then. . . . Perhaps in a heavily crowded land such as Japan has been since the seventeenth century, established patterns of conduct must be more rigidly observed than in lands where people live with more room about them and a wilderness to conquer. . . . It is significant that, with the advent of Tokugawa stability, the Japanese suddenly took a much greater interest in Confucianism than ever before. The Tokugawa period is the golden age of Confucianism in Japan. A stable, peaceful Japan needed a detailed book of rules, the way a war-torn land did not. Confucianism, heavy with the wisdom and prestige of China, fitted the need admirably, providing a perhaps overly emotional people with the external controls they required to form a well-regulated, peaceful society.*

It is tempting to turn from the historical development of Japan to the different emphases given various periods in the life of the Japanese child. As has been indicated in the literature, and as seemed true to me from fairly casual observations, the first five years of life for the Japanese child are predominantly those of unconditional love. The child is loved for what he is rather than in terms of what he can do. However, as school life approaches, and as a child must represent the family in the outer world, there is a shift to an emphasis upon the obligation the child carries as a representative of the family. These obligations continue through the adult Japanese person's life until the period of retirement and old age is reached. Once again in old age, as in childhood, a period of

* Reischauer, Edwin O.: *The United States and Japan,* 2nd ed. Cambridge: Harvard University Press, 1957.

freedom is available. And, as stated by Benedict, this leads to a somewhat different curve of life in Japanese culture than in American culture.

The patterning of these different curves of life would seem to offer a way to explore the question of possible differences in personality dynamics from one culture to another. This is a problem which has not as yet received sufficient detailed exploration although it has been emphasized in the work of Mead and Macgregor (28). Elsewhere (9), I have attempted to discuss this matter in terms of the defenses that are available to people under conditions of stress within the linked systems of *a*) physiology; *b*) personality; *c*) relatively permanent meaningful small groups, e.g., the family or friendships; and *d*) wider social structures, e.g., the community or nation. Such systems are open rather than closed in that what happens in one of them can affect another, and this process tends to be of a self-regulating nature. Moreover, the particular characteristics of any of these systems are, in differing degrees, influenced by the culture of the society in which they occur. It is not possible to discuss this matter more fully here, but as a minimum it is necessary to review some of the characteristics of the family system in Japanese culture.

As is well known, the family rather than the individual is the basic unit in Japan, and this continues to be true in practice despite changes in the legal system in the postwar period which favored the individual at the expense of the family. Traditionally the authority of the parents continues through life, and age carries with it great prestige and power. Women are subordinate to men; the main line of descent is through the eldest son; and younger sons and daughters take their place in descending order in a tight hierarchical arrangement.

In general in the Japanese family the tie between mother and son is not broken as completely as is true in the United States and the relation of the mother and eldest son is particularly strong. The eldest son's wife is usually chosen for him by his parents (or in any case, the marriage is more a relation between two families than between two individuals), and the wife comes to live in her husband's house where there is a constant, and usually tense, interplay between the mother, the son, and the wife. In disagreements the son often sides with his mother against his wife, and the wife then turns to her first-born son as a source of emotional satisfaction and of practical support for her later years, and thus the close relation of mother and eldest son moves into another generation. If there were time it would be possible to develop various aspects of this relation, and others such as that between father and daughter, much further.

Such a traditional family system is still tight today, but is showing increasing strain, and it is both the dynamics of the family in the traditional sense, and the strains upon it which must be considered as factors in the study of psychiatric illnesses. Many of the strains in the modern Japanese family come from the desire of young couples to establish their own physically and financially separate unit from either the family of the husband or that of the wife. This is a difficult matter because of the traditional obligations that both husband and wife have to their families. Moreover, the financial structure of the Japanese economy does not easily permit an individual to exist by himself on his own salary. Salaries in Japan are calculated on the assumption that a number of family members will be living together and that by pooling their income they will be able to live as a unit, whereas they could not live as separate individuals. Other strains on the family come from the changing values which have been introduced into Japanese culture after World War II through accelerated contact with the Western world—in particular with the United States.

Despite the interest Japanese people have in things Western, many Western ideas are fraught with ambivalence for the Japanese. A rather striking example of this occurs in the large and excellent department stores of Tokyo. Upon entering such stores one's attention is immediately drawn to the blonde and blue-eyed mannequins on which clothing is displayed, while the people who buy the clothing are black-haired and brown-eyed. In explanation of this it is likely that when Western clothing was taken over by the Japanese the entire cultural complex attached to the clothing was also taken over, so that the mannequins on which the clothing was displayed came, as in the West, to have blonde hair and blue eyes. Some substantiation of this comes from the fact that in the section of the store which specializes in the sale of the Japanese kimono the mannequins have black hair and Japanese physical features. On the other hand such an explanation does not seem entirely satisfactory, and, as pointed out in a popular article by Shibuzawa (38), there often seems to be the feeling that Western things are better than Japanese things; yet such a feeling is accompanied by other uneasy feelings that an acceptance of Western material culture and values involves a denial of Japanese culture and a loss of personal identity.

The above give some hints of the ferment of changing values in Japan. During 1954–1955 I attempted to get some preliminary indication of the directions of such shifts in values through the use of a value orientations schedule devised by Florence Kluckhohn and her co-workers as part of their study of five cultures in the Southwest (24). The schedule was administered to 619 subjects who came from two generations in three locations—a village, a small city, and an area of metropolitan Tokyo. The results of this work will be reported elsewhere, but the answers to the questions in the area of the relations of men with each other clearly showed some of the problems of culture change in Japan today. The questions in the relational area were phrased so as to elicit a preference, by means of a rank order, between lineal, collateral, and individual ways of relating to other people. Historically it seems likely that traditional Japanese culture had a first-order lineality with a second-order collaterality (35). In the sample, for those questions which dealt with family relations, this emphasis was reversed, and there was a first-order collaterality with a second-order lineality. However, the questions which dealt with political relations showed a first preference for collaterality and a second-order individuality, while the questions on economic relations produced a first-order individuality and a second-order collaterality. Moreover, when the subjects were asked to distinguish between their own values and the values of other people, there was a strong tendency to see others as more traditional than oneself. All of this would seem to indicate a process of culture change and shifting values.

Given a situation of flux today in Japanese culture, it is interesting to investigate the effect of this in terms of the traditional positions of elder and younger brothers in the family. In the small series of male psychiatric cases with which I worked in Japan it seemed that the eldest son was more rigid and constrained, and when he developed psychiatric difficulties these most often took the form of obsessive-compulsive defenses, depression, and overconformity in general. On the other hand the younger sons were more outgoing and spontaneous, and when they developed psychiatric difficulties these were more in the nature of impulsive acting-out disorders. These impressions are in line with the work of others in Japan. For example, on the psychological side, Miki and Kimura (29), using a questionnaire, found that the personality characteristics of the elder brother were manifested by self-control, moderation, neatness, kindness, leadership, and a sense of responsibility, while the personality characteristics most evident for the younger brother were manifested by gaiety, sociability, dependency, and humor. On the sociological side, there seems to be little doubt but that the eldest son tends to stay in the family and continue the family business, whereas the younger son seeks employment elsewhere. For example, the study done by Ujihara (46) of 400 factories with a total employment of over 14,000 male workers showed very clearly the preponderance of second or younger sons from agricultural families who were working in industrial employment.

Reference has been made earlier to the use of recreation and instinctual gratification (in alcohol, sex, massage, and hot baths) as sources of relief from the tensions and obligations of interpersonal relations in Japan. A further source of relief is to plead physical weakness or sickness, and a great deal is made of minor ailments and conditions of the body. At the same time, and it is hard for me at present to resolve the matter, there is a great emphasis on the importance of the physical perfection of the body. Very small imperfections, especially in women, are a much greater cause for concern and criticism in Japan than in the United States. For example, the "trace of a dark spot over Yukiko's left eye" which came and went with her menstrual periods, as described by Tanizaki (43) in *The Makioka Sisters*, was a source of agitation in the family and seriously jeopardized the arrangement of a marriage. Such matters require further study, but they are close to the kinds of symptoms often presented by psychiatric patients, and it is to more directly psychiatric material that the discussion now turns.

SOME HISTORICAL AND CONTEMPORARY ASPECTS OF PSYCHIATRIC ILLNESS AND ITS TREATMENT IN JAPAN

Upon initial impression much of Japanese psychiatry is similar to that found in Western countries since Japanese psychiatrists were trained first in Europe. This similarity is especially true of those aspects of research and treatment based on an organic etiology for psychiatric disorders. In comparison with the United States there is very little emphasis on psychodynamics. Interwoven with these Western influences are many aspects of administration and treatment stemming from Japanese culture. In what follows, my observations and those of others in Japan were made before the current extensive use of tranquilizing drugs, and such a factor must, of course, be taken into consideration in further study of this kind.

In Japan the development of psychiatric practice has been much less extensive than in the United States. In 1951, out of a Japanese population of slightly less than 85 million, there were about 20,000 patients in 148 mental hospitals with an average length of stay of 284 days, in contrast to about 700,000 hospitalized mental patients with an average length of stay of 829 days in the United States. Of the 148 mental hospitals in Japan in 1951, 4 were national hospitals, 17 were local public hospitals, and 127 were private hospitals. Equally, 132 of the 148 hospitals had less than 300 beds, so that the great majority were small private hospitals in contrast to the concentration in large public state hospitals in the United States (32). By the end of 1955 the number of mental hospitals in Japan had risen to 260, with a total of 44,250 beds—the great bulk of which were still in small private hospitals. It is apparent that privately owned small hospitals are of major importance in the total picture of psychiatric hospital care in Japan and that this is markedly different from the situation in the United States (11). Such increases in the number of mental hospital beds in Japan must, of course, be seen against the tremendous spurt in population growth which Japan has experienced. Population has grown from roughly 55 million in 1920 to approximately 90 million at the present time. Thus, the present number of mental hospital beds is probably no more nor less adequate than it was formerly.

The great increase in population growth in the years just after World War II presents many interesting questions with cultural and psychiatric implications. Merely to suggest one area of interest, in 1948 Japan passed a Eugenic Protection Law which made liberal provision for legal abortion. In 1949 the number of abortions was 9.1 per cent of the number of live births for the year, and this percentage steadily increased until in 1953 the number of legal abortions performed was over one million and represented 57.3 per cent of the number of live births (2, 26, 32).

While the proportion of American hospital beds used for mental patients is about one in two, the proportion of Japanese hospital beds used for mental patients is only about one in fifteen. As will be seen later, there are reasons to believe that the actual prevalence of mental illness is not particularly lower in Japan than what it probably is in the United States, and the question arises of where nonhospitalized psychotics are living in Japan. The answer would seem to be that they are taken care of within the family system, and also that the attitudes toward eccentric behavior are somewhat more tolerant and there are more small jobs available for such people in Japan than in the United States.

Of the 85,000 doctors in Japan in 1952 about 1,000 could be broadly classified as psychiatrists. Although the doctor-patient ratio is more favorable in Japanese mental hospitals than in the United States, there are few professional ancillary personnel, such as social workers, clinical psychologists, and occupational therapists. Such professions are, however, beginning to develop and will grow in the years to come. There are the usual nurses and attendants and, in particular, a special kind of practical nurse known as *tsukisoi*, of which more will be said later.

Of admissions to mental hospitals in 1952, the proportions in various diagnostic categories were as follows: 54 per cent were schizophrenic reactions, 12 per cent were syphilitic psychosis (including general paresis), 11 per cent were manic-depressive psychosis, and in decreasing order of frequency there followed toxic psychoses, psychoneuroses, epilepsy, involutional psychosis, mental deficiency, and psychopathic personality. It is, however, difficult to make comparisons with the United States because of wide variations between and within the countries in diagnostic criteria. It does seem likely that the proportion of senile patients in mental hospitals in Japan is much lower than that in the United States as a result of a combination of factors: the age structure of the population, the death rate among Japanese mental patients during World War II, and the ability of the Japanese family to absorb and care for the aged.

Adequate comparable studies on the number of mentally ill in the United States and Japan are not available. However, a sampling study (30) of the prevalence of mental illness throughout Japan was conducted using as its base date, July 1, 1954. This study attempted a complete survey of all families in 100 census districts—these districts being a stratified random sample drawn from a total of 3,690 districts. From this survey it was estimated that 1,300,000 persons throughout the country had sufficient problems to be classified as in need of psychiatric attention. Of this total, 450,000 were estimated as suffering from psychoses, 580,000 from mental deficiency, and the remainder from other disorders, such as narcotic addiction and psychoneuroses. There was little difference in the rate of psychosis between rural and urban areas, but a much higher proportion of the mentally ill in urban areas was hospitalized. There was an indication that psychosis rates were greater in lower income groups. It was estimated from the survey that 430,000 people who were not hospitalized required hospitalization. Of the total persons found in the survey who were considered to be mentally ill, only 2.5 per cent were in institutions, 1.4 per cent were being seen on the outside more than once a month by a psychiatrist, 4.8 per cent had more than one visit a month with professional personnel other than a psychiatrist, and 91.3 per cent were receiving no professional treatment. It would seem, therefore, reasonable to conclude that the small number of mental patients in hospitals is not attributable to the smallness of the number of mentally ill persons in Japan but rather to the lack of facilities. This means, then, that the large proportion of the mentally ill are either cared for in the family or manage to make their way somehow within the society, but outside of an institution.

Prior to the Meiji restoration there seem to have been three roots to the early practice of medicine and psychiatry in Japan. The first of these was the considerable influence of Chinese medicine, while the second was the influence of Dutch medicine which began in the period of intercourse with Europe during the latter part of the sixteenth century and just prior to the closing of the country at the beginning of Tokugawa regime. Throughout the Tokugawa period there was sporadic contact with Dutch medicine but it was not until after the Meiji restoration that European influences, particularly German and French, came to have a major effect on the organization of medicine in Japan (16). A third root of medical practice, particularly for Japanese psychiatry, was the influence exerted by certain Buddhist temples that came to specialize in the treatment of the emotionally ill.

The story of one of these Buddhist temples has been spread widely throughout Japan. The story is that the daughter of the seventy-first Emperor, Go-Sanjō (1069–1072), became abnormal when she was twenty-nine years of age, tore her clothing, talked to herself, and generally was recognized to be sick in spirit. The Emperor dreamed that he should send his daughter to the temple at Iwakura village near Kyoto. He acted upon this dream, and she stayed at the temple and drank the well water which was known to have spiritual qualities. Prior to her visit to Iwakura people had come to the temple for help concerning eye trouble. Later when she was cured through her stay it was felt that it was good for people who had mental difficulties to come and sit under the waterfall and to drink the water at the temple. In addition, there was a large Buddhist rosary around which the patients sat and prayed. This rosary is still in existence at the temple, and this type of "treatment" reminds one of an early example of "group therapy." *

Gradually the knowledge of the help people received at Iwakura spread throughout Japan and as time went by larger numbers of people

* I am indebted for the material concerning Iwakura to interviews with Dr. Eikichi Tsuchiya, the first superintendent of Kyoto Iwakura Mental Hospital. Further information on Iwakura, as well as similar places elsewhere in Japan, was obtained from Drs. Hayashi and Hirose of Matsuzawa Mental Hospital in Tokyo.

came for treatment. Many of these stayed for a long time at the inns or farmhouses in the area, and a sort of "psychotic village" came into being. Shortly after the beginning of the Meiji period a modern mental hospital with 200 beds was established at Iwakura. Following this, the patients received treatment at the hospital but continued to live in the inns or farmhouses. This system lasted until the beginning of World War II, at which time the Japanese military forces took over the hospital for their own purposes and this type of hospitalization was not re-established after the war.

The existence of a type of "family care" program at Iwakura was similar to that established at other temples in Japan, usually in connection with a waterfall under which the patients were placed as a sort of primitive shock therapy. Such systems of care of course invite comparison with similar situations in Europe, such as the care of mental patients in the village of Gheel in Belgium which has a history very parallel to that of Iwakura (22).

As Doi (12) points out, the first modern foreign influences on the development of Japanese psychiatry came from Germany and France. Dr. Baelz, a German internist, was invited by the Japanese government to help establish the Tokyo University Medical School and he lectured on psychiatry for the first time in Japan in 1879. However, the regular course in psychiatry in the medical curriculum was initiated at Tokyo University in 1886 by Dr. Sakaki, the first Japanese professor of psychiatry. Following Dr. Sakaki as professor of psychiatry was Dr. Kure, who returned to Japan in 1901 after four years of study in Germany under Kraepelin and Nissl, and it was Dr. Kure who essentially decided the course of Japanese psychiatry. Dr. Kure was particularly interested in neuropathology and attracted a number of bright students who pursued this interest so that it has become the most developed field in Japanese psychiatry.

As well as teaching at Tokyo University, Dr. Kure assumed the directorship of Sugamo Mental Hospital and introduced many progressive changes in treatment and administration. Under his direction patients were given increased freedom on the grounds of the hospital and the use of restraint was prohibited. In 1919, Sugamo Hospital changed its location and name and became the present Matsuzawa Hospital with a thousand-bed capacity (18).

In the past generation, Professor Uchimura of the Tokyo University Medical School has been responsible for training more psychiatrists in

Japan than any other person. Professor Uchimura received his initial training at Tokyo Medical School and then went to Munich for advanced training during 1925–1927. Like Dr. Kure, Dr. Uchimura's major interest has been in neuropathology, although he has done considerable research in other areas—one of which, of particular interest to anthropology, is the study of *imu* among the Ainu (45).

Prior to World War II the influence of the United States was not very great on Japanese psychiatry, although a few well-known psychiatrists received their training in this country—for example, Dr. Marui under Meyer in Baltimore, and Dr. Muramatsu at the Boston Psychopathic Hospital. Dr. Marui became professor of psychiatry at Tohoku University, while Dr. Muramatsu is at present professor of neuropsychiatry at Nagoya University. In recent years American psychiatry has come to have a somewhat greater influence, particularly on younger men.

Dr. Marui introduced psychoanalytic theories for the first time to Japanese psychiatry some thirty years ago as a result of his study in the United States. However, the result of his pioneer work was anything but a success and today psychoanalytic ideas are given little importance in Japanese psychiatry. Some of the reasons for this have been discussed by Doi (13), and, in what seems to me to be an overgeneralized fashion, by Moloney (33). There are many reasons why the Japanese have rapidly developed the use of physical and organic therapies, such as electric shock, insulin, and tranquilizing drugs, but have been rather slow to utilize psychotherapeutic or psychoanalytic approaches. For one thing, information about physical and organic therapies is more easily communicated and the results can be more readily and objectively evaluated. Beyond this, Japanese psychiatrists simply have had very little contact with psychoanalysis. But the lack of contact is not the whole story. Freud's work did not create the popular interest in Japan that it did in the United States. Nor could Dr. Marui first, or Dr. Kosawa later, arouse the interest of Japanese doctors in the study and use of psychoanalytic approaches. One of the lines of criticism of psychoanalysis in Japan closely follows that of Karl Jaspers, the German philosopher. This criticism holds that psychoanalysis assumes that man is able to understand and control his own existential situation. The criticism is particularly directed at American psychoanalysis because it is felt it implies that a wide range of choice is open to the individual, and that these choices can be made more effectively the more one is able to understand one's own problems. In Japan, however, the argument goes, the individual does not have such a wide range of choices open to him, and, particularly, boundaries on individual initiative are placed on a person within the structure of the Japanese family regardless of how much he is able to understand about his own position. An additional problem is raised as to how willing, or able, a Japanese patient would be to communicate the deeply personal feelings and motivations which are necessary parts of the psychoanalytic relationship (13).

Such generalizations of course do not have complete applicability, and they do not mean that psychoanalysis can never be practiced in Japan. In some groups in Japan, such as in certain intellectual circles, psychoanalysis has already taken root. But before it can be widely applied in Japanese society some modification in either Japanese culture or psychoanalytic practice, or both, may be expected.

Such comments about the importance of foreign contacts in the development of modern psychiatry in Japan should not be taken to mean that there has been a lack of original developments within Japan, for much original work has been done. One especially influential development solely within Japanese psychiatry is the type of psychotherapy for neuroses which was worked out by Dr. Seima Morita. Dr. Morita began his work about thirty-five years ago, and continued it as professor of psychiatry at Jikei University. His work has been further developed by Dr. Kora, and, in a modified form, has influenced most of the psychiatrists in Japan. This type of treatment will be returned to later in this paper.

Just as the effect of Japanese cultural values is likely to cause changes in the ways in which foreign techniques are put to use in Japanese psychiatry, so when reforms came about early in the history of mental hospitals in Japan, they did so in a manner somewhat different from that in the United States. The emphasis on reform in the United States came from the work of crusading individualists, such as Dorothea Dix or Clifford Beers, whereas in Japan a similar movement took its model from the loyalty of a retainer to his lord in the context of the family. This point may be illustrated by some events that occurred in Sugamo Mental Hospital during the period 1887–1894. The events were called the "Sohma incident," and attracted the attention of the popular press and the public throughout Japan. Although the authenticity of some of the details are in doubt, the medical records are available and the main outlines of the story have been verified (18). If, in the following account, the reader is confused by the intricacies of the familial setting of the Sohma incident, this is only to be expected.

The main character in the Sohma incident was Viscount Masatane Sohma, whose family had been a noble one during the Tokugawa period, and had continued its position of eminence in the Meiji period. The bare outline of the story concerns the fact that Viscount Sohma became psychotic and was confined against his will, first at home, and later in the Sugamo Mental Hospital from which he was kidnapped by his faithful retainer, Gosei Nishigoro. The background of the incident is involved, but it is apparent that there was considerable internal struggle for power in the Sohma family. Masatane's mother (named Otsuki) died when he was young and his father (named Atsutane) then took a concubine (named Ryu Nishigame) who bore him a son. Actually, however, the child was the son of the chief steward (named Naomichi Shiga), and the concubine and the steward plotted to have their child, rather than Masatane's line, succeed in the family. About these events, Hayashi writes:

According to Gosei's story, a son, Masatane, was born to the couple, Atsutane and Otsuki. After the death of Otsuki, the concubine, Ryu Nishigame, bore a son called Noritane. However, Ryu had illicit relations with the chief steward, Naomichi Shiga, and Noritane was in fact the son of Shiga. They conspired to take over the household and arranged things in such a way that Masatane married Toda Kyoko who was sexually frigid. Thus, they avoided having a heir to the family and at the same time drove Masatane crazy on account of sexual dissatisfaction. The conspiracy finally succeeded in 1876 when Masatane tried to attack with a spear Fukazo Tomita, the assistant steward, and was confined in a locked room as a lunatic. After that he was hospitalized twice in Tokyo Tenkyo-in. After the transfer of the hospital to Kagomachi, the Sohma family contributed a unit of the hospital consisting of one eight-mat room, one six-mat room, and a bathroom connected with a corridor. Masatane was hospitalized in this unit at the time that Gosei kidnapped him . . .*

The person responsible for awakening the interest of the public was Gosei Nishigoro, the faithful retainer. Gosei, later diagnosed as a paranoid psychopath, was convinced that he was a great leader, and he was extremely loyal to his master. He had been attempting unsuccessfully by legal action to get Masatane out of the hospital, and after repeated

* Hayashi, Susumu: *A Short History of Seventy-five Years of Tokyo Metropolitan Matsuzawa Hospital.* Tokyo: A pamphlet published by Tokyo Metropolitan Matsuzawa Hospital, 1954.

failures, kidnapped his master from the hospital in January, 1887. Subsequently, both were apprehended. Masatane was returned to the hospital, and Gosei attracted much support and captured the public imagination at the time of the trial that led to his imprisonment. The story was immediately picked up in the newspapers partly because there was a close parallel between the Sohma incident and the famous Japanese story of the forty-seven *rōnin* (masterless warriors). In this story, it will be remembered, the forty-seven *rōnin* had lost their master, Lord Asano, because Asano was obliged to commit suicide after angrily wounding his superior, Lord Kira, within the confines of the Shogun's palace. After several years of planning and much self-sacrifice the forty-seven *rōnin* revenged their lord by killing Kira and then themselves committed suicide.

In considerable part due to the stimulus provided by the Sohma incident the need for better laws regarding mental illness was dramatized and in 1900 the Law for the Supervision and Protection of the Insane was enacted and remained in effect until after World War II.

Turning to some of my observations during 1954–1955, it seems to me that the social structure of Japanese psychiatric hospitals is tighter and the control more rigidly hierarchical than is generally true for hospitals in the United States. Moreover, the Japanese hospital is organized much more in terms of a "family model," as is also true for many other types of organizations in Japan. This firm control within a family model has many implications for behavior at each level of the hospital. For example, the relation between the doctor and patient is clearly, if benevolently, authoritarian. There is no question who is the doctor and who is the patient. Perhaps because of this sharp status difference which provides a sense of security and inevitability, the casual relations between doctor and patient often appear to be more relaxed and friendlier than in American psychiatric hospitals.

One example of the somewhat different structuring of the relations between doctor and patient occurred during my first visit to Matsuzawa hospital. After talking for a while with the vice-superintendent, he mentioned that a group of the patients wished to meet me. This itself was surprising since it was not likely that a scholar who was visiting a state hospital in the United States would be told by a senior staff member that a group of the patients knew he was coming and wanted to see him. The action implied that the vice-superintendent had sufficiently close relations with the patients, and direct enough interest in them, to inform them that someone they might want to interview was coming to the hospital.

I went into the corridor and met four patients who, after a few minutes conversation, gave me a copy of the newspaper which they published as well as an English translation of it. That evening I discovered that the translation was of two articles in the newspaper—one was a criticism of Wiener's theory of cybernetics; the other was an essay on "patient government at Matsuzawa hospital." The latter article was particularly intriguing, and also a little disconcerting, as I had come to Japan to study the differences in psychiatric hospitals and was here confronted with a type of organization originally developed about ten years ago at Boston Psychopathic Hospital. Subsequent interviewing of both staff and patients indicated that the staff members were not very well acquainted with the concept of patient government but the patients were aware of the concept, specifically as it was used at Boston Psychopathic Hospital. It is interesting how this came about. About a year earlier the dietitian in the hospital had wanted information on diets for epileptic patients and had heard that work along these lines was being done at Boston Psychopathic Hospital. The dietitian asked one of the patients whose English was good to write to Boston for information about such diets. The patient wrote the letter, and Boston Psychopathic Hospital, in addition to sending the requested material, also enclosed some reprints on patient government which it thought might be of interest in Japan. When this material arrived at Matsuzawa hospital the patient translated the articles on diets for the dietitian, but was himself impressed with the concept of patient government contained in the additional reprints. Together with his fellow patients he explored this idea and they obtained further information about it through use of the library at the American Cultural Center. They then organized themselves as a patient-government group. It is not often that it is possible to catch diffusion in action so directly.

As is suggested by the behavior of the patients in the example just cited, I was impressed with the greater degree of contact with other human beings that seemed to be maintained among Japanese schizophrenic patients when compared with similar patients on the wards of state hospitals in the United States. As reports begin to come in from other cultures they seem to indicate that there is less withdrawal and avoidance among schizophrenic patients elsewhere when compared with those in our society. This may be due to attributes of interpersonal relations in other cultures, or to differences in ward environment and hospital structure, or to a combination of these and still other factors.

With regard to the social structure of Japanese hospitals it is interesting to look at a type of phenomenon described by Stanton and Schwartz (39) as disturbances in three- or four-person systems in the hospital in which the increased agitation of a patient can be linked with an ongoing disagreement between staff members who exercise authority over the patient. In the light of work in Japan I have come to believe that a certain tacit cultural premise or expectation concerning interpersonal relations underlies the phenomenon described by Stanton and Schwartz. As indicated in greater detail elsewhere (8), it may be that, in terms of American culture, both staff members and patients are in unspoken agreement that people can be moved quite a distance (knowingly or unknowingly influenced in their actions on behalf of another) in human relations. The boundaries of many relations in American culture are rather fuzzy—to a greater extent than in other cultures it is left to the individuals concerned to decide how wide a range of action and degree of intimacy are to be included in a relationship. In contrast, the boundaries of relations in Japan are very sharp and well known beforehand by the participants. Thus, when the patient and the staff members interact in the Japanese hospital, they are probably much clearer as to the limits surrounding their relation, and feel freer to act spontaneously within these limits because they are at the same time prevented by the tightness of the status system from developing the relation in other directions. One would not expect then, other things being equal, to find the kind of phenomenon noted by Stanton and Schwartz as evident in Japanese psychiatric hospitals. Such a structural reason for the lesser degree of violence and tension would seem to be one among several helping to account for this sort of difference, which has been noted by a number of observers who were in a position to compare the behavior of patients on wards in Japan and the United States.

In line with the emphasis on the family in Japan, it was usual in the past when a patient was sick for a family member to come to the hospital and care for his housekeeping and bodily needs. If it was not possible for a family member to come, then a person was hired by the family to perform these functions for the patient. In this manner a category of nursing personnel grew up called *tsukisoi*, and I had the chance to observe the work of these women in Japanese hospitals. *Tsukisoi* are women who occupy a position below the level of graduate nurses and more in a category with aides or attendants. They act as motherly servants and are usually with the patient for twenty-four hours a day, seven days a week. They sleep in the same room as the patient and serve as housekeeper and companion. Although the hospitals in Japan consider these women mainly in terms of their housekeeping functions, a very close relation often develops within the limits set by the relative positions of *tsukisoi* and patient.*

Different groups of *tsukisoi* specialize in caring for various categories of illness, and thus there are *tsukisoi* who work in general hospitals, tuberculosis sanitariums, psychiatric hospitals, and so on. When *tsukisoi* are not working on cases in a hospital they live in dormitories scattered throughout the city, which are run somewhat as extended families in charge of an elderly woman who has had much experience in her profession. It is useful to give some of the interview material from a visit to a dormitory for psychiatric *tsukisoi* as it serves to emphasize the strong familial orientation in the work of these women. Concerning the training of *tsukisoi*, the head of the dormitory said:

We had to learn how to get a feeling of mothering others. It is still so at present. These young *tsukisoi* have to learn what is the best way to think of the patient as their own precious and beloved person. . . . As you see, these young *tsukisoi* cannot possibly have a feeling of being a mother, so I teach them that they should face their patients with the feeling that they are brothers or sisters. . . . The patients come to depend on the *tsukisoi* if the *tsukisoi* has a strong feeling of serving as to a family member. . . . For example, the patient often asks the *tsukisoi* about such a small matter as whether it is all right to eat a piece of candy. . . . We build a feeling of love and mercy toward the patient, knowing that they are entirely depending on us. . . . [The writer asked about whether or not *tsukisoi* took a day off occasionally?] To tell you the truth people in the so-called modern world are quite useless. When I was young I did not lie down for twenty-one days while I was serving one patient. Japanese in the older generation did not consider about themselves and wanted to devote their life to others. In this regard I blame the American Occupation. They taught us only our profession and did not teach us our duty. But it is necessary for *tsukisoi* education to teach the real meaning of sacrificing.

The mention by the head of the dormitory of love, mercy, and sacrifice is interesting since the name of the dormitory is *Aijinkai*, or love and mercy organization. One can see here both the elements of helpfulness and tenderness in such an approach, and also the real power that is

---

* The following material on the use of *tsukisoi* and Morita psychotherapy is adapted from that appearing in the final chapter of a recent book by myself (8).

gained thereby over patients similar to the way in which women in the Japanese family exercise power through sacrifice.

The elderly head of the *tsukisoi* dormitory was not merely being old-fashioned when she emphasized the familial role of *tsukisoi*. This emphasis was also found in the interviews with a number of relatively young women who were employed as *tsukisoi* in a small private hospital. One of these young *tsukisoi* had formed a close relationship with her patient —an intelligent schizophrenic man who was in remission and had a strong obsessive-compulsive overlay. This patient had developed a private language with his *tsukisoi* by teaching her his special meaning for words, and over the course of some months they came to use quite an extensive vocabulary. At one point in their relation it was necessary for the *tsukisoi* to visit her family in the countryside and she was disturbed about doing so because another *tsukisoi* would not be able to care satisfactorily for her patient. Nevertheless, because her family business was pressing, she took the trip. Later, when asked for an example of the patient's private language, she mentioned, among others, what she had said upon returning from her trip.

She said: "After I came back from the country I described the scenery to my patient saying, 'When the leaves fall down, it is so pretty to see the ripe fruit on the tree.' My patient replied, 'It would be so nice if I could eat the ripe persimmon.'" I asked her what she had replied to this, and she said, "I thought he was pointing to my immatureness."

It is hard to retain the Japanese feeling of the above in translation. It reads much like an exchange of poems between lovers in the *Tales of Genji*. From this, and additional evidence on this patient's case, the *tsukisoi* would seem to be correct in her feeling that the patient was pointing to her immatureness, and also to the implication that he would like to eat her up. At the same time, despite this desire, the patient was also referring to the lack of ripeness of the fruit, and hence to the social and psychological distance which separated him from his *tsukisoi*. This matter cannot be analyzed more fully here, but it is hoped that the reader has been able to sense some of the unspoken or only subtly referred to emotional intimacy that existed between these two people within the context of the sharp distinctions between the role of the patient and that of the *tsukisoi* which were inherent in the tight social structure of the hospital.

The relations between *tsukisoi* and patient are not always as good as they were in the above case, and there is of course room for abuse in such work, along with the need to develop the right sort of training program for such personnel. Nevertheless, I felt it was unfortunate that during 1955 plans were being made for legislation which would do away with the use of *tsukisoi* in hospitals, with the expectation that their duties would be divided between graduate nurses and maintenance personnel. This was part of a laudatory attempt to raise the professional standards of nursing care, yet the attempt appeared to entail the sacrifice of one type of care for another that perhaps was not as well suited to the needs of psychiatric patients.

One of the most interesting types of treatment in Japanese culture is the method of psychotherapy for the neuroses developed by Dr. Seima Morita. Dr. Morita's influence has been great on Japanese psychiatry, although only a small proportion of psychiatrists use his method in unmodified form. During the first week of treatment the patient is isolated in an empty room, and all contact and activity (except eating and eliminating) are prohibited. Following this period the patient begins to communicate with his doctor through a diary upon which the doctor comments in writing several times a week. Also at this time the patient is set to doing simple manual tasks which will bring him into contact with nature. Emphasis is on the treatment of the patient through his daily life experiences, and it is felt that a direct approach to the constructive forces within the patient is to be preferred over an analytic approach to the obstructive, pathological conflicts in his personality. As Kondo (25) says, "First is the stress on the curative effects of nature; second is that of manual work; and third is the importance of the attitude called 'acceptance.'" The philosophy behind these procedures has its roots in Zen Buddhism.

Most of the neurotic patients who come for treatment at the hospitals using Morita psychotherapy are suffering from obsessive-compulsive symptoms or from hypochondriasis. Beyond this, and in line with the Japanese opinion that their own interpersonal relations are particularly difficult, Japanese psychiatry has created a syndrome which may be translated as anthrophobia (*taijin kyōfushō*). Anthrophobia is manifested by feelings of inadequacy, fear of meeting people, flushing, stuttering, and other signs of anxiety. These symptoms are certainly not unknown in American culture but we have not, in our psychiatry, focused on them so specifically as to group them in a special disease syndrome.

I had the opportunity of working for a few days in one of the psychiatric hospitals specializing in Morita psychotherapy. During this time a number of group sessions were held in which the psychiatrist had in front of him the diaries upon which the patients who were attending had been writing. At these sessions the following sort of exchange frequently took place:

PATIENT: Doctor, my heart pounds so fast.
DOCTOR: Anybody has a fast pounding on their heart when they run.
PATIENT: I feel that I will die because of my fast-pounding heart.
DOCTOR: How exaggerated, what is the matter with you? You have never died before. You had better not touch a problem you have never experienced. You have already gone to the doctor for an examination for heart trouble. That is it. Do you still want to die?
PATIENT: I don't have such a feeling any more.
DOCTOR: That is good. Try to write more on your diary. . . .

SECOND PATIENT: I yawned right after I became sick. It was the first yawn I noticed after I became sick, so I wrote about it in my diary. After writing this, I was so depressed by my stuttering. My anthrophobia and stuttering were mixed. I lost all of my memory.
DOCTOR: You have a great tendency to exaggerate such a small thing.
SECOND PATIENT: I am telling you the truth. I don't remember in what way I came to this hospital.
DOCTOR: If you don't remember anything, you should not remember your anthrophobia. . . .

Such therapeutic methods may sound authoritarian and repressive to Western ears, yet they have many advantages. Before judging, it would be well for the Western reader to understand something of the philosophical background out of which such therapy has grown (47, 48). Along these lines Stunkard (40) has pointed out some of the parallel aspects between Western psychotherapy and the interpersonal experiences in the training of a Zen monk. The one indispensable element in this training is the relationship between master and pupil. Beyond this a number of techniques are also used to advance understanding such as the *mondo* which is a brief dialogue between the master and his disciple. The dialogues of which *mondo* are comprised sound very similar to the type of exchange which took place in the group session in the psychiatric hospital as given above. For example, the following is often cited in books on Zen as a popular *mondo:*

Bokuju was once asked, "We have to dress and eat every day, and how can we escape from all that?" The master replied, "We dress, we eat." "I do not understand." "If you do not understand, [put on your] dress and eat your food."

The essential element in the *mondo* is an emphasis on the concrete and continuous confrontation of immediate experience. And for this purpose such techniques as the enigmatic answer, kicking, and the ridicule of the pupil by the master are used. As Stunkard (40) says, "The slappings and enigmatic answers appear designed to upset the student's expectation or set, and as such must be closely related to psychotherapeutic techniques for dealing with defenses against feeling." The goal of such training is the sudden flash of enlightenment, or *satori*, which is in some respects similar to what is meant by insight in Western psychotherapy.

In relation to the question of *satori*, Tanaka (42) points out that as a result of the state of consciousness in the human individual, life comes to be divided into two parts—that of acting and of observing. When enlightenment is reached these two parts are blended so that the ego which is observing essentially does not exist. As Tanaka (42) says, "At this point there is not space even for one hair between will and action." Such a statement of the attempt to do away with the distinction between acting and observing is close to some of the processes that go on in psychoanalysis, but the goal may be a different one. And this is much too involved a subject to be within the limits of this paper.

In general the process of Zen is well and charmingly presented by Herrigel (19) in the report of his experiences within the art of archery during the six years he worked as a professor in Tokyo. There are also the classic books of Suzuki (41), a good general treatment by Watts (48), and Benoit (6) has indicated some of the psychological background in Zen thought. At an earlier date, Alexander (1) made an interesting attempt to trace some of the similarities between certain aspects of Buddhism and psychoanalysis.

Such parallels between an Eastern religion (although the term is itself inappropriate, especially with regard to Zen) and a Western type of therapy suggest the wider problem of the similarities in the methods that have been developed to help or change people by many cultures. Certainly if the principles underlying Western psychotherapy are valid, they are so in part because they share in many of the, as yet, not thoroughly understood processes by which people are affected in their relations with others. At this point one is back again to the questions with which this paper began, and for which I have no pat answers at this time. I hope, however, that the material presented has at least indicated some of the interplay between pressures in Japanese culture and the emotional balance of people in it, and also that I have been able to suggest some of the ways in which treatment for psychiatric difficulties is differently phrased in Japan when compared with the United States.

BIBLIOGRAPHY

1. Alexander, Franz: "Buddhistic training as an artificial catatonia." *Psychoanalytic Review*, 1931, vol. 18, pp. 129–145.
2. Amano, Fumiko: "Family planning movement in Japan." *Contemporary Japan*, 1955, vol. 23, pp. 761 ff.
3. Babcock, C. G., and Caudill, W.: "Personal and cultural factors in the treatment of a Nisei man." In *Clinical Studies in Cultural Conflict* (Georgene Seward, ed.). New York: Ronald Press, 1958.
4. Belknap, Ivan: *Human Problems of a State Mental Hospital.* New York: McGraw-Hill Book Co., 1956.
5. Benedict, Ruth: *The Chrysanthemum and the Sword.* Boston: Houghton Mifflin Co., 1946.
6. Benoit, Hubert: *The Supreme Doctrine.* New York: Pantheon Books, 1955.
7. Caudill, W.: "Japanese American Personality and Acculturation." *Genetic Psychology Monographs,* 1952, vol. 45, pp. 3–102.
8. ———: *The Psychiatric Hospital as a Small Society.* Cambridge: published for The Commonwealth Fund by Harvard University Press, 1958.
9. ———: *Some Effects of Social and Cultural Systems in Reactions to Stress.* New York: published as a pamphlet by the Social Science Research Council's Committee on Preventive Medicine and Social Science, 1958.
10. Caudill, W., and DeVos, G.: "Achievement, culture and personality: The case of the Japanese Americans." *American Anthropologist,* 1957, vol. 58, pp. 1102–1126.
11. Crosby, Edwin L.: "Observations on Japanese hospitals." *Hospitals,* August 1, 1957, vol. 31, pp. 34 ff.
12. Doi, Takeo: "Some Aspects of Japanese psychiatry." Paper presented at the Neuropsychiatric Conference, FEC, U.S. Army Hospital, 8168th Army Unit, May 4, 1954.
13. ———: *Seishinbunseki* (Psychoanalysis). Tokyo: Kyoritsu Shuppan Co., 1956.
14. Freud, Sigmund: "Instincts and their vicissitudes." In *Collected Papers,* vol. IV, pp. 60–83. London: Hogarth Press, 1948.
15. ———: *Civilization and Its Discontents.* London: Hogarth Press, 1930.
16. Fujikawa, Y.: *Nihon Igakushi* (A History of Japanese Medicine). Tokyo: Shinrisha (complete edition), 1952.

17. Greenblatt, M.; York, R. H.; and Brown, E. L.: *From Custodial to Therapeutic Patient Care in Mental Hospitals.* New York: Russell Sage Foundation, 1955.

18. Hayashi, Susumu: *Tōkyō Toritsu Matsuzawa Byōin Nanaju Go Nen Ryakushi* (A Short History of Seventy-five Years of Tokyo Metropolitan Matsuzawa Hospital). Tokyo: A pamphlet published by Tokyo Metropolitan Matsuzawa Hospital, 1954.

19. Herrigal, Eugen: *Zen in the Art of Archery.* New York: Pantheon Books, 1953.

20. Huxley, Julian S.: "Evolution, cultural and biological." In *Yearbook of Anthropology* (W. L. Thomas, Jr., ed.). New York: Wenner-Gren Foundation, 1955, pp. 3–25.

21. Jones, Maxwell: *The Therapeutic Community.* New York: Basic Books, 1953.

22. Kilgour, A. J.: "Colony Gheel." *American Journal of Psychiatry,* 1936, vol. 92, pp. 959–965.

23. Kluckhohn, Clyde: "Universal categories of culture." *Anthropology Today* (A. L. Kroeber, ed.). Chicago: University of Chicago Press, 1953, pp. 507–523.

24. Kluckhohn, F. R., and Strodtbeck, F., et al.: *Variations in Value Orientations.* Evanston: Row, Peterson Co. (in preparation).

25. Kondo, Akihisa: "Morita therapy: A Japanese therapy for neurosis." *American Journal of Psychoanalysis,* 1953, vol. 13, pp. 31–37.

26. Koya, Y.; Muramatsu, M.; Agata, S.; and Koya, T.: "Preliminary report of a survey of health and demographic aspects of induced abortion in Japan." *Archives of the Population Association of Japan,* 1953, no. 2, pp. 1–9.

27. Marcuse, Herbert: *Eros and Civilization.* Boston: The Beacon Press, 1955.

28. Mead, Margaret, and Macgregor, Frances C.: *Growth and Culture.* New York: G. P. Putnam's Sons, 1951.

29. Miki, Y., and Kimura, Y.: "Elder brother-like and younger brother-like." *Japanese Journal of Educational Psychology,* 1954, vol. 2, pp. 69–78.

30. Ministry of Health and Welfare: *Seishin Eisei Jittai Chōsa* (Factual Survey of Mental Hygiene). Tokyo: pamphlet published by Ministry of Health and Welfare, 1954.

31. Ministry of Health and Welfare: *A Brief Report on Public Health Administration in Japan.* Tokyo: pamphlet published by Ministry of Health and Welfare, 1954.

32. Ministry of Health and Welfare, Division of Health and Welfare Statistics: *Vital and Health Statistics in Japan.* Tokyo: Ministry of Health and Welfare, two volumes, mimeographed, October, 1953.

33. Moloney, James Clark: *Understanding the Japanese Mind.* New York: Philosophical Library, 1954.

34. Opler, Marvin K.: *Culture, Psychiatry and Human Values.* Springfield, Ill.: Charles C Thomas, Publisher, 1956.
35. Pelzel, John, and Kluckhohn, Florence: "A theory of variation in values applied to aspects of Japanese social structure." In *Bulletin of the Research Institute of Comparative Education and Culture,* Faculty of Education, Kyushu University, English edition, March, 1957, no. 1, pp. 62–76.
36. Redfield, Robert: *The Primitive World and Its Transformations.* Ithaca: Cornell University Press, 1953.
37. Reischauer, Edwin O.: *Japan and the United States,* 2nd ed. Cambridge: Harvard University Press, 1957.
38. Shibuzawa, Hideo: "Yoko Moji Banashi" (Talk about European Languages). *Bungeishunjū,* February, 1957, Tokyo.
39. Stanton, Alfred H., and Schwartz, Morris S.: *The Mental Hospital.* New York: Basic Books, 1954.
40. Stunkard, Albert: "Some interpersonal aspects of an oriental religion." *Psychiatry,* 1951, vol. 14, pp. 419–431.
41. Suzuki, D. T.: *Zen Buddhism and Its Influence on Japanese Culture.* Kyoto: Eastern Buddhist Society, 1938.
42. Tanaka, Tadao: *Zen to Gendaijin.* (Zen and People in the Modern World), 2nd ed. Tokyo: Gengensha, 1955.
43. Tanizaki, Junichirō: *The Makioka Sisters.* New York: Alfred A. Knopf, 1957.
44. Teicher, M. I.: "Comparative psychiatry: Some references in ethnopsychiatry." *Revue Internationale d'Ethnopsychologie Normale et Pathologique,* 1956, vol. I, nos. 1 and 2.
45. Uchimura, Y.; Akimoto, H.; and Ishibashi, T.: "Ainu no Imu ni Tsuite" (Concerning Imu among the Ainu). *Seishin Shinkei Gaku Zasshi* (Journal of Neuropsychiatry), January 20, 1938, vol. 42, no. 1.
46. Ujihara, Shojiro: "Wagakuni ni okeru Dai-koba Rōdōsha no Seikaku" (The character of laborers in large factories in Japan). In *Shakai-teki Kincho no Kenkyu* (Studies of Social Tensions). Tokyo: Yuhikaku, published for Nihon Jimbun Kagaku-kai (Japanese Association of Human Science), 1953, pp. 217–275.
47. Watts, Alan W.: "Asian psychology and modern psychiatry." *American Journal of Psychoanalysis,* 1953, vol. 13, pp. 25–30.
48. ———: *The Way of Zen.* New York: Pantheon Books, 1957.

Bingham Dai
Departments of Psychiatry and Psychology
Duke University

9

OBSESSIVE-COMPULSIVE DISORDERS IN

CHINESE CULTURE *

This paper is a preliminary attempt to review the findings on three cases of obsessive-compulsive disorder in pre-Communist China with a view to raising some theoretical issues of general interest. These cases were studied by means of psychoanalytic methods but from a sociopsychiatric point of view.

According to Freud, obsessive symptoms are essentially substitutive infantile sexual activities to which the individual has regressed because of his inability to meet the demands of normal genital functioning after puberty or because of his failure to satisfy his libidinal desires in a normal way later in life (10, pp. 41–48). The kinds of infantile sexual impulses that are believed to have been repressed during latency but that are now reactivated during or after adolescence are said to be mainly anal-sadistic and autoerotic or, what is summarily called the pregenital sexual organization, as contrasted with the repressed early genital impulses that dominate hysterical symptoms (12).

Freud also observed that obsessive neurotics frequently showed the character traits of compulsive orderliness, parsimony, and obstinacy, which are believed to be reaction formations against the infantile pleasures regarding defecation or the results of sphincter discipline generally stressed during early childhood in Western society (11, p. 45). Applying this point of view to the study of Chinese character structure, one author

* This report constitutes a part of a study supported by the National Institute of Mental Health of the United States Public Health Service. It was presented at the joint annual meeting of the Society for the Study of Social Problems and the American Sociological Society at Detroit, Michigan, September 6–9, 1956. It is reprinted from *Social Problems*, April, 1957, vol. IV, no. 4, by permission.

observed, and correctly, that Chinese parents, as a rule, do not impose strict toilet training early on the child. "As a result," he added, "the Chinese are as free from compulsiveness about time and performance as they are unobsessive in all the other spheres of life" (17). For example, he referred to the Chinese inexact measures of weight and the lack of fanaticism in regard to absolute truth or abstract principles. Hence, he concluded, psychosomatic disorders, schizophrenia and psychoneuroses, especially those of the obsessive-compulsive variety, must be uncommon among them.

The facts, however, do not support such an optimistic view (4), for while the Chinese might not be compulsive about time, or what the Westerners consider as truth, in the days before the Republic, they were notorious for the minister's fanatic loyalty to his emperor, the son's obsessive filial piety to his parents, and the wife's superhuman chastity or loyalty to her husband, dead or alive. These fanaticisms, according to a recognized Chinese psychologist, have been responsible for a great variety of psychopathological phenomena throughout the long Chinese history (3). Equally compulsive and even more prevalent than these historical trends are the well-known Chinese preoccupation with symmetry, and proverbial passive-aggressiveness or ambivalence toward authority, which one author describes as aspects of the anal character (1). At present, the devotion of Communist China to a new ideology is certainly far from being unobsessive. And yet there is no reason to believe that the Chinese pattern of toilet training has changed drastically in recent decades. In other words, toilet training per se may or may not have anything to do with the genesis of compulsive character or obsessive symptoms (16, 20).

The sociopsychiatric approach views man consistently as a biosocial being (6). It makes full use of Freud's epochal discoveries of the "unconscious" and "infantile sexuality," but looks upon the latter as essentially a biosocial form of relationship between the child and his elders and as only one aspect of the role the child occupies in the total family constellation (21). It also takes full cognizance of the forces of culture which, through various social agents, largely define the roles or self-concepts of the individual in his various stages of development. It further emphasizes the importance of the immediate situation and seeks to understand behavior at any given point of time as a function of the total situation, which includes the individual as he conceives of himself and the social and cultural forces as he perceives them (18). From this approach, I have reviewed the most significant findings on three cases of obsessive-compulsive disorder that were seen at the Psychiatric Clinic of the Peiping Union Medical College Hospital. They will be called Chen, Lin and Lee. For lack of space, however, only one case will be summarized in some detail, while the other two will be referred to only when they may throw some additional light on the problems being discussed. A summary of Case 1 follows.

CASE MATERIAL

General Information. Chen was a twenty-one-year-old man * from a southeastern coastal province. He came from a small merchant's family, with seventeen people living in one household. He had an elementary school education. He was married at sixteen and had two children when he came for treatment. He was seen in 185 sessions extending over a period of fifteen months. His condition was greatly improved when his treatment was interrupted by the Japanese occupation of Peiping.

Situations Confronting the Patient at Onset of Illness. The immediate situation calling forth the first obsessive response from Chen was the severe illness of his two-year-old half-sister when he was twelve years old. One day as he was tearing a sheet of paper in school and letting the pieces fall on the floor, he was struck with the thought that unless he picked up those pieces of paper from the floor, his half-sister would die. So he did and there began his ever-expanding obsessive-compulsive symptoms.

It must be added that Chen's mother became ill when he was three and died when he was five. After that he became the adopted son of his elder paternal uncle and his wife, in addition to being his own father's son. The only other male child in the household was an older cousin, who was the son of his father's younger brother. Being the only son of two families was, apparently, a very privileged position, for according to the custom of his region at that time, such a man was entitled to have two wives to bear children for the respective families. Besides, he had always been his father's favorite until his father remarried and the beautiful and lively half-sister was born. His symptoms began one day after he was allowed to see this half-sister and noticed her erstwhile lovely face was covered with pock marks.

* This was his approximate age according to the Western way of counting. The Chinese infant is one year old before he is twelve months, and becomes one year older with each new calendar year.

Symptoms at the Onset of Illness and Their Later Development. As soon as Chen had obsessive thoughts of a destructive nature about the half-sister who was ill with smallpox, they had to be undone compulsively. This was accomplished mainly by thinking of somebody outside the family to take her place. Soon these obsessive-compulsive processes were extended to his older cousin, his father, and his paternal uncles, including his adopted father. His major complaint about these elder men in the family was that they were all authoritarian and often shouted at him when they wanted him to come home from play and sometimes hit him and caused him to be afraid of them. One special kind of resentment was directed toward the uncle who was his adopted father. Chen slept in the same bed, up to the age of nine, with the uncle and aunt and often knew when they were carrying on sexual intercourse. He was frankly jealous and hated his adopted father for possessing his adopted mother. On the other hand, he prided himself on being the most filial son to his elders and the most gentle-hearted person in general. Hence, his destructive thoughts involving them bothered him.

The following is a typical example of the way in which these authoritarian figures appeared in his obsessive-compulsive ruminations. As he was taking a step, he would involuntarily see the image of his father on the ground on which his foot stepped. Immediately he had to withdraw his foot and think of somebody outside the family to take his father's place, and, at the same time, he would shake his head and use his foot to go through the motion of erasing, to indicate the completion of the undoing process. These symptoms might involve any of the older men in the family and might accompany any move he might make, anywhere he might be. Thus, he might have just finished his toilet functions, but as he was getting up from the usual squatting position, he would involuntarily visualize his father's face among the feces and then he would have to squat and go through the whole undoing process before he could get up again. Since these obsessive-compulsive processes tended to repeat themselves, he would get stuck in one place for hours.

In the patient's obsessive-compulsive symptoms, no single body function or organ can claim monopoly or priority. For our purposes, a brief additional reference to the use of the mouth, perhaps, should be made. If he happened to think of his father when swallowing something, he had to keep swallowing six times in order to overcome his anxiety, for "1" represented his adopted father, "2" his father, "3" his younger paternal uncle, "4" his own son and "5" his half-sister, but "6" sounded like the name of a boy outside the family who had drowned. To swallow him, therefore, was better than to swallow his own relatives.

Symptoms involving the women in the family were of a different variety. They revealed two major impulses: first, to take possession of them directly or indirectly; and second, to be like them. Thus, while going to the open toilet at his hotel, he would think of his half-sister going to the men's toilet, and, at the same time, would feel as though he were his half-sister. Or in talking to the therapist, he would feel that his step-mother was talking to a man outside the family and also that he was his step-mother talking to the man. These thoughts, of course, had to be undone.

It should be added that sometimes his own son and daughter got involved in his obsessive thoughts too. This was more understandable when the patient revealed that when he had sexual intercourse with his wife, he often felt as if his wife were his adopted mother.

The Patient's Primary Group Environment and His Primary Self-concept. Chen's household at the time of his treatment included his own father, his step-mother, and three half-sisters; his elder paternal uncle, or adopted father, and his wife; his younger paternal uncle, his wife, and three children, one of whom was a boy two years his senior; and Chen's own family of four. Two older sisters had been married and lived away from home.

Reference has been made to Chen's special position in the household by being the only son of two families and by having been the favorite child of his father until the latter remarried and had younger children by his second wife.

Chen's relationship with his adopted parents deserves a special mention. His adopted mother had taken complete charge of him ever since his own mother became ill and could no longer breast feed him when he was three. Then he began to sleep with his adopted parents in the same bed up to the age of nine, after which he continued to sleep in the same room with them for several more years, but on a separate bed. As long as he slept with his adopted parents in the same bed, his adopted mother, as a rule, held his naked body close to hers which was also naked down to the waist. His adopted father slept next to his adopted mother but on the other end of the bed.

Chen recalled without great difficulty his strong sexual interest in his adopted mother, along with resentment against his adopted father. In fact, his incestuous interests seemed to increase with age instead of undergoing repression during what is known as the "latency period" in psychoanalytic literature.* Thus, he recalled that when he was seven, he woke up one morning and found himself aroused by the smell of the trousers his adopted mother had left in bed. Masturbation followed. Another time, during the same period, it was her belt that stimulated him. When he was nine, he woke up one morning and found one of his hands on her pubic hair. And there were a number of times when he experienced an erection during the night and felt compelled to withdraw from her embrace. In fact, getting up late in the morning and masturbating under the cover with thoughts about his adopted mother was almost a daily habit during that period.

Chen's incestuous impulses during this period were not confined to his adopted mother. He readily recalled his early erotic interest in his step-mother, his younger aunt, girl cousins and half-sister.

As to Chen's strictly autoerotic, especially anal-erotic, activities during his early childhood, there were very few recollections. Nor did he recall any traumatic experiences associated with toilet training. The only related fact he recalled is that he had enuresis almost up to the time of his marriage. As long as he was sleeping with his adopted mother, all he had to do when he felt the urge to urinate was to touch her, and she would take him to the toilet or give him the urinal. In view of the ease with which Chen talked about his incestuous and patricidal impulses that were strictly forbidden in Chinese culture, the relative dearth of recollections about anal erotism or toilet training can be explained only by the widely accepted fact that most Chinese mothers do not attach much importance to such matters. Chen's mother and his adopted mother were probably no exceptions.

Chen's status in the household may be summarized as follows. His father managed the family store and his older cousin was his assistant. It had been his father's hope that someday Chen would be able to take charge of the business, or at least, be an active partner in it. As a result of his illness, however, Chen not only totally escaped from this responsibility, but had the whole household continuously concerned about him. To use his own words, he often felt that he was "the only and the most important one" (*wei i tu chuan*), on whose recovery hung the future happiness of the entire household. He claimed that he felt this way most

---

* According to Freud, the latency period is from about the end of the fourth year to about the eleventh year when the first manifestations of puberty appear. (11, p. 47)

keenly when his symptoms began. This unique role that he felt he occupied in the household was dramatized in his dreams by having an
emperor live in a house like his, and the president of the country playing the kind of ball game he played.

However lofty and important this primary self-concept of Chen's
might have been to him, he was quite aware of its disadvantageous aspects. Before his authoritarian and indulging elders, he had become
overly submissive and compliant and had never learned to express himself effectively; he either kept silent or stuttered. To outsiders, he appeared to be a weakling and often was bullied or otherwise taken advantage of. Following his marriage at sixteen, which was arranged by
his family, he had diarrhea for two years. During the same period, he
attended the public elementary school and graduated at eighteen.
But while most of his schoolmates either went on for further education or began to work after graduation, he noticed that his symptoms
became intensified and he spent most of his time in seeking treatment.
In other words, Chen was keenly aware of the discrepancy between
what he was and what he would like to be at this stage of his development.

A SOCIOPSYCHIATRIC INTERPRETATION

The data presented above are amenable to various interpretations.
According to the classic psychoanalytic point of view, the prominence
of destructive or sadistic impulses in this case would lead one to think
that Chen must have regressed to the anal-sadistic stage of psychosexual
development owing to some obstacle to his genital functioning. The
difficulty here is that we have little information about Chen's anal activities during his infancy or childhood. The chances are that due to
the lack of early visceral discipline, no particular attention had been
called to the anal area, and therefore, there had been little to be repressed. Nor was there any real obstacle to Chen's normal satisfaction
of his libido, especially after his marriage, that would occasion its flow-
ing into what Freud called "collateral channels," that is, the pregenital
sexual activities (10, p. 48). What has been said was true of all the
three cases under review, as they were all married without their own
effort and their sexual relations with their wives—and in one case with
girl friends in addition—had suffered no serious disturbances.

Then there are the complications introduced by the almost equal prominence of genital incestuous and oral aggressive impulses in this case (2, 7, 8). Even if there were no self-contradictions in the usual psychoanalytic account of this case, we would still be dealing with the vicissitudes of the libido in an individual, instead of the problems of the individual as a whole in his relations with society and culture.

From the sociopsychiatric point of view, Chen's neurotic symptoms may be simply thought of as the serious, although ineffective, attempts made by an insufficiently socialized individual to be human or to maintain an acceptable and consistent self-picture in the face of conflicting needs and increasing cultural demands during adolescence. Under such a general frame of reference, each of Chen's major symptoms can be shown to be a function of the total situation at a given point of time, or in a certain period of his development, instead of a mere repetition of infantile sexual activities.

When Chen's obsessive thoughts first appeared, his lively little half-sister was ill with smallpox. Since his special position in the family and the indulgence of his elders, especially his adopted mother, tended to engender in him the concept of himself as "the only and the most important one," it would seem natural that he should consider this half-sister as his rival, especially for his father's affections, and that he should secretly wish that she were gone. But by the age of twelve, a boy, as a rule, has internalized some of the basic values of his culture; in this case one must take into account the Chinese concept of "brotherliness," which was taught as the only appropriate attitude toward siblings. Chen might have had murderous impulses toward his half-sister before without the sense of guilt, but could not do so at this age; hence, his obsessive thoughts involving his half-sister had to be accompanied by compulsive undoing.

Next came Chen's obsessive thoughts involving the misfortune of any one of the older men in the family, especially his father, his adopted father, and the cousin who was two years his senior. To the former two, Chen was the youngest and only male child and the most precious, and also the son they expected to be filial and obedient according to the Chinese cultural traditions. To Chen, they were the fathers whose love gave him the special position in the family, but whose authority was not to be challenged. This was the larger sociocultural field in which the son-father relationship should be seen, quite aside from the narrower angle of sexual rivalry between them which no doubt did, to a certain degree, exist. The older cousin was clearly a formidable rival, for by taking an active part in the management of the family store, he enjoyed the confidence of the elders and thereby forced Chen into the background.

Under such a patriarchal family atmosphere, it is understandable that Chen should experience intense hostile impulses toward these formidable figures, and that he should be unable to express them except in the form of symptoms, especially when, with the increasing rate of socialization during adolescence, the very harboring of these impulses became grossly inconsistent with the newly reinforced ideal of a filial son or nephew and of a brotherly cousin. Hence, the compulsive undoing whenever obsessive thoughts involving these elders appeared (14, 22).

Against the background of this difficult relationship between Chen and his male elders, his obsessive thoughts involving the older women in the family become understandable. The women were used in the fantasies either as targets for displaced aggression, as main sources of emotional support, or as objects of identification. But none of these impulses was acceptable to the newly reinforced adolescent concept of a filial son to both parents and a growing man to all the mother figures. Hence, the undoing processes accompanying these obsessive thoughts.

In all those obsessions in which the hostile impulses were prominent we were able to trace them to specific sociocultural situations in which Chen strove, on the one hand, to preserve his primary role as the "only and the most important" member of the family, and, on the other, to live up to what his culture expected him to be; that is, a filial son and a brotherly brother or cousin, as well as a productive member of the household (15). It was probably his awareness of his deficiency in the latter capacity that was responsible for the intensification of his symptoms during the period following his graduation from school and prior to his coming for treatment.

The same human need for consistency, creating anxiety and defense mechanisms whenever unacceptable impulses were active, was found in the other two cases, the details of which are not given here because of the limitations of space. Suffice it to say that in the case of Lin, having to study for his final examination in an elementary school was the situational context in which the desire to return to the primary role of being his mother's and father's only beloved son became intense and took the form of incestuous and passive homosexual fantasies; and in the case of Lee, it was the conflicting desires to be a patriot on the one hand and to cooperate with the enemy on the other, which constituted the core of his obsessive-compulsive symptoms, and the latter took the biosocial form of attempting to establish a passive homosexual relationship with the Japanese conquerors (5).

In all these obsessive cases, there were no evidences of a precocious ego development during infancy or early childhood which necessitated the repression of the "component sexual instincts" as is generally assumed, and which could be said to have been responsible for the compromise formations when they were reactivated during adolescence. It was rather the serious lack of ego development or socialization that rendered them incapable of complying with the requirements of culture during or after adolescence and that resulted in half-hearted attempts on their part to be what they thought they should be. On the one hand, they strove to conform to cultural expectations commensurate with their age and sex, but, on the other, they tried to hold on to the primary roles they had acquired earlier in the family.

SOME TENTATIVE CONCLUSIONS

Pending a more detailed analysis of the cases reviewed, the following tentative conclusions regarding obsessive-compulsive disorders in Chinese culture seem justified:

1. Obsessive-compulsive neurotic symptoms as well as character traits were found in China in spite of the fact that the Chinese mothers, on the whole, do not impose cleanliness training early on their children. Information gathered from the cases reviewed does not give support to the popular notion, derived from classic psychoanalytic theory, that obsessive-compulsive symptoms are invariably related to strict toilet training during infancy or early childhood. It is interesting to note that a Japanese psychiatrist has made similar observations on the basis of studies of Japanese patients (19).

2. The ambivalent or hostile impulses found among these obsessive patients did not appear to have any necessary relationship with anal erotism, as is assumed by the classic psychoanalytic theory of psychosexual development. Furthermore, these hostile impulses were not instinctual in the sense of being unlearned; nor were they primarily a matter of sexual constitution (13, p. 375). Instead, they were engendered in the course of the child's relations with specific social objects and cultural situations. The most important of these situations seemed to be the

patriarchal structure of the Chinese family and the traditional emphasis on filial piety and on respect for elders. This weight of parental authority is felt by the Chinese child in many areas. Being punished for early sexual misdemeanor is not as important a source of unconscious hatred of father as Freud asserts (13, pp. 342–343). Since disobedience or expression of hostility toward one's elders is strictly tabooed, ambivalence toward authority has always been a national character trait.

3. The sexual or biosocial forms in which the patient's primary selves or roles were expressed cannot be fitted neatly into the classic psychoanalytic stages of psychosexual development. The oral, anal, and genital, as well as the auditory, cutaneous, and cranial (especially in the case of Lin) body zones were used by these patients at different times and for various purposes much as, to borrow a metaphor from French, the forces on a battlefield are mobilized and dispersed by the general as the situation may require (9).

4. It is also interesting to observe that in all three cases, I was unable to detect a marked period of latency in which the pregenital and early genital sexual impulses were subjected to repression and thereby lay dormant. All available evidences point to a continuation of childish sexual interests until early puberty, when the process of socialization generally begins in earnest and the need for consistency becomes paramount. In fact, in the case of Lin, the information about whom was not gone into in detail here for lack of space, his recurrent incestuous dreams began to reflect censorship only after his treatment had progressed to a certain stage.

5. Thanks to Freud, the importance of the sexual aspects of neurotic symptoms is generally recognized today. Unfortunately, the meaning of the neurotic's sexual activities in terms of his self-picture and of his relations with fellow humans and with culture is still not sufficiently appreciated. So far as these Chinese cases of obsessive-compulsive disorder are concerned, it would be grossly misleading to think that their symptoms were only, or even principally, substitute infantile sexual activities. On the contrary, in all of these cases, the major issue seemed to be one of maintaining a consistent and acceptable self-picture and of being human according to the dictates of Chinese culture. It was when this all-important job of being human at the present was interfered with by earlier, but now unacceptable, need systems and behavior patterns that anxiety arose and defenses became necessary.

BIBLIOGRAPHY

1. Abraham, Karl: "Contributions to the theory of the anal character." In *Selected Papers on Psycho-Analysis*. London: Hogarth Press, 1949, pp. 373, 389.

2. Alexander, Franz, and Shapiro, L. B.: "Neurosis, behavior disorders and perversions." In *Dynamic Psychiatry* (Franz Alexander and Helen Ross, eds.). Chicago: University of Chicago Press, 1952, p. 122.

3. Chang, Yao Hsiang: "A historical study of the abnormal behavior of Chinese famous men" (in Chinese). *The Far Eastern Miscellany*, January, 1934, vol. 31.

4. Dai, Bingham: "Personality problems in Chinese culture." *American Sociological Review*, 1941, vol. 6, pp. 688–696.

5. ———: "Divided loyalty in war: A study of cooperation with the enemy." *Psychiatry*, November, 1944, vol. 7, pp. 327–340.

6. ———: "A socio-psychiatric approach to personality organization." *American Sociological Review*, February, 1952, vol. 17, pp. 44–49.

7. De Monchy, Rene: "Oral components of the castration complex." *International Journal of Psychoanalysis*, 1952, vol. 33, pp. 450–453 (reviewed in *The Annual Survey of Psychoanalysis*, 1956, vol. 3, pp. 74–75).

8. Fenichel, Otto: *The Psychoanalytic Theory of Neurosis*. New York: W. W. Norton & Co., 1945, pp. 274–277.

9. French, Thomas M.: "Some psychoanalytic applications of a psychological field theory." In *Contemporary Psychopathology* (S. S. Tomkins, ed.). Cambridge: Harvard University Press, 1943, pp. 226–228.

10. Freud, S.: *Three Essays on the Theory of Sexuality* (1905), translated by James Strachey. London: Imago, 1949, pp. 41–48.

11. ———: "Character and anal eroticism" (1908). In *Collected Papers, II*. London: Hogarth Press, 1950, pp. 45–50.

12. ———: "The predisposition to obsessional neurosis" (1913). In *Collected Papers, II*. London: Hogarth Press, 1950, pp. 126–127.

13. ———: "A case of obsessional neurosis." In *Collected Papers, III*. London: Hogarth Press, 1950, pp. 296–389.

14. Fromm, Erich: "Individual and social origins of neurosis." *American Sociological Review*, August, 1944, vol. 9, pp. 380–384.

15. Glover, Edward: "A developmental study of the obsessional neuroses." In *On the Early Development of Mind*. New York: International Universities Press, 1956, pp. 267–282.

16. Klineberg, Otto: *Tensions Affecting International Understanding*. New York: Social Science Research Council, 1950, p. 41.

17. LaBarre, Weston: "Some observations on character structure in the Orient, II. The Chinese, Part Two." *Psychiatry,* November, 1946, vol. 9, pp. 378–380.

18. Lewin, Kurt: *The Field Theory in Social Science* (Dorwin Cartwright, ed.). New York: Harper & Brothers, 1951.

19. Muramatsu, Tsuneo: "Japan." In *World Tension: The Psychopathology of International Relations* (George W. Kisker, ed.). New York: Prentice-Hall, 1951, p. 195.

20. Opler, Marvin K.: *Culture, Psychiatry and Human Values: The Methods and Values of a Social Psychiatry.* Springfield, Ill.: Charles C Thomas, Publisher, 1956, p. 50.

21. Parsons, Talcott: "The superego and the theory of social systems." *Psychiatry,* February, 1952, vol. 15, pp. 20–21.

22. Sullivan, Harry Stack: *Conceptions of Modern Psychiatry.* Washington, D.C.: William A. White Psychiatric Foundation, 1946, pp. 55–59.

Tsung-yi Lin
Department of Psychiatry
National Taiwan University

10

TWO TYPES OF DELINQUENT YOUTH

IN CHINESE SOCIETY *

Tai-pau, a nickname for juvenile delinquents, constitute a problem of growing concern to police, teachers, and parents, and an increasingly frequent subject of press comment in Taiwan (Formosa). Recent discussions of new legislation recommending a separate juvenile court and juvenile probation officers, the establishment of a juvenile prison which in three months was overcrowded, or the plan for a separate school for *Tai-pau* students—these together indicate the gravity of the situation as it was assessed by various authorities. The only child guidance clinic in Taiwan, The Taipei Children's Mental Health Centre, finds itself fully occupied with such youth referred by schools and parents, since its establishment two years ago. This community-wide concern leads to speculation as to causes of the upsurge in delinquency, and it becomes fashionable for adults, teachers, or street philosophers to blame Hollywood as being responsible for the whole matter. These same voices betray pride in giving accounts of the contrasting good old days.

When one carefully examines this problem of *Tai-pau* in Chinese society, however, one soon realizes that these *Tai-paus* have unduly overshadowed another group of adolescents known as *Liu-mang*. The latter are not less important as delinquents. The present paper will describe the behavior and structure of these two groups in relation to their sociocultural background, and some attempts will be made to understand the group dynamics involved.

* This paper was read at the Tenth Annual Meeting of the World Federation for Mental Health, Copenhagen, August, 1957.

TWO TYPES OF PEER GROUPS

DIFFERENCE IN SOCIAL BACKGROUND

While *Tai-pau* is a newly coined term, either for an individual delinquent, adolescent, or a group of such deviants, *Liu-mang* is a long-established term with a meaning of "vagrant" or "law-breakers." * This difference of nomenclature signifies a historical difference between the two groups, the former being of recent origin, and the latter a traditional one. These *Tai-paus* are found in small groups throughout big cities, whereas the *Liu-mangs* are more or less concentrated in certain old sections of both cities and small towns. *Tai-paus* are usually discernible from other youth by their conspicuous appearance and attention-seeking manners. Their favorite haunts or "nests" are the cinema, cafés, ping-pong houses, billiard clubs, or parks, but most of them live at home with their parents. It is more difficult to distinguish the majority of *Liu-mangs* from the rest of the population, unless one is acquainted with subtleties in their dress and manners. The *Liu-mangs* aggregate in those areas where typical Chinese urban life takes place. The winding narrow streets are crowded all day by noisy pedestrians and pedicab-shoppers carrying out business transactions and daily necessities. Small children run in and out of the houses in their games. The front rooms of the houses are used for business, while the back rooms and upstairs quarters are used for residences, often housing several families. When the working day is over, the family gathers to discuss its affairs, or the father plays chess, one-stringed fiddles, or visits friends. The market place and the courtyards of Chinese temples provide, in addition to their original functions, the best meeting places for adults or become the playground for children in the afternoons and evenings. The com-

---

* The term *Tai-pau* has its origin in the history of *Shi-shan Tai-pau* (Thirteen *Tai-paus*) in the Tang Dynasty. There was a famous general called Lee Keh-yung who had thirteen adopted sons. Due to the distinguished service of General Lee in wars and also to the promotion of all his adopted thirteen sons to the rank of *Tai-pau*, which was a highly respected position in the court, the Lee family become extremely influential in those days. Several of the thirteen adopted sons and many of their descendants and relatives, however, took advantage of their prestige and caused considerable trouble to the community. Thus, the respected term *Shi-shan Tai-pau*, which was originally used to celebrate the thirteen distinguished sons of the Lee family, came to have poor connotations. The recent increases of delinquent youth of good family background has some similarity with the above *Tai-pau's* troubles to the community in the old days, and the term *Tai-pau* has been applied to this group of problem adolescents. Thus, while the word *Tai-pau* has a long history, the use of *Tai-pau* to denote a specific group of delinquent adolescents in Taiwan is of recent origin.

plexity of these areas is increased by the presence of theatres, illegal gambling places, restaurants, and houses of prostitution, all of which attract a large number of outsiders.

Group Behavior of Tai-pau

A large number of *Tai-paus*, or the majority who absorb the attention of the authorities, come from middle- or upper-class families. They are mostly Middle School students or unsuccessful ones in ages ranging from fourteen to eighteen. The traditional value placed upon education in Chinese culture and the limited facilities for higher education, which is the highroad to secure jobs, combine to make scholastic competition acute, with resulting heavy pressures on the children from teachers and parents. This enormous pressure applies particularly to children of middle- or upper-class families. With such backgrounds, *Tai-paus* tend to play truant in small groups from three to four to as many as ten in their "nests" centering in the modern amusement sections of the cities. Movies, billiards, ping-pong, cards, eating or smoking in cafés, or sports in the park are among their favorite activities. When the money for these pastimes is exhausted or when a junior member is compelled to please his group leader in terms of expenditures or goods, improper means of getting money by lying, pilfering, blackmailing, or occasional thefts are the outcome. Although proportionally small in number, a few girls are found associated with *Tai-pau* in their group activities and are called *Tai-mei*. Sexual irregularities occur on occasion, but serious sex offenses are rare among them. Assaults of varying degrees of severity, but mostly minor, are another problem among *Tai-paus*. Such incidents of assault are frequently caused by intragroup conflicts or quarrels with non-*Tai-pau* students. Most of the serious assaults result from rivalries between different groups. The members are expected to follow the code of the group, as it has been determined by mutual agreement. Loyalty to the group is emphasized, and toughness becomes a virtue, the toughest boy usually being the leader. Thus, in forming a group, *Tai-paus* test the toughness of members as well as the leader by taking advantage of non-*Tai-pau* students, by teasing adults, or by fighting with other groups of *Tai-paus*. They defy policemen by disregarding laws and regulations. Practical jokes, sarcastic remarks, driving, dancing, stealing without being caught are all marks of cleverness. Conflicts between groups or with local police are the main cause for frequent change of "nests" or hangouts, and also account for the change in leadership. Such change of hangouts, membership, and leaders makes the cohesion of each group loose and transient, and the loyalty factor is weakened despite a strong insistence upon it. It is not uncommon for one group of *Tai-paus* to change its "nest" once in three months or to have its membership almost totally replaced by a new one every six months.

GROUP LOYALTY OF LIU-MANG

The majority of *Liu-mangs* are residents of the old sections of cities and small towns, and mostly from poor or lower-class families. Their education is seldom beyond the primary level and ages range from ten or twelve to twenty or more. While many of them are engaged in various odd jobs as unskilled workers (bicycle mechanics, shoeshine boys, shop attendants, candy vendors, etc.), a good number of them are unemployed. They are frequently seen chatting, playing Chinese chess, or gambling in groups of various sizes in or around the market places or temples at any hour of the day or night. The most organized public activities of the *Liu-mangs* are ceremonial occasions during temple festivals in the neighborhoods where they live. At such times, they take pride in helping elders plan, organize, and participate in temple activities. They collect contributions for the temple, sell *Chu-fu* (amulets used for individual or family protection against such evils as disease) and perform in dragon dances, as their favorite volunteer tasks. Each group, therefore, has a more or less close affiliation with a temple, and sometimes several small groups have a common affiliation with one. Thus, these small groups form a larger group. Loyalty, regardless of group size, stands above everything, with discipline often very strict and ranging from beating to lynching or ostracism. The practice of *Hsueh-ming* (blood-bond) is a good example of determined faithfulness. It consists of an oath in front of the temple god, taken by sipping the blood of a cock, whereupon the members swear eternal loyalty to the point of death. These boys call each other "*Chi-pai* brothers." They also decide the order or relative position of each member in the group, and this is henceforth strictly observed. While intergroup rivalry and conflicts exist at all levels, the members readily obey the judgment of the ordained leader in the hierarchy. Leaders are really professional *Liu-mangs*, having a strong voice in communal affairs through their connections with temples and community elders. They also have a strong grip on the economic affairs of the district through subordinate *Liu-mangs* who act as agents particularly in illegal activities, such as prostitution, gambling, or trade in stolen goods. Even black-marketing and narcotic peddling come into their purview. These leaders of *Liu-mangs* are frequently criminals of long standing with a person or a small group of people over them who, in turn, have the controlling power over *Liu-mangs* of a wider area. Power is exercised when there is serious inter-group conflict or trouble with authorities. Subordinate *Liu-mangs* are dutiful in relations to leaders and in observing their orders. They maintain the moral code of peers, while maintaining their own living through legal and illegal means.

ATTITUDE TOWARD THE COMMUNITY AND RELATIONSHIP WITH ADULT CRIMINALS

The behavior of *Tai-pau*, expressed by disregard of authority, contempt for traditional life-patterns, and imitation of Western forms of vulgarity cause concern and shame to parents and teachers more than they constitute a problem to the police. Only occasionally do involvements occur with legal authorities. Rather, the *Tai-pau* seem to be of moral concern to the community. Some adults even think them "cute kids." Their group activities create little real effects on the larger community except for this disturbing psychological impact. The relationship of *Liu-mang* to the community is of a different nature.

Liu-mang follow traditional patterns of life, and their group structure is intimately connected with that of the community. Their respect for or cooperation with community affairs, such as festivals, strengthens this tie. Furthermore, their lawful and illegal activities as a group contribute something to family and community in terms of economic gain. In the old days, they offered a kind of protection against outsiders. Their contempt for Western or "modern" life is expressed by their preference for native costume, their hostility against Western religious practices, and their dislike of Western music. As conservatives or traditionalists, they are often hailed by the elders. But the illegal activities committed by them in connection with prostitution, gambling, narcotic trade, or the crimes of assault (mostly related to rivalries, money, and women) make them despised and feared by people who are not in any way related. *Liu-mang* leaders with long criminal records are under constant surveillance by the authorities.

Table 10–1 summarizes the differences between the groups in terms of sociocultural background and group behavior and organization:

TABLE 10-1

Sociocultural Background	Liu-mang	Tai-pau
Historical	Traditional	New
Geographical	Old sections in cities and small towns	Modern theatre and amusement centers in big cities
Age	Wider range from 10 or 12 to early adult; high concentration in 14 to 18 age group	Predominantly between 14 to 18 years
Living	Residents of same district	Of same or differing districts
Educational	Not beyond primary level	Middle School and the unsuccessful student
Occupational	Unemployed or taking odd jobs to earn a living	Not working; many still in school
Social class	Lower and lower-middle	Middle and upper
Group Behavior		
Appearance	Indistinguishable from traditional dress	Student style with frequent western emphasis, i.e., blue jeans, aloha shirts, etc.
Participation in community affairs	Interest in temple and festival activities	No interest in traditional affairs
Favorite activities	Native games, drinking, gambling	Modern recreation: cars, movies, dances, etc.
Antisocial behavior	More organized, persistent and skillful	Sporadic, playful
Variability	Less variable, behavior transmitted to next generation	Variable with outside circumstances
Organization		
Size	Large: range from 10 or 20 to 100, infrequently over 100	Small: 3 or 4 up to 10
Membership	Boys only: stable membership	Both boys and girls: rapid turnover
Structure	Highly structured for long periods	Vaguely defined and of short duration
Loyalty	Absolute loyalty	Loyalty relative in time and degree
Group discipline	Severe: beating, ostracism	Less severe
Community relations	Infiltration into community affairs	Isolated

INTERACTION BETWEEN THE TWO GROUPS

Owing to separate geographical distribution and differences in favorite activities, the majority of the members of both groups have few contacts with each other. To *Liu-mangs*, the *Tai-paus* represent "play-boys," "leisure seekers," and "odd characters." The *Tai-paus* look upon the *Liu-mangs* as a potential threat, as people whom they should placate or else avoid. But quite often the *Tai-paus* have certain feelings of superiority because of the *Liu-mang's* ignorance of "modern" life and recreation.

COEXISTENCE OF THE TWO GROUPS

Whenever the two groups meet, either in person or in terms of interest and benefit, they show intense reactions to each other. They may become cooperative and comradely when forced to form a common front against a third party, or when they find it beneficial in pursuing some concrete objectives. When the situation calling for cooperation is over, however, the two groups separate again as before. If occasions calling for cooperation occur frequently between a group of *Liu-mang* and of *Tai-pau*, rather more permanent relationships may be established between them. In this case, the *Tai-pau* usually become an affiliate subgroup of *Liu-mang* or else they dissolve their own group and join *Liu-mangs* openly. The reverse of this process of regrouping rarely occurs.

COMPETITIVE RELATIONSHIP

The *Liu-mang* and *Tai-pau* can also be highly competitive in their relationships, without becoming openly antagonistic. One finds this type of relationship between the two groups when they engage in competitive operations. For example, they may compete in the amount of goods they can steal (as evidence of their smartness and toughness). This kind of relationship is usually noted between *Tai-paus* and junior members of *Liu-mang* only, the senior members of *Liu-mang* being rarely involved. It should also be added that this competitive relationship is usually transient in most cases.

ANTAGONISTIC RELATIONSHIP

The most frequently observed relationship, one of considerable social significance, is that of antagonism between two groups. Quite often such conflict starts from a trifling argument or accidental neglect. Even the slightest misunderstanding of members of two groups may be involved. But the outcome is serious group fighting, violence, assault or the development of feuds and revenge. The outcome of such conflicts may be one of the following: *a*) the defeat and dissolution of a *Tai-pau* group; *b*) the defeat of *Tai-pau* and their assimilation by *Liu-mang*; or *c*) the defeat of *Tai-pau*, who call for help from another group of *Liu-mang* with ensuing conflicts between the two *Liu-mang* groups. Of the three developments, the last one, although rare, is obviously the most grave.

The greater strength of *Liu-mang* groups when compared with *Tai-pau* is quite obvious. While the latter are constantly under threat of being dissolved or assimilated by the former, the *Liu-mang* is not only self-perpetuating, but increases by absorbing the *Tai-pau*. It should be added that not all *Tai-paus* belonging to a group which has been defeated are absorbed by *Liu-mangs*. Only a small fraction of *Tai-paus*, mostly leaders or those with long histories, become *Liu-mangs*. The rest find it too "different" or threatening to become *Liu-mangs*. They either form another group of *Tai-pau* in emergencies or separate themselves entirely from their peers. The distinction between the two groups is often blurred because of the above-mentioned interaction, or transformation and assimilation of the groups. Furthermore, one sometimes finds that the *Liu-mang* gradually adopt some of the *Tai-pau's* behavior or come to enjoy similar pleasurable activities. Or, one may find that the *Tai-pau* comes to use the *Liu-mang's* own language. This blurring of distinctions, however, does not necessarily abolish the practical and categorical differentiation of the two groups.

SELECTED CASES

A CASE OF A LIU-MANG

L.H.L., a twenty-seven year old male and unskilled laborer. Born the oldest son of a family of six siblings, he was forced to leave school after third grade to help his father in such jobs as pulling a pedicar or selling icecream on the street. He was described as an intelligent, obedient, good-natured boy. He found the expected duties at home tedious and exhausting. His mother was preoccupied with care of the house and the six children, while his father worked day and night to earn their living. He was constantly given jobs at home, taking care of the youngsters, sweeping the floor, shopping, or watching the fire of the oven. At the age of ten to eleven, he began to seek outside pleasures in association with neighborhood boys. Their favorite pastimes were to play Chinese chess, watch the outdoor Chinese plays, or find things to eat. If any of the group had money, they went to the market place or to the temples and sought diversions. The festival season of the temple was their happiest or best time. By helping with odd jobs in the temple, they could get some money or food, and best of all, there was a respite from home or work. The association with the gang and the temple developed after his joining a band of dragon dancers. Since this membership represented privilege and honor to him, he devoted himself enthusiastically to the activities of the gang. He worked or helped his father at home more and more irregularly. Parents complained, cursed or occasionally beat him, but this did not deter him. At the age of sixteen, he became a member of *"Chi-pai Brothers."* His father made him accept a job as a grocery storekeeper, but he did not retain it for more than three months. His job was changed more than ten times in the next three years. During this period, he was more frequently seen in bars, gambling dens, and houses of prostitution. Once he was caught stealing a handbag in a theatre and was jailed for three months. His police record multiplied as he stole, fought, and blackmailed. From being a "constant" or steady member of a *Liu-mang* gang, he rose to being their leader. He joined in narcotic peddling and became an addict himself. Living by selling drugs, by contributions from his subordinates and by some shares in a house of prostitution, he was finally caught as an addict and sent for treatment. The following are some of his phrases about his life: ". . . Tough life at home . . . poor parents who had to work hard . . . unfair to work, while other children went to school and played . . . wonderful to have buddies who are like you. . . . The people in the temple were really nice; they gave us what we wanted most. They respected you. . . . What's wrong with stealing? The rich people are worse liars and thieves. . . . We did things to fool those policemen . . . Any organization in selling the drug? By no means, Doc, you think I should say yes? No, I did it all by myself. [Actually, he did not want to reveal the names of his cohorts.]. . . . Do you ask me what sort of job I like? Doc, you tell me the kind of job which will make me feel secure to hold on to. I don't know anything else I can do. I just ought to be smart enough not to be caught next time."

A Case of a Tai-pau

T.S.H., a twenty-two year old male, eldest son of a reputable banker. The father was interested in education and religion. The mother was a painter, busy with social activities. Family life was described as being religiously oriented and happy. Discipline was strict. The boy did well in primary school, but failed to win admission to the Middle School which his father chose for him. After enrolling in an inferior school, he started truancy and spent extravagantly during his third year. Besides the monthly stipend from his father, he secretly asked for and received a considerable amount of money from his mother in addition. His father called him and the other children, separately or together, to preach the necessity of studying to become a successful person. The importance of spiritual purity was also emphasized. He concealed poor marks at school, but was finally discovered and severely punished. As a discipline, he was allowed only to read moral stories, classic novels, and to hear such music. Jazz, movies (unless accompanied), and dancing were prohibited activities. In turn, he surreptitiously frequented amusement districts, smoked, and drank heavily. When this became known to his father, he was severely punished again, and the regulation of his activities became still more strict. A younger sister, his father's favorite, was applauded for her skill at school and in painting. This made him feel all the more unwanted. He stopped talking to his father, only answering briefly any questions put to him. This was followed by brief absences from the city for a few days at a time, during which he engaged in all the prohibited activities. Each occasion was followed by punishment and also by the payment of his fabulous expenses by the mother. He became well known to the *Tai-pau* group as a good dancer and a boon companion. He stole a few things from home, but never stole outside. He borrowed money from relatives or friends, and the debt was left for his mother to pay. His contact with any one group of *Tai-pau* seldom lasted longer than three months. When he had money in his pocket, he assumed temporary leadership in the group. He seldom fought alone and only occasionally as a member of the gang. On such occasions, he fought bravely, but often regretted his deeds afterward. He managed, or rather his father managed, to help him to graduate from Middle School, and he came to Taipei to study in a second-rate college. Not liking to study, he spent his time in pleasure-seeking. His phrases run as follows: "It would be nice if I could succeed in getting through the college as my dad wishes. . . . I know I should study hard and shouldn't play much. . . . I don't know why I joined these *Tai-pau*. Maybe I just wanted company. . . . Dad is always right, but so right, I suppose, that I can't follow him. . . . You know when a person can't do what one is supposed to, he gets angry at himself. . . . Occasionally I despise myself and also my dad. Maybe I shouldn't. I often felt guilty in hating my dad. . . . The best time I had was when I played with friends, forgetting all other things. . . . I never did anything illegal, so I am not afraid of the police. But I like to fool them. It's fun. I feel like fooling my dad also; for he is such a respectable man."

A CASE OF A TAI-PAU WHO BECAME A LIU-MANG

L.Y.P., twenty-five years old, born into the family of a wealthy merchant by a concubine. The family lived in an old section of the city. The boy was treated differently in many ways from the rest of the siblings, who were sons of the first wife. He did poorly at school, and consequently more pressure was put on him to get better marks. His leisure time was spent in playing games at home since he was not allowed to play outside with neighborhood boys. He managed to enter a Middle School of poor reputation. Truancy, smoking, and fighting immediately became attractive to him, and his father was much annoyed by his behavior. Restrictions were imposed on his daily life with little effect upon him. He became a leader of a *Tai-pau* group and was regarded a "smart, tough guy" by the gang. He took much pride in demonstrating his skill in stealing, defying authority, teasing girls, and promoting trouble. This and neighborhood proximity forced him and his group into serious conflict with local *Liu-mang*. After considerable hesitation, he joined the *Liu-mang* along with a couple of his *Tai-pau* friends. The *Tai-paus* remaining did not wish to follow him. Upon his entering the *Liu-mang* group, he was forced to dip his cigarette into "white powder" (heroin or morphine) before smoking.* This ritual, so he explained, was a test of his willingness to do "everything." He became addicted and consequently did "everything" the others did, gambling, frequenting

---

* This practice of dipping into "white powder" might have been an isolated incident that was peculiar only to the group to which this boy belonged. It is, however, probable that this practice, although not widespread, did exist in some other groups. The consumption of heroin in Formosa has been greatly reduced as a result of measures taken by the Government in recent years.

prostitutes, stealing, fighting, and drug-peddling. The following are excerpts from his statements about his own life: "Life at home? No fun at all! I feel sorry for my mother, though. She and I were always discriminated against. The only thing they care about is the 'reputation' or 'face,' not my personal needs or feelings. . . . Teachers at school are just like my father. They don't understand. They ask you things that are impossible. . . . The kids (*Tai-paus*) are cute. We had a lot of fun. They respect you when you are 'tough and smart.' Does anyone not want to be popular? . . . Why I joined the gang (*Liu-mang*)? Once you are a member you are theirs; you are 'safe.' They treat you better than anyone in my family, except for my mother. They *trust* you. . . . Do I want to go back home? Well, I don't think so. I may if they change their attitude and don't interfere with my business. . . . It would be a good thing to have a steady job. Is there any? . . . Marriage? Do you think that I will get settled and sit tight at home by marriage? It might be a good thing, but I doubt it. . . . Policemen? You ought to know how to deal with them. They can be very O.K. occasionally. If they found you too tough to deal with, they'll let you go; but when you go too far, then you'll have bad luck. . . . Are you asking whether or not I believe in fortune or destiny? Of course. Human life is gambling throughout. Don't you agree? A child has already gambled when he comes into the world. If he wins, he is born to nice parents with a nice home. If he loses, he is born into a poor family. Everything that follows thereafter cannot change the course too much. You call it destiny."

DISCUSSION

Common Features. With some differences, *Tai-pau* and *Liu-mang* have essential features in common. The demonstrative, hostile, and aggressive behavior, the formation of groups outside the family with strong emphasis on group autonomy, the conformity and loyalty, and the defiant attitude to authority figures—all these features are the common characteristics of adolescent behavior. We may call them adolescent subculture. In a majority of instances, they imply no deviancy. Rather, they are expressions of the psychological and social needs of adolescents in a process of maturation toward independence. They are nonpathological insofar as they remain within the limit of what is customarily expected of adolescent behavior in each culture. This norm or culturally accepted element in behavior is well-illustrated by the observation that *Tai-pau* are hailed as "cute kids" by some adults, and *Liu-mangs'* participation in communal affairs is regarded as "helpful" by the community elders. This applies particularly to the activities of new members or newly formed groups of either *Tai-pau* or *Liu-mang*. Insofar as they transgress the limits of customarily accepted adolescent cultural norms, however, their behavior may be described as delinquent. This delinquent element is an expression of the now-exaggerated antisocial and hostile reaction of adolescents in response to environmental stresses.

Ethnocentric and Ethnoeccentric Subcultures in Current Chinese Society. Although adolescence has its own unique behavior patterns, or adolescent subculture, the behavior of the individual adolescent is strongly influenced by his past experiences, in particular his relationship with parents. An adolescent still develops his own system of values, roles, attitudes, and conceptions of self through contacts with his parents or parental substitutes who function as the carriers of the culture. The difference in behavior between groups of *Tai-pau* and *Liu-mang* is in part due to the existence of differing subcultures in current Chinese society.

The traditional dichotomy in Chinese society as being composed of privileged scholars and underprivileged illiterates further enhances the difference in attitude of the two groups toward Western culture. The families of *Liu-mang* are uneducated. Therefore, they have little or only casual contact with modern Western culture. They regard Western culture and the people "equipped" with it as a threat to their existence, and before this they retreat and hold to that conventional way of life which has traditionally provided the means of existence. Thus, they have an *"ethnocentric" system of values* with little interest in change. They emphasize the traditional systems of interdependence in Chinese society, such as Tang—surname association—or affiliation with the temple organization.

Modern Western technology and culture can only be learned through education, and it is only the privileged classes in Chinese society who have had the opportunities of education and consequently most contacts with the West. The parents of *Tai-pau* belong to such a privileged class. They are representative of a subculture in which modern technology, management, and a Western way of life are highly valued. Thus, unlike the parents of *Liu-mang,* their system of values and their expectations for their children are what may be called *"ethnoeccentric,"* and emphasize "progressive change of society" and "personal achievement."

Difference in Group Dynamics. It may be seen then that the differences of behavior between *Tai-pau and Liu-mang* in appearance, participation in communal affairs, and favored activities reflect the transmitted subcultural differences of their families. *Tai-pau* are less rooted to the community because of their valued emphasis on change, while

Liu-mang adhere to conventional life and show little inclination to accept such changes. For *Tai-pau,* the peer group seems to provide some feeling of pride in demonstrating their privileged way of life as well as providing a means of escape from stress. For *Liu-mang,* the peer group acts more as a channel of security and protection against threat. One important way in which this difference of subcultural origin is displayed in the families of the two groups is in the attitude of the parents toward the adolescent. Parents of *Tai-pau* are themselves extremely anxious and insecure because of their own anomalous position in an ever-changing culture. The rapid changes of values and goals in their culture put them in a situation similar to first-generation immigrants. They, therefore, tend to develop compensatory and highly rigid attitudes toward moral standards involving higher expectations of achievement for their children. Similarly, the relationship of the children to these parents is that of second-generation immigrants. To their parents, when overly strict, the children react with revolt and disregard. This attitude aggravates a parental lack of tolerance toward behavior deviating from the expected norm. Thus, a vicious circles is begun which drives children to an escape into peer groups. Parents of *Liu-mang* expect little of their children except for the labor involved in earning a living. Deviant behavior of children causes but slight concern as long as no trouble occurs. This difference of parental attitude toward deviant behavior of adolescents may explain the fact that *Tai-pau* cause more trouble to their own families, with consequent feelings of guilt, while the *Liu-mangs'* antagonistic behavior is directed more against outsiders.

Relationship to Adult Delinquent Society. A difference in degree of intimacy and in duration of contacts with existing adult deviant groups in the community—a criminal subculture—also plays an important role in the difference of *Tai-pau* and *Liu-mang.* The outward behavior, including criminal activities, strong group cohesion, hierarchic structure, and intimate community relations of *Liu-mang,* all indicate similarities with adult deviant groups. The adult criminal may be regarded as a continuation of the adolescent deviant into adulthood. The behavior and structure of the adolescent group is influenced by the adult deviant group which indoctrinates adolescents into adult patterns of crime. The distinction between these two is one of degree. The relationship of *Tai-pau* to adult deviant subculture is casual and loose. Fewer *Tai-pau* become members of such groups. Any transition of this kind is drastic and qualitative. The majority of *Tai-pau* form independent small peer groupings, which are less integrated in the community.

Female Participation. The difference in female participation with peer activities between *Tai-pau* and *Liu-mang* can also be regarded as reflecting the differing subcultural attitude toward female status. Although small in number, a few girls (*Tai-mei*) mingle with *Tai-pau* groupings. These girls may even occupy powerful positions in such groups. Sexual irregularities among boys and girls which contradict the traditional moral code of middle class society are occasionally reported. But no girls participate in *Liu-mangs'* activities publicly, and *Liu-mangs* frequent the houses of prostitution or the bars. Prostitutes often become mistresses of *Liu-mang* leaders and later join the adult deviant groups. In other words, while more free and public participation of females is occasionally observed among *Tai-pau*, as is often the case in modern society, the traditional attitude of male dominance prevails among the *Liu-mang*.

Similar Observations in Other Cultures. Two types of youth peer groups in current Chinese society occur and should be regarded as differing reactions of adolescents to two existing subcultures introduced by modernization or contacts with Western culture. Each possesses characteristic features of its own matrix (subculture) in terms of behavior, attitude, and structure.

Similar phenomena were observed in Japan before the war where *Mobo* and *Moga* ("modern boys" and "modern girls," equivalent terms to *Tai-pau* and *Tai-mei*) were differentiated from *Yakuza* or *Yota*, the equivalent of *Liu-mang*. Whether or not these phenomena are universal in Eastern countries or in other countries where subcultural divisions exist is a question. If so, one may term such groups as *Tai-pau*, the "modern Westernized" or "uprooted peer." The same sense of transiency applies to the matrix-subculture to which this group belongs. The situation in Japan has radically changed after World War II. The recent epidemic of menacing delinquent adolescents, called *"Taiyozoku,"* * signifies the existence of a seriously uprooted subculture or cultural segment.

One may even go a step further in viewing the relative number and

---

* *"Taiyozoku"* translates as "sun race," originally the name of a group of adolescents in a novel which was feverishly welcomed by youth when the epidemic of *Taiyozoku*-like peer behavior started.

strength of two peer groups, as reflecting the relationship of "modern" and "traditional" subcultures in a given society. The recent and rapid increase of *Tai-pau* in Taiwan may be regarded as a sign of the growing "modern" and "uprooted" subculture, due mainly to postwar urbanization and modernization. The relative persistence and dominance of *Liu-mang*, however, seem to indicate the existence of a still strong traditional culture at the base.

Morris E. Opler

Department of Sociology and Anthropology
Cornell University

11

FAMILY, ANXIETY, AND RELIGION
IN A COMMUNITY OF NORTH INDIA

Every study of Indian life and thought conveys a sense of the central importance of the family in the social system and the richness and variety of religious life, with its pantheon of gods and goddesses, its shrines and temples, and its ritual occasions. Any functional view of culture will anticipate some relationship and interpenetration between two such important aspects of the total round of life and some evidence of the impress of one of these facets of culture on the other. But this is a matter to be studied rather than assumed. Wider formulations about the nature of culture and the structure of religion may rest upon closer examination of these particulars. As an example of the kind of data useful in this connection, we present material from Senapur, a village in north central India intensively studied by Cornell University social scientists for the last decade. Senapur has a family and religious system fairly typical of the region. A review of the material suggests that the very importance of the family makes it a stronghold to defend. Anxieties relating to the perpetuation, stability, status, and prosperity of the family guide much of the ritual activity. In fact, a large part of the religious system is an elaborate apparatus for putting family members and family interests under the protection of benign supernaturals, and for defending the family from unfriendly supernatural attacks. Such ceremonies obviously assuage anxiety throughout a given calendrical year.

If one wishes to review the place which the family plays in religious matters in India, there are obvious directions in which to look. There are the life cycle ceremonies or rites of passage, the *sanskara* which mark the development of the individuals from birth to death and bring the members of the family together in pride, celebration, or sorrow. These

273

are rituals arranged by the family and largely attended by members of the family, though friends, well-wishers, and retainers of the family may also be present. Many of the ritual acts of these life-cycle ceremonies must be performed by specific family members or relatives on behalf of the central figure.

Again, if one looks over the information on religious *vrats* or vows, one is impressed by the high percentage of them which are stimulated by anxieties over the welfare of the family or its members. Fasts and vows to make offerings to a deity, to have a ceremony performed, and so on, are undertaken repeatedly to ensure the birth of a son in the family, to restore a sick family member to health, or to guarantee the success of some family venture. Visits to temples and shrines are likewise frequently associated with some crisis in the affairs or well-being of the family or one of its members.

Still another index of the solidarity and importance of the Indian family in religious matters is the place of tutelary deities. Even though a given individual may take the initiative in propitiating or communicating with the guardian spirit, the deity is considered to be attached to his family and may remain "in the family" for generations. Evil spirits and ghosts are considered to be attacking families and lines, rather than the individual who is suffering at the moment. The persecution of a family member by a ghost is a matter of grave concern and potential danger to those of this social unit.

The types of religious experience and activity mentioned to this point are those in which family interests and concerns might be expected to loom large. By examining the calendrical and seasonal rites, spread out in time and celebrated by the whole community, additional insight is gained. These are not the exclusive business of an individual or family group, and are often the vehicles through which societies express their major anxieties, religious purposes and attitudes.

The calendrical and agricultural rites of Senapur are determined by a lunar calendar. The lunar month is approximately 29½ days long; the twelve months of the lunar year add up to 354 days, 8 hours, and 48 minutes. In order to adjust to the solar or zodiacal year, an intercalary month is added about once in 33 months. Consequently, a date of this Hindu calendar will fall on different days of the Western (Gregorian) calendar in successive years. The range of fluctuation may be as great as two weeks in either direction. Thus any Western calendar date given for any Senapur rite is only approximate. *Cait*, which begins in about mid-March of the Western calendar, is the first month of the year as the Senapur villagers reckon it. The pertinent ceremonies will be introduced as they appear during the year from this point.

Before discussing family interests and participation in religious activities, it may be mentioned that the very failure on the part of some to observe calendrical or village-wide rites is frequently an evidence of family feeling. When a member of a family dies on the day of a calendrical rite, the bereaved family ceases to participate in the rite so long as the parents or children of the deceased are alive. Should a child be born to this family on this same day, however, the ban is lifted. It should be understood too, that only those calendrical or seasonal agricultural rites in which the interests or protection of the family, family members, and family property are central or important will be considered here. Both the nuclear family, consisting of parents and unmarried children, and the joint family, consisting of a married couple, their unmarried children, the married sons, and the spouses and children of these sons, are found in Senapur, although the joint family with its variants is the ideal and idealized type.

The first nine days of the year, beginning toward the end of March of the Western calendar, is a period when ghosts and spirits, propitious and unpropitious, are active. Most women and some men fast, at least on the first and ninth days of the period, make offerings to *Bhagavati Mai*, the Mother Goddess who controls disease, and pray to her to protect their families from sickness. If an ancestor or member has vowed to do so, a more elaborate ceremony is conducted on the ninth day by a family (*Chotka Basiaura*). This ceremony is much like *Barka Basiaura*, which is observed generally a fortnight later.*

Barka Basiaura occurs in early April when the hot, dry, dusty season, often marked by epidemic sickness, is at hand. *Sitala Mai*, the goddess of pustular disorders, visits homes on this day, and all must be made cool and clean to greet her so that she will leave with a kindly feeling toward the occupants and grant them immunity and health for the coming year. The house is plastered, the walls whitewashed, the drains are cleaned, and old earthenware pots are replaced by new. There is no cooking in the home but "cooling" food is prepared outside in advance. A family representative, usually the oldest woman, keeps a total fast.

* For a full account of these rituals see: Jack Planalp, *Religious Life and Values in a North Indian Village*. Ithaca: Ph.D. Thesis, Cornell University, 1956, unpublished. Pages 248–382 of this thesis deal with the calendrical rites.

A new, much-decorated pottery jar is installed in the kitchen with considerable ritual. From it are hung small silver figurines representing male members of the family. The women remain awake all night and before sunup conduct a series of ceremonies successively farther from the kitchen and house. These are intended to lead *Sitala Mai* out of the home and pleasantly on her way. Then the ceremonial jar is put in a safe place and every attempt is made to keep it intact during the next year. During the day following this all-night ritual no food is cooked; the family dines on food the women have previously prepared.

At about mid-April, on a day selected by the family for planting sugarcane in its fields, relatives and friends arrive to assist in this enterprise. The house is again freshly plastered and a vessel of water is placed in a corner, with a pestle upright in it so that the cane will grow as straight as the pestle and be full of juice, as the jar is with liquid. There are a number of other ritual acts and restrictions marking the occasion. Certain foods must not be cooked or given away on this day. Women are not allowed to assist in the field at this time nor are members of the oil-presser caste permitted there. No footgear may be worn in the field. During the work one man calls out the name of some god and the others repeat it in unison. The obvious purpose of this ritual activity and these practices (*Ukh Bhoj*) is to bless and safeguard the sugarcane fields of the particular family.

By the time of *Asarhi Jog,* a religious festival which occurs in mid-July, the monsoon rains have flooded the fields and lanes. This is the period of danger from snakes, centipedes, and scorpions. Consequently, *Asarhi Jog* is a rite of propitiation of snakes and an attempt to clear the home and fields of a family of reptiles. The house is swept clean and the floor of every room is strewn with appropriate offerings. The family head makes an offering in a field of the family near a hole thought to be that of a snake. In addition, a protective line of cow dung is made around the outside of the house. This protects against snakes particularly, but it is believed that any other dangerous animal, or even a thief, will meet death if he crosses it.

Pachaiya or *Nag Pancami* (literally "snake fifth") falls in early August when the rainy season is at its height, and again the purpose is to propitiate *Nag Baba,* or snake, and protect the house from his anger. In the morning, the women of the household sprinkle milk and parched rice in a circle around the outside of the house as an offering and protection. Cattle are decorated and given "medicine" on this day, but no ploughing is done lest snakes are molested or angered. The men spend much of the day in wrestling and other athletic endeavors.

Cauth or "*Kajali Day*" falls about mid-August. Women who have sons fast the whole day; unmarried girls fast until noon. The women go together to bathe at a tank, singing *Kajali* songs (songs with romantic motifs, sung only in the rainy season). They take barley seedlings which they planted on *Nag Pancami* and wash these. Upon their return, they tie a barley seedling to a tuft of hair at the back of the head of each male in the family. In the afternoon, the women gather at one another's homes to sing songs about romance or episodes from epics. Many of the songs deal with situations of great emotional force in family relations, such as the grief of Rama's mother when he was sent into banishment. The ritual activities of the women on this day are obviously meant to protect and bless the male members of their families.

Tij, which is celebrated about the first of September, is an occasion on which *Parvati*, the consort of *Shiva*, is worshipped. The purpose of the rite is to honor and bless the husband and perpetuate the married state. Wives and also unmarried girls who have already reached puberty observe a total fast, even from water. If, because of sickness or for some other reason, a woman cannot fast on *Tij*, she may not celebrate this ritual for the rest of her life. In the morning, the married women go to a tank to bathe. On the way they sing *kajali* songs. They sing one song in which each woman utters the given name of her husband. This is the only occasion a woman ever does this. Much teasing, laughter, and high spirits accompany the act. At the bathing place the women do a stylized dance.

Lalahi Chath, a ritual dedicated to *Lalahi Mai* or *Shashthi Devi*, occurs on the sixth day of the light half of *Bhadon* (early September) and the number six runs through many of the observances. The goddess honored is the one who is concerned with the affairs of married women and children and who grants and protects sons. Consequently, this is a festival conducted by women for the long life of their sons. Only women with sons participate. One woman of each family accepts special obligations. She fasts and collects wild rice, curds made from buffalo milk, a wild water grass used as a vegetable (*karemus*), and *mahua* (*Bassia latefolia*) flowers. If there has been a marriage or birth of a son in her family during the past year, she puts most of the food in six small, unbaked earthen pots. Over the pots are placed two pieces of fried bread. Some of the food, mixed together, is also placed on a metal tray. In families in which no marriage nor birth has occurred during the year, the food offerings are placed on leaf plates instead of in pots and the fried bread is omitted.

A protective circle of buffalo dung, large enough to permit all the women to sit inside, is plastered by some of the women near a tank early in the morning. In the center a moundlike figure of *Lalahi Mai* is shaped. At about mid-morning the women leave their homes and walk toward the bathing place. They carefully avoid stepping in the plowed fields as they go to and from the tank. To do this, even unintentionally, is inauspicious, and a woman to whom this has happened will never observe *Lalahi Chath* again. At the tank the fasting women bathe and then gather in the circle. Some blades of a sacred grass have been brought and these are fixed in the mound representing the goddess. Then the principal representative of each family tries to tie a knot in a blade of the sacred grass, using only the thumb and little finger of the right hand. This act, successfully performed, is thought to add to the length of life of the sons of the family. Each woman now makes two marks with vermilion on the receptacles containing the food offerings. Then she marks the mound representing the goddess six times and places branches of the *palas* tree (*Butea frondosa*) there. Now one woman tells six stories to her companions. At the end of each story the family representatives offer the goddess food from their trays. The tales, appropriately, recount how death or some disaster threatening a son was averted by meticulous observance of *Lalahi Chath*. Next the women eat foods they have brought and drink some water of the tank. They return home in procession, singing the type of song sung at the birth of a son. Some of the consecrated food which they have brought back is distributed to family members. The remainder is placed around the home. Some is placed in the grain-storage room and in the cattle troughs. The women who have fasted again eat wild rice and curds to break the fast. They may not drink milk or eat sugar on this day. The emphasis on curds from buffalo milk is noticeable in another connection. Anyone who comes to a house in the morning to request curds to offer in the ceremony should not be turned away. This custom has constituted a heavy drain on the caste that sells milk products. Using wild rice and uncultivated plants instead of rice and the more usual vegetable offerings, and curd from buffalo milk instead of products of the cow suggests that in this ceremony the deities of the forests and the wilds are being rallied to the protection of the sons. The care with which the women avoid cultivated fields at this time points in the same direction. There is evidence that in Bengal as well *Shashthi Devi* is associated with the forest and that women walk in the woods on this day (1).

Jiutia, the name of a rite in the latter part of September, is also the name of a necklace preserved by the female head of each family. It consists of small, elongated gold or silver beads strung on red and yellow cotton strings, one bead for each male member of the family. Formerly some of the elderly women wore the necklace at all times. The name of the festival and necklace is connected with the word for life (*jiu*) and on this occasion *Jiut Baba,* a personification of life itself, is honored and specially blesses males, particularly sons of the family. A woman begins to observe *Jiutia* only after she has borne a son, unless she wishes to do so in hopes that a son may come. When a woman observes *Jiutia* for the first time, she keeps her decision and fast a secret from all except the women of her family. She does not go with the other women to bathe, but bathes by herself in the cattle shed. It is not until the following year that she goes with the other women to bathe and worship.

About two hours before sunset the women start toward a bathing place, each carrying a number of items on a brass tray. One of these objects is an *areca* nut which is kept in a special place in the house year after year for this occasion. There is an unusual air of freedom during the journey. The women banter with men they meet on the way. A band of musicians may even head the procession. Women who are fasting and who will bathe wear old clothing; others wear new, brightly colored saris.

When they reach the bathing place, a woman of the water-carrier caste makes a large plastered circle of cow dung. She then molds a mound of cow dung to represent *Jiut Baba.* A Brahman marks the cow-dung image with vermilion and arranges sticks of wood around it. A woman of each family steps inside, faces south, and makes offerings. An oil cake is offered to kite and another to jackal. Now the fasting women rub oil cake in their hair, bathe, and brush their teeth with the twigs of a plant not ordinarily used for this purpose. During the bathing, they offer water to the "old ones," the ancestors, and dip under the waters five times. The atmosphere continues to be a relaxed one with much laughing and joking.

After bathing, the women gather around the sacred circle. The Brahman sets fire to the wood covering the cow-dung image. The women pour water in a circle around the outside of the fire. Then they throw branches on the fire. No one wishes to take the lead in this; each encourages the other to start until someone becomes impatient and begins. Once the wood is blazing, the women hold their brass trays over the image and hold their hands in prayer over the flames. Some hold their baby sons over the fire for a moment. The women now sit in concentric circles around the fire and throw rice and cotton seeds into it. The Brahman tells them stories appropriate to the occasion. Older women may act as raconteurs too. The Brahman walks among the women with a brass tumbler of water and each woman drops a coin of small denomination into it. The Brahman also collects clarified butter from the women and pours it on the image while he recites sacred texts. During these events, the women are careful not to touch one another, and any violation of this evokes resentment even if it happens unintentionally. Women who are without sons try to steal the *jiutia* of others and need not return it if they are successful. Therefore, no woman leaves her *jiutia* unattended when she goes to bathe. It is customary that men come to the general vicinity and play a traditional game (*baddi*) involving running, holding the breath, and touching and tackling members of the other side.

At sunset the women are ready for the return journey. Each lights a small earthen lamp and tries to bring it to her home still lit. It is considered a bad omen if the lamp goes out. She strews rice, a cooked grain preparation, and colored cotton seeds along the path. As she walks she carries on an imaginary conversation between two persons, one of whom is ordering the other to tell God that the mother of this son has kept a very strict fast on *Jiutia* and that the son should therefore be protected and blessed. Throughout the night the women prepare foods considered particularly palatable to their sex. At dawn they break their fast by swallowing five grains of a soaked grain preparation. Then those who have fasted offer food to the female ancestors of the house. After that all the family members partake of the food. As the final acts of the ritual suggest, *Jiutia* falls within the half-month period when ancestors are especially worshipped, and *Jiutia* is the day when the female ancestors are particularly remembered.

The worship of the female ancestors ends on this ninth day of *Pitri Paksh* or "Ancestral Spirits' Fortnight." But the worship of the male ancestors continues for the entire period, and the last day, called *Pitri Visarjan*, "allowing the manes to depart," is of special importance. During *Pitri Paksh* a man whose father is dead does not shave, apply oil to his hair, send clothes to the washerman, or indulge in sexual intercourse.

Further, he does not eat meat or fried foods, he takes a bath in the early morning rather than at noon, and at bathing time he offers five handfuls of water to his father's spirit, saying, "Father, take this to drink." A pinch of food of each kind may be set aside from the noon meal on each of the fifteen days, and the oldest woman in the family carries this to a *pipal* tree and places it there as an offering. On the fifteenth day, the women cook special food and place it in leaf cups, one for each male ancestor. A male of the family takes these containers to a field and offers them along with water to spirits of dead males of the family. To sever finally the spirits of dead ancestors requires an elaborate ceremony at a famous temple at Gaya, in Bihar State.

Toward the end of October there are four consecutive ritual days, two preceding the well-known festival of lights, *Divali,* and one following it. The first of these is *Dhan Teras,* literally "wealth thirteenth." It comes toward the end of October after several months of rain. The day is associated with housecleaning and plastering. New utensils are purchased and a supply of candy is obtained to be eaten on *Divali.* The next day is *Narak Caudash,* "hell fourteenth." On this day the old lamps are thrown out and a new lamp, fresh from the family potter, is put on the manure pile. The new lamps are thought to help the souls of the dead find their way to heaven.

Divali, which follows, is associated in Senapur with the lighting of the city of Ayodhya to welcome back the divine hero Rama and his wife Sita. The day is also associated with Lakshmi, the goddess of wealth, and is the beginning of the business and work year. As a gesture, a little of one's customary work is done on this day. Craftsmen try to produce the best possible examples of their trade and customers eagerly try to acquire whatever is made on *Divali.* The lighting of the small earthen lamps begins at seven or eight o'clock in the evening. The first one is lit in the courtyard of women of the household who then bow to it. The others are lit from this one and placed on all objects associated with the well-being of the family. There is a tradition for staying awake and gambling on this night, although these practices are mostly honored in a token manner now. They symbolically represent industry and watchfulness over accumulated wealth and the speedy acquisition of wealth. Those who do not stay up all night are awakened early, about four o'clock in the morning, by someone going through the house beating on a winnowing tray and calling loudly for the Goddess of Poverty to leave the home and for a God or Goddess of Wealth to enter. The next day, children, particularly

those of shopkeepers, make toy balances from the little earthen lamps
that have been lit on the night of *Divali.*

The day after *Divali* is *Godhana.* Married girls of the village home
on visits and the resident unmarried girls combine to carry out the ritual.
The girls who plan to participate fast and gather to prepare a ceremonial
square which they outline in sausage-shaped pieces of cow dung called
piria. Facing east within the square are placed two such objects. The one
on the north is decorated as a woman and is called *Godhani.* The one on
the south, representing a male, is called *Godhana Baba.* Within the square
are to be found a pond, a miniature boat and boatman, and other miniature molded objects, such as a grinding mill, mano, metate, mortar, pestle,
lingam, centipede, scorpion, and cobra. The girls bathe, dress in fresh
clothes, and gather at the ceremonial square before noon. Each girl brings
objects she will need on a brass tray. The molded images are bathed in
milk, offerings are made, and a lamp is moved over them in prayer. Then
each girl pricks her tongue with a thorn and says, "I will eat my brother,
my uncle, my father, my grandfather." It is believed that the lives of these
relatives, and especially of the brother, who is named first, will be length-
ened by this ritual. From fluffy cotton the girls make garlands for the
images. This part of the ritual is called "adding years to life." At this
point older women tell stories of affection between brother and sister.
Young married women who cannot attend often send trays by others. On
their trays they include earrings to symbolize the hearing of the stories.
After the storytelling is concluded, an areca nut is broken with a pestle.
The pestle is next used to smash the figures of the centipede, scorpion,
and cobra. Then each girl vaults over the square with the aid of the
pestle, which is put at the "stomach" of *Godhana Baba.* Each girl next
tries to tie knots in a sacred grass, using only the thumb and little finger
of the right hand. To accomplish this means long life for the one in mind
during the act.

At about 1:00 P. M., the girls bathe at a tank. There they repeat, "I
will eat my brother, etc." On their return, they give little sugar cups,
pieces of areca nut, gram, and rice to their brothers and to older male
family members. In exchange, they receive money or clothes. When a
girl and her brother are living in different places, she sends presents and
he will send gifts to her. The girls break their fast with curds and coarse
brown sugar. Later they eat other special foods. In the evening they
gather at a shed or enclosure where strips of dung from the sacred
square have been placed. Stories are told and devotional songs are sung.

For a month the girls gather here in the evening to listen to different stories.

Deva Uthan Ekadasi, which falls about November ninth, is associated in many parts of India with the awakening of the gods, and especially *Vishnu,* from a four-month sleep. But in Senapur it is associated with the cane crop and is also called *Nevan* or "new grain." At dusk a ritual representative of the family goes to the field. He takes with him smoldering cow dung, water, brown sugar, and clarified butter. Since they know there is the likelihood of getting fresh sugar cane to chew, the children follow him. The family representative makes a fire offering to *Mahabir* or *Hanuman.* He prays to Snake that the crop be abundant. Then stalks of sugar cane are cut. Five stalks are taken back and offered to the image of *Hanuman* in the home. A single stalk is saved for the fire that will be kindled at the time of the *Holi* festival. Some of the stalks are saved for the Brahman who serves as family priest.

Hariyari (from *hariar,* "green"), the personification of the crops, is honored on a Monday or Friday during the dark half of *Agahan.* Thus it usually falls during the latter half of November. At this time, seed grain saved from the planting of the winter crops is offered Mother Earth. Women grind the grain and make fried bread. Special foods which appeal to women are prepared. A woman who will represent the family goes to a field of the family and brings back five sprigs of a certain weed. On her return she places them, seven pieces of fried bread, and some of the special food on a brass tray. She kindles a small ritual fire and scatters clarified butter, incense, and coarse brown sugar on it. She pours water on the ground as a libation, bows five times, and prays, "Oh, Mother *Hariyari,* I am worshipping you so that there will be a good crop and all members of the family will be healthy." She may pray to *Dharati Mai,* "Earth Mother," or *Bhagavati Mai* in the same way also. In some cases, a male family member takes a plate of offerings to the deities in the field already mentioned or to *Khet Maharaj,* "Great King Field." The food that has been offered in worship is mixed with the rest of the food that has been prepared for this occasion and is fed to the family at the noon meal. At this time, a green plant may be put at the seating place of each male. By sprinkling water on it before he eats, each man makes an offering to *Hariyari.*

Piria marks the conclusion of observances that were initiated by the girls a month before on *Godhana* day. Again the girls gather to listen to stories and sing devotional songs. They fast throughout the next day. In the morning, they remove the strips of cow dung that were placed on the wall at *Godhana* and put them in a small pottery jar. They whitewash and decorate the room the way a special room is readied at the time of marriage. Each girl prepares thirty-two balls of rice paste with a kernel of corn in the middle. These they call *piria*, too, using the same term applied to the strips of dung. Just before dark the girls sing *en route* to a bathing place. Later, they return to the decorated room. The married girls daub vermilion dots on the wall, the unmarried girls use clarified butter. After that each girl takes a bit from each of the rice balls she prepared, molds these into two small balls, and swallows them with all the water she can drink on one breath. It is a good omen if she hears no noise while doing this. Now the girls may break their fast. Later they gather again to sing, tell stories and dance throughout the night. At daybreak, they go to the tank once more. They float *pirias* of rice and dung on the water, bathe, and return. During the day, the girls eat and share the remaining rice *pirias* with family and hereditary family servants. Like *Godhana, Piria* is observed to protect the brothers of the girls who participate.

The ceremony which is ordinarily called *Khicari* in Senapur is more generally known in India as *Makar Sankrant*. It celebrates the winter solstice. Sometimes it occurs in the month of *Pus* and sometimes in *Magh*, for it is variable within the lunar calendar (occurring on January fourteenth of our solar calendar). *Pus* is considered an inauspicious month, and when it occurs in *Pus*, it is the only set ceremony that does take place in that month.

On *Khicari* everyone is required to take an early bath. Even the sick or menstruating women do so symbolically by sprinkling a few drops of water on themselves. After bathing, each person touches a jar of uncooked rice and pulses. Some of its contents is given to the family priest and some is cooked as *khicari*, for *khicari*, which names the ritual activities, is actually a mixture of cooked rice and pulses. After bathing, some women make offerings to the sun and fire with sesame seeds mixed with brown sugar. In some families, sesamum is offered to the ancestors at this time also. Everyone dresses in clean clothes after the ritual bath.

Khicari is the most important time to send gifts to married daughters and sisters. A servant or family member takes clothes and candy to the women. Presents are timed to arrive just before or after *Khicari* rather than on the very day. Hereditary servants of the family and tenants pay their respects and receive food. The family priest arrives with new sacred threads for the males of the family and is generously remembered. Members of other castes bring token goods and receive food. There is an elaborate exchange of food by related or friendly families. During the day, parched grains and candy are distributed. In the evening, cooked pulses and rice are offered. During the afternoon, the young men play games in or near the village grove. *Khicari* is essentially a day when families remember those who have left the fold and asserts ties with those who are part of a network of social and economic relations.

Magh Cauth or "*Magh* fourth," as the name suggests, is observed on the fourth day of the dark half of the month of *Magh*. This would be about mid-January in the Western calendar. The fourth day of the Indian lunar calendar is associated with *Ganesh*, the elephant-headed god and son of *Shiva*, and on this day *Ganesh* is invoked on behalf of a son of a family. There is an association in Hindu religious thought between *Ganesh* and Moon, and so prayers to Moon occur at this time also. The full rite is observed by families in which a son has been born or married within the year. If there is no newly born or newly married son, the women of the household merely fast and pray.

When the family enters fully into the rite, the boy's mother and other women of the household fast. In the evening, the young woman who is taking main responsibility for the ritual activities (the *pujakarti* or "holder of the ceremony"), usually the mother, purifies a place on the courtyard floor with cow-dung paste, makes a design with rice flour, and molds an effigy of a lamb out of coarse brown sugar. The effigy is placed on a brass tray at the purified spot. When the moon is rising, the lamb is "sacrificed" by decapitation with a knife. Some families ask a Brahman to do this, but the more usual thing is to have the father's younger brother act in this capacity. The head is lifted up and offered to *Ganesh* with a prayer that the sons of the family be protected. Then the father's brother runs out of the house with the head. The "body" is left on the tray over night and is distributed the next morning to family members and friends as sanctified food (*prasad*).

After the sacrifice, the women break their fast. The *pujakarti* lights an earthen lamp, and as she moves it in a circle five times, prays to Moon. The women pray to *Ganesh* at this time, too. The observance of *Magh Cauth* is expected to bring good luck in the years ahead for the boy in whose name it is carried out.

Vasant Pancami, or "spring fifth," which occurs at about the end of January, is associated in classic Hindu tradition with flowers, especially

the flowers of the saffron, and with the goddess *Sarasvati*, the consort of
Brahma and patroness of learning and the arts. In addition to some ex-
ercises at the village school and the erection at the village grove of a
castor tree which will be burned six weeks later during the *Holi* festival,
the day is associated in Senapur with a first-fruits' rite (nevan) for the
winter crops of barley, peas, and gram which is generally similar to the
one held earlier when the sugar cane was ready. Five stalks of barley
are cut in the field of a family and taken to the home. There the women of
the household thresh, pound, and grind the grain, cook it with brown
sugar and clarified butter, and give some to each member of the family.
Green peas and gram are also roasted, pounded and distributed. Before
eating, the family members pray, give thanks to God, and ask that the
crops of the family continue to be good. The stalks are saved for the
Holi fire, for *Vasant* ushers in the season of preparation for *Holi*.

Shiva Ratri, which falls in late February or early March, is dedicated
to *Shiva*. Some believe that it is the anniversary of the marriage of *Shiva*
and *Parvati*. Many of the women of Senapur refrain from eating grain on
this day. Unmarried girls, especially, fast in order to get good husbands.

On the first day of the winnowing of the threshed crop (this can occur
any time between February 25 and March 10), a ceremony is traditionally conducted by each family on its threshing floor. A man of the
family kindles a fire in an earthen pot and scatters sacred substances
on it. Two Brahmans are feasted on a mixture of flour of roasted gram
and barley. Throughout the threshing, a ball of cow dung and some object
of iron, often the hand chaff-cutter, are kept on the pile of threshed grain
in the expectation that the grain will magically increase as a result of
their presence. Those working at the threshing floor must keep their heads
covered, and the hand scales used for weighing grain are turned upside
down when not in use.

Although *Holi* falls on the fifteenth day of the light half of the month
of *Phagun*, it is a period or mood as much as it is a specific day. The *Holi*
season actually begins with the replanting of the castor tree on *Vasant*
Pancami and lasts until at least the day after *Holi*. This is a period when
customary restraints are relaxed. Songs for the month of *Phagun* (*phagua*)
are sung, and these have extremely broad references and ribald phrases,
for *Phagun* is the month associated with masculine sexuality just as *Savan*
is the month of feminine passion. The *Holi* fire is usually kindled late at
night. It symbolizes for the people the destruction by fire of all filth and

impurity, physical or social. Since this is the last day of the year, it is important to destroy anything dirty or evil at this time, so that the entrance into the new year may be auspicious. Women massage their children with mustard paste, and the dirt and paste are collected, mixed with five cow-dung cakes, and sent to be burned in the fire. Bedbugs and lice are also gathered and burned to protect the house from such pests during the following year. An attempt is made to eradicate difficulties of other kinds too. Persons between whom there has been some unfortunate misunderstanding or enmity may call on each other as a pacificatory gesture. The fire is not only a means for the elimination of impurities, but a vehicle for the worship of *Agni*, the God of Fire. Thus grains and stalks saved from the new fruit rites are offered to *Agni* in the *Holi* fire. All try to see the *Holi* fire, at least from a distance, for it is inauspicious to fail to get a glimpse of it.

On the next day, the first day of the new year, the *Holi* spirit still reigns. In the morning, there is much bantering and throwing of mud and cow dung. The boys make sprayers of hollow bamboo and squirt colored water on those whom they meet. Within the extended family or lineage, there is considerable relaxation of usual restraints. *Holi* is the only day when men and women may touch each other publicly. The men enter the women's quarters and spray color and apply powder on the wives of elder brothers, cousins, and father's younger brothers, and the women retaliate. But the men are careful in their behavior toward their mothers, sisters, and the respected elderly women of the family, and they do not violate the restraint relationship that exists between them and their younger brother's wife. Groups of young women, "daughters" of the village, also enter houses and throw color on the daughters-in-law of their own age.

The new moon falls on a Monday about once in seven months. When this happens (*Somavati Amavashya*, "Monday New Moon"), some of the women of the village, particularly women of the caste of carpenters and smiths (*Lohar*), observe a total fast and make offerings to *Bansdeva* (*Vasu Deva*), the deified personification of the pipal tree. Their devotions are thought to benefit the health and ensure recovery from sickness of family members. The central conception is that the moon is in difficulty when it is dark but that it then waxes and recovers its light. In the same way a sick family member may be restored, it is felt, by the fasting and prayer on this day of a woman of the family.

SUMMARY

There are some forty calendrical rites observed in the village. Of these, twenty-five revolve sufficiently around family needs and purposes to have been selected for treatment in this paper. Obviously, in some of the rites described, persons who are not family members are drawn into the activities of the occasion. Thus, at *Khicari*, the servants (who are not only of different families but of different castes) are given presents, but what is being emphasized is their attachment to the family and their reward for services to it. There is an impressive amount of family orientation throughout. And this is not a generalized concept of family, but specific kin who are kept in mind.

It will be recalled that in a number of cases in which the intent is to seek ritual protection for sons, the women of a particular household do not participate or do not participate fully if a son has not been born into their immediate family since the time the ceremony was last performed. There are no general services for the dead in which the whole community joins; the fortnight devoted to the ancestors is a period in which each family worships its own deceased. That the Hindu family is an extremely important social unit is well enough known. But its prominence in the purposes and benefits of ritual, even of the calendrical type, gives some indication of how this position is reinforced by religion and how persistent and durable the sentiments surrounding it are likely to be, regardless of the economic, demographic, and political shifts foreseen at the present time. Underlying such concern, anxiety is obvious.

The count of calendrical rites largely colored by family considerations could be extended further. The important ritual pageant of *Ram Lila*, in which scenes from the *Ramayan* are dramatized, has not been included because it is sponsored by the whole community rather than by a single family. But its message is mainly devoted to family relations. It depicts, for instance, how a woman of a joint family, in seeking to promote the interests of her own son above others, once caused great difficulty. It portrays the grief of Rama's mother when he was exiled, the devotion and virtue under trying circumstances of his wife *Sita*, and the loyalty of his younger brother *Lakshman*, who insisted on following him into exile.

The influence of the family upon the calendrical rites is shown in still another way. It must have been evident that Brahman priests officiate rather infrequently in these rites. Not only are the rites meant to promote health and prosperity of the family and the individuals who belong to it, but most often family members plan, direct, and carry out the ritual acts.

Finally, it is clear that women have greatest responsibility in these ceremonial matters. In part, this reflects the male-centered character of the society. It is the women who must pray for the men of the family and propitiate gods and goddesses on behalf of husbands, sons, and brothers. But still more may be involved. Because of village exogamy, married women of this village and area come from different settlements. Their assumption of ritual responsibilities for the welfare of the social unit they have joined is an exceptionally effective way of identifying them with the most pressing interests and crises of the group. It would be useful to know whether women play as conspicuous a part in rituals of this type in regions where village exogamy is not the rule or where the male prerogatives are not so pronounced.

In accounting for the prominent place that women play in the conduct of such ceremonies, and especially those rites which have to do with the preservation and well-being of the family, it is well to keep in mind the high stake that Indian women have in the continuity of this social unit. Security, normal social life, and status depend on the perpetuation of the married state and the presence of healthy sons. The very thought of widowhood or the termination of the line is bleak and depressing. There is more than ordinary incentive and reason for them to carry out ritual tasks relating to the welfare of the family, both loyally and enthusiastically. Actually, anxiety is here overwhelmingly associated with ceremonialism. It relates to the problematic role of women in this society.

BIBLIOGRAPHY

1. Underhill, Muriel M.: *The Hindu Religious Year*. Calcutta: Oxford University Press, 1921, p. 104.

H. B. M. Murphy

Fellow of the Milbank Memorial Fund

12

CULTURE AND MENTAL DISORDER IN SINGAPORE

There are two very obvious difficulties in trying to relate mental health or mental disorder to the sort of cultural or social factors studied by social scientists. The first is the problem of defining what one is studying. The antithetical concepts of health and disease are value judgments. Hence, merely to describe certain behavioral characteristics in a people is meaningless for mental health until either the writer or the reader assesses these characteristics in terms of some definition, saying, although perhaps not explicitly, that he regards certain traits as unhealthy, etc. Such judgment implies a standard, and for any sociopsychiatric study to be meaningful that standard needs to be quite clear to the reader, something which in psychiatry is very difficult to achieve. Absolute standards or definitions in psychiatry do not exist, and although considerable agreement may be found concerning the nature and appearance of certain disorders there exist very few objective indices, and judgment remains essentially an individual matter. One has only to remember that psychiatric rejections at Armed Forces induction stations in the United States could vary from 0.5 per cent in one locality to 50.6 per cent in another to realize the possible variations in judgment of mental health. Except in extreme situations, judgments of mental health are not absolute but comparative, and hence it can be said that any attempts to survey the mental health of special communities should likewise be comparative. Either the same judge and same techniques should be used with two or more groups of people, being careful to allow for cultural bias, or one should use only such measures as are capable of translation, such as saying that a particular type of person would certainly be forced into a mental hospital if found in a particular part of the United States.

The second difficulty to be overcome is that of assessing the amount of disturbance, a procedure which is necessary if one's judgment is to

291

have any meaning. In the special type of study where a clinician is assessing the frequency of certain fairly common mental traits, or the more
dubious method of using so-called tests of neuroticism, etc., this offers
no problem other than that of ensuring strict comparability. But if, as is
more commonly the case, one is forced to use the coarser indices of disorder, then their relative infrequency presents a serious problem. The
average incidence of obvious psychosis is very roughly 1 per 1,000 per
annum, and the average incidence of suicide 1 per 10,000. To find any
cases of these disturbances at all, therefore, one needs to study respectively an average of 1,000 or 10,000 man-years; but to arrive at any useful
estimate of incidence one needs to study many times these numbers, a
point which is often not recognized either by psychiatrists or by those
who try to employ their findings.

Figure 12-1 may emphasize quickly what is meant if we take the not
atypical case of a survey which was done on a primitive community of

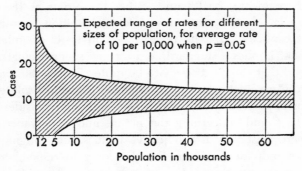

FIG. 12-1. Expected range of rates possible in 20 samples of
uniform size for an average rate of 10 per 10,000; by size of sample.

about 5,000. Five recent cases of psychosis were found, plus another 5
probable cases of longer duration, and on the basis of these findings an
incidence rate of 10 per 10,000 was reported with a prevalence rate of
20 per 10,000; these rates then being briefly compared to those reported
from another country. Figure 12-1 shows, however, that if that community had been visited in any other year, chance expectation is that
the same researchers would have met anything from no recent cases at all
to 9 recent cases, permitting them to offer for our edification any rate from
nil per 10,000, which could be claimed as exceptionally low, to 19 per
10,000, which is usually regarded as high. With such findings it would

only be legitimate to make comparisons with another population if the second group had a reliable rate of over 19.

These points are not fully relevant to the purpose of this paper, but they may serve to remind one of the difficulties which face any attempt to use psychiatric material in a study of cultures. Also, they may draw attention to the value of the few locations throughout the world where variety of culture, adequacy of psychiatric records, adequacy of population data, and sufficient population numbers can all be found together. Lebanon is one such place, Hawaii is another, but possibly the most suitable is Singapore, some data from which are here offered. These data are only a few of the more obvious or more appealing from a larger collection, and they are offered as much in illustration of method as for the light which they cast on the cultures concerned.

Singapore has three features which make it of special value in a study such as this. First, it is a meeting point of three Asian cultures, all of which are permitted to continue there almost free from pressures to assimilate to one another or to the ruling European power. Second, it has at the present time remarkably good census and social survey data. Third, it has for Asia a very good record of mental health care so that the population is used to the idea of mental hospitalization and can obtain it when they need it without waiting. At the time this study was made there were 1.8 mental hospital beds per 1,000 population, which was about the same as the state of Michigan. The main data to be discussed in this paper consist of the admissions to this hospital—the only one accepting mental cases—over a five-year period. Whether such admissions reflect the genuine levels of mental disorder in the various sections of the population is something which must always be asked, and the question will be taken up again shortly; but it may be remarked that this is only one of a variety of sources of data which are being used in the complete study, and where possible other checks have been used.

Singapore's population at the time of survey consisted of about 850,-000 Chinese, 140,000 Malaysians, 90,000 Indians, and 30,000 Europeans, Eurasians, and others. We propose to contrast some patterns of mental disorder in the three main Asian groups, relating these where possible to the more obvious aspects of their cultures, cultures which in their broader aspects are well known, although perhaps not quite in the form they were brought to Singapore or have been perpetuated there.

THE THREE CULTURES

The *Chinese,* so numerous that Singapore is properly considered a Chinese city, have nearly all come from the southern coastal provinces, the provinces where local dialects or languages persist, splitting the people into separate groups only doubtfully able to communicate with each other (10). These provinces are also the region where female emancipation was most advanced in China, women going to work in the mills, buying themselves out of marriage, and forming their own societies —sometimes with celibacy as their aim (13). Hence the Chinese in Singapore are split up into dialectal groups between which intermarriage is not common, and female labor, with the women coming not out of family life but from special residential clubs, is a special feature. Virtually all have come from a lower-class farming background, perhaps with a short intervening experience of Chinese urban mercantile life, and in Singapore many go back to the land, or take up any employment offered, thus distinguishing this immigration from those in Indonesia and Thailand where the Chinese are almost wholly merchants (12). The system of migration has been mainly by personal reference from one relative or acquaintance in the homeland to another in the new, but the system of residential clubs or *kongsis* which was mentioned for women also exists for men, forming a unique and important feature of Singapore Chinese life which apparently is not found among most overseas Chinese groups (13). In a sense such groups are reminiscent of substitute extended families. Although they may be organized according to village or membership of some sect, they are not confined to members of the same clan. The extended family in its true sense is not in the majority in Singapore (we are told it was not so common in China either) but it tends to be developed again after one or two generations of immigration somewhat along traditional lines.

Even without the extended family however, the individual Chinese at this time tended to remain very conscious of family or self, striving always for his own family farm or business and avoiding entanglement in wider social activities. Friendships and acquaintanceships are still made carefully with a measuring of benefits against obligations, and with a pervading sense of responsibility to one's family. One's earnings, business activities, and all important decisions are regarded as belonging to the family. Both within and without the family structure, emotional relationships and expressions tend to be restricted, and there is still emphasis on formal respect for elders and on propriety of conduct. Such loyalty to the family is at the core both of religious consciousness and of the great industriousness which pervades the moral system. Beyond ancestor worship their sense of religion is little practiced in ritual, but neither are the Chinese of Singapore much affected by superstition.

The *Malaysians*, although the next largest group, are less conspicuous in the streets than the Indians, for they are strongly attached to a village type of life, and it is rather in such village units than in the family that their social security rests. They have come partly from peninsular Malaya and partly from the larger islands like Java and Celebes, but although 40 per cent of the present generation are immigrants they tend to regard themselves as the natives of the Island. Malaysian cultures vary greatly with locality and such a mixed group could not normally be treated as having a single culture. But the form developed in Singapore appears to be generalized and to have crowded out immigrant influences through gradual acceptance. It is a gentle, easy culture, very different from the quarrelsome pattern one finds in the historic records of Malaya or in the present day Macassarese, but equally different from the intensely religious culture of the Balinese (1). Material possessions, success, and commercial aggressiveness are undervalued, while most highly valued probably is the rich emotional relationship between parent and child. Child-rearing is very permissive and affectionate; there is little emphasis on duty toward elders or toward husband. Divorce is common, and the extended family is quite rare (1, 11). In employment, Malaysians are moderately attached to the land, but also prefer work where loyalty is valued higher than individual initiative and where good leadership is given. Hence one finds them mainly as small-holders, but also as policemen and drivers; it is difficult to get them to enter into competitive commerce. They are almost wholly Muslim and very loyal to their religion, but without fanaticism or any tendency to produce their own religious leaders (who are mostly Arab) and without strict obedience in matters like fasting, etc. Their religion is shot through with many traditional beliefs in magic, so that being bewitched by someone is still a common explanation for sickness. Amok and Latah, traditional disturbances among the Malaysians, are almost unknown, but they are still somewhat prone to react to insult with violence.

The *Indians* are mostly southern Dravidians, speaking Tamil, and mainly Hindu by religion. Family structure in Singapore appears more in the form of a net of richly interacting nuclei than a single large unit under one roof and under one patriarch, although dominance and sub-mission are still important, both within the family and without. Caste is inconspicuous, and questions of whom one eats with almost nonexistent; but it is still important in marriage. The loosening of these systems, on the other hand, seems to have released energy for wider social activities, and one finds the Indian notably active in trade unions, societies, politics, and other community matters. Religion is important to them, as is artistic expression, and in both it is the richness and variety that are striking rather than the organization or clarity of thought and structure. Con-sistency of behavior is less valued than freedom and variety of emotional expression; this is reflected in family life, where child-rearing is affec-tionate and harsh by turns, where promises are made generously but with no intention of being kept, and where aggressiveness, both in the im-potent tantrums of the smaller child and the bullying of the older, are permitted or even encouraged (2). The Madras Indians were brought to Singapore mainly as contracted manual laborers and the administrative class for them was recruited from the educated Tamil Indians of Ceylon. This dichotomy has persisted, the mainland Indian being found rela-tively infrequently among the middle and upper social classes while the Ceylonese Indian is quite disproportionately represented among the professions. In both, superstition and in particular astrology are im-portant, affecting many people's lives.

RATES OF MENTAL HOSPITALIZATION

With these brief reminders of a few aspects of the three cultures we are considering, let us now see how mental disorder appears among them. Figure 12-2 shows the age-standardized incidence of mental hos-pital admissions as compared with the United States and Britain; we see immediately that while the average level of hospitalization is not very different from the West, the specific rates for the three groups are very different. The Indian rates are almost double the Chinese and the Chinese almost double the Malaysian; these differences apply to the psychoses as much as to the total admissions, to readmissions as well as first admis-sions, and to schizophrenia as much as to others. Since the same commit-ment laws, the same voluntary facilities, the same channels of admission, and the same doctors deal with all three groups, these differences cannot be due to some administrative factor.

As to cultural attitudes toward mental hospitalization affecting such marked differences, we rejected this after having made considerable inquiry on this question. The one point that did seem significant in these inquiries was that the Malaysians used all forms of modern medical care much less than do the other two groups, and so it seemed likely that

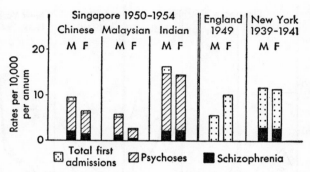

FIG. 12-2. Standardized rates of mental hospital first admissions in Singapore, 1950–1954, by ethnic group and sex, with comparable data for England and Wales and for New York.

Source of data for England: *Register General's Statistical Review of England and Wales for 1949: Supplement.* (Data for County Boroughs only.)

Source of data for New York: Malzberg, Benjamin, and Lee, Everett S.: *Migration and Mental Disease.* New York: Social Science Research Council, 1956.

they must be treating less serious illness themselves. However, an analysis of admissions into lighter versus more serious cases showed no support for this hypothesis. Taking only cases remaining in hospital more than one year, it was found that the Malaysian rates were still about half the Chinese, whereas one should have found on that hypothesis that the rates had moved closer. Also, parallel material from a prevalence survey of psychosis in Sumatra, or our findings on suicide, plus observations among the people all suggested that at the present time the Malaysians in Singapore do genuinely have a low rate of major mental disorder (14, 7). Our conclusions at this point are therefore that these differences in mental hospitalization do reflect genuine differences in incidence of major mental disorder, although the latter may not be of exactly the same magnitude as we present.

AGE DISTRIBUTION

Next, we may ask if they affect all ages or if we see as applicable to the whole population some difference that affects one period of life only —old age for instance. Figure 12-3 presents the answer, namely, that

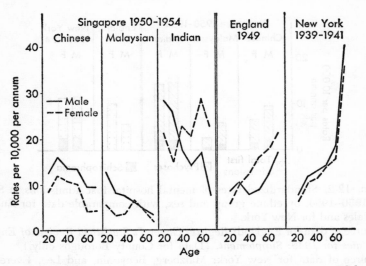

FIG. 12-3. Age-specific rates, by sex, of first admission to mental hospital, for three ethnic groups in Singapore, with comparative figures for Britain and the United States.

Patients whose age was not given varied between 5 per cent and 20 per cent of the Singapore groups, being higher for females than for males. To correct this bias, rates have been adjusted on the assumption that the cases with unrecorded age had the same distribution as the majority. An inspection of diagnoses made this seem justified; there was certainly no excess of senile and arteriosclerotic cases in that group.

Rates for England and Wales are for total direct admissions, not first admissions, since no satisfactory first admission data for a representative population in that country were available. These rates should be reduced by an over-all 27 per cent, but not necessarily equally at each age.

these differences apply roughly to all ages, but with some minor variations. Before we discuss these variations, however, there is another point which must strike one—the marked difference in profile that all three Singapore curves show as compared to those from the United States and Britain. In the West today, mental hospitalization rates nearly all rise with age. That was not always so, but even for the earliest data that we have, the curve tends to remain fairly level from the age of 30 onward, never showing a definite decline (6). On the other hand, we find almost everywhere in Asia where one can get such comparative rates, that there is a decline with age, the peak usually being not later than about the age of 30. And this difference becomes still greater if one considers certain groups, of whom the native-born or peninsular Malays are one. Excluding from the Malaysian male admissions those cases recorded as being of overseas origin (all are by no means of such origin, but only those who specifically call themselves Javanese, Boyanese, etc.), one finds in the present material and on two other occasions for which the hospital records happen to have survived the Japanese occupation of 1940–1945 the figures shown in Table 12-1. There one sees that the proportion of

TABLE 12-1

Percentage Age Distribution of Malaysian Male Admissions to Singapore Mental Hospital; 1950–1954 and for Limited Periods of 1917 and 1926–1927; Divided into Those Recorded as Malay and Those Recorded as Javanese, etc. Percentages to Nearest Whole Number

	1917*		1926–1927*		1950–1954	
	Malay	Others	Malay	Others	Malay	Others
15–24	43%	0%	14%	23%	41%	21%
25–34	43%	37%	57%	31%	35%	26%
35–44	14%	13%	24%	23%	15%	21%
45–54	0%	13%	5%	23%	7%	21%
55+	0%	37%	0%	0%	2%	10%
	100%	100%	100%	100%	100%	99%
N.	7	8	21	13	150	39

* For 1917 and 1926–1927 only single volumes of records had survived the 1940–1945 Japanese occupation; hence only small numbers are available for these years.

Malay male cases over the age of 45 was 0 per cent, 5 per cent, and 9 per cent, respectively, whereas in the United States in the present century the percentage of admissions over the age of 45 has usually been at least 50 per cent. These differences are only partly due to the lower expectation of life of the Malays, for in 1953, 21 per cent of the adult population (over 15) was estimated to be above the age of 45.

Now, one's first reaction to these figures may be to think that a decline in mental disorder rates in later life could be connected with a patriarchal family system and the exalted place which age is accorded in certain Asian cultures. But, as we have just seen, the most striking example of a decline of rates with age occurs in the Malay males, and Malay culture does not particularly revere or protect its elders. Offspring are not expected to work for their parents when the parents are able to work for themselves, for instance. Rather, parents will resume or take on extra work in order to find money for their grown children, money whose repayment is not a very serious obligation (1). Nor are the aged accorded special honor or status outside the family. Singapore Malay culture does not create special roles for its elders and the leaders of the community tend to be outsiders—Indonesians or Arabs—rather than from among themselves. Hence, the idea of lower Asian mental disorder rates in later life being associated with the special prestige which the Chinese and some Indian groups accord their elders becomes more doubtful. It may be true, but it is not the whole truth. Prestige, after all, is not something which necessarily leads to peace of mind, for it often involves extra responsibilities, a degree of isolation, and less easy emotional relationships with one's family. As we shall see later, the Chinese extended family does seem to give more protection against mental disorder in old age than does the simple family, but this manifests itself more as a function of the collective security of such a unit than of its hierarchical structure.

In relation to the other prestige orientation in the Chinese and Indian cultures, the extra status accorded to the first-born male, my data definitely suggest an increased vulnerability to mental breakdown, not a decreased vulnerability. Whereas one would expect in any sample of patients as many last-born as first-born * and as many first-born females as first-born males, one finds in Singapore that first-born males greatly exceed either of the other groups. This excess occurs both in the earlier half of life and in the later, and appears to be present in the Indians as well as the Chinese, but not in the Malaysians, although samples of Indians and Malaysians are too small for this to be certain. Hence, prestige in old age may not be so important for mental health.

But what old age does possess among the Malays (and what may be important for mental health) is relative freedom from a feeling of duty to exert themselves, and a rich emotional relationship both with children and with grandchildren. In the Malay culture an older man is not expected to exert himself either for the sake of his posterity or to prove himself to his neighbors, and hence as long as environmental conditions

* This is not necessarily true in a rapidly increasing population such as Singapore, or where the survival of first-male children is more highly valued than the survival of females. But such factors should not be so great as to cause the difference shown in the table. See Table 12-2.

TABLE 12-2.

Birth Position of Special Sample of Chinese Patients,
Coming from Families with Four or More Children

	Male	Female
First-born	19	7
Last-born	6	7
Others	20	39
	45	53

are favorable there is no inner drive to keep him working and worrying. On the other hand, the emotional attachment of children and grandchildren is an assumed fact, so that the old person does not need to seek emotional ties. Rather, the younger generation seeks this from the elder, providing much in exchange.

The evidence that this low Malay rate is connected with freedom from socioeconomic pressures can be found by examining certain situations where such pressures are increased from without. We need not list them all here, but simply state that in such circumstances, as during the world economic depression of the early 1930's, the Malaysian rate in Singapore was found to rise above that of the Chinese. Hence, the easy Malay attitude toward material needs and toward work, and their present comfortable milieu are probably contributory causes toward their remarkably low breakdown rates. But whether the emotional contact with children is important could not be further substantiated.

That was a diversion induced by the obvious differences in Asian and Western age breakdown trends, but this allows us to see some connections between culture and mental disorder in Singapore. Let us now return to the question of whether ethnic differences apply at all ages or only at certain periods.

SEX AND AGE DISTRIBUTIONS

Figure 12-3 shows that, while the Chinese female curve follows that of the male, the Indian and Malaysian female curves do not. This is not a point on which one can lay much stress since, unfortunately, the small size of the latter populations make these age-specific rates rather questionable. It is difficult to be sure, for instance, whether the apparent rise in the Malaysian rate at the menopausal period is real or accidental. All one can say is that in neither group is a significant fall with age to be expected, whereas it definitely does occur with the Chinese. And probably this difference can be related to fairly obvious cultural and social conditions, since neither the Malay nor the Indian women are as well equipped to meet the special social strains of middle age as are the Chinese. In the event of threatened or actual widowhood or divorce, the latter can rely on the help and usually the obedience of their children, their grandchildren, and their sons' wives; and, if they have no such relatives there are the *kongsis* for residence. Also, the Chinese woman is usually mentally equipped to seek employment, even though she may not have worked outside her home before. With the Indian middle-aged woman the family may be more affectionate, but it will also be more variable and less loyal. There can be an acute struggle with her son's wife for his affections, and her husband, now that she has lost her attractiveness, is likely to be more dominating, perhaps more violent and alcoholic. Also the Indian women are relatively isolated, not having a quarter of the city where they form their own communities, but being scattered among other groups. The Malay woman of that age, again, will be expected either to live alone or to return to the home of her parents or brothers if she is widowed or divorced. She is quite unadapted to seeking independent employment and will now be beyond the age of attracting another husband (this apparently being the usual solution, so that divorces tend to proceed as a chain reaction in this group). She will still have the affection of her children, if she has any, but the customary Malay failure to provide for future needs will result in some economic strain on her, and one must remember that we are not dealing here with a moderate rate of breakdown which fails to decrease, but rather an exceedingly low rate which is likely to be raised by any adverse circumstance. These are probably factors affecting the female curves.

Returning to the male graphs, let us consider breakdown rates and life experience at the ages of 15 to 24.

The Indian male rate is more than twice as high as the other two, and almost twice as high as it will be in middle age. Presumably, therefore, late adolescence is a period of strain for the Indian, and this is seen to extend into early adolescence when one examines comparative data on juvenile delinquency (one of our other sources of information). There one finds that the Singapore Indian rate of juvenile delinquency at the ages 10 to 14 is three to four times those of the other two groups. Similarly, the Singapore Indian suicide rate in the 15 to 24 period is unusually high, and there are places in India itself where there is as much suicide below the age of 20 and even below the age of 15 as above 45. Our mental hospital data thus agree with other data. Further, although juvenile delinquency is relatively higher among Indian boys it is worth noting that both in Singapore and in Madras such offenses are almost wholly against property, never direct assault, whereas when one comes to adult crime a most striking change is found. As Table 12-3 shows, the

TABLE 12-3

Offenses against Person and against Property in Two Samples of Singapore Crime Records; Juvenile and Adult; by Ethnic Group

	Chinese		Indian		Malaysian	
	10–14	Adult	10–14	Adult	10–14	Adult
A. Offenses Against Person *	46	70	1	37	4	21
B. Offenses Against Property *	275	287	84	43	44	98
Ratio of B/A	6.0	4.1	84.0	1.2	11.0	4.6

* Offenses against person exclude sexual; offenses against property exclude fraud; offenses against discipline and some other types of offense are not included in table.

ratio of the two types of offense among the Chinese does not change much with age and with the Malaysians it only doubles; but with the Indians virtual absence of direct bodily aggression has been replaced by abundance of such crime, the amount almost equaling that of the usually more common theft. This change in the Indian crime pattern takes place during the 15 to 24 age period and it is surely clear that there is some serious problem with the control of aggressive impulses in this culture. It is, as stated earlier, a culture where the motives of dominance and submission are of frank importance, particularly within the family, dominance depending partly on prescribed status, but partly also on age, seniority, and physical size (2).* Hence, the child is trained for overt submissiveness and covert resentment, while the adult is permitted to dominate in certain situations and to express aggression where he can; the change from the one attitude to its opposite will usually take place around the age of 20. We suggest that this is one reason, although only one, why mental breakdowns are so high at this age. In older life there are increasing culturally approved situations for the expression of dominance, but

* I am indebted to Miss Jean Dumas, who has studied children's fears in India, for the suggestion that the relative excess of theft among Indian children—and also in their fantasies—is due to the fact that aggressiveness is stimulated by teasing, etc., but deprived of direct expression by the simple fact that other people are bigger than oneself and can hit back harder (3).

around the age of 20 such opportunities are few although physical growth is completed and the submissiveness of childhood is no longer appropriate. Among Singapore Indian university students the handling of aggression against each other was an obvious problem, and aggressive feelings against the father were a frequent underlying cause for psychiatric consultation (8).

With the Malaysians the rate at this age is also relatively high, as high as the Chinese although still far below the Indian. We suggest that this emphasis in the 15 to 24 age period stems from a quite different cause. Malay childhood is easy, with very little frustration, the parents being affectionate but not overprotective or overdemanding. Adolescence sees great freedom to roam about in small innocent gangs or in paying casual visits to relatives and submission or a sense of duty plays little part in such upbringing. The strain at this point arises because it occurs when the youth must move out of the shelter of the parent's family, must find employment, must establish a household with a bride of other's choosing, and must face the unaccustomed frustrations of dealing with a wider society. Sexually the Malay youth is much more ready for marriage than his comrades from the other cultures, finding it more of a frustration not to be married, but he is poorly equipped to handle the more complex interpersonal relations which marriage brings (8). His wife, meanwhile, has been brought up to be very attached to her mother, and such upbringing has not led to a desire to get away. She is not likely to have a special attraction to her new husband, and she is often rather immature. The marriage may be neolocal, but as often will be with the wife's mother initially and may lead to mother-in-law trouble. The relative excess of Malay mental breakdowns at this age may well be a reaction to the frustrations which are now being met for the first time, and one finds that many of the cases appearing at this time are mild, acute affective psychoses of short duration and without apparent later relapse.

On the female side, the striking thing at this age is again the high Indian rate, which again is accompanied by a high suicide rate (7). Delinquency is low since these cultures afford little opportunity for it among females. Whether this picture is related mainly to the basic culture or to the special situation in Singapore is a matter of conjecture, but there is no question that the two combined offer a stressful situation to Indian girls. The key point, I think, is that there was until recently a gross imbalance in the sex ratio of the Singapore Indian population, and Indian males, whether local-born or immigrants, returned to their home village in

India to marry, bringing their brides back with them almost immediately. Since Southern Indian family life is characterized by a richness and variety of interpersonal relations, the Indian girl, brought up almost wholly within the family network, is very dependent on the uncertain emotional relationships it affords. At the same time, she is quite interested in establishing her own household. Leaving her family of orientation is usually easy even though in the first years she will be dominated by her husband's family, since at home in India this is likely to happen within the same village or region. But the girl who accompanies a strange husband to Singapore, while perhaps relieved of the customary mother-in-law trouble, is at once deprived of all her previous emotional ties without ever having been trained to depend on herself. The strain becomes particularly marked during the birth of the first child, since it is an Indian tradition that the girl should return to her mother and be fully pampered during and before this period of confinement. From Singapore such wives are still sent home to their mothers, if the husband can afford it, but if he cannot she is likely to be confined in a factory-like hospital, lacking the traditional Indian appurtenances, attended by people who usually cannot speak her language. So it is understandable that as much as one-quarter of these early mental breakdowns consist of [puerperal] psychoses occurring around the first birth, and that other breakdowns occur in connection with physical illness. Such breakdowns, fortunately, have a favorable outcome, but the rate of disorder which does not respond so well is still higher than for the other two groups. We see that after this first decade the incidence of disorder drops briefly, for now the woman has passed the initial difficulties and is still attractive enough to be able to find a new husband among the excess of males if her present one does not treat her properly. The age of struggling with daughters-in-law for her sons' affections has not yet arrived.

MALAY OCCUPATIONAL RATES

We see, then, that a consideration of culture can help in explaining patterns of mental breakdown. Can we reverse the process and consider some instances where attention to mental disorder patterns may enlarge our appreciation of a culture itself? Let us first consider the Malays.

There is in Malaya today considerable agitation and activity aimed at making the Malay competitive in business and commerce with the Chinese and Indians, who are seen as endangering his very existence by their economic inroads. It has proved difficult, however, to induce the people to take advantage of the special facilities or privileges offered them, and the question arises whether it is love of the land which holds the Malay back from such nonagricultural enterprises, or whether the wrong type of incentive is being offered, or offered in the wrong way. Perhaps the culture is in some way incompatible with such activities. If we knew which types of occupation had the highest mental health among the Malays we might possess a partial answer to this problem. A look at Table 12-4 offers some explanation.

TABLE 12-4

Mental Hospitalization Rates for Specific Occupational Groups; Malay and Chinese Males Only; Ranked in Increasing Order among Malays

Occupational Category	Malaysian	Chinese
1. Messengers and Officeboys	18.2	91.7 (13th)
2. Domestic Service	25.0	25.0 (1st)
3. Personal Services	28.0	59.8 (5th)
4. Hawkers and Vendors	33.3	67.3 (6th)
5. Drivers and Conductors	35.4	84.6 (11th)
6. Clerical and Administrative	41.2	50.8 (4th)
7. Agriculture and Fishing	41.5	46.8 (3rd)
8. Policemen, Postmen, and Firemen	48.0	80.0 (10th)
9. Shop Assistants	50.0	79.1 (9th)
10. Teachers	53.6	71.4 (7th)
11. Unskilled Laborers	74.2	76.5 (8th)
12. Trisha (pedalcab) Riders	85.7	95.9 (14th)
13. Business and Professional	85.7	31.4 (2nd)
14. Skilled Craftsmen, Technical	110.0 *	85.4 (12th)

* Rate for skilled craftsmen doubtful owing to overlap of categories.

Here we find that the data differ from those found in the United States (where mental disorder increases with decreasing social and economic prestige) and also differ from what is found among the Singapore Chinese. The categories which show the least mental disorder are clearly those not associated with wealth and prestige, or with agriculture, but those associated with least effort and least initiative. The categories showing the highest rates, on the other hand, are those in which the most effort—either mental, as in the case of business and professional men, or physical, as in the case of laborers and trishariders—is required. With the Chinese we see that the business and professional category has a low rate, while that of the messengers and officeboys has a high one, so that one cannot attribute special mental health characteristics to these occupations in Singapore outside of their significance in the respective cultural contexts. Also, the Chinese rate in the agricultural and fishing category is almost as low as the Malay, suggesting that it is not the "call of the land" which is so important to the latter, an impression which is supported by the finding * that while the Malay male rate in the central city zone is relatively high the female rate there—where one would expect the women to be uncomfortable at the lack of village life—is not so much higher than in the rural zone. These observations, therefore, suggest that it will be difficult to induce the Malays to enter happily and successfully into commerce and business while preserving their traditional culture, and that their special attitude toward material success and attainment may be a more important factor in that culture than attachment to rural village life. We would be the last to say that definite conclusions should be made on such evidence alone, but we do suggest their relevance in understanding the situation.

CHINESE DIALECTICAL MINORITIES

The next illustration concerns the Chinese dialectal groupings which I mentioned earlier. They show no important differences with regard to type of employment, social status, religion, sex ratio, period of immigration, and they share the same general cultural background.† But two questions present themselves. First, does the language barrier create different social conditions for the larger and the smaller dialectal groups? Second, in what way is mental health affected by such differences, if any exist? We know from other cultures that minority status can in certain circumstances be accompanied by a reduction in the expected amount of mental disorder, as with the Hutterites, while in other circumstances it can result in a marked increase in such breakdowns. What of the Chinese culture?

In discussing the answer which emerges from these data, we run into a new difficulty, a difficulty at least in as far as we attempt to relate such findings to cultural forces. Hitherto, we have considered either only total mental hospitalization, or total hospitalized psychosis, and we

* Not detailed here.

† The attitude of Cantonese women toward outside employment, and the attitude of the other Chinese toward a group called the Hakka, whom they regard as not truly Chinese, are important from some angles, but need not concern us here.

have not had to trouble with interpretations. Now, however, we come to a situation where the results from total hospitalization are not informative, but where most interesting differences are found when one considers particular diagnoses. So one must ask what occurs mentally in these different states, what mental processes are assumed to be at work which appear meaningful in relation to cultural and social influences. On this point it is very difficult to get any agreed answer, but purely for the purpose of stimulating discussion we wish to offer here some very rough hypotheses.

First, that major mental disorders can be divided roughly into two groups, the organic type reactions and the functional type. We suggest that the organic type reactions are usually associated with a breakdown in the physical mechanism of the mind, whereas the functional type rather represents faulty attempts at responding to situations. The organic type is usually associated with temporary or chronic overburdening of a mind weakened by factors like anemia, malaria, syphilis, or old age; if relief of one or more of the stress factors is possible, as in the case of malaria, then the mind can fairly easily and rapidly return to its former state. However, if there has been permanent damage, as with old age or syphilis, full retraining or recovery is rarely possible. With the functional psychoses, except in their mildest form, relief of single factors is not sufficient since a false habit of response has been acquired and must either be erased or retrained. We suggest further that with functional psychoses one can distinguish two main types, the affective psychoses and schizophrenia. For present purposes we look on the affective type as being faulty responses to some situation of emotional deprivation or loss, not necessarily recent. On the other hand, the schizophrenic type, in this schema, may be regarded as representing faulty attempts in handling some problem of ego control or ego organization, especially a problem arising out of conflicting or confused environmental pressures.

These are, of course, gross oversimplifications. We know, for instance, that many of the senile psychoses which we label organic are associated with emotional deprivation or with failure to adjust adequately to a society in which the old are given no satisfactory role, and such cases may be treated best as we would a functional psychosis. Nevertheless, with such recognition, these working hypotheses may be useful in the present context. See Figure 12-4.

There are no statistically significant differences between the mental hospital admission rates for the larger and the smaller Chinese dialectal groups in Singapore. On the other hand, there are close and significant inverse correlations between group size and incidence rate when we come to consider suicide, one type of organic psychosis, and the func-

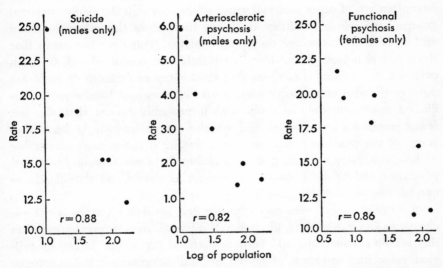

FIG. 12-4. Correlations between population size and rates for three types of mental disorder in Chinese dialectal groups in Singapore; by sex and type of disorder. No other type of disorder gave significant correlation with population size, but one case—male confusional psychosis—came close to significance (−.726).

tional psychoses, although not all for both sexes. One finds that suicide and arteriosclerotic psychosis are definitely increased among the minority males but not the minority females, while the functional psychoses, affective and schizophrenic combined, are increased for the minority females but not for the minority males. On the basis of the above hypotheses we can now suggest something about how minority status may affect the individual in a Chinese culture. The difference in the nonspecific organic type psychosis may indicate that the males have been exposed to chronic extra mental strain of such a type that the necessary response is known and simple but the effort is excessive. Such a strain, for instance, as making one's living under increased competition. That suicide should be increased among the same people is expected if one notes that in Singapore the two principle causes are physical disease and failed ambition. Further, the absence of any increase among the minority women of arteriosclerotic psychosis is matched by the fact that the women have no direct role in earning the family's livelihood among a polyglot society. For the woman of such a minority, the problem is to establish social contacts with her neighbors, neighbors who often are of other dialectal groups (for although the major dialectal groups have whole localities almost to themselves the minorities have no blocks or streets where they predominate). This does not mean that she will feel herself an outsider in a tightly knit neighborhood, for such evidence as we possess suggests that the Singapore Chinese do not form tight geographic units. But it may mean that she must handle more conflicting environmental demands, and it probably means that she has fewer emotional resources should a major source be lost. At least, that is one of the possible hypotheses; but whether it is the most acceptable or not, the facts regarding a relationship between female functional psychoses and minority group size remain as shown and should add to our knowledge of these people.

A correlation between minority size and breakdown rates is not exclusive to Chinese culture, of course. We have shown in previous studies that such a correlation could be demonstrated for suicide in certain religious minorities and for total mental hospitalization among Polish refugee groups in Britain, but the association of one sex with one type of breakdown and the other with a quite different type is something new which may have specific cultural significance (7, 9).

PRIMARY GROUPS

In these dialect minorities one found that although arteriosclerotic psychosis was increased, the senile psychoses were not, and were, on the contrary, somewhat decreased. Similarly with suicide, we found that although the rates increased with declining group size in middle age, they decreased with group size in old age, suggesting that perhaps the smaller minorities gave their old people better support. Now let us turn to another instance where one can find a variation in the incidence of senile organic psychoses among the Chinese, relating this to what we noted earlier about the Malays.

So far as we know, there exist no previous comparative studies on the incidence of mental breakdown in different types of primary groups. The subject is a very difficult one to approach, since definitions are not commonly agreed to and censuses rarely give the relevant information. But partly because of the interest in the subject, and partly as an illustration of what may be done with unpromising material, we think it worth while offering the partial results obtained by a very rough technique.

For six months all admissions were classified by the admitting psychiatrist in the Singapore mental hospital into four rough categories of primary group, plus a "rag bag" of others who did not fit this schema. The categories were: Simple family; extended (stem and collateral) family; *kongsi;* and single-person household, the last indicating not so much true isolates as earners with families overseas. Polygamous families were classified as extended when the wives shared the same household, but as "simple" (other factors being absent) if the wives ran separate establishments. Special situations like shop employees living and eating in an employer's family were put down as "other." We cannot claim that precise boundaries were used, or that each case was thoroughly checked before classification, since the psychiatrist was a very busy man. But in practice the majority of cases were easy to place. A *kongsi* was taken as a group of four or more persons of the same sex but not the same family, living and usually eating together.

The broad results are shown in Figure 12–5. For simplicity, only schizophrenia, the affective, and the organic type psychoses data are shown and, since the age distribution in the groups was likely to vary, a division into under thirty-five and over thirty-five is also made. For the moment we are considering only the cases, not the populations from which they arise, and the diagnostic distributions are given as proportions only, not as rates. In this way, two quite clear and statistically significant differences can be seen. First, the organic type psychoses are proportionately much less frequent in the extended family and *kongsi* groups than in the other two categories. Next, schizophrenia is proportionately much more common in the two-family categories than in the nonfamily. Both differences apply to both those under the age of thirty-five and those above, and the difference in organic type psychoses applies to all main categories included within that term.

Regarding the first finding, it seems highly probable that this reflects a difference in true incidence, since the variation in proportion is so great (6 to 10 times), and we suggest that it may be related to some property which the extended family and *kongsi* possess in common but which is lacking in the other two. We cannot say that they share a special hierarchic structure, or a social class, or an abundance of children, but what the extended family and *kongsi* do possess in common is the presence of a number of adults among whom decisions may be discussed and responsibility shared. The inference would, therefore, seem to be that either adult companionship or the sharing of responsibilities is in

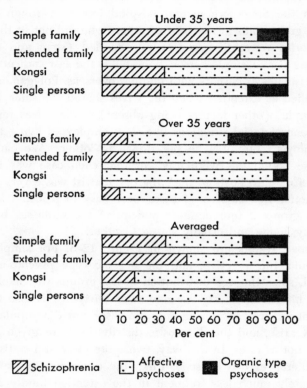

FIG. 12-5. Percentage distribution, by two age groups, of three types of psychosis in patients from four categories of primary groups. Cases not falling into the types and categories, e.g., mental defectives and neurotics, have been excluded for simplicity; percentages are to nearest whole number.

this culture associated with a reduction in the rate of organic type psychoses and hence, since the mental disorders of old age are largely organic, a reduction in the incidence of senile breakdowns. Were we only considering the extended family it would not be possible to decide whether a lowering of mental hospitalization in old age were especially associated with the presumed greater tolerance of such a unit toward its elders, with the presumed richer emotional interaction it may contain, or with higher prestige, etc. But when we find such organic type disorders to be relatively rare in the *kongsis* and in the under-35's as well, then it seems probable that any association is with the one main facet of life which they have in common—multiplicity of adults. And, if we relate these findings both to the age distribution of mental disorder among the Malays, which we considered earlier, and to our finding in relation to the dialect groups, then it seems that we must admit there may be some connection between the mental effort associated with responsibility and organic type of mental disorder. Where such effort can be avoided or shared, the rate seems to be lower; where it is additionally heavy, as with the dialect minorities, it is found to be increased.

This conclusion is consistent with current thinking in Western societies regarding the arteriosclerotic and senile psychoses, but when we come to our second finding an apparent contradiction to Western findings presents itself. In Western society we are accustomed to think of schizophrenia as the main mental disease associated with nonfamily living, whereas the affective disorders show little change in rate.* In Singapore, however, we find the proportion of schizophrenia twice as high in the family as in the nonfamily categories. As our data stand we cannot be sure whether this represents a real difference in rate, since it is not improbable that the nonfamily categories have a higher over-all incidence rate than the family. But even if one had to admit that the Singapore family groups had no higher a true rate of schizophrenia than the nonfamily, this would mean that the latter had a very much higher rate of the affective psychoses. So a contradiction remains between the Singapore findings and Western ones at this point. In fact, different analyses of the hospital data and estimates of the distribution within the population derived from social and housing surveys suggest that both associations occur, i.e., that the incidence of schizophrenia in families is slightly higher than in the nonfamily groups, and that the incidence of the affective psychoses is much higher in the nonfamily than in the family. Also, the incidence of schizophrenia in the extended family is probably higher than in the simple family type.

Limitations of space prevent our discussing the full implications of these findings. One way of looking at them would be to relate them to social involvement. If the provisionary assumptions suggested earlier

---

* A revision of the original Chicago work of Faris and Dunham by Ronald Freedman did suggest a correlation of the affective psychoses with migration. (Freedman, R.: *Recent Migration to Chicago.* Chicago: University of Chicago Press, 1950.)

for the two main types of functional psychosis are accepted, one of the corollaries would seem to be that the affective psychoses will be increased where there is a paucity of emotional social support, and vice versa, while schizophrenia will be increased where there is an excess of conflicting social pressures. Comparing Singapore and the United States in such terms, then, we might say that in the Asian location, family pressures and support are high and extrafamilial social pressures and support are low, whereas in the Western society family pressures are low but extrafamilial social pressures to conform or to acculturate are high. However, other hypotheses might be proposed; the reader will no doubt have some of his own.

CONCLUSIONS

This review of a few facts about mental disorder in the three main cultural groups in Singapore permits us now to attempt certain broad, if not especially original, generalizations about the effect of culture on mental health. First, there seems to be ample support in the high Indian and low Malay rates for the common current belief that child rearing affects adult stability. However, to suggest that this was the only, or even the main cultural factor would be wrong in the light of our data. Malay rates of breakdown rise above the Chinese when there is an increase in social economic pressure. Indian male rates apparently drop almost to the level of the Chinese in middle age when the desire for dominance can be most easily gratified. Clearly, therefore, the influence of child-rearing patterns on the development of adult psychosis is dependent in large part on the pressures and facilities which that culture offers to adults. Perhaps one might even say that successful cultures in their purer forms introduce balances and compensations whereby specific stresses have their antidotes.

The next factor which we may discern is the adverse influence of the imposition of responsibility or expectation. The first-born Chinese male showed a higher rate of mental breakdown than other birth ranks; the older person in a simple Chinese family showed more risk of breakdown than in an extended Chinese family or *kongsi* where responsibilities were shared, or than in a simple Malay family where, provided the environment was kind, responsibilities were largely avoided. As far as one can tell it is this factor rather than any other which is associated with the low rate of senile disorder which these peoples show.

Regarding the third probable influence, the influence of emotional ties, the evidence is less clear, but probably still relevant. None of the data point definitely to the greater emotional richness of the extended family or of Malay adult life as a factor in old age operating independently of the more potent sharing of responsibility and relief from effort. But where emotional ties do clearly operate is with the affective psychoses of the young Indian female immigrant, and with the involutional melancholia of the Chinese *kongsi* dweller for whom a sense of desertion of family must be partly operative.

Finally, there is the question of social demands and a conflict of needs or goals. For the Malay intellectual and business man, for the women of the Chinese minorities, and for the Indian and Chinese extended-family youth trying to readjust feelings of subordination and dominance, of independence and family loyalty, new responses are required and it seems as though the response may occasionally be a faulty one. These are the main factors which show hazily behind these data.

In addition, we have shown how an examination of mental hospital material can add to our knowledge of the cultures themselves. The limitations of such data are great, and as was said at the beginning, their application depends on the use of proper comparisons or controls. But I feel that there is justification in these illustrations for asking anthropologists to give such techniques their consideration, and for suggesting that such an approach be considered in other parts of the world.

BIBLIOGRAPHY

1. Djamour, J.: *The Family Structure of the Singapore Malay.* London: Colonial Office, 1955.
2. Dube, S. C.: *Indian Village.* London: Routledge and Kegan Paul, Ltd., 1955.
3. Dumas, J.: "A study of fears among the children of three Indian States." *Manasi,* 1954, p. 16.
4. Freedman, M.: *Chinese Family and Marriage in Singapore.* London: London School of Economics, 1954.
5. Goh, H. S.: *Urban Incomes and Housing.* Singapore: Government Printing Office, 1955.
6. Goldhamer, H., and Marshall, A.: *Psychosis and Civilization.* Glencoe, Ill.: The Free Press, 1953.

7. Murphy, H. B. M.: "The mental health of Singapore; I. Suicide." *Medical Journal of Malaya*, 1954, vol. 9, p. 1.

8. ———: "Cultural factors in the mental health of Malayan students." To be published in the conference volume of the First International Conference on Student Mental Health. Princeton: Princeton University Press, 1956.

9. ———, ed.: *Flight and Resettlement*. Paris: UNESCO, 1956.

10. Purcell, V.: *The Chinese in South East Asia*. London: Oxford University Press, 1951.

11. Shamsuddin b. Abd. Sam: *Patterns of Child-Rearing in Malay Families*. Dissertation on file at the University of Malaya Department of Social Studies, 1957.

12. Ta Chen: *Emigrant Communities in South China*. Shanghai, 1939. Also published by the Institute of Pacific Relations, New York, 1940.

13. Topley, M.: "Chinese women's vegetarian houses in Singapore." *Journal of the Malayan British Royal Asiatic Society*, 1954, vol. 27, p. 51.

14. van Loon, F. H.: "The problem of lunacy in Atcheen." *Mededeelingen von der burgerliche Geneeskundige Dienst von Nederlands Indie*, 1920, no. 10, p. 2.

Section IV

AFRICAN
CONTRASTS

Simon D. Messing

Department of Sociology
Hiram College

13

GROUP THERAPY AND SOCIAL STATUS
IN THE ZAR CULT OF ETHIOPIA

Therapists who employ the dynamics of modern group psychotherapy are being urged to take greater cognizance of the larger cultural and social backgrounds and experiences to which the treated patients and even the physicians are exposed (11).

In most societies which have developed specialized healing patterns for mental ailments, patients and doctors enact certain roles which govern the frequency, intensity, and meaning of their interaction. Factors of social structure, cultural values, and expected roles are always present, even when they are unacknowledged. Even the disturbed patient knows something of the performance expected of him when he falls ill. Indeed, his first task in the new role of patient is often to demonstrate his sickness, e.g., spirit-possession, so that society in general will accept him in this role.

HEALING OF THE SPIRIT IN ABYSSINIAN CULTURE:
BASIC FACTORS

An elaborate process of this kind can be observed in the old, traditional Zar cult of northern Ethiopia (Abyssinia). The center of this healing cult is located in the town of Gondar, on the highland-plateau. There, the major Zar doctors have their headquarters and their societies of chronic patient-devotees.

Common symptoms of possession by the Zar spirits include proneness to accidents, sterility, convulsive seizures, extreme apathy. The healer is himself Zar-possessed, but has come to terms with the spirit (quite

319

literally). His first task is to diagnose what specific spirit or syndrome of spirits ails the patient (8).

Everyone in the culture knows what procedure follows. The patient will be interrogated in the house of the doctor. There the doctor will lure his own Zar into possession of him, through a trance. The doctor's Zar is then used to lure the unknown Zar of the patient ("his horse") into public possession. Then the spirit is led to reveal his identity, by means of adroit cajolery, promises, and threats. The demands of the Zar are then negotiated through a lengthy process of financial bartering. Finally, the patient is enrolled for the rest of his life into the Zar society of fellow-sufferers, renting, as it were, his temporary freedom from relapse through regular donations and by means of participation in the worship of the spirit.

The patient, of course, knows this too and responds to the leading questions of the doctor, although often only after a considerable show of resistance. The latter is attributed to the activity of certain mischievous, minor spirits, whose only power is to create confusion. Final identity of the Zar is revealed by the patient's individual Zar dance (*gurri*), which the spirit obliges his human "horse" to perform in public, while the doctor watches and directs.

The chronic patients gain a number of benefits as members of the Zar society. The patient calls attention to himself as an individual, alleviating some of the consequences of low social status in the family or community. Most patients are married women, who feel neglected in a man's world in which they serve as hewers of wood and haulers of water, and where even the (Coptic Abyssinian) church discriminates against females by closing the church building to them. Married women in the predominantly rural culture are often lonely for the warmth of kinship relations, for typical residence is in a patrilocal hamlet, which is exogamous. Members from the lower classes, such as Muslim (mostly Sudanese) minorities, find social contact across religious barriers in the Zar cult. Ex-slaves, many of them descended from alien African tribes (Shanqalla), are also admitted to full membership in the Zar cult. Finally, occupational and economic benefits are dispensed by the Zar doctor, who functions also as treasurer of the society, but does not render any financial accounting. Thus, he has the opportunity, rare on the simple material level of traditional Abyssinia, to accumulate capital which he invests in economic enterprises, e.g., brewing honey-wine, and which further enhances the reputation of his special powers.

Active opposition to the cult comes from husbands, who fear the sexual and economic emancipation of the wife. Although there are no orgies of the kind assumed and suspected by outsiders, membership in the Zar cult does give opportunities for liaisons. Passive resistance comes from priests of the Coptic Abyssinian Church, who profess to condemn the Zar cult, but do little to counteract it. This may be because many priests secretly believe in the cosmology of Zar themselves, particularly in spirits that are regarded as Coptic Christian (others are Muslim or pagan).

Incipient symptoms vary with certain ecological seasons, notably the onset of the nine-month dry season. Then the spirits are regarded as emerging from the confinement of the dreary, cold rains. The landscape blossoms forth. The epidemiology of possession suggests that many patients try to emerge from their psychological and social confinements in that season. Furthermore, the major Zar celebration occurs just before the "little rains" which coincide with the onset of the Coptic Lent. The Zar season closes with an annual convention (*āmāt bāl*) of Zar doctors the night before Lent. (Western carnival—Mardi Gras—is otherwise unknown to the Coptic Abyssinians.)

INDIVIDUAL VULNERABILITY AND SYMPTOMATOLOGY

Every human is considered potentially vulnerable to being possessed by a Zar spirit or spirits. But humans differ considerably in degrees of vulnerability. Certain situations are considered particularly inviting to the Zars. Most of these situations are points of psychological or social stress.

Heredity, usually mother to daughter (paralleling the dominant patrilineal principle in Abyssinian culture) predisposes some victims. Some mothers even promote this transfer on purpose, if the individual Zar has been turned into a powerfully protective spirit (*weqābi*). They carry out this transfer in a ceremony of physical contact, accompanied by a covenant of continued devotion.

A sort of psychic predestination predisposes some persons. They are chosen by the Zar for their melancholy natures or weak personalities, e.g., alcoholics. In some cases the illness plays the role of a religious revelation, which calls the chosen into the Zar cult.

In this connection it is interesting to note that not only weaknesses create points of stress that attract a Zar. Some Zar spirits choose their victim for unusually attractive qualities, e.g., the beauty of a woman who has been much praised, or the enchanting voice of a chorister (*däbtära*) of the Coptic Church. It seems that envy and jealousy play a role, although a minor one, in the theory of causation.

More significant are features of cross-sexual persecution in human situations that attract certain Zars. Possession is very often regarded as a state in which a spirit is having sexual intercourse with his human victim of the opposite sex. A woman who sleeps alone renders herself vulnerable to a male Zar. A man who sleeps alone and has a seminal emission blames it on a female Zar. The convulsive seizures of a male patient are commonly regarded as evidence that a female Zar is experiencing sexual climax with him. Similarly, when a woman patient cannot be readily coaxed out of her state of apathy, she is regarded as being slept with by a male Zar.

Confused sexual identity, which may be a symptom of schizophrenia, is also explained in terms of cross-sexual persecution. If a female Zar possesses a male patient, he manifests characteristics regarded in the culture as feminine, such as silly gaiety and teasing behavior. If not awakened quickly, such a state is regarded as dangerous, for it may destroy his masculinity. Women possessed by a male Zar manifest it by draping their toga (*shamma*) in male fashion; some even seek out and wear ornaments of old-time male warriors, such as lion mane, leopard skin, etc. She insists that she does this on request of her male Zar who likes to see his "horse" dressed suitably to represent him.

Symptoms of hysteria usually begin at night, and take the pattern of seeking escape. The patient tries to run out of the hut at night, with great clamor and drama, to "roam with the hyenas." Restraint results in rage, even self-injury. Kinfolk usually tie the patient with ropes until contact with the Zar doctor can be made. The latter usually has cultivated a stare that can calm cases of hysteria, so that diagnosis can proceed. Without saying a word, the doctor grasps the upper arm of the patient (for male Zars attack the shoulders first and then squat on the patient's back until they descend into the victim, during the period of full possession). When the patient has been sufficiently calmed, the doctor loosens his grip and lightly caresses the upper arm and shoulder. This indicates that he is unafraid to establish contact with the spirit, and that the situation is well in hand. Most victims of hysteria are women.

Extreme apathy indicated possession by an evil Zar. The patient, often a woman, withdraws into a corner of the hut, sits there huddled, refuses food. Kinfolk immediately come to her aid, for if she were to remain long in this state her Zar could "ride his horse to death." Therefore, until a Zar doctor can be sent for, kinfolk and neighbors come quickly, sing to the patient, dance for her, try to move her into joining them, promise her whatever she desires, and never leave her alone.

A period of incubation is believed to precede most cases of possession, especially in women victims. The male Zar possessing her may be jealous of her human husband, may wish to bring about a divorce so that she can be free to join the Zar society of devotees. If she is already pregnant, the Zar may cause a miscarriage, either because he likes his victim "pure," or to take revenge on the husband for miserly refusal of a chicken or young goat requested for the Zar sacrifice. The Zar then takes the human fetus as his love gift (*mäqwädäsha*). When a male Zar appears to a human female in a dream, in the shape of a husband visiting his wife, this indicates that he is in a benevolent mood. But if he appears in the dream in the shape of a black dog (Ethiopian dogs are typically reddish) or of a snake, this indicates anger.

ZAR COSMOLOGY AND SOCIAL STATUS

In order to appreciate the complex role of the Zar concept in this healing cult, the cosmology of the Zar must be understood, even though the Abyssinian myth of the origin of the Zar spirits is probably a superimposed rationalization.

They are regarded as having originated in the Garden of Eden, where Eve had given birth to thirty children. One day, the Creator came to visit and began to count the children. In apprehension, Eve hid the fifteen most beautiful and intelligent ones. As punishment, the hidden ones were condemned to remain always hidden, nighttime creatures. Consequently, they envy their uglier and weaker human siblings, who are daytime children of the light.

The world of these hidden Zar spirits mirrors Abyssinian feudal and ethnocentric society. Some Zars are powerful lords, others serve them like retainers. Some Zars are classified as "rich man's Zar," others as "poor man's Zar." Spirits that are Coptic Christians are regarded as superior in social standing and education to Muslim and pagan spirits. Those who have their abode on the highland-plateau of Abyssinia, home of an ancient literate culture, are regarded as superior to Zars whose home is among the lowland, Sudanese, and ex-slave tribes.

One intellectual Zar is credited with having taught mankind the use of fire and cooking, by lending from his own flame atop a rock that juts out from the Red Sea. He and some other benevolent Zars can be persuaded to teach healing medicines.

THE ROLE OF THE PRACTITIONER

Such potential benevolence is utilized by the Zar doctor. Once a patient himself, he has learned to control the situation and has turned it into a profession. But both he and ordinary possessed are referred to by the same term "balä Zar."

To become a recognized doctor, he must have certain talents. One is the ability to cultivate the stare that can calm cases of hysteria. Another is linguistic ability, for he often speaks in Zar language, which Abyssinians regard as a completely different esoteric language. Actually, it is an argot composed of deformed Amharic (the major of the three Abyssinian languages) paraphrases and foreign loanwords (7).

Before he begins practice, the Zar doctor identifies his own personality more and more with that of the most powerful of the spirits possessing him, so that he can use his power against the lesser mischievous ones. In his name he opens a coffee tray (gända) in his own house, which symbolizes the altar of the cult.

Female Zar doctors almost always claim professional sanction through transfer of power and knowledge from their mothers. This is paraphrased as "transferring the monkey."

Male Zar doctors, in order to compensate for this lack of inheritance, often substitute a myth of contagion. They may claim that they had been kidnapped by Zar spirits during childhood and released in adolescence. Male Zar doctors make arrogant and extravagant claims more often than female doctors. Confronted with the technological superiority of the European, the male doctor may try to reduce the effect by claiming that only the night before he had magically visited the stranger's homeland and is familiar with all his gadgets. Male doctors often dress like old-time Abyssinian warriors and, like them, anoint the hair so that it stands up stiffly and ferociously.

In contrast, female Zar doctors, often regarded as superior to male ones, rarely show arrogance. When not in a violent trance, they usually assume the phlegmatic composure of the Abyssinian noblewoman. This was the usual poise of Woyzäro (Lady) Sälämtew, chief Zar doctor of Gondar in 1953–1954, although she herself was of low-class descent in Abyssinian society.

Thus, in the traditional form of the Zar cult, it was mainly the doctor who improved his (or her) social status. Gondar itself has about a dozen powerful Zar doctors, mostly female. But there are hundreds of Zar country doctors in the surrounding rural areas, mostly male, and less powerful.

DIAGNOSIS THROUGH DEMONSTRATION

In most cases of sudden symptoms of possession first aid is given the patient by kinfolk or neighbors. At nightfall, the patient is conducted to the house of the Zar doctor. The scene inside is warm with illumination, burning incense, and the assembled membership of the devotees, all chronic cases themselves. A relative hands an entry gift referred to as "incense money" to a disciple, who passes it quietly to the doctor behind a screened platform. The doctor ignores the new arrival until the spirit has taken full possession. Only then does the doctor emerge, her eyes bright and curious, her gestures commanding. She greets her flock and orders drinks for everyone. The male reader-composer of liturgy of the Zar cult intones old and new hymns of praise to the Zar. He is accompanied by the rhythmic handclapping of the worshippers. This ritual recharges the interrogation whenever the latter becomes difficult.

The Zar doctor pretends that she has guessed the identity of the spirit who plagues the patient. But this spirit must be made to confess in public so that negotiations can be made. The patient is asked leading questions, beginning with his recent activities and whereabouts. This may offer important clues. If answers are not satisfactory, the patient (i.e., the Zar speaking through him) is accused of lying. Gradually, the answers become more satisfactory. The doctor alternately lauds and threatens the spirit, giving the patient no rest. The latter is made to confess shortcomings, such as neglect of family, of kinfolk, of the church, and of course of the Zar himself, who may have been insulted in some unintentional way. Finally, the patient dances the individual whirl (*gurri*) of his particular Zar, identifying him through minor variations in the clockwise or counterclockwise rapid movements which end in temporary exhaustion. Still later, the patient learns to intone the proper war chant (*fukkārā*) of his spirit. Sometimes, several nights are needed to achieve this final expression.

MITIGATION OF SYMPTOMS THROUGH CHANNELING, ACCEPTANCE, AND GROUP MEMBERSHIP

The Zar doctor does not proclaim the final diagnosis until he has also studied the social and economic status of the patient. For an important part of the doctor's function is to match the social class of Zar with the socioeconomic class of patient. The Zar of poor and low-class members usually belongs to the class of "pages serving great Zars" (*wureza*). Such poor patients may work off their dues by "serving the tray." Sometimes, when a doctor regrets his earlier overestimate of a patient's financial position, he may "transfer" his expensive Zar to another devotee better able to bear the offerings demanded.

The symptoms of the patient are thus channeled in such a manner that will fulfill both his psychological and social needs. He is not made into a deviant from society. He learns to accept his ailment and come to terms with it. His new social role within the Zar society is similar to his position in the social hierarchy of the outside communty. But he is no longer a lone, unidentified individual in that outside community. He now has the backing of the Zar subculture and social organization.

The acceptance by the patient of his new role is ritualized. The Zar doctor helps him to transform the Zar spirit into an attitude of benevolence, of protection (*weqabi*). The aim is to reduce the sufferings in frequency and severity, in exchange for periodic offerings of animals, ornaments, incense money, etc. Most Zars are never exorcised. This is attempted only in a few stubborn cases, where possession is attributed to certain evil female Zars, whose "contracts" are regarded as unreliable anyway. In this case the doctor transfers the spirit to a spot near the path in the bush, where he can pounce upon an unsuspecting stranger. In his place, the patient is assigned another Zar as protective spirit, from among the Zars currently available in the house of the Zar society, and without a "horse" to serve them.

A more active and positive channel to mitigate symptoms and prevent relapse is in the group membership itself. Here is the sympathy of fellow-sufferers. Here are the opportunities to find interpersonal response and recognition in the interaction across barriers of sex and social class.

Here, hypochondriacal complaints can be expressed, and domestic problems aired. Economic security is provided through employment secured through the Zar doctor, or by spinning cotton in the doctor's house.

Moreover, every chronic patient-devotee, is assigned two human protectors referred to as "*mizē*," appointed from the society of devotees. In the ritual of possession, it is the duty of the *mizē* to be near the patient every time another possession occurs so that the patient is not injured (e.g., by flying ornaments during the violent twirling). But the real significance of the role of *mizē* is derived from the meaning of the term, literally "best men" who attend the bride at a wedding, and forever after protect her even against her own husband. In the outside community, *mizē* are usually appointed from among the husband's kinsmen, so that they can be trusted not to break up the marriage and because of patrilocal residence. The analogy is carried even further in the Zar cult. The new patient-devotee is referred to as "*mushärra*," newlywed to the Zar. The Zar does not resent the "best men," much as human bridegrooms do not show resentment against them. It is rather considered a reinforcement of the marriage bond, allowing for arbitration in case of discord.

Since most patients until recently were married women, they have all experienced and appreciated the *mizē* system, even though it may have broken down and not functioned well in their individual marriages. In human marriage in Abyssinian culture, the *mizē* are usually older but of the same generation as the bridegroom. One of them acts as the primary best man (*ser mizē*), the other as secondary (*gelgel mizē*). It is their duty to impart sex education to the bridegroom before the wedding, if necessary, and even to assist in the deflowering of a recalcitrant bride by restraining her, if need be. During the wedding ceremony, the *mizē* are sworn in. The formula is for the bride's father to say to the bridegroom: "Call for us two guarantors for her eyes, head, and teeth," whereupon the *mizē* step forward and take the oath to protect the bride from bodily harm. For that evening she leaves the parental hamlet. But the *mizē* act as go-betweens, so that she can maintain contact with her kinfolk at this point of stress. Two days after the wedding, the *mizē* travel to her former hamlet to report on her well-being and good treatment. On their return, they carry an invitation to the bridal couple to come for a three-day visit. On that occasion, donkey loads of household staples are given the bride. A month later, this is repeated.

In the Zar cult there is a literal analogy of this function. The Zar spirit is often regarded as the role of husband. The *mizē* are older persons of the patient's generation, who might have been elder siblings and have more experience in life as well as in the cult. This creates close human ties even within the primary group of the Zar society. They are always on hand to restrain an incipient hysteria, awaken the patient from incipient apathy, prevent injury in case of a convulsive fit, reduce proneness to accidents. Their psychological role is probably as important as their physical function.

THE CHANGING ZAR CULT AND SOCIAL MOBILITY

While the Zar cult continues in full force in Abyssinian culture in Gondar, certain significant changes can be traced from the early 1930's when a French expedition observed it there, and when I studied it in 1953–1954 (10).

Attempts are now made to conceal it from the rare foreign visitor, and in Addis Ababa the cult has been entirely suppressed by the government.

More significant is the change in the membership, leadership, and location of the cult, even in Gondar.

In 1932 the center of the Zar cult and house of the chief Zar doctor was located in the "respectable" Coptic sector, called *Bäata*, of the town, on top of the truncated hill that forms the geographical center of the town. The chief practitioner was an Amhara (dominant ethnic class of Abyssinia) lady in good standing with the Coptic church (2, 3, 5, 6).

In 1953–1954 the cult was centered in the old Muslim suburb called *Addis Aläm* at the bottom of the hill, now a slum even by local standards. It is inhabited largely by poor Amhara, half-Sudanese Muslims, and ex-slaves. They now constitute the majority of the regular members of the Zar cult, and many of these low-class members make use of it to achieve upward social mobility. Almost every dusk during the active season, a few city Amhara climb down the hill to participate or to consult the chief practitioner on a matter of business. The latter claims that from time to time clients come by airplane from as far as Addis Ababa (since there is no passable direct road). The chief doctor is a middle-aged woman, and many of her devotees are females engaged in spinning between sessions, much like twenty years ago. But now she, as well as many of her devotees, are part-Sudanese, although she speaks the upper-class Amharic language well. She has a reputation of considerable achievement both in her healing and her business activities.

If the cult survives the present suppression, one may form a prognosis of its continuance, not only in the healing activities, but as a syncretic link between Copts and Muslims, Amhara and Sudanese, ex-slave and upper class. One may even anticipate a revival of the Zar cult, if and when the industrial age comes to Ethiopia and technological change brings further problems of social adjustment. The Zar doctors have a tradition of initiative otherwise absent in the tradition-bound society of old Abyssinia, and provide a healing leadership for those persons who, because of psychological or social problems, find it difficult to carry on their normal roles in the general community.

SIMILARITIES BETWEEN TECHNIQUES OF THE ZAR CULT AND WESTERN GROUP PSYCHOTHERAPY

Western therapists who employ group dynamics are increasingly aware of the need for reference, what one might call an "active, positive, primary group" within the group. The Zar cult constitutes such a reference.

A number of modern therapists have begun to attempt to build up cultural awareness and respected identities (11). But some aspects of what they do unwittingly and sparingly have been built into an elaborate and complex pattern in the Zar cult for centuries past.

Modern group psychotherapy began only at the beginning of the twentieth century with Pratt, designated by some as "the father of group psychotherapy." He discerned a common problem in lower-class tubercular patients connected with the isolation and sense of secrecy and shame associated with this disease, its recognition, and management. Accordingly, he used the group technique to create hope and give patients instructions. Despite developments since then, current group psychotherapy is as concerned today with role conflicts exhibited within individuals and in groups as it was then (11).

The group setting has many advantages. It is collectively more powerful than the therapist himself, and the patient feels less helpless. This makes him less fearful. In the Zar cult the patient is even more personally supported by the two *mizē*.

By identifying the specific ailment, learning to accept it and live with it, the patient-devotee of the Zar cult perceives and organizes his instinctual impulses into thoughts and language that enable him to function properly in relationship to his environment. His former compulsive pattern of behavior is no longer compulsory, once the individual is aware of it and has a genuine feeling that there is an element of choice and manipulation. This is done for him by the Zar doctor.

One of the limitations of the modern group setting is that each individual receives less attention than he would if he received individual therapy (12). This factor is mitigated in the Zar cult by the appointment of the two *mizē*.

The success or failure of modern group therapy depends upon whether or not the group therapist is successful in helping the group members to a gradual understanding of their resistances in terms of the history, origin, and meaning of the resistances (12). These resistances and their gradual understanding are ritualized in the Zar cult as described earlier.

There is a marked tendency in the group setting to assuage intense feelings which tend to disorganized behavior (12). The repeated experience of clashing with group members and eventually adjusting to this continuously changing social reality, which becomes more familiar and more understanding as time goes by, tends to promote the growth of feelings of self-confidence and self-esteem with resulting improvement in general functioning (12). In the Zar cult, the practitioner sometimes has to keep order by wielding his stick and even using it occasionally, especially among relatively new members who become bored and inattentive more frequently than long-time members. The ultimate function of the Zar cult is not to create a deviant society, but to recreate self-esteem, recognition, and security, so that the patient can carry on his normal role in the outside community.

A modern psychiatrist expresses the hope that group therapy may "develop leaders who will guide society on its path" (12). The Zar doctors have been providing leadership in addition to their capacity of healing for many centuries past.

The processes of healing in the Zar cult, although they are systematic, could hardly be called scientific in the narrow modern sense. Apart from the ritual, the Zar doctor is overly concerned with the social status of his patient. But perhaps a number of prescientific lessons can be learned. Not the least of these is that every human being is vulnerable, and that certain social situations render him more vulnerable than others.

A significant similarity between the technique of the Zar cult and Western psychotherapy, basic in the former but not always in the latter, is expressed by the Danish psychiatrist, G. K. Stürup. He states that his own success is not based on curing the psychopaths but in transforming them into "nice psychopaths" who are capable of adapting themselves to ordinary life (13). This has been the ultimate aim and achievement of the Zar cult.

CONCLUSIONS

1. The "Zar" is a catchall for many psychological disturbances, ranging from frustrated status ambition to actual mental illness.

2. Healing is in context of a culture that is socially much more organized than commonly found under the shaman type. The Zar cult thus reveals many aspects of social structure, such as feudalism, the position of women, etc.

3. Since no patient is ever discharged as cured, the Zar cult functions as a form of permanent group therapy. The chronic patients become devotees, "nice psychopaths" in some cases, who form a close-knit social group in which they find security and recognition.

4. The Zar cult is not actually a deviant cult. Its significance in maintaining the status quo in society has traditionally been greater than improvement of social status. By matching the social status of patient and spirit, the doctor (inadvertently) functions in maintenance of the social structure of old Abyssinia. The patient must confess neglect not only of the Zar but of his other social duties also. The Zar spirit in turn becomes protective and helps the patient carry out his normal role in the outside community.

5. In recent change the motivation is shifting toward employment of cult membership for upward social mobility. This can be observed from the epidemiology of possession itself. In the past a neglected wife would punish her husband through having her Zar extort economic sacrifices from him on threat of relapse. Now, ex-slave and low-class persons are increasingly being chosen by the Zar. Both seek escape from their social confinements in the Zar cult.

6. Although some of the processes of this healing cult can hardly be regarded as scientific group therapy because of too much concern by the Zar doctor for the social status of the patient, a number of significant similarities can be traced. Perhaps some lessons can be learned from the permanency, the limited aims, and the techniques of channeling symptoms in accordance with the social and cultural backgrounds.

BIBLIOGRAPHY

1. Griaule, Marcel: *Mission Dakar—Djibouti, 1931–1933*. Paris: *Minotaure II*, 1933.

2. Leiris, Michel: *Le Taureau de Seyfou Tchenger (Zar)*. Paris: *Minotaure II*, 1933, pp. 75–82.

3. ————: "Le Culte des Zars à Gondar" (Etiopie Septentrionale). *Aethiopica*, 1934, vol. 2, pp. 96–103, and 125–136.

4. ————: *L'Afrique Fantôme*. Paris: Gallimard, 1934, pp. 336–337, 440.

5. ————: "Une Rite Médico-magique Etiopien: Le Jet du Danqara." *Aethiopica*, 1935, vol. 3, pp. 61–74.

6. ————: "La Croyance aux Génies 'Zar' en Etiopie du Nord." *Journal de Psychologie Normale et Pathologique*, 1938, vol. 1–2, pp. 108–126.

7. Leslau, Wolf: "An Ethiopian argot of a people possessed by a spirit," *Africa*, 1949, vol. 19, pp. 204–212.

8. Lifchitz, Deborah: *Quelques Noms de Maladie en Etiopien*. Communication au GLECS, Séance du 21 Fevrier 1940. Paris: Sorbonne, 1940.

9. Littman, Enno: *A Song about the Demon Waddegenni*. Leyden: Publications of the Princeton Expedition to Abyssinia, 1915, vol. 2, p. 311.

10. Messing, Simon D.: *The Highland-Plateau Amhara of Ethiopia*. Doctoral dissertation, University of Pennsylvania, Philadelphia, 1957.

11. Opler, Marvin K.: "Group psychotherapy: Individual and cultural dynamics in a group process." *American Journal of Psychiatry*, 1957, vol. 114, pp. 433–438.

12. Spotnitz, Hyman: "Group therapy as a specialized psychotherapeutic technique." In *Specialized Techniques in Psychotherapy* (G. Bychowski, ed.). New York: Basic Books, 1952, pp. 85–102.

13. Stürup, G. K.: *Danish Psychiatry*. Copenhagen: Schenberbske Forlag, 1948.

George De Vos

School of Social Welfare
University of California

and

Horace Miner

Department of Sociology
University of Michigan

14

OASIS AND CASBAH—A STUDY IN
ACCULTURATIVE STRESS *

ALGERIAN CULTURE AND PERSONALITY IN CHANGE

The Algerians we shall consider are known to the French as "Arabs" and, in fact, a thousand years of residence in North Africa has not obscured their racial and cultural ties to Arabia. Nevertheless, since the French occupied Algeria over a century ago, the Arabs have been subjected to marked acculturative influences, particularly in the French-dominated cities. The research reported here is specifically addressed to understanding the nature of the relation between Arab culture and personality under the impact of French urban influences.

In considering Arab culture, we have departed from the traditional anthropological method of describing culture traits in terms of the usual, average, or preferred behavior. Such descriptions possess a useful econ-

* De Vos is responsible for the scoring of the Algerian Rorschach protocols and for their interpretation. Miner collected the cultural data and administered the tests during fieldwork made possible by a grant under the Fulbright Act and another from the Horace H. Rackham Fund. The authors wish also to acknowledge the assistance of Bernard Berk, Akira Hoshino, Takao Sofue, and Mayumi Taniguchi in the processing and statistical analysis of the primary data.

The material utilized in this chapter is treated with a somewhat different emphasis in an article by De Vos and Miner: "Algerian Culture and Personality in Change," *Sociometry*, 1958, vol. 21, pp. 255–268 (6), and in Chapter 10 of a forthcoming book by Miner and De Vos: *Oasis and Casbah—Algerian Personality and Culture in Change* (9).

omy for some purposes, but they tend to give a false impression of homogeneity. Particularly in an investigation of the relationship between psychological and cultural phenomena, it seems desirable to express the cultural norms in terms of distributions of individually varying behavior. When this is combined with individual personality data, each person, as well as the culture group, becomes a meaningful item of analysis.

For our purposes, "personality traits" will refer to those basic psychological structures which are expressed in the generalized tendency of an individual to relate himself to various life situations in some characteristic fashion. Operationally defined, these traits will be those which emerge from the analysis of Rorschach protocols in conjunction with personal observations, but not depth interviews.

The basic design of the study involves the synchronic comparison of Arabs living in a small oasis in the northern Sahara with other Arabs who were born and reared in this oasis but who left it some time after adolescence to take up residence in the city of Algiers. These characteristics of the two groups minimize the degree of cultural difference which might be expected between them but maximize the probability of homogeneous origins of the two groups. The importance of the latter is obvious in a study in which group differences are to be interpreted as due to acculturative change. The possibility of selective urban migration cannot be ignored, but comparison of the two groups on the basis of a substantial body of family background data provides assurance as to their similarity of origin. The only selective factor apparently operating is that of economic pressure, but the necessity for migration out of the oasis is so great and so general that even the families which are economically more secure contribute sons to the urban movement. Such differences in background as were found were controlled in the comparative analysis.*

THE SETTING

The date-growing oasis of Sidi Khaled has a resident population of 5,300. The population has doubled in the last century, but further expansion of the agricultural economy is stifled by lack of water. As a result, two thirds of the men between the ages of twenty and fifty must now seek unskilled work in the cities of France and North Africa. A few of those who go to the city return after failing to find work or after accumulating a little capital. These returnees exert some acculturative influence in the oasis, and a French school has sporadically exposed a

* A full report of the investigation is in the process of publication (9).

small group of boys to the three "R's." Despite these influences, life for most of the oasis dwellers continues in terms of traditional Arab culture.

Those who move to Algiers find themselves in a new physical world, peopled with what appears to the newcomers as domineering French and with Arabs who have already altered many of their beliefs as a result of long interaction with the French. The secluded courtyard of the oasis gives way to the crowded apartment. Opportunities to work are controlled by the French or by relatively acculturated Arabs, and there are both economic and status advantages to adopting Franco-Arab city ways. To find a role in the life of the city, the migrant is inescapably forced, or lured, into adopting its patterns of life.

Within this oasis-urban comparative framework, we shall consider the cultural and Rorschach data collected in 1950 from sixty-four Arab men, largely between the ages of twenty and fifty. Twenty of these men, to whom we shall refer as the "oasis group," either have never been outside of the oasis setting or have had less than four months' residence in the city. The "urban group" consists of twenty-eight men who have lived more than a quarter of their lives in the city. All have resided there longer than five years and most for more than twenty. The sixteen Arabs who had amounts of contact intermediate between these oasis and urban groups are excluded from the comparisons to be considered, but they figure in the over-all analysis of Arab personality.

An attempt to work with subjects selected on a random basis proved utterly impractical. The oasis and urban groups, therefore, cannot be said to be representative. Both groups of subjects were, however, chosen so as to provide a wide range of age, occupation, and prestige. Despite the informal method of selection, the oasis and urban samples are similar in terms of their basic demographic characteristics. Each of the subjects was interviewed concerning the same areas of culture and a Rorschach test was administered to each.

SOME PSYCHOLOGICAL VARIABLES RELATED TO CULTURAL CHANGE

For purposes of this presentation * we shall deal mostly with those Rorschach variables that showed significant relations to specific cultural beliefs and opinions. The measures that showed the closest relationship to cultural traits were not the Rorschach variables usually scored in

---

* A more detailed presentation of the statistical treatment of all the Rorschach data will be presented in Chapters Eight and Nine of a full report now in process of publication (9).

quantitative analysis but *a*) over-all indices of rigidity and maladjustment, using a method of assessment developed by Seymour Fisher (7),
and *b*) a system for scoring the affective implications of the content of
Rorschach responses developed by De Vos.* These scoring systems have
been used previously with both American and non-Western data (3, 4,
5). There were certain model psychological patterns found in the protocols that did not differentiate between the urban and rural groups but
were highly characteristic for the group as a whole.

There were, for example, characteristic thought patterns in evidence
that conformed remarkably to a pioneering Rorschach study by Bleuler
and Bleuler done with Moroccans twenty years ago (2). Many individuals
tended to create percepts full of arbitrary juxtapositions on the one hand
or arbitrary discriminations on the other. The records were replete with
modes of thought suggestive of what would be diagnosed in Western
records as obsessive-compulsive character defenses. In the more extreme
cases the type of illogical juxtapositions brought forward in the organization of the responses, as well as the modes of rationalizing the responses
given, were strikingly similar to those found in paranoid records in
Western groups. An examination of certain individuals with sufficient
background evidence available demonstrated that the patterns of thought
indicated in the Rorschach were indeed related to behavioral evidence.
In a number of instances the test seemed to differentiate as well between
Arabs as it does between Americans, assuming sufficient knowledge of the
cultural background. In the main, the determinants of responses and the
location used were similar for both the rural and urban groups. However,
certain differences in the use of color, shading, and inanimate movement
distinguished the urban-dwelling Casbah group from those of the oasis.
The picture is a consistent one in which the urban group inferentially
demonstrated more tendencies toward diffuse anxiety, less conscious control over affective reactions, and more tension over the control of impulses.

On over-all assessment of rigidity, using the rigidity scale, the Arabs
scored extremely high. The group as a whole obtained a mean score over
one standard deviation above the mean of a sample of American nor-
mals. This mean was considerably beyond measures of rigidity as applied

---

* In this system the affective implications of the content are scored according to a
number of discrete categories of hostility, anxiety, etc. These categories are combined
for quantitative treatment into over-all indices of hostility, anxiety, body preoccupation, dependency, positive, miscellaneous, and neutral content. See De Vos (3) for
the criteria used in scoring according to this system.

to maladjusted American groups (see Table 14-1). On the maladjustment scale that was applied to the records, the mean score obtained for the group as a whole was directly comparable to that of an American neurotic sample and over two standard deviations above the mean of the American normal group.

TABLE 14-1

Rorschach Indices of Rigidity and Maladjustment in Arab and American Samples

		ARAB			AMERICAN		
		Oasis	*Urban*	*Total Sample*	*Normal*	*Neurotic*	*Schizo-phrenic*
	N	20	28	64	60	30	30
Rigidity	Mean	51.0 *	46.3 *	50.1 *	27.7	30.8	32.2 §
	S.D.	10.3 †	20.2 †	14.0	15.3	15.3	16.8
Maladjustment	Mean	63.3 *	61.8 *	62.2 *	34.0	65.8 * ‡	80.6 * ‡
	S.D.	19.8	26.1	20.2	16.2	31.7	23.8

Key to levels of significance:
 * Significance of difference from American normal .001
 † Oasis-urban Arab difference significant at .001
 ‡ Neurotic-schizophrenic American difference significant at .01
 § Schizophrenic-normal American difference significant at .05

While it does not follow that the Algerians should therefore be considered neurotic as a group, behavioral evidence was sufficient in a number of cases to indicate intrapsychic disturbance in certain capacities to adjust. In other cases, however, no overt maladjustment was perceivable.

The maladjustment and rigidity measures are not independent as to the variables scored. There is some tendency for individuals with excessively high rigidity of necessity to show these rigidity variables in the maladjustment scale as well. However, this sort of relationship is not always in evidence. These scales tended to covary only in the case of the urban group. In some of the Casbah records the maladjustment scores were related to the presence of inflexible ego defenses, not readily adaptive to changes in the environment.

One might raise the question, at least in regard to these over-all results with Algerians on a maladjustment score, of whether the type of personality integrations found modal for Arabs are sufficiently different

TABLE 14-2a

Comparison of Indices of Affective Symbolism

N %	ARAB Oasis 20		ARAB Urban 28		ARAB Total Sample 64		Normal 60		AMERICAN Neurotic 30		Schizophrenic 30	
	Mean	S.D.	Mean	S.D.	Mean	S.D.	Mean	S.D.	Mean	S.D.	Mean	S.D.
Hostility	6.8	8.6	10.0	7.9	8.5	7.4	9.4	7.1	11.6	6.9	8.3	7.7
Anxiety	19.1	14.2	18.7	14.9	18.3	14.1 *	13.8	7.6	22.6 ***	11.8	23.7 ***	14.1
Body preoccupation	2.0 †	3.6	10.1 †	19.0	5.7	12.4	4.1	4.9	9.3 *†	12.8	19.3 ***‡	23.2
TOTAL unpleasant	27.9 †	17.5	38.8 †	23.8	32.5	22.8	27.3	12.0	43.5 ***‡	13.2	51.3 ***‡	20.0
Dependent	7.1	7.1	6.1	8.0	7.0	8.3	4.6	4.6	7.0	7.4	6.0	6.8
Positive	13.2	10.7	9.4	9.2	10.4 **	9.4	17.2	10.9	11.9 *†	9.8	6.9 ***†	5.8
Neutral	49.3	19.6	43.0	37.5	45.3	29.0	49.3	15.6	35.3 ‡	19.2	34.6 ***	19.1

Key to levels of significance:

3 symbols = .001
2 symbols = .01
1 symbol = .05

* Comparison with American normal
† Comparison between oasis and urban Arabs
‡ Comparison between American neurotics and schizophrenics

Categories do not total 100% because of omission of "miscellaneous."

from those of Americans or French to involve special problems in adjustment to Western life.

No significant difference was found between the oasis and urban groups in either mean rigidity or mean maladjustment. In the city, however, the mean rigidity score is somewhat lower and shows significantly greater variability due to the appearance in a minority of individuals, including those more successful in acculturation, of lower rigidity scores.

TABLE 14-2b

Presence of Significantly High Scores in Hostility or Body Preoccupation

	Hostility *	Body Preoccupation *	Either or Both
Oasis (N = 20)	3	1	3 ⎫
Casbah (N = 28)	7	6	12 ⎬ P = .05
Total Arab (N = 64)	10	7	15 ⎭

Presence of Mutilated or Distorted Humans, or Tension Responses
(Such as Explosions)

Scored under Hostile Symbolism	Humans Mutilated or Distorted (Hsm and Hhad) †	Tension Response (Hhat) †	Either or Both
Oasis (N = 20)	6	1	7 ⎫
Casbah (N = 28)	13	8	17 ⎬ P = .05
Total Arab (N = 64)	28	10	34 ⎭

* 1 S.D. above mean of normal Americans:
hostile, 16%+
body preoccupation, 10%+

† See "A Quantitative Approach to Affective Symbolism in Rorschach Responses" (3) for a full description of criteria for scoring content.

These records are more comparable to American norms. The number of these records is not sufficient, however, to lower the mean significantly below that of the oasis group, since the city group also has a number of individuals with high rigidity that covaries with high maladjustment. The oasis group's rigidity and maladjustment scores did not covary. The most rigid records were in no case among the highest in maladjustment.

Turning to the analysis of symbolic content of the Rorschach protocols, the proportion of unpleasant content was found to be significantly higher among the city Arabs, particularly in the content categories indicative of body preoccupation or hostility. These results, as was indirectly indicated by the results with color and shading and inanimate movement determinants, suggest that urban residence produces increased psychic stress for the Arabs. Two patterns of adjustment which appear with some frequency in the city are only rarely found in the oasis. One centers around greater rigidity and internalization of aggression suggested by anatomical preoccupations. Such records contributed heavily to the high mean maladjustment score found in the urban group. Another pattern suggests the development of a more complex, flexible ego, but one which must cope with heightened internalized tendencies for aggressive hostility to be overtly expressed. In this latter pattern a considerable amount of tension over hostility is projected outward and the environment tends to be peopled with hostile and dangerous human forces. It is reasonable to believe from the Rorschach evidence that the degree of threat which the French represented to these Algerians was a reflection of intrapsychic stress as well as the continuing effect of objective political and economic issues.* (See Tables 14-2 a and b.)

PERSONALITY VARIABLES RELATED TO SPECIFIC CULTURAL BELIEFS

These characteristics of the urban Arab as compared to those living on an oasis are in some cases related to changes in culture in a direct manner. The ensuing discussion will, therefore, consider the interrelationships among three types of variables: a) the personality characteristics just discussed; b) urban contact; and c) cultural beliefs associated with the seclusion of women, the punishment of children, and those connected with certain supernatural beliefs.†

Seclusion of Women. Concerning the seclusion of women, we note that from the time of puberty they are carefully isolated from the sight of men other than their husbands and close kinsmen. A woman's life tends to be narrowly restricted to her home, and when she does leave its confines, she must be veiled and accompanied.

---

* Goldfarb (8) reports in a study of the American Negro the presence of anatomical content and responses in which the human body is perceived mutilated in some form in 88% of the cases included in Kardiner and Ovesey's study, *The Mark of Oppression.* The similar responses were notably present in Japanese immigrants to America (4) in contrast to those living in Japan. Abel and Hsu, although using a different interpretation, report anatomy responses prevalent in Chinese-Americans (1). The similarity of this sort of symbolic content in such widely disparate minority groups attests to certain possible common intrapsychic coping mechanisms related to the environmental stress of a depreciated minority status.

† Tests of significance of relationships are based on chi square, using a correction for continuity, or, particularly when theoretical cell frequency was below 5, Fisher's Exact Test was employed and the resultant probability doubled to provide the closest approximation of a two-tailed test.

The relation of three seclusion customs to the personality variables was explored, as will be seen from Table 14-3. The degree of veiling required and the terminal age for the seclusion of women both showed a statistically verifiable consistent relationship to rigidity and maladjustment. The more restrictive customs were preferred by Arabs who were very high in these qualities, and, interestingly enough, somewhat low in symbolic indications of hostility and body preoccupation in the content of Rorschach responses. Concerning the acceptability of wife's mother as her chaperone, however, there is a striking lack of relationship to the

TABLE 14-3

Levels of Significance of Relationships Between Rorschach and Cultural Variables *

	High Rigidity	High Maladjustment	Medium or High in Positive Content	High in Hostility and Body Preoccupation
Cleanliness				
Meticulous or Clean	—.10	—.10		
Seclusion				
Requires veiling of one or both eyes	.10	.01		—.10
Forbids wife to go out with her mother				
Wife's seclusion ends at 56 years or older	.001	.01		—.15
Punishment				
Beats severely or prefers beating	.05			—.15
Uses isolation				
Uses food deprivation	—.05	—.10	.05	
Supernatural				
Uses charms			.05	—.01
Believes in genii				—.15
Believes in power of Sahhara				—.05
Protects against or has been affected by evil eye			.05	—.01
Interprets his dreams				
Believes in power of Guezzana				

* Total Sample analyzed with two-tailed tests of significance. Minus signs indicate an inverse relationship between the variables.

psychological variables, despite the seeming similarity of the personality implications of the three seclusion customs.

If we place the evidence in the general context of what was learned about Arab personality, we conclude that the rigidity of the relatively maladjusted Arab, whose psychic problems are inferentially markedly sexual in origin, imposes strict controls on his women. In the tendency for an inverse relationship to exist between severity of restriction and hostility or body preoccupation symbolism, we see evidence that the rigid, maladjusted Arab who follows such restrictive practices does not tend to develop more internalized and intrapsychic conflicts over the handling of his aggressions. In a sense, they are "taken out on the women" in acceptable cultural ways which produce no overt or even covert hostile tensions.

The above cultural expression of personality characteristics is based on analysis of the total Arab sample. Beyond demonstrating its existence, it should be revealing to see how these apparently functional links between culture and personality operate under acculturative influences by contrasting urban and rural groups.

Considering veiling norms first, we note that the shift to the more liberal requirement of allowing the exposure of both eyes is so general in the city that only four of the urban Arabs continued to insist on more complete covering. The demonstrated personality implications of differences in veiling practice are, therefore, essentially an expression of the oasis situation.

The relationship of maladjustment to veiling is significant in the oasis group taken alone where there is still possibility of measuring differences in attitudes. It is revealing, however, to examine the urban "traditionalists," despite their small number. Of these four more restrictive Arabs, all are high in rigidity, three are high in maladjustment, and three are low in both hostility and body preoccupation, paralleling the oasis findings.

It is meaningful to ask if the change in cultural norms occurred despite the apparent psychic "utility" of the oasis norms in personality integration, or whether the changes in cultural attitudes are paralleled by personality shifts attendant upon urban residence. We have already seen that overall indices of rigidity and maladjustment do not change in the city, but Rorschach content symbolizing hostility and body preoccupation increases. The total evidence indicates, therefore, that change in attitudes toward veiling goes on despite its significant relationship in the oasis to certain personality traits and basic attitudes toward women which do not change with movement to the city. The urban increase in hostility symbolism or anatomical responses is consistent with the decline in severity in attitudes toward veiling. As will be further discussed in relation to supernatural belief, it would not be unreasonable to assume that the external social pressures of the Casbah affect cultural beliefs. With urbanization, the certain changes in psychological integration occur, since the individual finds himself bereft of beliefs and practices that make possible certain adjustments around these culturally condoned beliefs and behavior that circumvent intrapsychic conflict. The person who is more stripped of reassuring religious and social beliefs is also more exposed to the French world and what is perceived as its threatening domination.

There is less change in prevalence of attitudes between oasis and Casbah as to the age at which a woman may come out of seclusion. The relationship with content symbolism rigidity and maladjustment scores,* nevertheless, is similar to the results with veiling, namely those who are most rigid and maladjusted are more severe in adherence to custom, whereas those who give more hostile or body preoccupation content are prone to be less severe.

Punishment of Children. The psychological implications of the methods employed in punishing children are markedly varied. The use of isolation as a punishment shows no relation to the personality measures employed. The use of severe physical punishment is characteristic of the most rigid Arabs and of those who do not tend to show marked hostility or body preoccupation. But unlike seclusion customs, such beating of children shows no relation to maladjustment. Beating does not become less severe in the city, nor does rigidity decrease, but the expression of preference for such beating as the best form of punishment does decline. The Arab seems to beat his sons through rigid adherence to the pattern learned on the receiving end in childhood. The father's domination of his children is not altered by contact with the French, but he is probably not so likely to express, at least to a non-Arab, what he knows will be taken as an unduly punitive position.

The most rigid Arabs, however, are significantly less likely to punish children by depriving them of a meal, limiting their food, or even delaying their meals. The explanation here seems to be that beating is the usual form of punishment and only the less rigid Arabs are likely to depart from

---

* In the oasis, age out of seclusion is significantly related to rigidity at the .02 level, and in the city at .08. In the oasis the relationship to maladjustment does not reach significance, but in the city it is significant at the .05 level.

the pattern and employ other means. Interestingly, it is also those who tend to be better adjusted and who give more positively toned affectual material in the Rorschach who punish by food deprivation. Such Arabs show no less tendency to use physical punishment. It is as though those who use deprivation to punish their children do so with the feeling that "it is for their own good." Despite the association of the stable personality factors with food deprivation, this kind of punishment increases in the city (P = .06).

Supernatural Beliefs. Rigidity and maladjustment, which showed such striking relationships to the preceding culture traits, are not related to any of the six supernatural traits analyzed. However, the relation of maladjustment to belief or disbelief in fortune-telling *guezzanas* was significantly different in the city and oasis (P = .02). In the desert eleven of the twelve disbelievers are very high in maladjustment. It is possible that a religious interdiction of fortune telling is responsible for the tensions associated with this custom, but the direction of the relationship would have been hard to predict.

The most marked personality concomitant of the supernatural beliefs rated is the inverse relationship which exists between the intensity of four of the beliefs and indications of hostility or body preoccupation. As with seclusion customs, approved belief in supernatural forces seems to function to obviate the formation of aggressive sets either turned outward toward others or directed inward against the self that appear in Rorschach content symbolism. Customs concerning charms, the evil eye, and love magic of the *sahhara* show this pattern at statistically significant levels,* while belief in genii shows a trend of similar nature. The only beliefs which diverge from this pattern are the two involving prognostication. As a concomitant of the inverse relationship of four of the traits to types of unpleasant Rorschach content, two supernatural beliefs show significant relations to positive content in the test.

One may provisionally conclude on the basis of these results that the personality implications of the supernatural traits hold without regard for acculturative changes. Customs concerning charms, genii, and *sahharas* wane significantly in the city, where there is a concomitant increase

---

* We have seen that fortune telling is significantly and differently related to maladjustment in the oasis and city. Similarly, the use of dream interpretation is directly related to low anxiety in the city (P = .05) and the city differs from the oasis in this regard (P = .11). The only other significant finding with respect to supernatural traits in the subsamples was the inverse relation of use of charms to hostility and body preoccupation in the urban group taken above.

in evidence of hostility and body preoccupation symbolism. But concern over the evil eye, which has similar personality implications, is not altered by urban contact. In fact, all of the evidence we have presented indicates that culture change goes on in response to social pressures, without much regard for the previous personality implications of the traits involved. It would certainly have been impossible to predict which culture traits would change on the basis of our knowledge of their psychological significance for the individual in the oasis and our knowledge of the personality shifts attendant upon urban contact. There is probably some sort of threshold beyond which given personality types cannot adjust to certain cultural behaviors. Our investigation, however, seems to indicate a marked tendency for personality predispositions and cultural configurations to develop new kinds of equilibria during acculturation.

It is important to point out also that half of the urban group came to the city when they were fourteen years of age or older and three-quarters were over nine years old. The changes which they underwent, both culturally and psychologically, demonstrate that the effect of early training and experience is not conclusive in personality formation. It is the continuity of influences through life, and not just the impact of early influences alone, that makes men as they are.

In summary, then, the evidence from Rorschach protocols, when viewed in relation to seclusion practices, discipline of children, and religious beliefs, shows a consistent pattern, namely that attentuation of traditional beliefs in the urbanized Arabs is related to increasing intrapsychic tensions that are expressed in symbolic form in Rorschach content in a number of individuals. The minority position of the more acculturated urbanized Arab is reflected in internalized personality adaptations in which the social environment is more directly experienced as hostile and threatening. He must cope with the implications of this psychological set intrapsychically. Direct expression of reactive hostility was not readily possible. Attention is more directly focused on feelings of being directly oppressed in relation to the dominant French. Those who adhere more tenaciously to traditional beliefs may demonstrate greater rigidity in certain instances and score higher on maladjustment indices, but in adhering to social and religious beliefs they are not forced into patterns of adaptation that cause them to experience social relationships as directly involving a great degree of personal threat coming from their own projected hostility. The fact that analyses of materials on urban American Negroes living in New York (8) show similar Rorschach patterns of personality integration is highly suggestive for understanding the effects of minority group status on individual integration where pronounced rejection by the dominant group makes actual assimilation impossible.

A Note on the Cultural Setting of Arab Personality Formation

The above discussion concerns itself with certain demonstrable differences between urban and rural oasis Algerians. Elsewhere (6) we have discussed how these differences between the oasis and Casbah groups are far overshadowed by similarities in personality that are part of a modal configuration. These modalities suggest the effects of certain culturally widespread experiences in psychosexual development.

The Rorschach records in our sample are most characterized by ego defenses related to problems over the internalization of disciplinary controls and unresolved feelings of threat from an overwhelming authority figure. While there are numerous signs of regression to what, in Freudian terms, is described as "anal sadism," the Algerians as a whole are less characteristically concerned with the earliest stage of ego development in which personal relationships are concerned with nurturance. Oral symbolic material is not lacking, but it is not more prevalent than that found in numerous other groups.

Looking from the Rorschach to the culture one finds that the fear of attack found in the Rorschach is directly explainable in terms of the behavior of the culturally dominant father who in exercising his prerogative is often given to uncontrolled rage and physical abuse. The Arab adult is free to display violent affectivity toward women and children with no real pressure of sanctions to modulate or suppress such behavior. Fear of retribution checks such free displays outside the home, but within its confines a man is free to display genuine affection or anger quite freely. Since there is an expectation that an angry father will resort to physical abuse if sufficiently angered, a child learns to avoid direct provocations by any direct challenge of authority.

There is little room for logical discussion, and objective fact is not often used as a way of settling issues. The relationship of a wife to a husband does not allow for the experience of temperance or regard for the opinions of women. Nevertheless, part of the cultural tradition of women is how to handle men by guile and deceit.

One method the child learns in relating to others which seems to be modally adapted at certain periods of development is passive submission.

This passive submission has certain sexual components. Early experience associates mother and other female adults and siblings with sexual stimulation. Later, very strong internalized sanctions are imposed against continued orientation toward these earlier sex objects. These sanctions are hypothetically related to the type of classical attempt at resolving the oedipal rivalry described by Freud in his theory of the formation of neurosis. The very severe threat represented by the father is resolved by giving up the world of women, and the culture supplies a pattern of behavior that ideally suits this form of partial resolution.

The young boys leave the world of women and younger children to join in the almost exclusive world of men found outside the walls of the home. The young boy has a strong need to belong to this world of men. There is a culturally prevalent pattern of inducing young preadolescent males to the homosexual practices of older males. Homosexual submission as a means of placating a more dominant figure can be considered a culturally modal defensive maneuver, but the temporary assumption of a passive, submissive relationship in directly sexual terms arouses strong needs for a compensatory assertion of one's masculine identity in a world where to be a woman is so heavily disparaged. The young preadolescent, therefore, with further development attempts to become in his own eyes and those of others a virile male.

This experience of many of the preadolescent Algerian males entering the man's world is not unlike that of the newcomer entering the exclusive male world of a prison. The younger weaker-looking inmates are first "pressured" for their commissary privileges. If they succumb, "pressure" to submit to homosexual advances follows. As in the prison, little opprobrium is attached to the dominant individual among the Algerians who is seen as "masculine" in so using another individual, but as in the case of convicts, there is nothing but contempt for the passive individual who cannot psychologically or physically protect himself. If homosexuality of the passive sort continues into adulthood, the man is despised by others. The most severe term one can call an Arab is that of naming him a passive homosexual.

As in a prison, a great deal of time and energy goes into demonstrations of virility and masculinity. However, it is apparent that this emphasis on manliness does not lead to very easy or satisfactory relationships with women. The converse of the emphasis on virility is the concern with impotency widespread in Arab culture. Diffuse feelings of threat and feelings of inner inadequacy are disguised in more consciously tolerable distrust and intense suspicion of women. Now repressed homosexual proclivities receive conscious representation in jealousy fantasies concerning the potential behavior of one's own women with other males. Shaky over one's virility, women are blamed for sexual inadequacy, as in the case of men who accuse their wives of using *sahharas* to make them impotent. Potential rage toward possible initiators of adultery with one's wife goes hand in hand with underlying oedipal fantasies of adultery with the wives of others.

It is not difficult to relate these patterns to unresolved childhood rages toward an aggressive, dominant, and fearsome father. What is not as clear is what the effect of polygyny within the home has on the nature of the image of the father and that of the mother. It may well be that it serves further to heighten the impression of father's authority and dominance and suggest the alternative submissive role as a mode of relating.

Since an immature individual who perceives himself as weak usually retreats from actual conscious rivalry or rebellion, the conscious feelings expressed toward the father emphasize respect rather than hostility. And so it is with the Arabs. One notes in most instances an active respect in men for their fathers. The better-adjusted men resolve possible difficulties by making an active identification with their fathers.

It was noteworthy, however, that in those cases of individual Arabs who behaviorally had achieved such an identification, the sense of threat from outside forces had not disappeared from their Rorschach records. Even with an active identification with the role of an active dominant male, one must continue to defend himself against his former passive proclivities. Paranoid-like projection and obsessive compulsive character defenses are in common use to prevent a return to passive submission. It would seem that relatively few attain the dominant, active role without a severe struggle of some sort.

Once attaining some modicum of personal economic independence, the Arabs tend toward asocial seclusiveness in family life, each within his own domain. A man makes of his own home a fortress against outside attack, yet memories of his own deviousness plus the above personality considerations make him mistrust even those within. For as a child he probably observed how family members can intrigue against one another for the father's favor, or how they can combine in deceiving him. One learns how not to trust most people. Relationships of trust do not extend to women or subordinates, but are limited to certain kinship ties where stringent social sanctions define the limits of behaviour, or to close personal ties between men that sometimes have an unconscious homosexual flavor.

Not all men achieve a dominant masculine role. The nature of the extended family is such that it readily permits the entry into a passive economic relationship with a brother, brother-in-law, or other near kin. The household can include one or more such dependent families. Such a relationship can be satisfactory to both. The support of kin attests to one's attainments as a family head. For the dependent, on the other hand, it allows for a cessation of struggle against passive proclivities, into a sometimes devious submissiveness—or into an adulation of the dominant figure as a paternal surrogate.

As we have suggested indirectly from our analysis of the Rorschach in the process of personality formation, supernatural beliefs can be presumed to bolster inner defenses. There is definite evidence that those individuals who actively employ supernatural forces have less internal tension.

Some of the supernatural beliefs and practices of the Arabs seem to be directly relevant to prevailing fears and concerns. It is not difficult, for example, to equate concern with love magic and the relatively common fear of impotence. The nature of the description of how one is attacked and penetrated by genii is almost a direct reflection of various forms of Rorschach symbolism found in certain records attesting to a fear of penetration. It is interesting to note the consciously emphasized heterosexual nature of the genie's attack in that certain informants aver that men are only possessed by female genii and the converse is true for women.

The fear of the evil eye is not limited to Arab culture, but its prevalence among the Arabs attests also to a fear of attack from the outside. Belief in the evil eye with its emphasis on the destructive power of the eye of an envious person when turned on a desired object possessed by another, whether there is conscious intent or not, suggests again fear of penetration.

In the more stable social order of the relatively isolated oasis we found firmer beliefs and tendencies toward more secure though highly constricted personality patterns. Conversely those who moved to the Casbah tend to suggest lessening belief on the one hand and more symbols of intrapsychic stress on the other. Even those who achieve a more adequate adaptation to their new half-Western and half-Arab environment often show serious lack of development of more objective emotional and intellectual controls and the prevalence of a readiness to project fears and hostilities—all of which suggest that relationships between individuals remain difficult and uneasy.

BIBLIOGRAPHY

1. Abel, T. M., and Hsu, F. L. K.: "Some aspects of personality of Chinese as revealed in the Rorschach test." *Rorschach Research Exchange* and *Journal of Projective Techniques,* 1949, vol. 13, pp. 285–301.

2. Bleuler, M., and Bleuler, R.: "Rorschach's ink blot test and racial psychology: peculiarities of Moroccans." *Character and Personality,* 1935, vol. 4, pp. 97–114.

3. De Vos, George: "A quantitative approach to affective symbolism in Rorschach responses." *Journal of Projective Techniques,* 1952, vol. 16, pp. 133–150.

4. ———: "A comparison of the personality differences in two generations of Japanese by means of the Rorschach test." *Nagoya Journal of Medical Science,* 1954, vol. 17.

5. ———: "A quantitative Rorschach assessment of maladjustment and rigidity in acculturating Japanese-Americans." *Genetic Psychological Monographs,* 1955, vol. 52, pp. 51–87.

6. De Vos, G., and Miner, H.: "Algerian culture and personality in change." *Sociometry,* 1958, vol. 21, no. 4.

7. Fisher, Seymour: "Patterns of personality and some of their determinants." *Psychological Monographs,* 1950, vol. 64.

8. Goldfarb, W.: "The Rorschach experiment." In A. Kardiner and L. Ovesey: *The Mark of Oppression.* New York: W. W. Norton & Co., 1951.

9. Miner, Horace, and De Vos, G.: *Oasis and Casbah—Algerian Culture and Personality in Change.* In preparation for publication.

J. B. Loudon

Institute of Psychiatry
Maudsley Hospital, London

15

PSYCHOGENIC DISORDER AND SOCIAL CONFLICT
AMONG THE ZULU

My aim in this study is to examine the relation between certain kinds of ritual and certain forms of psychogenic disorder occurring among the Zulu of South Africa. The theoretical emphasis is as much on what clinical medicine may be able to tell the social anthropologist as on how the anthropologist may be able to help the practicing physician.

The ritual in question has been discussed by Gluckman (2) in a recent publication, and is known as the *Nomkubulwana* ceremony. In essence, it consists of a rite performed only by women, at the time when the new crops have just begun to grow, in honour of a goddess; the ostensible purpose of the ritual is to ensure fertile crops. But it also appears to have deeper significance, in that it seems to express—in an institutionalised and publicly approved form—the normal subordination of women to men, by giving vent to the tensions created by that subordination. For the ritual is characterised by the temporary assumption by women of certain cardinal features of male behaviour and of male dress; furthermore, the modest demeanour which is normally expected of Zulu women is replaced, for the duration of the ritual, by flagrantly obscene actions, accompanied by lewd utterances. The men meanwhile abstain from participation in, or even observation of, this ritual of rebellion, as Gluckman has called it; furthermore, they are anxious that it should take place and accept, as their positive contribution to its effectiveness, the passive role of nonparticipation.

Gluckman's male informants made it clear that they were convinced that the *Nomkubulwana* ritual would help to produce bountiful crops; and he states that "a dropping of normal restraints, and inverted and transvestite behavior, in which women were dominant and men sup-

351

pressed somehow were believed to achieve good for the community—an abundant harvest" (2). "The ceremonial operates seemingly by an act of rebellion, by an open and privileged assertion of obscenity, by the patent acting-out of fundamental conflicts both in the social structure and in individual psyches" (2). But it is not clear from Gluckman's account whether or not there is any evidence to show that either the men or the women were conscious of the symbolism involved in the ritual, insofar as it may be a catharsis. In the absence of any such evidence, one must agree with Nadel (5) in claiming that "the social effectiveness of symbols lies in their capacity to indicate, and if they indicate nothing to the actors, they are, from our point of view, irrelevant and indeed no longer symbols—whatever their significance for the psychologist or psychoanalyst."

Gluckman's analysis of the *Nomkubulwana* ritual is both plausible and impressive. But, insofar as the fundamental conflicts are "both in the social structure and in the individual psyches," it would gain greatly in weight if supported by data obtained from individual participants. This individual aspect of social conflict is crucial to the exploration I am attempting and I shall return to it later. Here it is as well to stress how widespread in Africa are mechanisms whereby social unity appears to be achieved, maintained, and emphasized through the acting-out of fundamental conflicts in the community. These mechanisms are a feature common to a variety of rituals occurring in widely different social contexts. Thus not only do women behave with orgiastic licence in "a vestigial fertility rite," as Bryant considered the *Nomkubulwana* ceremony to be; but the same element is found in funeral ceremonies and in rituals intended to drive away crop pests. Junod (3) describes the lewd dancing and obscene back-chat of Tsonga women at funerals and says that their menfolk tolerate their behaviour as a necessary though embarrassing feature of important occasions.

In his comments on the *Nomkubulwana* ritual, Gluckman puts forward a number of propositions, some of which are of special interest in the context of this essay. For example, for how long is the cathartic purging effective? How does the ritual itself keep within bounds the rebellious sentiments aroused? Why is the reversal of roles so important a part of the ritual mechanism? In how far is it true that the marital situation imposes great and only partially subdued strains on Zulu women? What is the relation, if any, between their rituals and such things as conversion hysteria and spirit possession, to which Zulu women are peculiarly liable?

An approach to some of these questions may be made by examining the development of the individual in contemporary Zulu society, concentrating attention on those features of the life history of the child and adult which seem to have relevance for the discussion which follows.

Outstanding among the essential features of the Zulu social system is the agnatic lineage. Exogamous clans, tracing common descent in a putative patrilineal line over six to nine generations, form the most important divisions of the Zulu nation. Lineages within clans are usually residential units, and segments of lineages form the nuclei of villages. A number of segments living in one neighbourhood form a district group relative to other similar groups, of the same clan and of other clans. There are rights and obligations, such as residual inheritance rights and obligations to help one another, between fellow clansmen. Members of segments hold rights in each other's herds and lands, and consult on personal questions.

Each exogamous clan obtains wives from other clans by giving cattle which transfer to the husbands and their agnates rights to all the children of the wives, whoever the genitors of the children may be. A child is absolutely a member of his mother's husband's lineage, and all his rights of inheritance lie in it, and not in his mother's lineage.

The kinship terminology clearly distinguishes paternal kin from maternal kin, and behaviour toward the latter is much less formal and submissive than it is toward the former. A man's formal ties and major responsibilities are centred in his father's people, but his mother's relatives are very important in his life and it is with them that he enjoys social relations of which affection and easy informality are the keynote.

Marriage is frequently polygamous and marriage to two sisters is approved. Divorce is comparatively uncommon, even today, and it does not form a common subject of discussion. Children are highly valued and there is an obligation on the family of a woman who proves sterile on marriage to send a substitute to raise children for her by her husband. There is nothing the maturing Zulu woman fears more than childlessness. Sterility leads inevitably to substantial loss of a woman's social and economic status. It seems probable that the number of sterile or relatively sterile women among the Zulu is steadily rising. The incidence of venereal disease has risen by many hundreds per cent over the last twenty-five years, not only in the urban areas, but also in the rural parts of Natal, whether Native Reserve or European-owned farm. Furthermore, the number of illegitimate children born has also increased tremendously among the Zulu, in particular if one interprets the word "illegitimate" in the widest sense as meaning the birth of children whose parents are not merely unmarried, but who never live together for more than a few weeks or months at the most. These babies are not only particularly liable to be congenital syphilitics, but the lack of stable background, experience and care on the part of unmarried and unattached mothers, the frequent use of foster parents with all that it means in terms of hopelessly inadequate artificial feeding, all combine to raise still further the infant mortality rate.

About 300 out of every 1,000 live Zulu children born die before their first birthday, and about 200 more die between their first and fourth birthdays. The comparable rates for whites in South Africa are 36 per 1,000 and 4 per 1,000, respectively. The major aim of Zulu marriage is the rearing of children; the women may thus be justified in showing some anxiety about their success or failure as mothers. For even if they prove fertile, they know that many children fail to survive their early years. The anxiety is not less because they do not know that the chances of a child so surviving is little better than even, or because they have no notion of the comparative figures I have presented.

Zulus do not necessarily expect to marry for love, but Western concepts need not affect the emphasis to be placed on this. Rather should we examine the status of the newly married woman in her husband's household. Apart from the restraints imposed on and accepted by all women—such as their legal position as minors under the care of father, mother, husband, or son—the bride is subservient in her new home to her husband's mother, and, to a less extent, to the other senior women in the household or district. This subservience may last for many years. Until she had borne a child, she may not partake of certain foods, such as milk or *amasi*, and the position she eventually attains as an old woman, when she may be the real, if not legal, head of the family, is only reached over a period of many years, during which her lot is very arduous. To Western eyes, a woman of sixty often looks twenty years older, after a life of regular child-bearing, constant domestic tasks, and continual fetching, carrying, hoeing, and weeding.

Women are generally considered to possess inherently evil qualities. They come to their husband's household as members of another clan and look to their own ancestors for spiritual support rather than to their new domestic ancestors. Their menstrual discharges may be good in that they are the source of children, but they are also bad, being a source of great danger to men, cattle, and crops. In ritual their role is subordinate, and any magic they perform is usually bad magic; but they have one means of performing good ritual actions—namely, by becoming diviners. Nevertheless, they more often become sorcerers as a result of their inherently evil natures; such women are believed to have sexual familiars, among which the most notorious is Tikoloshe, a hairy dwarf of obscene propensities.

Women are thus both threats to the social system as the source of danger of various kinds, but also the mainstay of the social system, in that they are the cultivators of the fields and the providers of children. Linked with them are cattle; cattle, the major asset of all Zulus, which confer wealth, position, and prestige, change hands primarily at marriages. The cattle go one way, the women the other; the cattle as *lobola* (bride price) to the women's kin, and the women as brides to the men's households to rear new generations. Cattle have enormous ritual value, and on all important ritual occasions a beast is either killed as a sacrifice, by means of which a man may receive the blessings of the ancestors of his agnatic lineage, or it passes from one group to another, as at marriage. At marriage, moreover, the bride is incorporated into her husband's group by touching the gall bladder of a beast sacrificed at the wedding ceremony. Cattle are, however, entirely taboo to women. They take no part in herding or milking them; nor are they allowed to enter the *isiBaya* or cattle enclosure, one of which forms the central feature of every Zulu homestead. In theory this rule applies as much to young girls and old women as it does to women of child-bearing age; but, in practice, the senior wife of the head of the household may enter the *isiBaya* when she becomes mistress of the *kraal* on the death of her husband's parents.

Women are thus excluded altogether from any dealings with the preeminent economic and ritual activities of any group—whether her own kin group or that of her husband. On the other hand, they are expected to carry out all the other economic activities of the household that have no ritual significance. These occupations include the care of the fields and gardens, with the laborious hoeing and weeding involved, the preparation of food and drink, the cutting of special grass for thatching, and the collection of fuel and water. Thatch grass, fuel, and water may not be obtainable near the homestead, and a journey of a mile or more may be required to get them. The cutting of thatch grass, however, is a seasonal activity and is carried out by parties of women in the dry season. But fuel and water may have to be collected every day or more than once a day, the heavy loads being transported by hand for considerable distances. Furthermore, as Zulu homesteads are almost invariably built high on the sides of hills, a relic of the days when the nation was organized for war, the women have to carry their loads up hill. The use of pack animals is almost unknown, and men never assist in the prosaic but burdensome tasks of the household.

The daily life of the Zulu woman is thus most arduous, and her activities are little diminished either by pregnancy or the need to care for young children. In either case she merely has an added weight to carry with her on her household and agricultural tasks and expeditions, which continue to be performed until labour commences, and which are resumed soon after the birth of the child.

In spite of common belief to the contrary, these constant outdoor physical activities do not result in childbirth being any easier for Zulu women than it is for women in other parts of the world. In addition, certain observances related to the actual process of parturition tend often to hinder rather than help the birth; and the anxieties inseparable from childbirth have particular features for the Zulu women undergoing labour in a household dominated by her mother-in-law and many miles from skilled assistance or the care of her own kinswomen.

The newborn Zulu baby is forbidden the breast for the first day or two. Until the first flow of milk appears, it is fed with warm water in which a little *amasi* (sour curds) may be mixed. For the colostrum is believed to be harmful and poisonous, in the sense of being physically harmful, rather than in the sense of being magically harmful although physically innocuous. If the baby does not appear to suck satisfactorily when put to the breast, however, the older women of the household may decide that the mother's milk is poisonous in the sense of being magically injurious or bewitched. In many instances, this decision appeared to be influenced by a woman's antagonism toward her son's wife, partly because she was an intruder from a potentially hostile kin group and partly on account of personal incompatibilities. In such matters, a young wife needs to be very patient and determined, and the anxiety of the conflict tends to decrease the flow of milk. These babies are thus often given food other than breast milk, and it is safe to say that very few of them manage to survive.

Zulu mothers make much of their babies, kissing and fondling them openly and with pride. This is particularly the case when the babies are male. Women enjoy breast-feeding, and babies are fed on demand; while still very small, they are put to the breast whenever they wake, and when a little older, they are fed whenever they cry. Children live in close contact with their mothers until they start to walk, being carried on the back during the day while the women are engaged in their work in the home or in the fields. During the night the child sleeps beside its mother, under her blanket.

In some cases, however, as soon as a child is being given supplementary foods as well as the breast, it may be looked after for part of the day by other women in the household or by its older siblings or by other children specifically detailed for the task. This is particularly the case where the mother is employed for part of the day by Europeans. In such instances, weaning may not be a major problem. For weaning does not take place until the child is about two years old, either when the mother becomes pregnant again or when she wishes to do so. Sexual relations between husband and wife are forbidden while she is breast-feeding; while a woman may cease to suckle a child because she has in fact resumed coitus with her husband, in only one instance out of many hundreds of cases did I come across a Zulu woman who became pregnant while her previous child was less than eighteen months old.

When a child of about two years of age, who has become accustomed to being cared for by older children or by women other than its mother, is taken off the breast and made to sleep in a separate hut with its brothers and sisters or with its grandmother, the effect of weaning may be minimal. In cases where the child has spent most of its life hitherto close to its mother's body, the results of the sudden banishment may be more dramatic; such children sometimes become considerable problems, especially as they are now put on to a diet consisting largely of carbohydrate. By and large, however, it is my view that the suddenness of the weaning and the comparative lack of interest shown in the weaned child by a mother with a new baby to consider are counterbalanced by the late age at which the weaning takes place and by the fact that most Zulu children are accustomed to being looked after by many people besides their mother by the time they are two years old.

While it has been shown that a woman is sometimes said to be magically harmful to her own children, it does not appear that children ever likewise endanger their mother, in spite of the fact that the Zulu believe all children to be born with an unavoidable and inherent taint which, unless suitably treated, may infect adults. Failure to take proper steps to rid a child of *isiGweba,* as the taint is called, may result in a number of ailments when the child grows older; in particular, the child may be sexually depraved or lecherous when it grows up. Adults who come into contact with a child insufficiently purged of this congenital taint are thought to be made peculiarly prone to skin diseases and to be afflicted with lechery.

The visible sign of *isiGweba* is the meconium, a greenish-coloured material excreted by all newborn infants before they have taken sufficient nourishment to start producing the normal, bright yellow faeces. It is possible that there is also an association in the minds of Zulu women between the green meconium and the greenish slimy faeces character- istic of infantile gastroenteritis and infant malnutrition. The first is a sign of congenital evil, and the second is a frequent precursor to the death of children.

Soon after the birth of a child, a concoction of various herbs and roots is blown into the rectum through a hollow reed. This is done in the first instance to rid the child of its meconium and the associated congenital taint. But the process is repeated daily for periods varying from a few days to some months. In addition to these enemata, the process known as *ukuGweba* is also carried out. One or more plant stems are thrust into the child's anus and swiftly revolved in it until blood is drawn. The custom of *ukuGweba* is apparently more specifically con- cerned in preventing the congenital taint having its effects on the child than are the enemata. The process may be continued daily for a few weeks and then at longer intervals for about a year, small twigs being substituted for plant stems as the child grows older and, presumably, as the mucosa of the anal canal becomes hardened to the treatment it re- ceives; for it seems that blood must be drawn for the treatment to be effective. At the same time a small cow's horn with a perforated point is used as an enema in place of the reed used while the child is still small. The enemata appear to be continued for general reasons of health rather than for any specific purpose. Indeed, enemata are a major feature of Zulu household remedies, and are administered frequently, and to peo- ple of all ages, as much as a precaution as for the relief of particular symptoms.

When the Zulu child reaches the age of four or five, he or she is ex- pected to help look after new babies, while small girls, in particular, are expected to make themselves useful around the homestead. As they grow older, boys take over such jobs as herding stock and guarding crops against pests, while girls assume greater responsibility for the more arduous duties of fetching and carrying water and firewood. It is, for example, the young girls who are expected to keep the fires replenished in the sleeping huts during the cold nights of winter.

The Zulu girl soon learns that the world is a man's world, and she is taught how to behave toward her elders and in particular toward her father and her paternal kin. When she reaches puberty, she comes under the control of older girls, who tend to be organized into gangs under a leader dominant in the age set. The younger girls are instructed in the techniques of external intercourse and in the way they should behave with sweethearts, but they are not allowed to put what they learn into practice without the permission of the older girls. Above all, their demeanour is supposed to be modest and they must at all costs avoid becoming pregnant until they are betrothed.

Although the *ukuGweba* process (as described above) is applied to both male and female children, the effects of failure to carry it out are thought to be particularly marked in the case of girls. Thus, a girl who is notorious for her lechery, but who may be careful or fortunate enough to avoid becoming pregnant before marriage, will be said to have been insufficiently treated by *ukuGweba* in her infancy. On the other hand, a modest and well-behaved girl who becomes pregnant before marriage and who does not get married before her child is born, although not condemned as lecherous, used to be ostracized on social occasions, and even today is treated neither as a marriageable girl nor as a married woman.

It will be seen that the practice of *ukuGweba* is not intended to prevent girls becoming pregnant before they are married. Nevertheless, all social emphasis is on the need for women to avoid premarital pregnancy, while premarital sexual intercourse is institutionalised in the form of external intercrural intercourse. In this way a girl's virginity is retained while the normal physiological needs of young adults are satisfied in a way socially acceptable to the Zulu people. The customs still pertain wherein a girl's mother or grandmother carries out regular inspections to make sure that the girl remains a virgin. This is not because virginity, as such, is highly valued by husbands or by anybody else, but because a girl who is no longer a virgin has obviously been running the risk of becoming pregnant, if she is not already so.

From early childhood, as this brief analysis of the development of the individual has shown, the Zulu female is imbued with the subordinate nature of her social and personal role. Before puberty her freedom is more restricted than is that of her male contemporaries, and her work more arduous and time-consuming. After puberty, until marriage, she continues to work in her parental homestead; at the same time, she becomes practiced in a socially accepted form of sexual intercourse, in which she is enjoined to keep her passions curbed and her legs crossed, and from which she obtains considerably less satisfaction than her lover, although she is expected to be an enthusiastically active partner. When she marries, she acquires both the dignity of her new status and the frustration resulting from the transfer to a strange household and from the restraints associated with her membership of a potentially hostile and strange kinship group. Finally, she is expected to be a successful wife and mother, a dutiful daughter-in-law, and the eventual mainstay of her husband's house and family.

The relation, if any, between the *Nomkubulwana* ritual and certain forms of psychogenic disorder among the Zulu will now be examined.

In the first place, there is some historical evidence which, although suggestive, must not be taken as establishing any form of causal connection between the two. The *Nomkubulwana* ceremony was no longer performed in Zululand, according to Gluckman who did his fieldwork there, in the 1930's. Nor did I observe it in the 1950's, although I believe it may still be performed in a very modified form in the more remote districts. At any event, it is clear that the ritual is more or less obsolete, and that it became obsolescent at or before the beginning of the twentieth century.

Now it is interesting to note that a relatively specific form of psychogenic disorder which is very much more common among women than among men appears to have manifested itself at about the same time, and to have greatly increased in incidence in the past fifty years. The disorder appears to have many features in common with what is known to Western medicine as conversion hysteria; in many instances the cases also have marked anxiety symptoms, this being particularly true of male patients.

In the district in which I worked the disorder is known to the Zulu as *ufufunyana*. There are other words which are also used to describe it, and Lee has shown that they are all relatively recent additions to the Zulu language, although somewhat similar conditions appear to have existed in the past under other names but not to anything like the same extent. A man of over eighty informed me in 1951 that the condition was very rare indeed when he was a young man; he attributed the increased incidence to the gradual loss of parental authority over daughters.

The Zulu class *ufufunyana* as a Bantu disease, a term they use to cover all conditions which they believe to occur only among their own people and to be susceptible only to indigenous Zulu methods of treatment.

A person is said to be suffering from *ufufunyana* if there is no organic cause of the disease but rather the cause is said to be witchcraft or spirit possession. The disease is accompanied by stereotyped dreams—particularly dreams about flooded rivers, flood water, or just water; other frequent themes include crowds of dead people, Indians, short, black-bearded men, snakes, and baboons. But in a group of eighty-seven female cases seen by Lee, eighty-five volunteered that their dreams were mostly about water.

The most noteworthy features of the condition, quite apart from whether one accepts the standard Freudian interpretation of the dream content associated with it, is that it is most commonly associated with overt worries on the part of the women patients about sterility and child-birth. A control group examined by Lee did not appear to dream about water to anything like the same extent. Another noteworthy point is that the symptoms are more strongly stereotyped and Lee points out that "the Zulu neurotic could be said to suffer from highly socialised psychoneurosis"; the symbols occurring in the dreams are not only the same, in many cases, as those used by Europeans, but the symbols themselves appear to have become a culturally necessary part of the Zulu concept of *ufufunyana*.

There are three further considerations which cannot fail to stimulate discussion, but I mention them only under the category of conjectural additions to the evidence which I am trying to put together.

The first is that many of the men who visited me as patients, and who were suffering from *ufufunyana* appeared to me to be latent sexual inverts; this opinion is no more than a subjective view, or "clinical impression," based partly on the general demeanour of these men, but mostly on the fact that they were unsatisfactory husbands. In other words, not only were these men suffering from psychoneurotic symptoms of the *ufufunyana* type, but they were fastidious, unaggressive, shy, and frequently impotent. Needless to say, few of these men came complaining of *ufufunyana;* some were brought by friends or relatives for one reason or another, and some came suffering from physical conditions, such as wounds or dysentery, which were in no way related to their *ufufunyana.* Now it seems reasonable to suppose that a certain percentage of Zulu men are latent homosexuals; my informants strongly denied that this was true, but they also stated that it was well known to be common among what the Zulu call the Nyasas—that is, the Africans from Central and East Africa, many of whom come to the Union to work. But I was also informed, by a man who had served a sentence in gaol in Durban, that homosexuality is common in prisons; and I heard a number of anecdotes relating to the *lobola* transactions which go on between one prisoner serving a life sentence and another who has a "marriageable" juvenile prisoner under his control, care, and protection. It therefore seems possible to suggest that these male inverts suffering from *ufufunyana* may have been reacting, by developing a psychoneurosis, to their inherent reversal of roles, which has no sanctioned outlet—at least, none outside prison.

The second point is not so nebulous. The district in which I worked, while almost entirely rural, has one factory employing over 1,000 Africans; it also is linked with the large urban areas of Durban and Pietermaritzburg by a main road and railway. Thus, men who leave their homes in the Reserves to work in the towns, as is customary, for periods varying from six months to two years or more, are able to get home at relatively frequent intervals. In particular, men go home when their presence as the heads of families is demanded, as it is on ceremonial occasions, and when such crises have arisen as legal disputes, serious illnesses, and sudden deaths. They also go home when there are things to be done which only men can do, either for practical or ritual reasons. The most important of these is ploughing, which is done with cattle; only men can handle and use cattle.

By contrast, a neighbouring district of Natal is further removed from towns and industry, and communications are comparatively rudimentary. Migrant labourers are therefore unable to visit their homes while away and so many of the men are absent that much of their work and many of their responsibilities fall on the shoulders of the women. Now, what is most interesting is that many of the women in this district who suffer from *ufufunyana* trace much of their anxiety to the fact that they are forced into this reversal of social roles, whereas none of the women in my district has any anxiety on that account. While this contrast is most illuminating, I wish it could be established whether or not there is a greater incidence of *ufufunyana* in a district where migrant labourers are away from home for long intervals. At present this cannot be done.

The third point is this: *Ufufunyana* appears to be very much more common among women related to diviners than it is among the general population. Some families have a tradition of providing diviners, and the women of such families appear to be particularly prone to *ufufunyana* and to becoming diviners.

Ufufunyana, therefore, is an illness without demonstrable physical lesion; the symptoms are caused, precipitated, or reinforced by circumstances, and by social environmental factors. *Ufufunyana*, therefore, whether classified as an anxiety state or a hysteria, manifests itself in ways and for reasons common to the whole human race, but the ways and reasons have a Zulu slant. It may be doubted whether the study of psychoneuroses, from the point of view of this specific slant, will tell us anything about the Zulu that cannot be found out by the study of the social system which provides the environmental backcloth for the illness. The "way in" to some aspects of the social situation may be easier in one approach than in the other. But the final goal is likely to be the same.

I now wish to examine very briefly some other aspects of mental abnormality and disease among the Southern Bantu. Although there are no reliable figures whatsoever with which to compare the known incidence among other societies, it is safe to say that schizophrenia is the commonest form of chronic insanity among them, as it is among Europeans. Most cases appear to be of the simple or of the hebephrenic type, and the paranoid form is relatively uncommon. The manic-depressive psychosis also occurs but the depressive type is very rare, and some writers appear to believe that it is almost entirely confined to so-called "Westernised" Africans.

The most significant organic reaction types are those resulting from malnutrition and from chronic infections, particularly syphilis. For our present purposes, we may ignore mental deficiency except to mention, as a matter of some interest, that mongolism does not appear to occur among the Bantu.

Epilepsy is not uncommon, and the only case of suicide among my Zulu patients, over a period of two years, was an epileptic. He was a man of about forty who had been treated with sedatives for some time, and he was brought to me one day by the farmer on whose land he lived. He walked from the truck in which he had been brought to my surgery —a distance of about 50 yards—and, without speaking, removed the scarf he was wearing round his neck. This revealed a large wound of the throat, from which the tissues had retracted to form a hole big enough to take the closed fist, in the depths of which the vertebral column was easily visible; needless to say, he had by chance avoided the large vessels on each side of the neck, but he died about two days later in hospital from the gross infection of the lungs which almost inevitably occurs in such cases. The act had been performed with a pair of scissors while the rest of the household were out at work in the fields.

Nothing very conclusive is implied if I add that, in a small area over a comparatively short period, 1 suicide occurred among 25,000 Africans in 2 years, while 3 suicides occurred among 3,000 Europeans in the same period; the rate of suicide in the United Kingdom is about 1 per 10,000 of the population per annum, while in my district the rates for Africans and Europeans were 1 per 50,000 and 1 per 2,000, respectively, per annum.

By way of contrast, I can point to the fact that in the same period I was a medical witness at the trials for homicide of only one European, three Asiatics, and no less than fourteen Africans; the number of cases of assault I dealt with among the Africans of the district averaged more than ten a month, quite apart from the far larger number that I treated but which never came to court. The possible theoretical implications of these figures we may discuss later. Whether Laubscher's (4) generalisation that "races who are prone to the externalisation of aggressive tendencies in an impulsive manner have low suicide rates" is true or not, the Bantu have a high homicide rate and a low suicide rate, and depressive psychosis is very rare.

In addition to the various manifestations of mental abnormality which have been briefly mentioned, there are those conditions which have been grouped together in the general adaptation syndrome; these are disorders which are thought to be due to stress of one sort or another, and which occur less commonly in those who suffer from psychoses and psychoneuroses than they do in others. Outstanding among these conditions are a number which are common enough among Asiatics and Europeans in South Africa, but which are either very rare indeed or very much less common among the Bantu. Duodenal ulcer, asthma, coronary thrombosis, hyperthyroidism, migraine, and psoriasis are good examples of disease entities with which all European doctors are very familiar, but which occur very rarely among the Bantu. While dietary and hereditary factors, among others, may lie behind the very varied incidence of these so-called "psychosomatic" conditions among different populations, the present indications are that the major factors may be traceable to the social environment alone. Further discussion of the evidence for this statement cannot now be undertaken, since this aspect of comparative social pathology is still an almost unexplored field.

It remains to be considered whether studies of individual psychology and psychopathology are able to increase our understanding of social processes in any way, and, in particular, whether some of the potentially traumatic features in the life of the young Zulu girl and of the Zulu woman can be taken to underlie the cathartic *Nomkubulwana* ritual, in which—to quote Gluckman again—there occurs "the patent acting-out of fundamental conflicts both in the social structure and in the individual psyches."

The purposes for which the ritual is performed are not immediately obvious to the observer. Moreover, the purposes given by the male informants—namely, the promotion of the fertility of the crops—may be different from the purposes which might have been given by female informants, had they been asked. The purposes of the purely technical aspects of ritual activities may be adequately revealed by such statements, but ritual activities often assimilate technical acts, the explanation of which may be mistakenly assumed to provide sufficient answer to the symbolic aspects of the ritual. The meanings expressed by the symbols may not be capable of expression in words by the performers themselves, although they may know the meanings intuitively. Indeed, it may be that the analysis of the *Nomkubulwana* ritual provided by Gluckman, which we have already discussed, conforms to the analysis which would emerge if the intuitions of the women performers could be examined. Since the ritual is no longer performed, any attempts to explain it in terms of individual psychology can only be in the nature of conjecture; and, even though this aspect of Gluckman's analysis seems most reasonable, that may well be because we share with him the preconceptions of human motivation which form the basis of the attributions of its purpose.

If we discard, for the moment, the given purposes and the supposed reasons for the ritual, we may direct our attention toward the effects of the ceremonial acts. These are of two types, and may be considered in two different ways. First, we may consider the effects from the point of view of the suppositions of the performers—in this case, both the active female performers and the negatively active male performers. Second, we may consider the effects which the observers—that is, Gluckman and ourselves—see to be in fact produced. The effects will then appear to be, on the one hand, psychological, direct, and immediate, and, on the other, social and secondary in nature.

While it is possible to consider the psychological effects and ignore the more remote social effects, it is impossible to consider the social effects without taking into account the effects on the individual psyche. As we are dealing with an obsolete ritual, it is largely an academic exercise to spend much time considering what may have been the psychological effects, although it follows from what has just been said that some attention must be paid to them if we are to postulate the effects on the social structure of the ritual as well as seek its aetiology there. But one can also approach the problem from another viewpoint and ask the following question: Why should the ritual have become obsolete when the fundamental conflicts which appear to have been resolved by it have not, so far as one can see, diminished in quantity, even though they may have changed in other ways? The tensions created appear to find outlets elsewhere, some of which have been discussed in the foregoing pages. It is in the discovery and elucidation of these outlets that the techniques and approach of clinical psychology may find application in the field of social anthropology. But the methodological problems involved are such that, on launching out to examine them, I am—to say the least—sailing a leaky boat into inadequately charted waters. So far as compartive psychiatry is concerned, we are dealing in the main with data provided by the physician, whose approach is essentially clinical. In other words, he is primarily concerned with symptoms leading to a diagnosis, on which treatment and prognosis can be based. Confronted with such urgent and practical problems as deciding whether or not a particular patient is likely to be a danger to himself or others, he is often far less concerned with the theoretical implications, for other disciplines, of his material than many people who have only seen psychiatrists on the stage or screen would ever believe.

Certain hypotheses may, however, be put forward. For example, the evidence suggests that psychoneurotics play a large part in leadership situations among certain preliterate peoples, and that their influence in initiating and maintaining rituals of the abreactive type may be considerable and may certainly be out of proportion to their numbers among the population. It seems probable that the same restraints and repressions, experienced by all Zulu women to much the same degree from early childhood, will lead to tensions shared by all the women and finding satisfactory release in a ritual of rebellion. But this is not to say that the tension is such as to demand such release, or, in fact, any release, except in a small minority. It may be women among that minority who were responsible for the ritual being maintained. Whether it is cause or effect, now that the ritual has died out, those who have special psychological characteristics are apt, as Firth (1) says, "to find in spirit mediumship a way of passing beyond the bounds of ordinarily recognised social alignments." In other words, release of a socially approved type has been obtained by these women in the profession of diviner and in the so-called separatist African churches of the more bizarre variety.

But those who, for one reason or another, do not or cannot find release in such quasi-institutionalised modes of behaviour turn to the individual mechanism of stereotyped psychoneurosis. For this is what *ufufanyana* undoubtedly is: an illness without demonstrable physical lesion, the symptoms of which are caused, precipitated, or reinforced by circumstances in the social environment. The illness manifests itself in ways and for reasons common to the whole human race, but the ways and reasons have a Zulu slant.

Now the study of this particular psychoneurosis, from the point of view of this specific slant, leads us straight back to Gluckman's phrase about "fundamental conflicts both in the social structure and in the individual psyches." To Nadel it seems "the most obvious thing in the world that, if I wish to be certain about the mental make-up of a group . . . and if I wish to define the cultural patterns of behaviour in terms of 'basic' psychological agencies, I must examine them where they are ultimately rooted—in the individual."

It has been said that the aetiology of the psychoneuroses is to be sought in the social environment. As far as the psychoses are concerned, Adolf Meyer, speaking of schizophrenia, attributes it to "the progressive failure of adaptation of individual to environment." On the other hand, at least 50 per cent of cases of schizophrenia have a family history of mental disease. Laubscher is of the opinion that environmental factors have been overstressed in concepts of the nature of schizophrenia, because it occurs among the Bantu in spite of the high degree of protection afforded by their culture. One may agree with the first part of this statement, but I, for one, would tend to disregard the second part entirely. It does not appear to be possible, at the present stage of our knowledge, for useful assessments to be made of the degrees of protection afforded by any culture.

The crucial point in my argument is this: insofar as individual psychology may be concerned with the environmental backcloth of mental disease, it may tell us much about the social system of the peoples with which we are dealing. But it only provides an easier "way in" to some aspects of the social situation. The approach of social anthropology may be more difficult, but it seems unlikely that individual psychology and psychopathology will tell us anything inherently different and new, or tell us anything that cannot be found out through the study of social systems by the accepted methods of sociology and "microsociology."

Furthermore, if mental disease is conceived of in terms of a combination of intrinsic and extrinsic factors, anything the psychological approach tells us about the former is not directly relevant to our study. It is true, of course, that the incidence of certain types of mental abnormality and the part played by hereditary factors in their causation will have an effect on the social environment; but this effect can as easily be judged by the sociologist examining the social environment as by the psychiatrist examining the mentally abnormal individual. On the other hand, anything the psychological approach tells us of extrinsic factors is not in any way different from that which the social anthropologist may himself observe and deduce from his study of society and its values. In fact, the social anthropologist is more likely to be of use to him in revealing new social fields unapproachable except through the individual.

Nevertheless, attempts to build up a social personality, a sort of average individual for any one society, must start in the search for consistent manifestations at the personal level and must, therefore, lead us to trace the development of the individual, as I attempted to do in my outline of the development of the Zulu individual. Even then, we will have to be satisfied with tendency statements only, which are irksome to many of us.

BIBLIOGRAPHY

1. Firth, R.: *Elements of Social Organization.* New York: Philosophical Library, 1951.

2. Gluckman, H. Max: *Rituals of Rebellion in South-East Africa.* Manchester: University of Manchester Press, 1954.

3. Junod, H. A.: *The Life of a South African Tribe.* London: 1927. Paris: Neuchatel, 1912.

4. Laubscher, B.: *Sex, Custom and Psychopathology.* London: Routledge, 1937.

5. Nadel, S. F.: *The Foundations of Social Anthropology.* Glencoe, Ill.: The Free Press, 1951.

Section V

ANGLO-AMERICAN
PATTERNS

G. M. Carstairs

Institute of Psychiatry
Maudsley Hospital, London

16

THE SOCIAL LIMITS OF ECCENTRICITY:

AN ENGLISH STUDY

The development of psychiatric practice in Britain has been punctuated, and accelerated, by recurrent episodes of self-criticism and of re-evaluation of prevailing theories. We are living through such a period just now, a period in which major premises of psychiatric treatment are being reconsidered.

In particular, the functions of the mental hospital are under scrutiny. It is being seriously debated whether these hospitals provide the best treatment for patients with long-lasting mental illness, and whether such patients might not be better treated elsewhere. "Treatment in the community" is the slogan of the day. This has found expression in the report of the recent Royal Commission on the Law Relating to Mental Illness and Mental Deficiency:

The recommendations of our witnesses were generally in favour of a shift of emphasis from hospital care to community care. In relation to almost all forms of mental disorder, there is increasing medical emphasis on forms of treatment and training and social services which can be given without bringing patients into hospital as inpatients, or which make it possible to discharge them from hospital sooner than was usual in the past. . . . The extent to which patients with long-term disabilities could live in future in less isolated residential homes must depend partly on the willingness of the general public to tolerate in their midst some people with mild abnormalities of behaviour or appearance. We believe that the increasing public sympathy towards mentally disordered patients will result in a higher degree of tolerance in this regard. But even without this, many of the patients now in hospital should be immediately acceptable as members of the general community. . . . Whatever form of accommodation is favoured in any particular locality, we are convinced that the aim should be a deliberate re-orientation, away from institutional care in its present form and towards residential homes in the community.*

The discerning ear may note a certain didactic tone in these recommendations, even a note of dogmatism. "We are convinced . . ." say the members of the Royal Commission; and the tenor of their convictions is so humane and benevolent that one hesitates to point out that they are based not on facts but on the personal convictions of a number of eloquent partisans. "Community care" may well prove to be an advance in treatment for patients of certain types; but for which patients, and in which circumstances, yet remains to be demonstrated.

In some respects the modern zeal for community care for the mentally ill is a reversion to ideas which were current a century ago, during the heyday of "Moral Treatment" of the insane, and which later suffered eclipse. Dr. Kathleen Jones, in her admirable study, *Lunacy, Law and Conscience; 1744–1845* † (to which I am indebted for a number of the following citations), has written the social history of the care of the insane in the period of its emergence from superstition, malpractice, and neglect to the high standards of humanitarian care which were achieved, in some hospitals at least, in the mid-nineteenth century. Both she and the American medical historian and psychiatrist who recently described the subsequent decline of standards of treatment between 1860 and the 1930's (2) relate ideas about mental illness and its treatment to contemporary currents of thought in philosophy, politics, and religion.

In John Aubrey's "Natural History of Wiltshire" (written in the latter half of the seventeenth century), we have an account of an earlier pattern of community care: "Till the breaking out of the Civill Warres, Tom o'Bedlams did travell about the countrey. They had been poore distracted men that had been putt into Bedlam, where, recovering to some sobernesse, they were licentiated to goe a-begging . . . they wore about their necks a great horn of an oxe in a string or bawdric, which, when they came to an house for almes, they did wind."

Tom o'Bedlams could count themselves fortunate in being thus licensed to beg, because at that time, and for more than a century to follow, the mentally handicapped were not, in general, distinguished from the rest of mankind, and were subject to the prevailing harsh

* *Report of the Royal Commission on the Law Relating to Mental Illness and Mental Deficiency*. London: Her Majesty's Stationery Office, 1957.

† Jones, Kathleen: *Lunacy, Law and Conscience; 1744–1845*. New York: Humanities Press, 1955.

measures against vagrancy, theft, and misdemeanours—unless they were flagrantly insane, and then their fate was even harsher, in the primitive madhouses of the time. During the eighteenth century, mediaeval beliefs about insanity as spirit possession were giving ground, at least among the educated minority, to more naturalistic explanations. The influence of natural theology led some to the belief that the sufferings of the insane must be a just retribution for sins committed in this life or in a previous generation; and the argument that madness represented a surrender to man's baser, animal nature provided a further excuse for harshness of treatment.

Rationalisations of this kind are not found only in connection with mental illness: anthropologists have reported innumerable instances of societies in which illnesses of all kinds have been attributed to the wrath of the gods against human transgressions, and are treated accordingly. I myself have lived among a community of Hindus who regarded leprosy as the consequence of one's having (in this life, or in a past one) committed the ultimate sin of killing a cow.

At the turn of the eighteenth century, the view of insanity as a medical affliction, a disease of the brain, began to gain ground—helped not a little by the long-drawn, and at first remittent, illness of George III and of other notables of the day. (Walter Bagehot was to write, later in the century: "It has been said, not truly, but with an approximation to the truth, that in 1802 every hereditary monarch was insane.") Medical treatment, however, was inspired by Hippocratic concepts of the accumulation of evil humours in the body; and its cuppings, bleedings, and purgings were scarcely less arduous than the whippings and exorcisms of earlier days.

"Moral treatment," on the other hand, was a by-product of the Romantic movement, and of Methodist and Quaker emphasis on the worth, obligations, and rights of the individual. For the first time, opportunity for achievement began to be regarded as the right of every individual, not the privilege of a few. The Quaker establishment, the York Retreat, was the first to extend this degree of consideration even to the insane, housing them in decent conditions, treating them with personal consideration. At the Retreat patients were regarded as belonging to "our family": they were not denied the civilising experiences of normal social intercourse, and were urged to retain the discipline of good manners. In the early nineteenth century this example was followed in many enlightened hospitals, by Pinel at the Bicêtre, by Conolly at Hanwell, by T. S. Kirkbride at the Pennsylvania Hospital, and by W. A. F. Browne at the new Crichton Royal Hospital in Scotland, to name only the most celebrated. Each of these maintained that the insane should be treated in accordance with their moral rights as individuals, and should be encouraged to retain their social responsibilities; they demonstrated that under this libertarian regime many who were formerly regarded as "dangerous madmen" could be enabled to return to society.

In mid-nineteenth century, English psychiatry was celebrated for its advocacy of "no restraint" and of "open doors" to such an extent that some German sceptics described our mental hospitals as "a veritable fools' paradise"; and yet before the century was out, the generous principles of moral treatment had passed into almost total eclipse. Patients were herded together in large numbers in the new County Asylums under a regime which kept them alive but denied them dignity or personal worth. The emphasis was now all on "inherited taint"; the mentally ill were viewed as the losers in the struggle for the survival of the fittest. Since inherited neuropathic degeneracy was believed to be the cause of their condition, there was little hope of cure. Once again, as in the Dark Ages, the insane were regarded as possessing neither the sensibilities nor other mental attributes of human beings. In overcrowded locked wards, exposed to long years of idleness and regimentation, many patients succumbed to a progressive dementia which we now recognise as being attributable as much to the conditions in which they lived as to their illness.

Sporadic protests against these dehumanizing conditions were made by enlightened psychiatrists from time to time, for example, by Eugen Bleuler and his successor, Hans Maier, and by Hermann Simon, the advocate of "More Active Therapy" (11, 12), all of whom urged that the patient should return to his ordinary life as soon as the most severe symptoms had cleared up, irrespective of whether he still had mild psychotic disturbances of volition, hallucinations, or delusions. In order to facilitate this process of early discharge, Maier urged that relatives, local authorities, and general practitioners should be instructed and helped in the care of such patients.

To suggest that the fifty years preceding the Second World War represent a period of neglect of the mental hospital patient would be to do a grave injustice to the many energetic and humane pioneers of social therapy to whom Sir David Henderson paid tribute in his Maudsley Lecture (7), and yet these were the exceptions rather than the rule.

During this period, which covers not only the major work of Freud and his school but also that of Adolf Meyer and of Sir David himself, Meyer's foremost British disciple, great things were happening in psychiatry: but as yet few repercussions had penetrated to the back wards of the mental hospitals. It was, perhaps, the rapid development of empirical physical treatments in the last two decades which did more than anything to stir mental hospital practice out of its stagnation. The mentally ill were shown to be in some cases curable, in all cases susceptible to some degree of rehabilitation. This has lent force to the arguments of those psychiatrists who urge that mental disease should be treated as an illness, like any other. This is a laudable slogan when it is used to combat unreasoning prejudice. Unfortunately, it is not quite true.

Mental illness *does* differ from physical illness in its intimate dependence upon social factors. An illustration of this is given in a paper in which Feldman, Susselman, and Barrera (5), reviewing the results of recent policies of active electric shock treatment for schizophrenia, pointed out that many patients had made partial recoveries and had then been discharged to their families, who were unable to understand, or to cope with, their remaining disabilities. As a result, a large proportion of these cases relapsed and returned to hospital. As Aubrey Lewis pointed out in his paper "Health as a Social Concept" (8), the recognition of mental illness is bedevilled by the fact that many symptoms of insanity can also be experienced by the sane, and must be assessed in relation to the social setting in which they occur. Nonconformity is not necessarily a sign of mental illness: there may even be occasions [such as the outbreaks of ecstatic chiliastic cults which Professor Norman Cohn described in his recent book, *The Pursuit of the Millennium* (3)] when to retain one's sanity is to mark oneself out as abnormal.

It appears in fact that there is *no* clear-cut criterion of what constitutes a psychiatric case. Whether a person is regarded as in need of medical treatment is always a function of his disturbance of behaviour *and* of the attitude of his fellows in society. This very lack of a precise definition of mental illness can be regarded as an asset; it may well make it possible to reconcile public opinion to a greater degree of tolerance of the mentally ill than has hitherto been the rule. This is particularly important for the treatment of those who suffer a long-lasting handicap, whether on account of mental deficiency or as the aftermath of a serious mental illness. The present century has seen great advances in our acceptance of collective responsibility for handicapped members of society. The report of the Royal Commission on the Law Relating to Mental Illness may well be the herald of a further advance to grant the mentally handicapped their due share of consideration and social support.

Before its recommendations can be translated into action, however, we shall need to know much more than we do about peoples' attitudes toward the mentally ill, on the one hand, and the capacity of chronic psychotics to regain some measure of social competence, on the other.

As yet, very little has been done in Britain to ascertain popular attitudes concerning mental illness, but a number of studies have been carried out in recent years in America and Canada. The most ambitious of these to date has been the "Survey of Popular Thinking in the Field of Mental Health," directed by Shirley Star for the National Opinion Research Center of the U.S.A. Interviews were carried out with several thousand respondents in a number of states, noting information about the education, marital state, religion, military service, occupation, and economic position of the informants. Some of Dr. Star's preliminary findings are as follows:

The public tends to equate mental illness with psychosis. People are only imperfectly aware of the existence of minor emotional disorders. As a result, confusions and contradictions exist in public attitudes to mental illness. Many believe that neuroses are only minor or early forms of severe psychoses.

In the interview, brief case histories of a violent paranoid, a withdrawn schizophrenic, an anxiety neurotic, a compulsive-phobic personality, an alcoholic, and an instance of childhood behaviour disorder were given: only the first of these was classified as mentally ill by anything like a majority of people.

Confusion arises from a tendency to accept a broad definition of the concept of mental illness in theory, but to narrow the concept down to psychosis in practice.

Many people regard the "nervous system" as a physical entity, separate from the brain and the rest of the body, and attribute minor mental illness to disorders of this system.

Mental illness is regarded as a term of opprobrium: withheld out of charity.

Respondents believe that "understanding people" is a matter of common sense, everyone can do it. They seek immediate, visible, concrete factors as the explanation for normal motivation and for mental illness. Remote causes, and childhood experiences are ignored.

The ordinary person would be more hostile to the psychiatric viewpoint if he were not ignorant of it. Instead, psychotherapy is seen as explanatory, rational, exhortatory, re-educative: consists essentially in giving good advice.

Neuroses are regarded as minor, transient complaints; simple to cure by common-sense methods—a moral problem, whereas psychoses are a medical problem. Responsibility for recovery is placed on the neurotic; hence recourse to a psychiatrist is regarded as a confession of failure.

Psychosis is feared because it is believed to be a sudden, irreversible serious illness; unpredictable, and so a threat to everyone. All psychotics are believed to be potentially dangerous, and certainly disturbing to live with, hence the "tendency to extrude the mentally ill from society, if not from consciousness." Fear and distrust extends to ex-patients also (13).

British psychiatrists have no difficulty in recognising in this account attitudes toward mental illness which they also commonly encounter in the relatives of their patients; but a community-wide survey of these attitudes has yet to be made. In Britain, as in America, there has been a quickening of public interest in this subject during recent years. The British Broadcasting Corporation has contributed to this by sponsoring a series of radio and television programmes on the problem of mental illness. The TV series, "The Hurt Mind," broadcast in the first weeks of 1957, attracted a particularly wide audience.

In connection with this series, Dr. W. A. Belson, of the B.B.C. Audience Research Department, conducted inquiries with two samples representative of the London TV viewing public. His aim was to ascertain their attitudes to mental illness and their response, if any, to the television programmes on "The Hurt Mind." His findings coincided in many respects with those of Dr. Star, except that his London sample showed more optimism about the results of treatment, and greater trust in mental hospitals. Informants who had seen the TV series responded, in some degree, as the authors of the programme hoped they would do: they showed a moderate increase of confidence in the ability of medical men to cure mental illness and in certain specific kinds of treatment which had been demonstrated. (Incidentally, such was the bias in favour of physical treatment in these programmes that there was a significant increase in the number of those who thought that psychotherapy was a form of physical treatment. A triumph for propaganda indeed!) Questions were asked at the same time about viewers' willingness to associate with the ex-patient or with the person who is at present receiving treatment for a mental illness.

It was noticeable that this willingness was most readily forthcoming in respect to relatively impersonal contacts, such as mixing in the street or in shops, working or living next door to an ex-patient, or keeping up a casual acquaintance with him: from 80 to 90 per cent were prepared to go this far. Appreciably fewer persons expressed a readiness to accept an ex-patient as a close personal friend, or as an employer or employee; and only one in five could accept the prospect of an ex-patient's marrying into their family or being left in charge of their children. In all of these areas those who had seen the programmes gave positive replies in a higher percentage of cases; but the differences, although small, were all in the desired direction (1).

In these respects, the B.B.C. experiment in popular education appears to have been more successful than the Canadian community education project described by John and Elaine Cumming in their contribution to the book, *Health, Culture and Community* (4).

In 1951, the Cummings launched a six-months "concerted effort to bring about a measurable change in attitudes to the mentally ill" in a small country town in western Canada. In spite of their strenuous endeavours, using films, pamphlets, articles in the local newspaper, programmes on the local radio station, meetings, and group discussions, they found, on repeating their attitude measures at the end of the six months, that no significant change had occurred, except that the inhabitants showed a considerable amount of hostility toward their interviewers. The authors have been very candid in reporting the failure of their endeavour, which they attribute to the acute anxieties aroused in the community when their accustomed beliefs on this subject were disturbed. They found thinking on mental illness to be confused and inconsistent: "Behaviour that would seem clearly pathological to a psychiatrist would be dismissed by many respondents as 'Just a quirk' or by saying 'He'll get over it' or 'It takes all sorts to make a world.'" When the informants were shown six typical case histories, nearly all recognized that describing a paranoid schizophrenic was a case of mental illness, but only a quarter to a third so identified the descriptions of cases of alcoholism, simple schizophrenia, and severe depression; and only 4 per cent thought that the accounts of delinquency and of compulsive behaviour in children denoted mental illness.

Their only consistent criterion for mental illness was admission to a mental hospital. Once it was known that this had taken place, the same behaviour that formerly was judged "normal" would be considered as "abnormal." This was taken as evidence of a social pattern. The community needed some workable way to handle the difficult problems of mental illness, and their solution was to deny the abnormality of peculiarities of behaviour until they reached a certain pitch and then to brand the deviant as insane, and to insist upon his total removal from their midst.

It is possible to quarrel with some details of the authors' procedure, and to suggest less abstruse reasons for their lack of success; but the experiment was instructive even in its failure. As is the case in the majority of similar studies, these workers appear to assume that there is a "correct" attitude toward the mentally ill, which is held by the psychiatrist: they saw their task to be one of wrestling with the "invincible ignorance" of the community.

Charlotte Schwartz, in a recent paper analysing the ways in which the wives of twenty men admitted to mental hospital for the first time with a psychotic illness defined their husbands' difficulties, has advanced a very different point of view. She makes it plain that these wives were very loath to recognise their husbands' behaviour as psychotic; indeed, they went to great lengths to minimise the seriousness of any abnormalities, and to attribute them to a physical illness or to a temporary aberration, but she points out that this blindness to the abnormality of their husbands' behaviour is as appropriate to their social role as wives (and perhaps as helpful to the patients) as is the psychiatrist's clinical assessment of the case in his role as doctor. She goes on to say: "My analysis suggests that it is neither particularly desirable nor possible for relatives to take over the total psychiatric orientation towards the patient's problem," and again: "I think that much of the present block in helping families reintegrate patients into the community lies in the fact that the problem tends to be approached as if there were one answer or one set of principles by which all families can be guided in their relationships with patients. Sooner or later, the practice of ascertaining what is functional for families of different subgroups must be adopted. Those who deal with the mentally ill must come to consider the specific values, the particular role definitions, and the unique ways of living and relating to each other that constitute the life of a variety of subgroups from which patients come to the mental hospital and to which they will return" (10).

It will be appreciated that very little is yet known about the attitude of the public toward mental illness when it falls within their own personal experience, nor about the factors which determine the success or failure in social adaptation of a person who is handicapped by chronic

mental disability. A study carried out in London in 1956–1957 by members of the Medical Research Council's Social Psychiatry Research Unit *
was designed to throw some light on these problems.

In this study, the records of seven large metropolitan mental hospitals were consulted, and the names of all male patients between the ages of 20 and 65 who left hospital between 1949 and 1956 were noted. This yielded a total of 240 respondents, including many who had left hospital (or had been withdrawn by their relatives) against medical advice, and 18 who had effected their discharge by escaping from hospital and avoiding recapture within the statutory period of 14 days. By dint of considerable pertinacity, the three investigators succeeded in completing follow-up interviews with members of the household of 229 (95 per cent) of these patients, including 18 of the 23 patients who had eloped (to use the American expression).

The follow-up was designed to cover an extensive schedule of inquiry covering 160 items, of which some could be ascertained from hospital records, but the majority were dealt with in a one- to two-hour interview with the "key person" in the household to which the patient returned. Usually the key person was his mother, wife, or other relative; in other cases, his landlady, the warden of a hostel, or a friend; in a few instances, where the patient lived alone, he was himself the principal informant.

In assessing the outcome of these patients' return to the community, we adopted two criteria. According to the first, "success" was defined as avoiding readmission to hospital within the twelve months following discharge. "Success" in these terms was achieved by 156 (68 per cent) of our 229 cases. These were in turn assessed in terms of the level of social adjustment which they had achieved one year after leaving hospital, using a scale which took account of the patients' independence of support, employment record, and interpersonal relations. Of those surviving in the community, 102 (44.5 per cent of the total sample) were rated as functioning at a fairly satisfactory level, whereas 54 (23.6 per cent) were making an unsatisfactory social adjustment. Of the latter, 20 could only be described as family invalids.

Analysis of the inquiry schedules indicated which items in the patient's clinical histories and in their posthospital experiences correlated

---

* Mr. G. W. Brown and Miss G. T. Topping collaborated with the writer in carrying out this study in which we were advised by Professor A. J. Lewis, Honorary Director of the Unit.

with the two criteria of outcome. Here, the special characteristics of these chronic mental patients became apparent. Whereas in follow-up studies of total admissions to mental hospital diagnosis and duration of illness are very important factors, the former was significantly related to outcome in this study, and the latter criterion discriminated only between patients with less or more than four years' history of illness. On the other hand, there were some divergences between the schizophrenics, who formed two thirds of the total, and the heterogeneous group of "other diagnoses": for example, the schizophrenics who were first admissions did not fare better than the rest, but among those with other diagnoses the first admissions had a significantly better outcome.

For the sake of simplicity, the present discussion will be confined for the most part to the outcome of the schizophrenic patients.

The analysis showed, as might be expected, that the patient's degree of recovery at the time of discharge was of major importance in his future progress: those discharged "recovered," "relieved," or "not improved" showed a descending percentage of successes. Nevertheless, this factor was not of exclusive importance, as was shown by the fact that 29 out of 58 patients discharged against medical advice, and 11 out of the 18 elopers were definitely known to have "succeeded" according to our first criterion; but it was clearly of such importance that it was used as a check on all other significant correlations with outcome to make sure that they could not be ascribed to this same factor.

Several other items were found to be significantly related to the patients' outcome: these included the levels of occupation and of social responsibility attained before the onset of the illness (it was a particularly adverse sign where there was a discrepancy between a patient's formal and his actual status in the household). In the posthospital situation, however, two factors appeared to be of particular importance: *a*) if the patient succeeded in holding a job for even part of the year, his chances of success were significantly better than if he did not ($p<.001$); *b*) the proportion of "successes" differed significantly ($p<.01$) with the type of living group to which the patient went on leaving hospital, as can be seen in Table 16-1.

Both of these correlations remained significant if only patients rated "relieved" on discharge were considered. They set the background for the more detailed examination of "what was going on" in the households to which patients returned.

In planning this study, it was anticipated that the two most important

TABLE 16-1

Successes and Failures in Different Social Settings
(Schizophrenic Patients Only)

	Success	Failure
Institutional *	7	7
Parental	55	31
Marital	7	7
Other Kin	20	4
Lodgings or Living Alone	17	0
TOTAL	106	49

* These were for the most part men who stayed in Rowton Houses (large work-ingmen's lodging houses) or Salvation Army hostels; they included 8 men who went from one to another such temporary residence and were classed as "no fixed abode."

determinants of the outcome would be the patients' mental state and the attitude of those in his immediate environment. Both of these expectations were realised. Table 16-2 shows the declining ratio of successes to failures in households of progressively less welcoming tenor. The likelihood of a patient's being readmitted to hospital within the year was significantly greater in those cases where his presence restricted the activities of other members of the household (p<.001).

TABLE 16-2

Attitude of Others in Patients' Household

	Success	Failure
Welcomed by All Members	72	6
Tolerated by All Members	28	14
Welcomed by Some, Not by Others	18	18
Unwelcome	9	17
Rating Not Applicable or Not Ascertainable	29	18
TOTAL	156	73

$X^2 = 40.904$, 3 d.f., p<.001.

The attitude of the key person in his household was also rated as either "positive" or "doubtful or negative." This dichotomy correlated highly with the patients' outcome (p<.001); so also did the division of households into those in which the ex-patient was viewed as "possibly dangerous" or "certainly not" (p<.001). In the latter instance, it was noteworthy that in only 25 per cent of cases did relatives view these patients as potentially dangerous, although there was an actual history of violence in 38 per cent of the total. This suggests that the common stereotyped opinion, "mental patients are dangerous" (which has a substratum of truth), becomes favourably modified by the first-hand experience of psychosis in the family; here, as in many other contexts, imagined dangers are more fearful than actual ones.

In an earlier age, these contrasting attitudes were illustrated by Dr. Johnson's saying: "If a madman were to come into this room with a stick in hand, no doubt we should pity the state of his mind; but our primary consideration would be to take care of ourselves. We should knock him down first, and pity him afterwards." Yet the same Dr. Johnson said, apropos of the madness of his friend, the poet Christopher Smart (whose eccentricity had become so marked that he would beg people to kneel down in the street to pray with him): "I would as lief pray with Kit Smart as with anyone."

A somewhat analogous finding was that patients whose admission to hospital had been the occasion of considerable social disturbance in their home neighbourhood did *not* fare worse after discharge than those whose illness had given rise to no such disturbance. This might be due to the interval of several years between admission and discharge; but it did suggest that a disturbance arising during a crisis of mental disorder was not remembered vividly enough to prejudice the patients' chances later on.

Patients who suffered from an incapacitating physical disability fared neither better nor worse than their fellows; but when another member of the household was so handicapped, the patient was less likely to succeed.

In studies of this kind, it is the unexpected findings which are the most instructive. Here, the most surprising observations were those shown in Table 16-1. In assessing chronic patients' suitability for discharge, psychiatrists tend to act on the assumption that those who have parents or a spouse willing to receive them will have the best prognosis; but here it is shown that in neither of these settings do patients succeed so well as do those who go to live with more distant relatives, or in lodgings. Only the 17 chronic schizophrenics who went to live in large public lodginghouses (changing one institutional environment for another in some respects less agreeable than a mental hospital ward) showed a less favourable outcome than those who returned to their immediate family.

TABLE 16-3

Outcome in Contrasting Social Settings

| | All Schizophrenics | | Schizophrenics Rated "Relieved" on Discharge | |
	Success	Failure	Success	Failure
Intimate Family Groups (parental and marital)	62	38	44	22
Other Private Households (remoter kin, lodgings, or living alone)	37	4	25	2
	$X^2 = 11.01$, 1 d.f., p<.001		$X^2 = 6.73$, 1 d.f., p<.01	

The contrasting outcomes of patients who go to households where they have intimate family ties and of those who go to more impersonal households are shown in Table 16-3. The "impersonal" setting is seen to be associated with a favourable outcome, and this association is still highly significant when only schizophrenic patients rated as "relieved" at the point of discharge from hospital are considered.

The parental domestic situation has in common with the marital that in both the ex-patient is involved in close personal relationships; they differ in that a wife expects her husband to work and to carry his responsibilities as head of the household, whereas parents are readier to accept "their boy" as a dependent, in need of support. As a Harvard group of investigators has recently shown, these contrasting expectations tend to be fulfilled: at one year after discharge, patients living in marital settings were found to be functioning at a higher social level than those living with their parents (6). The same was true of our respondents: significantly more of the patients in parental than in marital settings were rated as showing unsatisfactory social adjustment one year after leaving hospital, and this bias remained even if only patients recorded as "relieved" were considered, so that it could not be ascribed simply to the parents' greater readiness to give a home to the "sicker" patients.

There do, therefore, appear to be some factors in the parental situation (in an important number of cases) which actually militate against the patient's chances of maintaining a social recovery; these toxic factors can plausibly be identified as a) intrusive emotional contact, and b) low expectations of role performance. It was observed that in the parental group those patients who did go out to work, thereby both interrupting the day-long, face-to-face relationship and asserting their economic independence, had a much more favourable outcome than the rest, although among them were several with quite marked residual symptoms. In contrast, patients who go to live with remoter kin or in lodgings are left to themselves to a greater extent, and it is assumed that they will be able to fend for themselves; these are the patients who have shown the most favourable outcome.

Yet another item from our interview schedule gives some additional support to this argument. Whenever it was possible to do so, we rated the dominant mode of relationship between the patient and the others in his household under one of six different categories. We found that the outcome differed in very significant degree (p<.001) between these several categories, being worst where the patient was faced with unconcealed hostility, and progressively better where the patient tended to dominate the household, where he was subjected to firm discipline, where he was treated with especial indulgence, or where he was left to go his own way. The outcome was by far the best where there was a situation of mutual give and take between the patient and the others in his household (in such settings 38 patients succeeded and only 2 relapsed) and this could not be entirely attributed to the patients in this group being in a better mental state than all the rest.

It appears, therefore, that the chronic schizophrenic patient who returns to live in the community will be most likely to succeed if he is able to ensconce himself on the periphery rather than in the center of active social relationship. His most pressing need is to be helped to find work, and the fact that he has still some symptoms of his illness need not prevent his performing a job quite satisfactorily; but unemployment makes even the "recovered" schizophrenic more liable to break down. The ex-patient needs help in finding work, and also in establishing his own wary contacts with his fellow men; but he prefers that this help should not be too insistent—most of the time, he asks only to be left alone. In our study a surprisingly large number of patients received regular help from someone who did not belong to the household in which they went to live, and these patients showed an appreciably better than average outcome (p<.02).

Since the beginning of 1957, the writer has had the opportunity to conduct an out-patient clinic at Maudsley Hospital, catering specifically to chronic schizophrenics living in London. As the cases accumulate it is becoming evident that much can be done to help these patients—and their families—to adapt themselves to the best advantage to the lasting aftereffects of this crippling disease. Each case presents its individual complexities, and yet certain regularities can also be observed. One consequence of the study briefly discussed in this chapter has been to heighten one's appreciation of the positive social factors which exist even in the seamier side of metropolitan life. So often has "social isolation" been invoked as a harmful, even a schizophrenogenic, concomitant of life in the metropolis, that it is surprising to find that for some ex-patients a certain degree of isolation from intimate personal contacts is a helpful thing. Here, too, the anonymity and the casual acceptance of eccentricity which are conspicuous of living in London become positive assets. There are times when, observing the not infrequent social deviants who talk aloud to themselves or assert their peculiarity in their dress or in their bearing without attracting undue notice, one is reminded of the interchange between Hamlet and the Clown:

CLOWN: He that is mad, and sent into England.
HAMLET: Ay, marry: why was he sent into England?
CLOWN: Why, because he was mad; he shall recover his wits there; or, if he
          do not, 'tis no great matter there.
HAMLET: Why?
CLOWN: 'Twill not be seen in him there; there the men are as mad as he.

In this passage of self-mockery, Shakespeare was the spokesman for a society which was sufficiently self-confident both to accept eccentrics in its midst, and to recognise its own eccentricities.

One reason for the continuance of irrationally severe public prejudices against the mentally ill (as against homosexuality) may well be that these aberrations represent the emergence of tendencies which exist in all of us, but which are both feared and denied. The problem of the ex-patient in the community is not only the patient's problem, but also that of the community. It remains to be seen to what degree our contemporary urban society can tolerate the presence of socially withdrawn and even conspicuously abnormal persons in its midst without succumbing to the temptation to shut them away out of sight again. Aftercare and social work on the lines indicated by the study reported above can help the ex-patient to establish a modus vivendi with his environment, and so may prevent the recrudescence of his illness; but in the last resort it is the level of tolerance of the community toward the mentally handicapped which will set the limits of effective "community care."

BIBLIOGRAPHY

1. Belson, N. W. A.: "The Hurt Mind." An enquiry into some of the effects of the series of five television broadcasts about mental illness and its treatment. London: British Broadcasting Corporation, 1957.

2. Bockoven, J. S.: "History of moral treatment." *Journal of Nervous and Mental Disease,* 1956, vol. 124, pp. 167 and 292.

3. Cohn, N.: *The Pursuit of the Millennium.* London: Secker & Warburg, 1957.

4. Cumming, J., and Cumming, E.: "Mental health education in a Canadian community. In *Health, Culture and Community* (B. D. Paul, ed.). New York, Russell Sage Foundation, 1955.

5. Feldman, F.; Susselman, S.; and Barrera, S. E.: "Socio-economic aspects of the shock treatment in schizophrenia." *American Journal of Psychiatry,* 1947, vol. 104, p. 402.

6. Freeman, H. E., and Simmons, O. G.: "Mental patients in the community: Family status and performance levels," *American Sociological Review,* April, 1958, vol. 23.

7. Henderson, D. K.: "The 19th Maudsley Lecture: A revaluation of psychiatry." *Journal of Mental Science,* 1939, vol. 85, pp. 1–21.

8. Lewis, A.: "Health as a social concept." *British Journal of Sociology,* June, 1953, vol. IV, no. 2.

9. *Report of the Royal Commission on the Law Relating to Mental Illness and Mental Deficiency,* London: Her Majesty's Stationery Office, 1957.

10. Schwartz, C.: "Perspectives on deviance—wives' definitions of their husbands' mental illness." *Psychiatry,* 1957, vol. 20, pp. 275–291.

11. Simon, H.: "More active therapy." *Allgemeine Zeitschrift für Psychiatrie,* 1927, vol. 87, pp. 97–145.

12. ————: "More active therapy." *Allgemeine Zeitschrift für Psychiatrie,* 1929, vol. 90, pp. 69–121.

13. Star, Shirley: *Attitudes to Mental Illness.* Chicago: National Opinion Research Center Study. Mimeographed, 1952.

Edward A. Kennard

Chief, Anthropology Section
Veterans Administration Hospital, Perry Point

17

MAJOR PATTERNS OF THE MENTAL HOSPITAL *
—U.S.A.

The increasing shift of the practice of modern medicine from the home and community to the contemporary hospital reflects the vast increase in technical medical culture and attendant specialization in the division of labor. Although many general hospitals now have wards for the treatment of neurological or psychiatric disorders, most severe psychiatric disorders are treated in mental hospitals which are part of county, federal, or state hospital systems. The contemporary mental hospital reflects not only current ideas, both psychiatric and legal, but also inevitably embodies practices representative of earlier ideas not yet completely superseded.

The hospitalized mentally ill in our society constitute a residual class of individuals, whose behavior deviates in marked fashion from the expectations of others, despite knowledge of the individual's age, sex, status, and situation. Other segregated populations, such as inmates of prisons, are also deviates from the normative order, but they are distinguished as "being able to help themselves" and therefore, morally bad, while the psychotic is considered "sick" and legally not responsible for his behavior.

The contemporary mental hospital can best be understood in terms of three sets of themes derived from contemporary psychiatry, the history of mental hospitals in the United States, and the structure of the hospital and its relationship to the structure of society.

* Unless specific reference is made to other hospitals, the information is based on research conducted at the Veterans Administration Hospital, Downey, Illinois, a 2,400-bed psychiatric hospital serving the Chicago metropolitan area.

CONTEMPORARY PSYCHIATRY

The Diagnostic and Statistical Manual of Mental Disorders classifies mental illness in two major groups: 1) organic—impairment or damage to brain tissue, and 2) disorders of psychogenic origin or without clearly defined physical cause or structural change in the brain (1). These categories correspond to the major concerns of the neurologist and the psychiatrist. The latter category is subdivided for convenience into three major subtypes: 1) psychotic, 2) psychoneurotic, and 3) personality disorders.

The major revolution in psychiatric thought stems from Freudian theory and its derivatives, since it provided a consistent theory of the development of the human personality, and many hypotheses of the mechanisms involved in the development of aberrant behavior patterns. Harry Stack Sullivan wrote, ". . . there is nothing unique in the phenomena of the gravest functional illness. The most peculiar behavior of the acutely schizophrenic patient is made up of interpersonal processes with which each one of us is or historically has been familiar. Far the greater part of the performances, the interpersonal processes, of the psychotic patient are exactly of a piece with processes which we manifest some time every twenty-four hours." * And T. A. C. Rennie said, ". . . any human being in a process of adaptation has only a certain number of psychological and physiological defenses that he can employ. These various psychological defenses are common to every human being. There is no essential difference in the psychotic and his psychological defenses or devices from the less psychotic, from the neurotic, from the so-called normal, except in one or two significant factors. The first is the severity or degree of utilization of certain mechanisms. The second is the impact and force of certain disorganizing, internal drives which are greater or lesser in some persons. And third, most significant of all, is the capacity of that person to organize, to synthesize the conflicting trends, to hold them in balance—all that we analytically subsume under the term 'ego-strength' of the person. In these three manifestations I think we can see the entire gamut of psychiatric illness played out with the the same kinds of psychological and physiological mechanisms that

* Sullivan, Harry Stack: *Conceptions of Modern Psychiatry*. Washington, D.C.: W. A. White Psychiatric Association, 1946.

everybody—normal, semi-normal, half sick, seriously sick—uses in the continuum of adaptation." *

Popular images of the private practice of psychiatry are derived from the psychoanalytic model, which shares significant features with the private practice of other branches of medicine, especially in the doctor-patient relationship. From the work with neurotic patients, most of whom are able to fulfill their social roles and with whom the psychiatrist can communicate verbally, has come most of the current knowledge of the various forms that unresolved conflicts experienced by the patient take. The whole catalogue of phobias, obsessions, compulsions, and psychophysiological conversion of anxiety to one or another organ or organ system is interpreted as a defense of the self, although a maladaptive one, and hence a symptom of pathology.

In psychodynamic theory, the particular defensive reaction pattern manifested is assumed to be related to the life history of the individual, and particularly to patterns of response to others learned in the earliest years of socialization. Frequently, in an effort to uncover the sources of conflict, the present situation which brings the patient to the psychiatrist is given less weight than the antecedent events of his earlier history.

Various modifications of both theory and practice have occurred as a result of the experiences of many psychotherapists, and the exigencies of the situations in which they practice, resulting in the various schools and variations in technique. In addition to the traditional depth or uncovering therapy, there are directive therapists, supportive therapists, nondirective counselors, group psychotherapists, practioners of psychodrama, those who limit their practice to children, and others.

THE MENTAL HOSPITAL TRADITION

American society did not always hospitalize its psychotic members. They have in earlier years been kept in jails and almshouses, and sometimes auctioned off to the highest bidder (8). However, in the 1830's and 1840's the founders of American psychiatry developed a small hospital, and a mode of management that they referred to as "moral treatment," which did not consist so much of specific therapeutic measures as a humane regimen and the assumption that the recuperative

* Rennie, Thomas A. C.: In *Interrelations between the Social Environment and Psychiatric Disorders.* Papers presented at the 1952 Annual Conference of the Milbank Memorial Fund. New York: Milbank Memorial Fund, 1953.

powers of the patient would assert themselves and lead to recovery if not obstructed (11).

In that era, the superintendent-physician was in daily contact with all of his patients, and saw them in a variety of situations provided by the routine. He and his attendants shared hospital living with the patients twenty-four hours a day and seven days a week. Furthermore, the pattern of life in the hospital was not sharply differentiated from that of the towns and farms of the day. Nor was American society as stratified and differentiated as it is today (29).

However, in the second half of the nineteenth century, increasing population, and particularly the waves of immigrants, exerted such pressure upon mental hospitals that they were rapidly increased in size. The physician became an administrator, remote from both patients and attendants. "Physicians of colonial ancestry who were filled with compassion for the mentally ill who had a similar heritage were often revolted by the 'ignorant uncouth insane foreign pauper.' . . . It would be no wonder if the insanity of a highly educated, intelligent and refined person should not be increased rather than cured, if the person is brought into close contact with those who were always coarse in their habits and taste, rough in disposition, and filthy in their dress." *

Accompanying his shift in attitude, increase in size of the institution, and the abandoning of the practices of the era of moral treatment was a greater emphasis on organic factors in etiology. The Worcester State Hospital, which had recovery rates of 50 per cent in the 1830's, showed only 5 per cent in 1880. It was in this era that the patterns of segregation, control, and custody became dominant in the mental hospitals.

It was in the mental hospitals that the various somatic therapies became established as the treatment of choice for many of the psychoses. Starting with experiments with metrazol and carbon dioxide shock treatments, by the end of the 1930's they had been superseded by reliance upon electroconvulsive and insulin coma therapies as the major kinds of intensive treatment. And in refractory cases psychosurgery in the form of lobotomy has been performed as a method of last resort. Since 1955 the greatest reliance has been placed upon tranquilizing drugs.

* Greenblatt, Milton; York, Richard H.; Brown, Esther Lucile: *From Custodial to Therapeutic Patient Care in Mental Hospitals.* New York: Russell Sage Foundation, 1955.

INSTITUTIONAL SIZE

Even today, although there is more evidence of the effects of sheer size upon the formal institutional structure, most mental hospitals are large. Compared to short-term general hospitals, the difference is striking. Of the 6,970 short-term hospitals in the United States, 4,000 are less than 100-bed capacity, and the average is only 106 beds (15). However, the capacities of state mental hospitals are of an entirely different order of magnitude. California has nine state hospitals with an average population of 3,293; New York, eighteen with an average population of 4,344; Michigan, six averaging 4,381; Louisiana, two with 3,384; and Texas, eight with 1,884. These figures include some huge hospitals, such as Milledgeville, Georgia, with an average resident population of 9,448, Manteno, Illinois, with 7,375, and Pilgrim State Hospital in New York with 9,765 (4).

In addition, the thirty-nine psychiatric hospitals of the Veterans Administration care for 54,000 patients, yielding an average population of 1,400. However, all new psychiatric facilities built since the end of World War II by the VA have been of less than 1,000 bed capacity. They, in turn, are part of the hospital system of the Bureau of Medicine and Surgery, one of the three major divisions of the Veterans Administration, which operates 173 hospitals and numerous clinics. In 1956 the Veterans Administration employed over 176,000 in performing all its functions.

As Theodore Caplow pointed out in a recent article: "Each giant organization has a central record keeping system with standard procedures for budgeting funds and accounting for their expenditure. Each has a bureaucratic or rational personnel system with fixed grades and ranks, methods of formal evaluation, and a continuous dossier for every member. Each maintains some form of public relations activity to present its point of view to the outside world. Each has a set of internal values which are strongly defended by functionaries with high status and mildly supported by the rank and file. Each uses a broad range of experts, including planners and statisticians." *

Central office control of each of the constituent units in the total organization is maintained primarily through budget control and personnel control. Personnel control is largely exercised through central office

---

* Caplow, Theodore: "Organizational size." *Administrative Science Quarterly,* 1957, vol. 1, pp. 484–505.

control of the appointments to the top twenty-five positions in the hospital organization. Usually these positions are filled by promotion or transfer from another hospital within the Veterans Administration system and hence, seniority and experience within the system become significant factors in maintaining the consistency in the pattern of organization and of procedure in each of the constituent hospitals of the larger organization.

The other major means of central control is through the allocation of funds for operating expenses. Each hospital has a rated capacity usually measured in terms of beds. The cost of operation for any given year is based upon the average daily cost of hospitalization for each patient. At the beginning of each fiscal year a figure representing the estimated average daily patient load for the ensuing year is made and allocations from the central office are made on this basis. Should the actual number of patients hospitalized and treated during any given year fall significantly below this figure, the local hospital is faced with a withdrawal of funds consistent with the reduced workload.

In addition to these two major means of control, the central office provides all hospitals with detailed manuals of procedure, regulations interpreting the law under which the hospitals operate, and technical bulletins dealing with standardized procedures or new techniques in the care and treatment of patients suffering from particular diseases or disabilities.

TYPE OF ORGANIZATION

In a discussion of types of work organization, Jules Henry described the psychiatric hospital as one of multiple subordination, in that the work to be performed was split into many specialized tasks or operations (12). In the VA hospital, the manager is a physician and psychiatrist, with two major assistants. The assistant manager is a layman concerned with all those divisions that are not concerned with patient care and treatment, and the director of professional services has responsibility for all of the medical and paramedical services. These include the surgical, medical, neurological, pathology, and radiology, as well as the psychiatric services. These all operate under the formal authority of physicians. Other services under his control are nursing, dietetics, dental, physical medicine and rehabilitation, special services, psychology, social service, pharmacy, and several smaller units.

Cutting across the functional organization is a spatial one, which groups patients and treatment personnel in buildings and wards. There are more than thirty buildings housing patients, and some of these are divided into four separate wards, providing more than seventy units.

Patients are classified not only diagnostically and prognostically, but also in terms of age and sex, and other medical disabilities in addition to their psychiatric problems. Thus, two wards are devoted to female patients and two wards are devoted to psychiatric patients who also suffer from pulmonary tuberculosis. There are also small wards for medical, surgical, geriatric, and neurological cases. However, 1,680 are classified as male psychiatric. Among these there are two major divisions within the hospital. The primary distinction is between Acute Intensive Treatment Service, to which all newly admitted patients are assigned, and the various wards of the Continued Treatment Service.

The greatest concentration of medical and ancillary personnel occurs on the Acute Intensive Treatment Service. Following admission and diagnosis, every effort is made to assist the patient in achieving a remission of symptoms so that he can be discharged, or failing that, sufficient improvement in his condition so that he can likewise be discharged. Consequently, the greatest number of discharges from the hospital occur from this service and the greatest turnover of patients also occurs on this service, since those who do not respond are transferred to one of the wards of the Continued Treatment Service.

The basic problem of the mental hospital is not those patients who respond to existing therapeutic techniques and whose course in the hospital is relatively short even though stormy, but the large number of patients who fail to respond to any existing therapy and must continue to be cared for since they are unable to care for themselves. A survey of the male patient population drawn from the metropolitan Chicago area in 1954 showed the following figures in terms of length of hospitalization: Twenty-five years and over, 198; twenty-one to twenty-five years, 90; sixteen to twenty years, 112; eleven to fifteen years, 138; six to ten years, 327; and zero to five years, 489. While, in theory, a patient can be discharged after any length of hospitalization, the chances decrease with every year the patient spends in the hospital. This is not exclusively a matter of the patient's level of functioning and contact with reality, but the attenuation of all other social relationships (7, 22).

For the hospital staff, the perception of the hospital environment and each individual's place within it is given by two sets of factors: professional identification and ward assignment. Thus, to the hierarchy of status in a mobility blocked organization is added the hierarchy of wards. Everyone on the ward is responsible to the ward physician as far as the treatment and management of his patients is concerned. But nurse, psychologist, social worker, and ward clerk are also subject to the legitimate authority of the head of his particular service. In such an organizational structure there is pressure for autonomy both by the ward staffs and by the functional services.

Since the end of World War II, there has been a great expansion in both number and kinds of hospital personnel. The hospital is affiliated with a University Medical School, and under a Dean's Committee, resident physicians in psychiatry receive the first year's training of a three-year program at the hospital. This affiliation also brings to the hospital every week psychiatrists and neurologists as consultants, who provide both didactic lectures on psychodynamics and clinical demonstrations with selected patients. This program is designed not only for its educational function, but also to keep the professional staff abreast of current research and developments in medicine, and particularly in psychiatry.

Clinical psychologists were added to the staff after 1948, and psychology also has a training program, affiliated with four university graduate schools, which provides two years of supervised experience in a medical setting, the first year of which takes place in this hospital. Later experience is given in a general medical and surgical hospital and in a mental hygiene clinic. Most of the staff psychologists at the hospital are products of this program, either here or in other areas of the Veterans Administration.

Psychiatric social work is another postwar development in the VA hospitals. Its responsibilities center around relationships between the hospitalized patient and his nonhospital world. The social history following admission, maintaining contact with his family and employer, making arrangements for both discharge and trial visit (a conditional discharge), and participation in diagnostic and disposition staffings are its major functions. It, too, has a nine-month in-service training program affiliated with two graduate schools of social work.

The Nursing Education Service also has a thirteen-week program in psychiatric nursing for student nurses drawn from ten affiliated hospitals, so that at any given time there are approximately forty of them, assigned to the Admission Service and the Female Service, where the greatest variety of cases are found.

Each of these four groups is also involved in the formal training program of each of the others.

All of these professional groups, and the nurses and psychiatric aides are physically located on the wards, but ward geography is so arranged that only the aides and the student nurses spend any significant portion of their time in the day-room areas with the patients. The physician, the psychologist, and the social worker deal with patients individually in their offices. Table 17–1 indicates the distribution of staff among the various buildings and services, and the capacity of each building.

Although much of hospital life centers on the wards, there are many treatment programs and activities that take place in special clinics and other areas of the hospital. Two of the largest services dealing with patients off the wards are Physical Medicine and Rehabilitation and the Special Services Division. The former includes the occupational therapists, physical therapists, corrective therapists, and others who function in special buildings or clinics, and have the patients brought to them for treatment. Special Services are concerned with recreation. It operates two theatres, two recreation buildings, including canteens, a swimming pool, gymnasium, dances, musical activities, an athletic field, a golf course, three libraries, and a whole series of special programs. It also has charge of the coordination of the activities of some forty-odd volunteer groups, whose members contribute a variety of services to the hospital.

In order to coordinate these functions each ward has a master schedule, which lists for each day of the week not only the routine activities focusing on maintenance and control—getting up, going to the central dining hall for meals, bathing, shaving, visits to the canteen—but also assignments of individual patients or groups to any of the activities of PM&R or Special Services.

In recent years, there has been less emphasis upon control, and more willingness to test a patient's capacity to function in a series of hospital situations. This has led to the classification of wards in terms of privileged, partial privileged, and locked. The ideal pattern of movement for the Continued Treatment wards is from locked ward to one with partial privileges to full privileges, and ultimately to discharge from the hospital. Actually, the constant redistribution of patients among the

TABLE 17-1

Staffing Pattern of the Psychiatric Services, Day Shift, 7/9/57

	NP-TB		Female		AIT*	Continued Treatment							Convalescent			TOTALS
														2005-6		
	126	8	125	1	124	50	51	65	66	9	11	5	7†		2025W	
M.D.	2	2	2		6	½	½	½	½	⅓	⅓	⅓	1	1	1	17
Psychologists	1		1		2	1	1	0	0	0	0	1	1	1	3	12
Social Workers			1	1	2	½	½	Case	Supervisor			1	Supv.		2	8
Head Nurses	2	1	2	½	2	½	½	½	½	½	1	½	2	1	1	16
Practical Nurses	4	1		4		1	1	1	1	½	½	1	2	1	1	18
Aides	17	10	28	10	23	10	10	14	12	7	5	4	21	5	3	179
Consultants	1		2		2										1	6
Patients	115	146	140	134	144	157	160	145	164	149	94	67	137	180	287	2,219

* AIT: Acute Intensive Treatment Service
† Bldg. 7: Acute Section, Continued Treatment Service

400

wards is modified by the pressure of admissions, the need for emergency space on the acute service, and the failure of some patients to manage in a less restrictive environment. Inevitably, ward staffs interpret patients' potentialities for improvement so that they can retain some of their best patients and lose their most troublesome ones.

PATIENT ROLES

In hospital society, the greatest social distance exists between patients and all staff members. Although there are many social roles that patients play, depending upon the ward and the patient's position within it, the most significant one is being a patient. In many respects becoming a patient involves a reversal of all role obligations previously assimilated. Bizarre behavior that brought censure and commitment upon him is tolerated—even expected—as long as it does not threaten the safety of himself or others. He makes no decisions for himself, money and valuables are kept for him, movement is restricted, and when able he is expected to perform work details without compensation (6, 16).

In the Downey Hospital, newly admitted patients are not only given a booklet outlining what they can expect from physician, nurse, social worker, psychologist, the part that special therapies play in the program, but also information on routine, mail, visiting days, canteen visits, and recreation. In addition, newly admitted patients are given an orientation in groups by a clinical psychologist, which includes something of what is expected of them as patients. Whether the indoctrination is as effective as the experience of the patient in finding a place in ward society, either by relating to other patients or by relating successfully to the hospital staff or by becoming a day-room isolate is immaterial (7). That this is one of the effects of hospitalization is borne out by the evidence of the answers to a six-item sentence completion test. Of seventy-four answers to the sentence, "The most important thing in the hospital is to_____" over half the patients gave compliance with hospital rules in such forms as "obey," "act right," "be good," "behave," and "not cause disturbance."

Since the requirements of the patient role, even in productive endeavors, are scaled down to fit his needs and level of functioning in the interests of therapy, mental hospital culture tends to defeat its own aims in social rehabilitation. The normative order for the disordered is sufficiently at variance with the norms of most known groups in our society so that the patient who achieves a good hospital adjustment is less likely to adjust to the world outside the hospital gates.

Although there are a variety of special programs to bridge the gap between the hospital and the community, they involve relatively few patients at any one time. The night hospital plan, the employee-member program, and a motivation clinic are all designed to accustom the patient gradually to meeting the conditions of a world governed by social norms.

The grouping of patients has nothing to do with their previous social characteristics and experience. Diagnostically they are overwhelmingly schizophrenic reactions, with all subtypes represented. Recency of onset of illness, organic complications, age, and current level of functioning are the significant criteria of classification. And within ward society, they are classified by characteristic social behavior—the bosses, the patient-aides, the hallucinators, the clowns, the watchers, the messengers, the collectors, the traders, and others (27). Race, ethnic group membership, former occupational status, and other indicators of expected social behavior are ignored. In this sense hospital life is discontinuous with all previous experience, with the possible exception of military service.

SOCIAL AND CULTURAL BACKGROUND OF PATIENTS

The problem of incidence, type, and distribution of various forms of mental illness in various communities has engaged increasing attention in recent years. One source of data as to how extensive is the problem of the psychoses in contemporary society is revealed by state mental hospital statistics. The World Almanac for 1957 gives the following figures: Out of a total resident population in state hospitals at the end of the year, there were 529,997. During the year 167,071 were admitted to hospitals; of these 114,976 were first admissions. During the same period of time 109,253 patients were discharged from state hospitals and 40,250 died. Yet it seems clear that the incidence of psychoses as measured by those hospitalized in state institutions is partly a function of the availability of mental hospital beds. If one compares the total number of mental hospital beds in a given state with its population, we find that New York has a capacity of .63 per cent, Pennsylvania .37 per cent, and Tennessee .22 per cent. The evidence of psychiatric surveys and mental hygiene clinics indicates that there are psychotic individuals who are either cared for at home, in private institutions, or manage to make a marginal adjustment in spite of their illness (2, 17).

The early ecological studies showed a correlation between the socially disorganized areas of urban centers and the incidence of schizophrenic reactions (28). Recent efforts at case finding, represented by the studies of Stirling County, the Wellesley Project, the Yorkville Project, and the New Haven Survey (14), have sought to specify a number of concrete social and cultural factors which contribute to the etiology of the various diagnostic types recognized in contemporary psychiatry. To the extent that stress and conflict constitute a significant contributing factor, it has been postulated that ethnic groups whose patterns of life differed in significant ways from the core of American culture would have a greater probability of developing mental illness (21).

In two recent studies comparing the manifestation of symptoms of matched groups of Irish and Italian schizophrenics from New York, it was demonstrated that there were systematic differences in overt symptomatology as well as in fantasy and that these were related to the cultural patterns centering around child rearing, male and female roles, and processes of identification found in each of these two groups (17, 23). This would seem to confirm the fact that although the psychological mechanisms involved are similar, the specific content of disordered behavior is related to and relevant to the experience of normal individuals reared in such groups. This idea is further confirmed by Stainbrook's observations on the differential characteristic behavior of schizophrenic patients in the province of Bahia, Brazil, in contrast to the types of behavior he was accustomed to from his experience in hospitals in the United States (24).

The New Haven Survey, dealing with the relationship between the social structure of the community and the treated prevalence of psychiatric disorders, showed that although all types of psychiatric disorders occurred in all five of the classes, their frequency was far from proportionate to the numbers in each class (20). Although classes I and II constituted 11.3 per cent of the normal population, they constituted only 7.9 per cent of the psychiatric population. Class V, which constituted 17.8 per cent of the normal population, constituted 36.8 per cent of the psychiatric population. In classes I and II, the neuroses provided 65.3 per cent of the disorders and psychoses, 34.7 per cent. In class V the neuroses only constituted 8.4 per cent of the disorders and the psychoses accounted for 91.6 per cent. Specifically so far as the incidence of schizophrenic reactions was concerned, classes I and II were represented by 3.4 per cent of all diagnosed cases of schizophrenic reaction. Classes IV and V provided 89.8 per cent of all of the cases diagnosed as schizophrenic reaction (13). The survey also revealed that the higher the class position of the patient, the more reliance was placed on psychotherapeutic methods, and the lower the class position of the patient, the more reliance was placed upon organic therapies or no specific treatment at all.

In another study of the relation of social stratification to psychiatric practice, based upon patients treated in an out-patient clinic where the economic factor was not significant, it was discovered that class position was significantly related to acceptance for treatment, experience and skill of the therapist to whom the patient was assigned, and the duration of treatment (19). It seems clear that with the higher class patients who share more features of background experience and modes of communication with their therapists than do lower class patients the establishment of a therapeutic relationship based upon symbolic communication is easier and more rewarding. The fact that the lower class patient has little understanding of what is involved in a therapeutic relationship, but rather seeks some quick or magical solution to his difficulties is reflected not only in these data, but also in the observation of others who have worked in mental hygiene clinics. In a study of 1,216 cases referred to a Veterans Administration hygiene clinic, it was revealed that 32 per cent of the cases were not offered treatment. Of the remaining cases, 27 per cent refused to undertake treatment even though it was offered to them. For those who undertook treatment, the median length of treatment fell between six and seven interviews; in two-thirds of the cases treatment was terminated by the patient himself (9). It is quite clear from this evidence that effective psychotherapy not only requires a good therapist, but it also requires a good patient.

Since by this definition good patients represent a small minority of the total patient population in a hospital, the competition for good patients is one of the fairly constant features among the professional personnel on the hospital staff. Furthermore, the good patient is most likely to be one who can be effectively treated in the period immediately following admission and is consequently discharged and no longer a member of the hospital population. Since the Downey Hospital is only one of four that serves veterans in the Chicago metropolitan area, the patients who are likely to respond to psychotherapeutic methods are those that are least likely to be transferred to this hospital.

THE DIAGNOSTIC CULTURE

Psychiatrists, psychologists, and social workers are the primary participants in what has been called the diagnostic culture. Essentially, it consists of interpreting not only the behavior of patients in the lexicon of psychiatry, but employing psychodynamic terminology in "interpreting" the behavior of colleagues and as the preferred means of communication with one another. Stanton and Schwartz pointed this out as one of the blocks to effective communication. ". . . many psychiatrists seemed to pride themselves on ignoring the face value of what their colleagues said to them, focusing instead on what they believed 'to be really going on'." *

It is usually assumed that the individual's selection of psychiatry as against other branches of medical specialization, clinical psychology rather than social, experimental, or genetic, and psychiatric social work rather than other types of family case work was determined by preoccupation with his own problems. Many of them have undergone psychoanalysis and others discuss it as a future possibility.

In this system, the behavior of staff members is interpreted exclusively in terms of the individual's psychological needs, and it is utterly divorced from social role, occupational status, or administrative process. The legitimate authority of an office becomes the authoritarianism of the personality of the occupant of the office. Compliance with role expectations is evidence of passive-dependence. And conscientiousness is interpreted as compulsiveness. However helpful this may be in understanding symptoms that patients manifest, it impedes rational discussion of hospital problems or the resolution of recurrent difficulties.

In addition to their common participation in the diagnostic culture, each of these occupational groups has its own special mystique. The psychiatrist is supported not only by the medical tradition, but also by the psychiatric tradition. Legally and medically he must make the critical decisions of diagnosis, somatic therapies, and disposition. In many instances this may, in fact, consist in the validation with his signature of what has been the collective decision of the treatment team, but his pre-eminent role is built into the institutional structure.

The psychologist's functions center around diagnostic testing, psychotherapy, and research. Since the diagnostic function is largely limited

* Stanton, Alfred H., and Schwartz, Morris S.: *The Mental Hospital.* New York: Basic Books, 1954.

to the new admissions, great emphasis is placed upon psychotherapy with selected individual cases or in groups. However, since this does not differentiate the role of the psychologist from that of the psychiatrist, his distinct professional identification centers around the mysteries of testing. Although psychologists were critical of psychiatrists as ward administrators when the hospital was fully staffed with physicians, many of them have had to assume this role during the past two years. They have found, for the most part, that the position limits and determines the role and that they have no more time and energy for psychotherapeutic activities than did their predecessors even if suitable patients could be found.

The social worker identifies professionally with the patient and his family. Concern with relations with the family, arrangements for trial visit and discharge, and the patient's social history are the distinguishing features of his role. However, any of these three groups may accept a patient in therapy in the hospital, just as they do in mental hygiene clinics.

Since the patients come primarily from lower-class backgrounds, and the professional staff is of middle-class origin or aspiration, the problem of therapy based upon symbolic communication is a difficult one (19). Even the effort to employ the techniques of patient government as a form of group therapy proved of limited utility, since the factors of class and ethnic background in one such group left more than two-thirds of them nonparticipants or minimal participants, and hence deriving no benefit from the process of social interaction (5).

That this problem is not limited to the mental hospital patient is attested by the following statement in an article dealing with the role of the psychiatrist in teaching comprehensive medical care: "The special advantage of a printed case history offsets one of the major problems in undergraduate psychiatric education, namely, the nature of the patient material. In many medical centers students have most, if not all of their patient contacts with the indigent, poorly educated person, eking out a marginal existence in slum areas. The lives of the student's patients are so foreign to his own, and are frequently so overwhelming as to hamper any real understanding between them. It is equally true that when in practice, he will be dealing with such patients only during the time he devotes to teaching." *

* Greaves, Donald C.: "The role of the psychiatrist in teaching comprehensive medical care." *American Journal of Psychiatry*, 1957, vol. 114, pp. 42–46.

Although many recent efforts have been directed toward discovering the extent to which the wards can be converted into therapeutic milieus, the specification of patient roles in geographic and social space, and the conscious employment of these factors in moving patients to a better level of functioning, they are still experiments, and not part of the hospital regimen (18, 28).

In a success-oriented society, in a medical tradition in which new "miracles" are announced with great regularity, it is difficult for the staff to sustain effort, and retain confidence in whatever knowledge and techniques they have acquired as part of their professional training in the face of the massive resistance of the long-term psychotic patients. The successfully treated leave the hospital; the others remain as a challenge—or a reminder. It is no wonder that there is more concern with morale in the mental hospital than there is in the military organizations (27, 28).

It may well be that the security provided by the hospital represents a "secondary gain from illness" on the unconscious level. It is also possible that, in any given case, life in the hospital provides the patient more rewards and fewer deprivations than he has ever known on the conscious level. Schizophrenics are not the only patients for whom illness has become a way of life.

BIBLIOGRAPHY

1. American Psychiatric Association: *Diagnostic and Statistical Manual of Mental Disorders.* Washington, D.C.: American Psychiatric Association, 1952.

2. Barrabee, Paul, and von Mering, Otto: "Ethnic variations in mental stress in families with psychotic children." *Social Problems,* 1953, vol. 1, pp. 48–53.

3. Caplow, Theodore: "Organizational size." *Administrative Science Quarterly,* 1957, vol. 1, pp. 484–505.

4. Council of State Governments: *The Mental Health Programs of the Forty-eight States.* Chicago: Council of State Governments, 1950.

5. Croog, S. H.: "Patient government: Some aspects of participation and social background on two psychiatric wards." *Psychiatry,* 1956, vol. 19: pp. 203–207.

6. Cumming, John, and Cumming, Elaine: "Mental health education in a Canadian community." In *Health, Culture, and Community* (Benjamin D. Paul, ed.). New York: Russell Sage Foundation, 1955, pp. 43–69.

7. Cumming, Elaine, and Cumming, John: "Affective symbolism, social norms, and mental illness." *Psychiatry*, 1956, vol. 19: pp. 77–85.

8. Deutsch, Albert: *The Mentally Ill in America*. New York: Columbia University Press, 1949.

9. Garfield, Sol L., and Kurz, Max.: "Evaluation of treatment and related procedures in 1216 cases referred to a mental hygiene clinic." *The Psychiatric Quarterly*, 1952, pp. 1–11.

10. Greaves, Donald C.: "The role of the psychiatrist in teaching comprehensive medical care." *American Journal of Psychiatry*, 1957, vol. 114, pp. 42–46.

11. Greenblatt, Milton; York, Richard H.; Brown, Esther Lucile: *From Custodial to Therapeutic Patient Care in Mental Hospitals*. New York: Russell Sage Foundation, 1955.

12. Henry, Jules: "The formal structure of a psychiatric hospital." *Psychiatry*, 1954, vol. 17, pp. 139–151.

13. Hollingshead, August B., and Redlich, Fredrick C.: "Social stratification and schizophrenia." *American Sociological Review*, 1954, vol. 19, pp. 302–306.

14. *Interrelations between the Social Environment and Psychiatric Disorders*. Papers presented at the 1952 Annual Conference of the Milbank Memorial Fund. New York: Milbank Memorial Fund, 1953.

15. Lentz, Edith M.: "Hospital administration—one of a species." *Administrative Science Quarterly*, 1957, vol. 1, pp. 444–463.

16. Myers, Jerome K., and Schaffer, Leslie: "Social stratification and psychiatric practice: A study of an out-patient clinic." *American Sociological Review*, 1954, vol. 19, pp. 307–310.

17. Opler, Marvin K., and Singer, Jerome L.: "Ethnic differences in behavior and psychopathology: Italian and Irish." *The International Journal of Social Psychiatry*, 1956, vol. 2, pp. 11–22.

18. Pace, Robert E.: "Situational therapy." *Journal of Personality*, 1957, vol. 25, pp. 578–588.

19. Redlich, F. C.; Hollingshead, A. B.; and Bellis, Elizabeth: "Social class differences in attitude toward psychiatry." *American Journal of Orthopsychiatry*, 1955, vol. 25, pp. 60–70.

20. Redlich, F. C.; Hollingshead, A. B.; Roberts, B. H.; Robinson, H. A.; Freedman, L. Z.; and Myers, J. K.: "Social structure and psychiatric disorders." *American Journal of Psychiatry*, 1953, vol. 109, pp. 729–734.

21. Ruesch, J.; Loeb, M. B.; and Jacobson, A.: "Acculturation and disease." *Psychological Monographs: General and Applied*. Washington, D.C.: American Psychological Association, 1948.

22. Simmons, Ozzie G.; Davis, James A.; Spencer, Katherine: "Interpersonal strains in release from a mental hospital." *Social Problems*, 1956, vol. 4, pp. 21–28.

23. Singer, Jerome L., and Opler, Marvin K.: "Contrasting patterns of fantasy and motility in Italian and Irish schizophrenics." *The Journal of Abnormal and Social Psychology*, 1956, vol. 53, pp. 42–47.
24. Stainbrook, Edward S.: "Some characteristics of the psychopathology of schizophrenic behavior in Bahian society." *American Journal of Psychiatry*, 1952, vol. 109, pp. 330–335.
25. Stanton, Alfred H., and Schwartz, Morris S.: *The Mental Hospital*. New York: Basic Books, 1954.
26. Sullivan, Harry Stack: *Conceptions of Modern Psychiatry*. Washington, D.C.: W. A. White Psychiatric Association, 1946.
27. von Mering, Otto: "Legend and mores of patient care." *Danville State Hospital Mental Health Bulletin*, 1955, vol. 33, pp. 1–15.
28. von Mering, Otto, and King, Stanley H.: *Remotivating the Mental Patient*. New York: Russell Sage Foundation, 1957.
29. Weinberg, S. Kirson: *Society and Personality Disorders*. New York: Prentice-Hall, 1952.

Section VI

SOME
MODERN PROBLEMS

A. Kardiner

The Psychoanalytic Clinic
Columbia University

18

EXPLORATIONS IN NEGRO PERSONALITY

The interest of the social sciences in human personality lies largely
in the circumstance that society, not being an organism, has no built-in
homeostats. This means two things: that if there are any social regulators, they must be built into the individual. In their absence, social en-
forcement of regulations has become a fixture of most societies, ancient
and modern. Force or polite coercion is generally represented by policy
or by conventions maintained by a majority or some dominant segment of the community. When social regulation is placed on an optional
basis it is generally ineffectual, unless backed by fear, as in the case of
most religions.

Since man's socialization is governed so little by inborn regulators
and is maintained largely by cultivated ones, most of which become
automatized during growth, the genetic process of the development of
the individual is of the greatest importance in the understanding of
what emotional factors are conducive to holding society together or
tending to cause human relations to disintegrate.

This idea is not new. It has long been known by those who control
governments that deprivation can cause human beings to revolt against
those whom they deem responsible for their suffering. This kind of
reaction is generally limited to the deprivation of hunger. And since
Marie Antoinette recommended "let them eat cake," no Western government has ignored the threat of physiological deprivation as a powerful
factor in undermining a willingness to be socially compliant.

Short of this, however, human beings have shown themselves capable of tolerating social inequalities of varying degrees, from slavery
to various forms of caste and social stratifications that carry with them
most serious deprivations. A case in point is the American Negro today.

413

Here, in this essay, the issues about the American Negro are concerned with the following questions: *1*) Does this social discrimination affect personality? *2*) What is the best way of finding out in a reliable manner what these effects are?

Among the psychological methods of investigation there are none, in my opinion, that are able to explain so much of the underlying currents as the psychoanalytic. It is the only three-dimensional study of personality available today. This does not mean that this method does not have defects; but it does give more information.

The psychoanalytic method is, however, very time consuming, and it is not applicable under present arrangements to statistically relevant samples, even if one is interested only in incidence of social phenomena. This is an issue that the quantitative-minded sociologist generally cannot understand: that the study of incidence of unemployment, for example, is a very different *kind* of undertaking from investigating whether living under conditions of persistent social discrimination molds the personality in a specific manner. The first procedure looks for the distribution of one isolated trait or phenomenon at a time, but the latter involves a study of a special influence on the *total* personality. One does not need thousands of cases to establish the latter type of finding ordinarily. The psychodynamics of neuroses were, after all, established by Freud through a study of about ten published cases.

One may pause on this issue because in an essay published by Dr. Ovesey and myself (1), the actual number of depth studies were carried out on twenty-five cases. This was a point which was considered statistically insufficient. Had the study been called by such a title as the present "Explorations in Negro Personality," it would have aroused less protest from Negroes themselves. Another psychiatrist suggested that in order to find out the truth about the Negro we would have to study him "transculturally." I do not know what a transcultural psychoanalytic study is but would venture to suggest that such study be undertaken by a transcultural psychiatrist in a transcultural environment.

The method chosen by Dr. Ovesey and myself was to pick out the really operating adaptive constellations and relate these to known effects of life circumstances to which the subjects were exposed during growth.

Social discrimination in its simplest terms means the lack of access to available opportunities for gratification, self-enhancement, expression, etc. The exploitation of one human by another for his utility value for food (cannibalism), labor (slavery) and sex (forced concubinage) has long been known. The form most common in man is probably enforced concubinage. The latter has enduring social consequences in the form of a so-called "race problem," when the offspring have characteristics of both parents.

As long as the enslaved have no social rights, the characterological consequences may have little special historical relevancy, with one exception. The enslaved may revolt or refuse to work. Then it becomes a choice, to the enslaved, between survival or increased deprivation, or even death. When the slave is liberated and admitted to citizenship, then the characterological consequences of his bondage become socially relevant insofar as the degrading conditions and continued discrimination markedly influence his relations to the society in which he lives.

From this point of view the American Negro is highly instructive. His original cultures were almost completely destroyed but for a few vestigial remains, and the cultural equipment of the Negro became American. He was surrounded by much the same stimuli for social mobility and for improvement of status in the form of a higher standard of living as other groups. The one enduring variable between Negro and white today is therefore the persistence of social discrimination. We are interested in the effects this major factor has had on the Negro and on the community in which he lives.

It is now almost a century since the Negro was emancipated from slavery. His present social environment is therefore, in part at least, the result of this changing status occasioned by emancipation. Chief among these special features is the much studied character of the Negro family. This factor, discussed by E. Franklin Frazier and others, has a high priority because the family, in turn, decides many aspects of the development of the Negro child. The basic fact is that the Negro mother has remained the center of the household and the father distinctly secondary, especially in the lower classes. The reasons for this were that the mother had the social advantages including more sustained employment and general recognition as the responsible family member. Marriages consequently were less stable than among whites. This feature is complicated in many ways by the factor of migration of the Negro male from the South to the North, and is the chief characteristic of the lower-class Negro family in urban centers. As we shall see, the middle and upper classes are more like the white family.

This means, in other words, that the Negro lower-class family often is unstable and disorganized, hardly providing an environment where the most effective integration can take place. The absence of a stable male spouse and father leads to other consequences like the doubling and tripling of the households in addition to "broken homes," that is, broken homes of the nuclear family type with one member missing. The opportunities for effective integration are thus curtailed, in the sense that the family does not provide the protective environment it should to prevent characterological distortions.

We can state this case somewhat as follows: The Negro faces the social condition of discrimination with serious impairment of adaptive equipment. The situation here described is likely to undergo a great change in the next generation. The opportunity of the white to discriminate against the Negro is likely to be sharply curtailed by the pressing need for his (the Negro's) services in science and industry. The Negro as a source of lower-class labor is gradually becoming modified, and the younger generation of Negroes who have professional or skilled artisan possibilities is growing larger. These new opportunities are bound to reverse the social trends that formerly made it difficult for the Negro to enjoy pride in himself.

The central problem of Negro adaptation is in mastering the self-referential aspects of social discrimination. This merely means that oppression creates a self-image that is not lovable. Not approving of oneself means the collapse of pride and self-esteem. Thus, the end product of the behavior of others toward the Negro is a somewhat low opinion of himself. This is an ever-present and unrelieved irritant because the individual requires constant restitutive measures in order to keep functioning.

A compact way of representing the whole adaptive scheme is seen in the diagram on page 417.

In the center of this scheme is the depressed self-esteem (the self-referential part) and aggression (the reactive part). The rest are maneuvers to prevent the manifestation of either the depressed self-esteem or the aggression, to make things look different from what they are, and to replace the aggression with a more acceptable ingratiation and passivity. Keeping this system going makes one ill at ease, mistrustful, and lacking in confidence. The entire system is the kind that compels those emotions which would have the effect of rendering the individual socially cooperative and affectionate to remain impounded.

The low self-esteem leads to self-contempt and idealization of whites, which in turn nourishes the futile wish to become white by

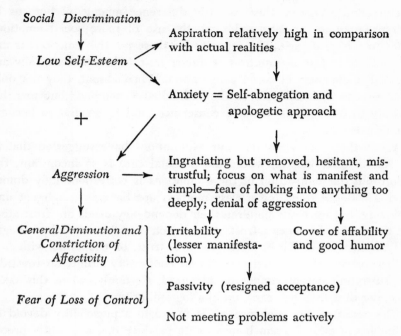

magical means. Since this magic is unattainable, the result is hatred of the whites, as well as self-hatred. One sees also what may be called projected self-hatred, i.e., hatred and contempt for Negroes. The low self-esteem can, in turn, mobilize compensations in several forms: apathy, hedonism, living for the moment, and even criminality.

The intrapsychic techniques for handling suppressed rage are numerous. Among the most common is to deny the rage, which may also transform it into the form of gaiety and flippancy. Another fate of suppressed rage is that it may ricochet back upon its subject in the form of guilt and depression. Psychosomatic channels may become another avenue or pathway in the form of headaches and hypertension.

This adaptational scheme is of course used by each individual in accordance with whatever personality patterns have been established during growth. There seems to be a considerable difference between such adaptation patterns integrated during growth in the lower as contrasted with the upper classes. The latter tend to approximate white middle-class standards—at any rate, on behavioristic levels.

The emotions that promote peaceful cooperation and affection are not inborn except in the form of an Anlage. They are therefore acquired or cultivated. Whereas there is little difference among all humans in their capacity for anxiety and rage, the use of more social emotions varies to a high degree. The capacity for these positive emotions is unfortunately not just a gratuitous character trait. When present, they are essential implements of social cooperation. When absent, they not only influence the personal fate of the individual concerned, but mar his capacity to form ideals, to have conscience, and in general to become socially educable.

While there are variations, our explorations have suggested that in the Negro lower classes, where the parental care is so inconstant, the opportunity for cultivation of these emotions is correspondingly diminished. No doubt some lower-class mothers are far from negligent and nonloving, but for many children their dependency needs are frustrated, and the mother becomes a frustrating object. A child reared by a negligent mother cannot be expected to love, trust, or cooperate with her. In the absence of love and care, social conformity brings no rewards; the frustrating parent cannot be idealized. Certainly, when this takes place, her directives can carry no binding authority.

The result of any such process is to create a personality devoid of confidence in other human beings, or to produce one constantly preoccupied with mistrust. This vigilance is purely protective. Often, the lower-class Negro must operate on the *proven* fact that to him the world is hostile. In the lower class, this inner conviction is counteracted by a perpetual struggle to relate to others in purely formal ways. It has been noted that he may become an inveterate joiner in clubs or cliques with high-sounding names and much ritualism. These organizations are often known to be pervaded by continuous discord. In other words, there are attempted compensations for a lack of capacity for relatedness; but, for the greater part, this effort miscarries.

The capacity for relatedness has a bearing on the necessity to idealize someone. This tendency means two things to the individual: 1) Whom do I admire, and 2) Whom would I like to resemble? The problem is very complex for the lower-class Negro for a simple reason. The society's general notion of an idealized hero is always portrayed as *the* white man. However, this may act on the Negro like a slow poison. It leads to more self-hatred. Perforce the manifest idealized figure for the colored person must be Negro. Of recent years, Negroes of high accomplishment have been more frequent, and many of them have thereby rendered their people a high service in that such figures, especially when their acclaim comes from Negro and white alike, tend to become real culture heroes. Such, for example, is the case with a wide variety of symbols such as Booker T. Washington, Marion Anderson, Ralph Bunche, etc.

Conscience mechanisms must suffer in the lower-class Negro child particularly because the parent, chiefly the mother, cannot inspire or satisfy much dependency. The father is generally not an authority figure. The failure of the home to be a protective environment inevitably leads to great accumulation of inner tensions, a constriction of affect, and an indolent conscience. Hence, the parent has no authority to enforce discipline by threat or example. Obedience, on the other hand, brings but little reward. Antisocial tendencies, when they do develop, can therefore be controlled only by fear of detection. Since the caste situation creates its ceaseless frustrations, the control of aggression is a constant and necessary preoccupation of its victims. In order to establish some kind of internal equilibrium, the following are some of the devices used: flashy and flamboyant dressing; the frequent use of narcotics and alcohol; gambling, chiefly in the form of playing the numbers racket. These are not pleasant outcomes, but neither is the erosion of self-esteem.

This same general situation may exist in the upper classes with some notable differences. The necessity of maintaining what Shaw called "middle class morality" (and living standards) imposes a terrific strain on personality. Any uncompromising acceptance of "white ideals" makes it harder to deal with lowered self-esteem and the management of the aggressions generated by the caste situation. The entire psychodynamic system may be further aggravated by the opportunity to develop better conscience mechanisms and higher ideals. It is questionable whether the better conditions during growth can compensate for the still greater struggle to maintain higher ideals. From some of the personality studies it would seem that the upper-class Negro has built up at the same time a sense of guilt toward those of lower classes because of his greater success. Such success is construed as a betrayal of his race and as aggression against it. In some instances this feeling is so strong as to be tantamount to a success phobia.

If acceptance of white ideals ends for some in overshooting the mark, then the task of adaptation becomes correspondingly harder. The difficulty is created by arbitrary or discriminatory obstacles placed in the

way of achieving the white man's ideals. This compels the Negro either
to place greater pressure on himself to buck the social barriers, or in one
form or another to deny their existence.

For what they are worth, the Rorschach tests, on twenty-four subjects who were a basis for the above conclusions, gave the following results indicated by Dr. William Goldfarb (1).

Intelligence was about the same as in whites. Intellectual efficiency
was, however, reduced in 92 per cent. Deep anxiety and aggression were
present in all the subjects tested. There was marked conflict about these
aggressive urges in 96 per cent. Suspiciousness, emotional isolation, and
deficient rapport with others were present in all subjects, as were apathy,
passivity, and compliance. According to Goldfarb, status differentiations
did not register any detectable differences in the Rorschach tests.

In the Thematic Apperception Tests, as interpreted by Mrs. E. D.
Kardiner, the results were about the same as in the Rorschachs (1).
However, some of the features stood out with greater clarity, as did, for
example, the mechanism of denial. This is illustrated in the response
to a card showing night, gloom, and fog by such a contrasting reaction
as "a spring scene with flowers." A distortion of this magnitude cannot
develop as an isolated phenomenon. Another feature that emerges with
great clarity is the equation: aggression plus control equals emotional
flatness. The sheer effort used in controlling aggression can choke off
other forms of affect. The T.A.T. also brings into sharp relief the confused social roles of male and female and the mutual hostility of each
to the other.

At the same time, the difficulty with any psychodynamic approach to
personality is that it specializes mainly in maladaptation. There are
undoubtedly a great many individual exceptions to the general picture
here described. But from our data, we have no way of appraising their
statistical incidence. As a matter of fact, for the present no such complete
study exists.

A description of problems of the personality of the lower-class Negro
has several uses; among these, two are most important: 1) It gives a
picture of the influence of a particular form of social deprivation on
effectiveness and happiness; and 2) it also gives us some clues to the
effects of these personality features on the social life of the Negro.
Neither of these objectives is in high repute in the social sciences. Nor
are they likely to gain any footing there for several reasons. They require
an "imported" technique and so are contrary to any insular traditions of

specific social sciences. Such objections notwithstanding, there is no other technique that can tell us just what the effects of social oppression are on human beings, and what the consequences are for the entire community of having an oppressed minority. Other techniques might speak of "loss" without indicating how the loss occurs.

If we approach this latter problem from its most extreme form, i.e., slavery, some aspects emerge with great clarity. Slavery is the most extreme form of subjecting another human being to utilitarian ends. But since the object thus exploited *is* human, there must be some kind of identification between persecutor and "persecutee." This generates a sense of guilt which in turn makes it imperative to degrade the object further to justify the original action. The result is to hate the abused object, the rationalization being that the attributes of the Negro really excite this hatred. These attributes, where they are social or personal, are acquired in the process of accommodation to a lowered status. But all this is conveniently forgotten by the white because it degrades the white man to recognize his responsibility in the picture. As long as the Negro in slavery accepted his degraded status, the white man could develop a convenient amnesia for this responsibility.

However, when the Negro was emancipated and demanded equality of access to existing opportunities, this demand was interpreted by the white man as a fall in his own status, which could only be restored by more hatred and more brutality. Such was the threat as he conceived of it. The increase in brutality and hatred could only cause the white man to have more fear of retaliation.

The social effects of discrimination on the Negro thus tend to become self-perpetuating. Economically, no doubt, they pay off, too. But looked at psychologically, the Negro father who abandoned his children was likely himself to be the product of a broken home. He was generally brought up in the custody of a foster parent who treated him cruelly or saw that he got the worst of it in his conflicts with his stepsiblings. He did not grow up with a very exalted ideal of masculinity, which he heard disparaged by his female relatives who were the more dependable mainstays of his life. Thus, a cycle is perpetuated in which the mother image is not an attractive one either. If the mother worked, she unintentionally subjected her son to deprivations. His attitude to the female, therefore, became exploitive and untrusting. He knew that the female had better economic chances. His frantic efforts to retain the dominant position in the family often ended in failure and despondency. If he left to take a job in another city, this step could be transformed into a permanent status of separation or informal divorce. The female, thus abandoned, led a harassed existence between work and caring for the young. Her role as a protector to the child was impaired, and the whole setting for cooperative relatedness was destroyed. This meant that the capacity for idealization and conscience suffered as well.

The chief interest in these latter features lies in their relation to the social cohesion of the Negro. This concept needs some definition. It could mean that the Negro has little capacity to act in concert with others to improve a common lot (2). The Negro has shown great unanimity of opinion and feeling, and hence unity, in connection with the problem of Negro status. This kind of situation, however, does not test social cohesion fully. It is like an emergency which calls for unity, a fire or an earthquake. It is still possible for people who have little capacity for social cohesion to meet such emergency situations successfully and then retreat to their position of emotional isolation and remain there once the emergency is over.

There are several features of Negro personality that militate against a high degree of social cohesion. The necessity to impound most forms of self-assertion and to that extent to identify with his white oppressor are such limitations of emotional development. Sometimes this does not happen, but unfortunately often it does. Such a constellation historically could lead to "passing" with its presumed advantages and its great (though concealed) sense of guilt. When members of a group fly from each other by secretly wishing to be like their oppressors, then their social cohesion is bound to be very low. On the other hand, one can legitimately raise the question of what use the Negro had for social cohesion, since the social cohesion that mattered most to him was that which he had in common with other American people whose culture and destiny he shared. Historically, such avenues were not open to him.

In this connection, the Negro is most often compared with the status of the Jew. The fact is that they are not comparable in many ways, although they have some features in common. A correct comparison would have to be made with the ghetto Jews, not those of England or America. Somehow, the Jew of the ghetto was able to do certain things that prevented social disaster from overtaking him. One difference is that the Jew's culture was not destroyed, nor did he seek to appropriate the culture of his hosts until he either became successful or until the ghettos themselves were abolished. The social discrimination has never, of course, been as severe as that toward the Negro. The self-hatred of the Negro could, therefore, not develop to the same extent in the Jew. As a consequence of these conditions, family cohesion has been greater for the Jew. Violent forms of self-hatred are to be seen in Jews today, to be sure, but only as severely neurotic elaborations. These may generally employ such magical devices as marrying non-Jews or conversion to one or another church, depending on whether one seeks security (in which case Catholicism may become the religion of choice) or prestige (when such a group as Episcopalian may be preferred instead).

In fact, it is the contrast between the *social* fate of the Negro and the Jew that points up where the damaging effects of social discrimination register most severely. The difference lies in the break-up of the culture of the Negro, which made it necessary for him to identify himself with the white, while at the same time his opportunities to realize the white man's social goals were seriously blocked. To this loss of pride in himself, when male, was added the relatively or slightly superior position of the Negro female. These two features combined to destroy the cohesion of the Negro family and thereby to impair the opportunity for the young to cultivate those emotions on which social cohesion depends.

BIBLIOGRAPHY

1. Kardiner, A., and Ovesey, L.: *The Mark of Oppression*. New York, W. W. Norton & Co., 1951.
2. Rose, Arnold M.: *The Negro's Morale*. Minneapolis: University of Minnesota Press, 1949.

Marvin K. Opler

Department of Psychiatry
University of Buffalo School of Medicine
and
Department of Sociology
University of Buffalo

19

CULTURAL DIFFERENCES IN MENTAL DISORDERS:

AN ITALIAN AND IRISH CONTRAST IN

THE SCHIZOPHRENIAS *

—U.S.A.

A group of disorders known as schizophrenias has long perplexed psychiatry. The French psychiatrist, Morel, called them Dementia Praecox, meaning a serious pathological state beginning early in life. Equally fatalistic, Kahlbaum's descriptions in German distinguished certain types in 1863 and 1874, each one having an insidious and disastrous course. Before the end of the nineteenth century, Kraepelin had published his famous classification of 1896 in which he argued that each type of schizophrenia was an organic or endogenous illness and one not due to external causes. At first Kraepelin felt this organic pathology was centered in the brain, but later he observed striking differences in the form and frequency of the illnesses occurring in Java, Malaya, and elsewhere. By this time, Bleuler influenced Kraepelin to add a fourth type, simple schizophrenia, to the three types of illness named by the latter. But Kraepelin's more important concession to environmental explanations was to shift to discussions of metabolic disorders accounting for the different forms and frequencies of the schizophrenias in various populations of the world.

* This paper was originally published in *The Psychiatric Quarterly*, July, 1959. Reprinted by permission.

Bleuler's classic, *Dementia Praecox or the Group of Schizophrenias*, appeared in 1911. Where Kraepelin had contrasted populations from far-flung regions of the world, hinting at racial and constitutional differences, Bleuler focused on a narrower range of peoples—from Holland, Thuringia, Upper Bavaria, Saxony, and even the people of Berne and Zurich. The latter were certainly similar in physique, but had "different reactions." Bleuler mentioned Irish and English differences in the illness state. He adduced the work of Kraepelin and Ziehen where they had observed epidemiological variance in several populations. Bleuler not only noted differences among peoples of similar racial type and discarded Kraepelin's metabolic explanation, but he described various *psychological processes* where Kraepelin had discussed *symptoms* and ascribed organic causes to account for them. Bleuler therefore noted that a psychological process can underlie a cluster or pattern of symptoms and their accompanying organic states. As such, patients were responsive to the impact of environmental conditions. Their individual reactions could be deflected, arrested, or channeled into a new course, depending on the treatments applied. Bleuler's assertion that certain types were responsive to given treatments was strengthened by his observation of spontaneous remission in others. He introduced the hope that schizophrenias were open to treatment and voiced his belief that factors of group background "and external circumstances should be found."

While Bleuler was interested in the epidemiology of schizophrenias, the passages in his great book are tantalizingly brief on this subject. One must look further to find a public health, or preventive, approach to this problem. Even before Bleuler, the reformist setting of postrevolutionary France provided the answer. Pinel's student, Jean-Étienne D. Esquirol (1772–1840) wished to sharpen the acuity of clinical observations with a more psychological as well as quantitative approach to the emotional life. In a reaction against the rationalists of the Enlightenment in France, Esquirol charged that they were preoccupied with intellectual aspects of mental disease and with the pigeonholes of classification. Instead, he said, one must stress the roles played by emotions and values in human relations. Realizing that such information was difficult to perceive and to accumulate systematically, Esquirol favored the gathering of statistical or epidemiological data with a view to preventive techniques in even the most serious schizophrenic disorders.

The convergence of these psychological, environmental, and preventive approaches was developed in the American scene by Adolf Meyer (1866–1950). At the Henry Phipps Psychiatric Clinic of the Johns Hopkins Hospital, Meyer and his colleagues built solidly on these earlier foundations. Preventive psychiatry was emphasized in the term, "mental hygiene," which Meyer located in the earlier literature but succeeded in popularizing. His system, called psychobiology, recognized each patient's problem as a complex of biological, psychological, and environmental influences reflected into his total personality. This encompassing view was called "a distributive analysis of relevant factors," but it led to the first massive epidemiological study of mental illness in urban surroundings, the Eastern Health District of Baltimore. This striking research, including the schizophrenias, was carried out by Lemkau, Tietze, Cooper, and others in an interdisciplinary team of behavioral scientists.

Meyer not only stimulated epidemiological research, but like Bleuler he stressed the existence of several types of schizophrenia and differences in their prognosis or probable course of illness. The responses to environment in every phase of their development or treatment were influenced by the psychological and cultural factors entering into a patient's self-conceptions or self-deceptions.

Contemporaneously with Bleuler in Switzerland and Meyer in America, the Freudian movement became interested in treatment of milder neurotic disorders. Meyer's notion of conflicts growing "realistically" out of experience and promoting habitual incapacities was replaced with conflicts dependent upon deeply rooted unconscious drives. Meyer's concept of the larger environment and its lifelong impact was shrunk to the narrow proportions of early parent-child and sibling relationships almost exclusively. Despite this, the Freudian system contributed heavily to an understanding of schizophrenia. Pierre Janet had earlier spoken of "the loss of a sense of reality." Bleuler had described "conflictual ambivalence," a concept borrowed from Freud, as leading to the withdrawn or shut-in "autisms" characterizing certain kinds of schizophrenia. In the Freudian system, this loss of reality contact was linked to the flooding of impulses from unconscious dynamic or symbolic sources, often poorly controlled and little understood by the patient. There was a defensive substitution of a world of one's own where reality failed. While the focus was upon the defensive mechanisms themselves, obviously an environmentalist revision of the system could point out that they were used against the stresses of life experiences and within social settings. If such defensive mechanisms distorted reality, how could they become habitual unless growth was blocked or reality appeared to be threatening?

It is clear that psychiatry had succeeded in typifying the general nature of schizophrenias while remaining largely preoccupied with the cause and course of these diseases in individuals rather than in groups. Today, more is known about the particular needs of a given case than about its general detection or prevention in the community. Psychiatry has delineated types and discovered processes in schizophrenias, but has only occasionally considered epidemiological backgrounds, or promoted a general understanding of the nature of schizophrenias. In quite another field of science, anthropology has busied itself with aspects of human existence distinguishing one group from another. It has located compelling and pervasive meanings in cultures which influence behavior. In brief, psychiatry as a medical science perfected knowledge of patterned behavior in individuals and in pathological states studied in western European cultures. The social science studied patterned behavior in groups with emphasis on ranges and contrasts in conduct, both normative or "normal" and aberrant, and located throughout the world.

Recently, social psychiatry has developed to bridge the gap between such constantly converging fields. For example, the World Health Organization commissioned a British psychiatrist, J. C. Carothers, to gather data on mental illnesses in Africa. This resulted in a monograph in 1953, bristling with regional variations. The present author in the same year began a more comprehensive survey of the distribution of various types of mental illness among the peoples of the world. This work was published in 1956 under the title of *Culture, Psychiatry and Human Values*. Again wherever reliably reported, epidemiological and acculturation studies showed various symptom pictures and led to consideration of their differing etiology.

For one thing, it appeared that mental illnesses differed from the organic deficiency diseases or from germ-specific ailments in several ways. In schizophrenias, for example, they drastically and dramatically involved the total personality. Often they implied the instability and disturbance experienced by groups of individuals in their cultural environment. Thirdly, and reflecting upon the recent overoptimism about "tranquilizers" and "wonder drugs," these serious illnesses had for decades defied the search for easy solutions and instead required a whole process of re-education over time. Because of their insidious nature, total personality involvement, and particular environmental influence, we seemed, especially in schizophrenias, to focus attention upon the unique individual all too exclusively. Most conceptions of schizophrenia implied —despite Bleuler, Meyer, and Freud—only the private aberrations of essentially deranged minds.

It seemed that typical strategies of research in public health and preventive medicine might be applied. In organic illnesses, such leads had proved valuable. Haven Emerson, in 1931, had found ethnic, or cultural, differences in measles, diphtheria, and scarlet fever rates which proved important in understanding the transmission of these communicable diseases. The year following, Clifford Abbott used the method to explain endemic developments of simple goiter. W. L. Aycock and J. W. Hawkins surveyed regional, cultural, and family relationships in leprosy, and R. D. Friedlander did so for pernicious anemia. In New York State, M. Calabresi had found different rates for diabetes, heart disease, pneumonia, and tuberculosis among Italians, Irish, Germans, Poles, and British. Following the Bigelow and Lombard studies in 1933 on the different frequencies of cancer at certain sites, H. F. Dorn and M. E. Patno, each, in 1954, renewed the case for ethnic differences in cancer development. F. R. Smith, in 1941, and E. L. Kennaway, in 1948, discussed cultural background differences in cervical and uterine cancers. A social scientist, Saxon Graham, reported a county in Pennsylvania where rheumatism, arthritis, high blood pressure, and diabetes showed low rates in the first generation of some ethnic groups, with an increase in the second generation and leveling off in subsequent generations.

A few of these illnesses had been claimed for some time to be psychosomatic in character. H. Blotner and R. W. Hyde noted, in 1943, the high incidence of certain forms of diabetes in Irish and Jewish male populations. Others noted high rates among Italians. Alcoholism was found among Irish to be a common accompaniment of more fundamental personality disorders. On the other hand, Diethelm's recent book on chronic alcoholism notes that certain groups, such as the Chinese in New York, are free of this symptom for a variety of social and cultural reasons. Haggard and Jellinek specify almost equally low rates of alcoholism for Italian and Jewish populations.

Klopfer, in the *Psychiatric Quarterly* of 1944, and Malzberg, even earlier, claimed to have found different frequencies in major mental illnesses among such groups as Italian, Irish, and German immigrants. In the same year as Klopfer's report, R. W. Hyde and associates found striking variations in Selective Service rejectees from the Boston area.

Again such groups as Chinese, Irish, Italians, Jewish, and Portuguese were compared, although, unfortunately, gross diagnostic categories were used such as psychoses, neuroses, mental deficiency, psychopathic personality, and chronic alcoholism. Only studies by E. Stainbrook in the Bahian region of Brazil or J. C. Carother's compendium of African data discussed schizophrenia centrally and even these authors discerned diagnostic variations more than a difference in the etiology and developmental course of the diseases. When one turns to the *Diagnostic and Statistical Manual on Mental Disorders,* developed by a Committee of the American Psychiatric Association, one finds no clue to a cultural etiology. Nine headings were utilized for schizophrenic illnesses exclusive of such personality disorders as "schizoid personality." Kraepelin's subtypes, like the hebephrenic or catatonic, were preserved to emphasize certain clusters of symptoms, but the symptoms themselves were overlapping and the older terminology of autism, hallucinations, and disturbances of thought and affect was recurrent throughout the list.

The crucial point is that the correct weighting and profiling of symptoms makes etiological sense about the development of a specific illness and not another. Only this can provide a differential diagnosis. Extensions of our knowledge of psychotherapy of schizophrenias, by Sullivan, Diethelm, Hill, Fromm-Reichmann and others, suggested that interpersonal relations and stresses implicit in various cultural backgrounds were basic, perhaps, to different disease processes.

The author explored this hypothesis earlier, in the period 1938–1943. Studying small samples of schizophrenics at Morningside Hospital in Portland, Oregon, he noted differences in patients who were Eskimo, Aleut, Tlingit, or Tsimshian in cultural background, and further differences in those who were Alaskan whites. The hospital used was a federal institution for persons from Alaska and surrounding regions. Unfortunately, the samples were inadequate and represented only those hospitalized in the five-year period. However, they did bring into focus differences in cultural background and acculturation processes. Along with these factors went distinctions in disease development and suggestions, useful for the psychiatrist, as to possible treatment.

It appeared that schizophrenias are not a collection of air-tight entities, since different cultural backgrounds defined variations in family and social structure, reflecting into pathology. As such, schizophrenias could highlight, rather than obscure, severely emotionalized conflicts rooted in culture. It was the latter element which had provided the family or the individual with systems of value, habits of thought, patterns of action, and even the attitudes toward interpersonal relations which proved to be so fundamental.

In 1954 and 1955, following studies of eight ethnic groups, it was decided to study hospitalized schizophrenic samples of certain cultural backgrounds. The community groups, from a section of New York City, were Irish, Italians, Germans, Hungarians, Czechs, Slovakians, Puerto Ricans, and older American families. The schizophrenic samples, from the same area and reported on here, were of Italian or Irish background. Besides wishing to explore cultural differences in schizophrenias, we hoped to provide a check on data obtained from random samples of persons residing in each functioning ethnic community. For each study, the normative community in New York, with its functioning picture of family life, good and bad, provided us with all the hypotheses necessary for understanding the schizophrenic illnesses in each specific group.

In the community, we used anthropological field surveys, questionnaires applied to a random sample of adults, and intensive family studies of subsamples. In the hospital, we were able to amplify these methods of community research with anthropological interviews and observations of patients, with psychiatric records and conferences, and with an independently operating battery of thirteen psychological tests. The psychological test battery was devised by clinical psychologists of the Franklin D. Roosevelt Veterans Administration Hospital and in particular by Dr. J. L. Singer and his staff at the hospital. The total project was designed by the author who assumed responsibility for assembling the anthropological data. Working with patients, with psychiatric staff, with preliminary records of psychiatrists, social workers, nurses, and occupational therapists, a complete account running parallel to psychological tests was developed on each patient by the author. When the data were completed on total samples of Italians and Irish, the author and Dr. J. L. Singer intercompared their independently gathered data on each sample.

The samples resulted from a total census of four contiguous hospital buildings conducted by the author. All female schizophrenics of Irish or Italian background had previously been studied to determine, beyond the community studies, differences in male and female roles in illness states. These samples of female patients were inadequate statistically, but interesting on psychodynamic grounds. The male patient census of four buildings drew samples of 40 Irish and 37 Italian male patients, each clearly diagnosed as schizophrenic and representing our field study area. Patients were accepted into the sample only if without record of cerebral brain damage and if they had not been involved in psychosurgery. Practically all had received shock therapy. Other than this, no organic causation or treatment beyond the usual barbiturates had been recorded.

The patients, entirely by chance, were limited to the first, or immigrant generation; the second, or children of immigrant; and the third generation. When all 77 subjects had been studied intensively by anthropological interviews, psychiatric methods, and complete hospital records, each was referred to the clinical psychology staff composed of Dr. Singer and colleagues. Among the psychological instruments, reported on elsewhere, it was decided to use the Rorschach, Barron's Movement-Threshold Inkblots, Porteus Maze, Thematic Apperception Test, Time Estimation and Motor Inhibition Tests, Lane Sentence Completions, and other behavioral ratings. These instruments, plus anthropological interviewing and ward observations, provided independent ratings of functioning to which past history and consultation with psychiatrists could be added. Ten Irish and 7 Italian patients were too ill to complete the test battery and were studied independently by the combination of anthropological and psychiatric means. They are not included in the tables below, since psychological tests were incomplete. However, they conform closely to the differential pattern of their ethnic group as hypothesized and discovered in matched samples of 60 patients, 30 Irish and 30 Italian, studied by all three methods, psychiatric, anthropological, and psychological.

In the matched samples of 60 patients, the mean age of Irish was 32 years as compared with the mean for Italians of 30.5. (Age limits for both groups were 18 to 45 at the beginning of the study, when the census was taken; it had shifted, of course, to 20 to 47 two years later when the study was completed.) For last grade of education, an Irish mean of 10.5 grades matched the Italian of 10.9. Intelligence potential, computed in Wechsler IQ averages and again by means, disclosed an Irish sample of 108.4 closely matching the Italian 105.5. Length of hospitalization was hardly different, with a mean for the first year of 1949.8 for Irish; and 1949.5 for Italian. In marital status, by actual count 25 Irish and 22

Italians were unmarried, although none of the remaining few marriages, when studied, could be counted distinct successes. Therefore, the variables matched or controlled for both samples were age, sex, educational level, intelligence, first year of hospitalization, marital status, absence of organic or chronic conditions, and origin in the field study area. Only marital status showed, for Irish, a slight and possibly culturally influenced excess of celibacy. Yet illness and its particular pathology had made both groups primarily celibate, as we shall see.

Regional differences are important in Italian culture and less so among the Irish. As concerns this variable, we were again fortunate in eliminating it along with those just compared above. All Italians but one could trace ancestral lines from the extreme south of Italy (Naples southward) or from Sicily. Luckily, all Irish traced ancestry to "southwest" Irish counties and villages. The one lone North Italian who occurred in the census and came into the sample consequently proved to be an interesting exception to his group in both his psychodynamic and cultural patterns.

The tables given below summarize seven variables of a total of ten found to be significant in distinguishing Irish and Italian male schizophrenic patients. Earlier, at the outset of the research, we hypothesized these differences as accounting for two patterns, highly contrasting, in the etiology of each type of schizophrenia. We may begin by first explaining the differential terms used in accounting for each variable.

For reasons to be given below, we hypothesized that neither group would have a clearly male sexual identification in the illness state. Schizophrenics are notoriously troubled by homosexual strivings. However, it matters greatly in the total balance, or imbalance, of personality how such sexual strivings are shaped and whether they are latent or overt in character. Certainly, Italians stress even more forcefully than Irish the importance of masculinity for the male and femininity in females. However, they equally emphasize the expression of sexuality, as they do any human emotion or passion. In males who are schizophrenically ill and in whom both self-identity and sexual identification become impossible, the Italian model hypothesized was overt homosexuality, or a confused and active bisexuality which refused to pattern directly after the clearly male image of dominant and authoritarian fathers and elder brothers. Most of our Italian patients were, indeed, younger siblings who had moved quickly and impulsively, judging by their life histories, through a confused latent phase of sexual repulsion from a male role and into overt manifestations of homosexual behavior. The Irish, by contrast, both in our hypotheses and in fact, were fearful of a male role but repressive of homosexual trends based primarily on anxious attitudes toward mothers and other female images. One Irish patient who escaped this latent homosexual trend lost his mother at age three although he was still fearful of domineering women. Another solved the problem by attaching passively to a woman exactly twice his age whom he economically exploited in her confused senility. The vast majority of Irish male patients were latent homosexuals who avoided the female world, but repressed overt manifestations.

In keeping with these characteristics, the majority of Irish patients struggled with sin and guilt preoccupations concerning sexuality, whereas Italians had no sin or guilt preoccupations in this area. Instead, the Italian case histories and current ward behavior showed behavior disorders in the realm of poorly controlled impulses, weak personal attachments, and widely fluctuating or flighty emotional affects. The attitudes toward authority in the two groups diverged in parallel fashion, Italians having been verbally rejecting or actively flouting of authority in tests or case history, while Irish were hypothesized to be compliant for the most part, with only the most passive forms of outward resistance in evidence.

We hypothesized that the delusions, based on compensatory imagination in schizophrenics, would become fixed in Irish patients, and assume in them the typical paranoid forms of omnipotence or suspiciousness and persecution. While delusions are ordinarily developed in many forms of schizophrenia, it was hypothesized that, on the contrary, they would be largely absent among Italians, or if present would rarely be systematized or maintained with great fixity. Practically no Italians proved to have the highly systematized and elaborated delusions found frequently in the Irish patients, as we had hypothesized, so that the table below deals with the other factor of fixity. On the other hand, for reasons of clearer bodily emphasis, or in Schilder's phrase, "body image," we claimed Italian schizophrenics, male or female, would be given to hypochondriacal complaints and somatic or bodily preoccupations. As concerns alcoholism in case history, we expected to find this more frequently in Irish patients than in the Italian. The tables given below summarize these seven variables, which must then be considered in their meaningful etiological sense.

	Irish	Italian	Total
Variable 1: Homosexual Types			
Latent	27	7	34
Overt	0	20	20
TOTAL	27	27	54
Variable 2: Sin and Guilt Preoccupations			
Present	28	9	37
Absent	2	21	23
TOTAL	30	30	60
Variable 3: Behavior Disorder			
Present	4	23	27
Absent	26	7	33
TOTAL	30	30	60
Variable 4: Attitude Towards Authority			
Compliant	24	9	33
Rejecting	6	21	27
TOTAL	30	30	60
Variable 5: Fixity in Delusional System			
No	7	20	27
Some	23	10	33
TOTAL	30	30	60
Variable 6: Somatic (Hypochondriacal) Complaints			
Present	13	21	34
Absent	17	9	26
TOTAL	30	30	60
Variable 7: Chronic Alcoholism			
Present	19	1	20
Absent	11	29	40
TOTAL	30	30	60

Statistical measures indicated that each of these variables was highly significant in delineating differences between Irish and Italian schizophrenics.

Having just indicated a skeletonized set of differences between our two samples, it remains to account for the development of each kind of pathology. The previous community surveys in New York City contained for each ethnic group a whole continuum of persons and families whose behavior ranged from normative or "normal" standards of conduct to those who were aberrant or deviant. Having studied well or moderately ill Irish and Italians in their family settings and community groups, one could distinguish for each group its distinctive cultural contributions and backgrounds, its particular pace of cultural change, and its typical or special patterns of stress in family conflicts. Each group, Irish, Italian, Puerto Rican, or others, sanctioned or interdicted outlets for emotional expression. In the range of persons and families from the healthy and well-balanced to those evidencing pathology, the cultural patterns even where undergoing change provided the necessary framework for understanding the meanings of emotional stress and conflict, both in the pathogenic families and individuals and in those who seemed to be presumably symptom free. The crucial point for each cultural group of the eight studied was that it was the normative side of the continuum, the on-going ethnic group, which helped define the kinds of conflict or repression, the types of emotional expression, the system of values, or the functioning of the family for each individual. While Freud had stated long ago that neurosis is the price paid for civilization, instead we found that each culture or subculture contained its designs for living. In each, consequently, there were various stresses and strains, and well-functioning families as well as pathogenic ones. Creative and negative features typified the genius and the pitfalls of each cultural system. As a result, we conducted no search for a single etiology of mental illnesses such as characterized the nineteenth century, but instead insisted upon viewing each family and each patient in his meaningful cultural setting.

Therefore, three variables not included in the above tables were considered of primary significance. All were prior in effect or earlier acting than those already listed. The first, which we shall call Variable A, dealt with the possibilities in each cultural group, by virtue of its family system, for the development of negative and destructive emotions of various sorts. While it is true that in schizophrenias elements of hostility and anxiety may coexist in different degrees, the amount of each emotion in such admixtures and the means by which it is expressed or controlled is the really crucial matter. D. H. Funkenstein's contrast between anxiety states premised on fear and those based upon hate is relevant here. We added that this dichotomy in the schizophrenias (fear versus hate) be taken together with Freudian considerations as to whether these emotions were expressed or denied outlet in typical family structures of a given cultural group. We noted that in Irish families, particularly those poorly organized, the central figure is usually the mother. Her authority extends to all matters of household management, including not only child-rearing but the major decisions governing the home. She achieves this status by reason of her matronage and not infrequently conceives of the distaff as the symbol of authority, of family domain, and of emotional control. Historically, Irish fathers of the southwest counties were frequently in straitened economic circumstances, and were shadowy and ineffectual figures in the home. It was hypothesized, on the basis of this type of family structure, that anxiety, tinged with fear and hate, would be the resultant emotion in Irish male patients who as sons had been raised to view themselves as "forever boys and burdens." In two-thirds of the Irish cases, this primary anxiety (with some hostility usually compressed by fear) was directed toward all female figures. In only three cases of a total forty did the father appear more centrally, and in these the entire pattern of illness shifted to the "Italian model" in most details. In one of these, as stated above, the mother had died when the patient was three years of age.

In sharp contrast, Italian cultural values set greater store on male parental or eldest sibling dominance while at the same time reinforcing more direct expressions of the resultant hostile emotions. This acting-out of feelings brought more hostility to the fore in poorly repressed conflicts with fathers or elder male siblings. One Italian patient, for example, entered the acute phase of illness at the time of his elder brother's wedding and expressed himself, with floridly violent accusations, against his father. In practically all cases there was a strong repulsion from the father, elder brother, and even surrogate authority figures. The Italian mothers, in such instances, were often subtly rejecting and preferred the oldest son. In some cases, the mother, playing a subordinate role in the family, had compensated by assuming a mildly seductive and pampering role in relationships with the son. One could trace the effects of a harsh and punitive or domineering father. The mother compensated for her own feelings of neglect at the father's hands by building up hostile forms of impulsiveness in these sons, along with features of poor emotional control. Italian patients, even when labeled like Irish as schizophrenics with paranoid reaction, had more prominent problems of emotional overflow (schizo-affective features) which took the form of elated overtalkativeness, curious mannerisms, grinning and laughing hyperactivity, or even assaultiveness. Even hostility directed toward oneself came into evidence when elated excitements gave way to inept suicidal attempts. One-third of the Italian sample showed such periodic excitements with confusion and emotional lability (catatonic excitements) while the other two-thirds were subject to extreme mood swings in which the depressed and quiescent periods gave way to destructive outbursts, elation, suicidal behavior, or curious mannerisms. In brief, all Italian patients had so much affective coloring, aimed primarily at male figures and images, that the paranoid schizophrenic label seemed to fit them poorly.

A second primary difference in the samples, which we shall call Variable B, dealt with the central tendencies in each culture for channeling emotional expression. To some extent, this expression of the emotional life in each ethnic group applied also to female patients. Italian culture generally sanctions the freer expression of emotions, and emotion may be expressed, in lower class groups particularly, in bodily action. The Irish, on the contrary, are famous for a greater constriction of activity and their most endearing trait, which no doubt compensates for this constriction, is an equally rich fantasy life. In Freudian theory, fantasy may substitute, almost vicariously, for action. We have, indeed, already noted the intensity of emotion and its expression in activity in poorly controlled Italian patients. The counterpart in the Irish sample of patients was a fantasy substitute for action. While Italian patients might oscillate between hyperactivity and underactivity, or show an inability to time their activities, thoughts, or emotions effectively, the Irish, with no such difficulties in estimating time or guarding their emotions, showed an inversely large proportion of rich and extensive fantasy. Their more deeply repressed conflicts consequently took a more delusional and paranoid form. One Irishman, for example, repeatedly gave for two years a most lurid series of accounts of the death of each family member, blaming his mother for a horrible accident which befell the father. The father had died at a ripe old age in a hospital of a common ailment. With each monotonous recital, the father's death in front of the home became more blood-stained and painful. The mother became a cold, emotionless, and witchlike figure described in an affectless tone and cursed in a magical, ritual manner.

Linked with these two primary variables of family authority structure and the channeling of emotional expression were other cultural variables affecting the emotional life. With Italian males, more direct feelings of hostility flooded up from shallowly repressed levels, connected with feelings of repulsion from a father, elder brother, or surrogate authority figures. As concerns sexual identification (Variable 1 of tables), two thirds of the Italian sample showed active homosexual tendencies which had at one time or another been overtly practiced. This rejection of a male identity and strong repulsion from male role fitted the variables already considered—hatred of the father, lack of stability in the mother, and the cultural sanctions for expression of emotion. Impulsiveness, acting-out, and the emotional overflow might be expected among the ill of this cultural group. This acting-out of impulse was often noted in a background of sociopathic escapades common in childhood or in youth. For the same variables, the Irish male patient, beset with anxiety and fear of female figures early in life, likewise lacked possibilities of a firm male identification, but here the fear was centered on the opposite sex, and the sexual repressions and sin or guilt emphases of the culture made for a repressive, latent form of homosexuality. Instead of the open refusal to be male, or repulsion from male role as in Italian patients (nonidentification in Italians), the Irish had instead a fearful or anxious lack of positive male identification. Here the latent homosexual tendency was controlled by added distortions and repressions. If repressed sufficiently, the Irish patient was pallidly asexual. Only three, as the tables indicate, managed to achieve or maintain the asexual balance in repression. Of twenty-seven who were latent homosexuals, the distortions of body image had occurred already in some who had bizarre delusional misidentifications as to their sexual characteristics. One such delusional form may serve to illustrate the patient who believed his entire bodily structure in the front was covered by an "apron"; this apron had certain feminine characteristics, like periodic bleeding or the capacity to distract the patient's thoughts ("affecting my thoughts," adversely, of course).

Beyond family structure, type of sexual identification problem, and the channels for emotional expression in each culture lie a further series of consequences for emotional stress and its pitfalls in poorly organized families. The sexual misidentifications (in Irish males) and nonidentifications (or refusals to identify properly in the Italian series) are contrasting types which occur in quite different defensive emotional structures. In this sense, Variables 2 and 3 of tables may be considered concomitant variations or further consequences on the basic themes of stress problems in family structure and affective controls. Obviously, personality traits exist and function together in the total business of living. Thus the concepts of sin and guilt, particularly in the sexual area, were built up in the Irish patients and were readily accessible in their cultural stock-in-trade. Not only did twenty-eight Irish patients torment and exacerbate themselves with such sin and guilt formulae, but twenty-one Italians of similar faith did not apply sin and guilt irritations to their sexual ideologies. Again, with the Irish, such formulae often became delusional and persecutory. A particular kind of mythology, prominent among nonliterate peoples, and concerning a toothed, castrating vagina, occurred in the setting of incestuous guilts about feelings toward sisters and other female relatives in several Irish cases. Contrary to this, twenty-six Irish patients showed no evidence in the hospital or in life history of having been involved in any sociopathic behavior, whereas twenty-three Italians showed repeated and marked evidence of behavior disorders. As we have seen, the attitude toward authority (Variable 4 of tables), more consciously expressed in instruments like Sentence Completions or exemplified in life histories and ward behavior, indicated a similar difference in attitude, with twenty-four compliant Irish patients to almost the same number of more rebellious Italians.

Variable 5 of tables explored the prediction that the Irish patients, with their anxious fantasies, their latent and repressed homosexual trends, and the indoctrinated "sex-is-sin" feelings of guilt would be forced to build fixed delusional systems. While Irish patients used this delusional or fantasy defense against their sexual misidentification problems and shattered self-esteem, the Italians mainly expressed their sense of defeat and hostility in mood swings, excitements, and impulsive behavior. Thus delusional fixity occurred in a ratio greater than three to one for Irish, while exactly two-thirds of the Italian patients had no delusions manifest during the study, and half the remaining ten had only changeable and minor delusional episodes. On the other hand, as might be expected, the Italian patients distinctly led in Variable 6 of the tables, in the frequency with which hypochondriacal complaints about imagined somatic disorders were mentioned. For Variable 7 of the tables, only one of the Italian patients had ever been chronically addicted to alcohol although every individual liked wines, whiskey, or beer. In the Irish, on the contrary, almost two-thirds had sought an escape from problems in protracted periods of alcohol addiction.

In discussing this relationship between environment and mental illnesses, such authors as Stanton and Schwartz in their book, *The Mental Hospital* or Fromm-Reichmann in her *Principles of Intensive Psychotherapy* have discussed patients' reactions to ways of handling them, to interaction processes on the ward, or to different psychotherapeutic approaches. These authors concede a general validity to the idea that no patients, not even schizophrenics, live in a cultural vacuum. But neglected in the literature is the related thought that the course of illness and the very structuring of personality bear a cultural imprint. All nine variables discussed thus far show an inner consistency and integration of defenses which constitute two separate kinds of illness. Psychiatrists in treating *each* type can be more effective if they understand these linkages of culture and personality. What Sullivan called "the schizophrenic ways of life" can be related and regeared to more positive cultural determinants only after we understand the differences in family structures, in self-identification problems, and in methods of emotional control which have made up the characteristic blend in any balance of defenses.

A final or tenth variable was therefore used in the study to describe this balance of defenses. We found it favoring fantasy and withdrawal patterns for the Irish to the extent of paranoid reactions. The Italian patients suffered from disorders of poor emotional and impulse control. The Irish were most anxious in relations with persons of opposite sex and the shaping of basic personality contained notions of male inadequacy, fear of females, and latent homosexual tendencies intensified by sin and guilt preoccupations. With the Irish, self-esteem and identification were destroyed together, and weakness, inadequacy feelings, suspiciousness, and paranoid delusions had taken over. Hence the bodily somatizations and hypochondriacal complaints, common in Italians, were rare in the Irish. Delusions became fixed in paranoid channels, and fantasy and distortion were used to preserve the system intact. These were the quiet, anxious men, fearful of anything which might separate them from the protection of the ward and their well-regulated delusional systems.

Obviously, the Italian patients were different not only on each count, but in the total pattern of symptoms. As such, they represented other problems in management and therapy. A family structure, diametrically different from the Irish, favored overt expression of homosexuality. The different cultural emphasis on emotional expression led to the acting-out of impulse. The strength of anger in this emotional lability, the motor excitements, or flaring-up of affect could now throw the patient into confusional affective states, or into the excitements, periodic and sometimes destructive, which characterized an even greater proportion. This balance, or typical resolution of defenses, was most important in the actual handling and maintenance of rapport with each patient.

Cannon, Wolff, Funkenstein, and others have each written on the subject of physiological consequences of such long-standing emotional states. Possibly the attack on these problems will benefit from further physiological understanding. Equally important in the psychotherapy which accompanies and vitalizes such methods will be the joint contribution, no doubt, of both psychiatry and anthropology. The former is expert in the guidance of the individual case, and the latter is helpful in indicating the types of family organization and social experience which influence all behavior, normative or pathological. Future research in social psychiatry is now required on various mental disorders, and it is hoped that further explorations of this type will be carried out elsewhere.

Victor D. Sanua

Research Fellow
Harvard Medical School

20

DIFFERENCES IN PERSONALITY ADJUSTMENT
AMONG DIFFERENT GENERATIONS OF
AMERICAN JEWS AND NON-JEWS

The problem of acculturation and assimilation of immigrant groups in their adopted culture has long been a subject of considerable discussion among anthropologists. Of special interest is the personality adjustment of the marginal man. The concept of marginality, aside from its economic meaning, has been evolved to describe members of ethnic groups who are not completely identified with either the dominant in-group or their own minority out-group, and yet who are forced by necessity to maintain cultural ties with both.

Marginality is sometimes considered as a no-man's land in which the individual stands between two cultures, the two extremes of his position being, on the one hand, a wholehearted or complete identification with his minority group, and on the other, an attempt at complete assimilation with the majority. In between, or marginal to either, we have the individual who tries to make an adjustment involving both cultures, with all the attendant conflicts of ambivalent identification, rejection, guilt, and frustration.

It has often been stated that there is a greater incidence of suicide (6) and mental disease among immigrant groups and a higher rate of juvenile delinquency, particularly among the second generation or native-born of immigrants. In such cases, it is claimed that the children are not entirely assimilated, and yet are in conflict with their nonassimilated parents. Sometimes this conflict results in what has been commonly called "self-hatred" for the second generation (19, 26, 31).

Concerning the major contributions of social scientists to the study

443

of Jewish peoples, most of the work appears to have been incidental to other main purposes of the study (25, 28, 48). We obtain scattered data on the Jew merely because he happens to be part of the total population studied. There are, however, innumerable studies and surveys carried out additionally by Jewish agencies and community groups, but these data are usually assembled mainly for a specific purpose of reform. There are no large-scale scientific studies using modern psychological methods to discover if there are such things as Jewish cultural characteristics. One anthropological study, *Life Is With People*, by Zborowski and Herzog (53), is primarily an historical account of the *shtetl* or small community. Handlin's works (22, 23) are valuable as history, but are not strongly psychological studies.

What we find in the psychological literature is mostly a series of studies comparing the "intelligence" of the Jew and non-Jew. During the past two decades, about twelve studies have appeared in psychological journals reporting on the emotional differences of Jews and non-Jews, based on use of personality inventories. The findings of many of these endeavors are regarded as inconclusive and sometimes even contradictory. Some writers, like Koenig, have explained this dearth of research among Jews because of the group's extreme sensitivity (30). It seems that most such research discloses differences which are not welcome among educated middle-class Jews, since there is so much emphasis upon acculturation within this class group.

In his review of the published literature on Jews, Glazer has been able to draw out two important social characteristics of the Jew: He seems to have advanced more rapidly and is more prosperous than any other ethnic group; and, further, he intermarries very little. In the latter connection, although he becomes culturally indistinguishable from other Americans, the line of separation from the majority group remains somehow sharper than the line that separates other white immigrant groups from the majority group (16).

Loewenstein, in his book, *Christians and Jews*, makes a survey of so-called Jewish cultural characteristics and then uses psychoanalytic theory to explain these (34). Only a few such characteristics are given below. For example, in Loewenstein's account, Jewish parents usually show very strong attachment to their children. However, he notes that boys receive preferential treatment when it comes to religious education. The Jewish mother is regarded as overanxious about providing adequate nourishment for the children and as weaning them later; further, in their overprotectiveness they make their children fearful of physical danger. On the other hand, in the behavior of both parents, a use of the intellect by the child meets with warm approval. Such children may become highly "rational," obsequious, and lack fighting spirit; they may try to placate the powerful rather than express true submission. Finally, they may compensate for a very profound sense of inferiority. Under the pressure of disturbing historical memories, the Jews are "prone to feel themselves insulted and attacked whenever a gentile so much as pronounces the word 'Jew', and the mildest anti-Jewish remark may throw them off balance, plunging them into outraged silence or excessive rage. Only rarely are they able to meet such remarks calmly or to parry them with a humorous reply" (34, p. 144).

Loewenstein is well aware, of course, of the limitations of such general observations and he urges a more objective approach to the study of "Jewish personality." He raises the question whether some of these characteristic behavior patterns are common to *all* Jews because of their similar history, or whether participation in various national cultures has made for subcultural differences.

Lewin's contribution to the subject of the emancipation of the Jew seems to be pertinent at this point (33). The adult, according to him, acts during most of his life not simply as an individual, but as a member of a social group which is itself subdivided. He may, in some instances, act as a member of a religious group; in others as a member of a political party; and often as a member of a family group.

In filling these various roles, or in shifting his behavior to suit complex situations in which he finds himself, conflict arises. This is especially true when there is no compatibility between various roles one is obliged to fill. There is often an element of uncertainty about just where one "belongs." Minority groups seem generally to share this type of problem. When the Jew lived in the ghetto compactly, boundaries were clear-cut for him—often painfully so. He wore a badge which set him off from the dominant group, which he regarded as being "strangers." In developing his own language and patterns of culture, the in-group feeling led often to extreme conservatism, orthodoxy, and ethnic solidarity which, in turn, helped considerably in the survival of the group against difficult odds.

With the emancipation period, the ghetto walls in western Europe disappeared and there the Jew was able to move freely. However, when this happened, the Jewish group lost both its compactness and solidarity as boundaries became less well defined. Consequently, with relaxation of pressure from the outside group, the trend for the Jew became the acquisition of the dress, habits, and languages of the dominant majority. Behind such facades, nevertheless, there was little complete assimilation or real relaxation in the life of the Jew.

Instead, as he became "marginal" to two cultures, this spelled an even greater tension. Once he gained independence and individuality, his problem increased, because he was constrained to cope with this hostile world by himself and "on his own." Previously, the point of application of external forces had been on the whole group, allowing the individual at least the security that comes from group membership.

While in the ghetto, therefore, and with no desire to go beyond the walls, the Jew was well aware of the impassable barriers in his way. There was "no positive valence," using Lewin's terminology. But once allowed to move out, there was a goal to be reached which was, however, not easy to attain. Conflicts arose in the path toward assimilation. These conflicts, according to Lewin, created tensions which led to restlessness and less-balanced behavior. While forging ahead, the Jew found himself between two worlds. The roots of actual evils for this marginal individual are not the real or formal aspects of his belonging to many groups. They lie, rather, in his feelings of not firmly belonging anywhere but in the competitive, striving world. It would appear that the psychological problems of the marginal man involve the crucial factors of role conflicts and divided loyalties. A person without strong identification is, in Handlin's image, "the uprooted." This uprooting began on European soil. One of the positive factors in psychotherapy is to make the patient feel his worth and value as one who is wanted by significant people in his environment. The analogy between the clinical and social situations may be clearly seen.

A similar social phenomenon substantiated by empirical findings has been reported by Wilson and Lantz (52). They found that the southern Negro pays a heavy toll in mental illness for his partial emancipation. It appears that Negroes, when refusing to abide by the white man's "dictum" of where one "belongs" in society, occasionally lose the security of the earlier position. With marginality, they lose firm group identifications. Bewildered and disturbed when the road to acceptance by the dominant group is filled with obstacles, the result is conflicts, and the faster acceleration of an incidence of mental illness among Negroes. Of course, we are speaking here of the inevitable results of partial and incomplete emancipation where full freedom is still far from guaranteed.

A more experimental approach has been developed by Kerckhoff and McCormick (27). They found that the greatest incidence of "marginal personality" characteristics is found with Chippewa children who are inclined to identify themselves with the dominant group but who, at the same time, encounter a relatively impermeable barrier because of their pronounced racial features. They found that differences in the permeability of the barriers by individuals are less important in producing disturbances if the identification is with the subordinate in-group.

After an exhaustive study of psychologically inspired literature, the writer located only ten studies where the pencil-and-paper test of personality was used in the United States to differentiate Jews from Gentiles. Major findings are summarized in Table 20-1. In examining these results, it will be noted that some psychologists report that Jews seem to be more unstable, while others report exactly the opposite. In most cases, significance of the differences on scales of neuroticism is very low.

Sward and Friedman, who appear to have made the most extensive research of differences between Jews and non-Jews, point out certain limitations of their study, including the fact that personality inventories do not present a picture of actual differences between the two groups (46). This is what they have to state in this connection:

In the face of a labyrinth of Jewish adaptations at various times and places, the present research hardly aims to ignore the complexity of the Jewish psyche as defined in the literature (Arnold Zweig, Feuchtwanger, Sholom Asch, *et al.*), or as observed in daily intercourse. It simply denies a wholesale difference in subjective temperament. Our admittedly select sample of American Jews diverge only slightly from the normal introspective picture. The defender of a "typically Jewish temperament" in America is only compelled to define his terms." *

Brown, in discussing his study in which Jewish boys appeared slightly better adjusted than Gentiles, formulated a hypothesis to account for the greater incidence of functional psychosis among Jews, as was claimed by Malzberg (37). Brown explained that the incidence of neuroticism among Jews increases as they come in contact with adult social reality (12). The heavy emphasis upon intellectual achievement in Jewish

* Sward, Keith, and Friedman, Meyer: "Jewish temperament." *Journal of Applied Psychology*, 1935, vol. 19, pp. 70–84.

homes gives the child the illusory sense of limitless "vertical mobility." During his early years this makes for good adjustment; but when the time comes for choosing a career and he discovers that discrimination limits the mobility factor, disillusionment then follows, with its accompanying anxiety states and depression. This drive toward achievement gains momentum, nevertheless, resulting in "over-reaction and compensatory behavior." The larger number of functional psychoses represents a further stage of this same process and illustrates the conflict between a powerful vertical thrust and a restricted social ceiling.

However, Brown's alleged finding, that Jewish high-school boys are less neurotic, may be artificial. In other words, the personality inventory, as now constituted, is not sensitive enough, nor is it suited to the task of discovering significant differences in maladjustment between Jews and non-Jews. It was felt, perhaps, that the use of a projective test might give some evidence of the expected differences between Jews and non-Jews. In a following section, the author discusses what these two tests are designed to "measure."

Bernard classified four types of adjustments which could be effected by the "marginal man" who feels himself isolated and who wants to achieve a greater sense of security. Taking the Jew as an example, one alternative is for the individual to decide that he will reject the Gentile world and live entirely within the fold of his own group. This isolation or clannish behavior is found among a few Jewish groups in New York City. Some have cited the Syrian Jews, who, as a group, have maintained something like the "ghetto" mentality. They avoid association with Gentiles as much as possible. Their social life revolves around their own synagogues which serve not only as religious meeting places but also as community centers for recreational purposes. Very few enter professions, and most of them are engaged in commercial occupations. Practice of traditional Judaism is sometimes to the extreme. Many will not answer the telephone or ride on the Sabbath. Some women do not even carry handbags on that day. Needless to say, intermarriage is almost nonexistent, not only with non-Jews, but even sometimes with Jews of different origins, although to a lesser degree in recent years. Another "ghetto" is the "Yeshiva" community of Williamsburg.

The other alternative would be to reject the Jewish world, and adopt the religion of the dominant group. Bernard points out that there are enough unsuccessful cases to terrify and daunt those who might be tempted to follow this road.

TABLE 20-1

Summary of the Research of Personality Differences between Jews and Gentiles

Name and Year	Test	Sample	School	Findings
Garrett (15), 1929	Laird P. I.	Freshmen: 75 Jews, 119 Non-Jews	Columbia	Greater instability among Jews; difference not significant
Thurstone (49), 1929	Thurstone	Freshmen: 127 Jews, 694 Non-Jews	Chicago	Greater instability among Jews; difference not significant
Sward and Friedman (46), 1935	Heidbreder Inferiority	Freshmen: 163 Jews, 163 Non-Jews	Minnesota	More variability among Jews; more inferiority feelings among Jews; both not significant
Sward and Friedman (46), 1935	Bernreuter	College students: 114 Jews, 114 Non-Jews	Western Reserve	Jews have higher neurotic score; not significant; women more neurotic in general; age least significant variable
Sward and Friedman (46), 1935	Bernreuter	High School Students: 40 Jews, 40 Non-Jews	Pittsburgh	Jewish boys less neurotic; sex more important variable
Sward and Friedman (46), 1935	Bernreuter	Adults: 80 Jews, 80 Non-Jews	Pittsburgh	Jewish adults higher neurotic score; scores of foreign-born fathers higher than American-born fathers; national origin no effect on non-Jewish scores
Sward (47), 1935	Bernreuter	Item analysis of previous study	Pittsburgh	Jews show more: gregariousness or strong social dependence; submissiveness; drive and overreaction; various anxiety states and symptoms of mood changes
Sukow and Williamson (45), 1938	Rundquist-Sletto	Freshmen: 163 Jews, 1166 Non-Jews		Jewish students, on the average, have more marked tendency toward maladjustment
Sukow and Williamson (45), 1938	Bell	Freshmen: 49 Jews, 366 Non-Jews		No significant differences between the two groups

TABLE 20-1 (*continued*)

Name and Year	Test	Sample	School	Findings
Sperling (44), 1942	Human behavior inventory:	Athletes: 80 Jews, 80 Non-Jews	New York	No significance in total adjustment scores between Jews and non-Jews:
	introversion-extroversion;			Jews more extroverted
	ascendance-submission;			Jews more ascendant
	conservatism-liberalism;			Jews more liberal
	Allport's values			Jews have higher theoretical and social scores
Brown (12), 1940	Brown University inventory	Students, 13 years old: 67 Jews,	Minnesota summer camp	Jewish boys manifest better school adjustment;
	Furfey D.A. scale	91 Non-Jews		Jewish boys more mature
Long (35), 1943	Bell	College students: 73 Jews, 74 Non-Jews	Mental Hygiene Clinic, Detroit	No over-all difference; Jews show better social and emotional adjustment, but less home and health adjustment
Gordon (17), 1943	Willoughby Personality Schedule	College students: 159 Jews, No Non-Jews	Minnesota University	Majority of Jewish students as well adjusted as non-Jewish students
Shuey (43), 1945	Bell	Freshmen: 397 Jews, 101 Non-Jews	New York University	Social adjustment of Jews indicated by more favorable scores

The third way to solve the problem of marginality would be to renounce both Gentile and Jewish worlds, assuming that they are completely irreconcilable. This, too. inevitably produces conflicts in individuals. It is expected that people who do this compose the social and political nihilistic groups.

The fourth and final way to solve the problem, according to Bernard, is to select the esthetically acceptable from both the dominant and minority cultures. This is the most rewarding, but by no means the easiest method. "To salvage what is lovely, to reject what is ugly—this involves an unending scrutiny of values. No comfortable relapses into unconscious acceptance or rejection of values on the basis of tradition or prestige" (7, p. 291).

In addition to the above classifications, another could be added on the basis of the author's experience. Some individuals are indistinguishable from non-Jews as long as they are outside their own milieu. But once they are in their own homes, they become the authoritarian masters of the house. They wear the traditional "yarmulka" or skull cap. They follow in detail the ritual prescriptions of the Mosaic Law, although no such obligation is felt, once outside their home.

In the course of research, the author interviewed a well-known scholar at Columbia University. As the interviewer was about to take a few notes, the scholar, with some embarrassment, observed it was the Sabbath and said that he would not want his children to see anyone writing, since this would set a bad example. According to Jewish tradition, any work, including writing, is prohibited on the Sabbath. Further, no one is supposed to "touch light" on that day. While opposing writing as a bad example, the scholar allowed his own children to watch a televised football game, against religious injunction. Although the pencil was taboo, television was not. This is but one example of the selective application of cultural rules on a situational basis. But contradictions are constantly juxtaposed in cases of this sort.

In general, in a world of rapidly shifting or migrant populations and rapid communication, the immigrant group presents a special problem of adjustment to new environment. It is during this transitional period of gradual absorption to the dominant group that social and psychological consequences occur. The time of the great waves of immigration from Europe is now history. But the present-day problems of large movements of population still include the 600,000 Puerto Ricans in New York City, the Mexicans in the West, and migrant laborers from the South, who are now residing in the great industrial centers of the North.

It has already been pointed out in the early part of this chapter that there has been little research on Jewish personality. However, many studies, particularly in the last few years, have emphasized the anti-Semitic personality, i.e., by Adorno, Frenkel-Brunswik, *et al.* (3), Ackerman and Jahoda (2), and Bettelheim and Janowitz (8). It is felt that this orientation, the study of the biased individual, has neglected the study of the object of bias, the marginal man. A first serious attempt to do this is the study of the American Negro in a book by Kardiner and Ovesey, called *The Mark of Oppression* (26). Kardiner supplements his analytical study with Rorschach tests. An adequate scientific study of the adjustment of the American Jew as a member of a minority group has yet to be attempted.

METHOD

The purpose of this study is to explore the adjustment of Jewish students belonging to different generations, as revealed by an objective and projective test. Samples of first, second, and third generations of Jewish high-school students having Orthodox, Conservative, and Reform affiliations were chosen for testing. The study was conducted in New York City. The intragroup differences were explored, and the scores obtained were in turn compared with scores obtained from a sample of non-Jewish students. Findings of this research are presented in the framework of a pilot study in order to demonstrate the type of data that can be obtained and the various analyses that are possible.

Deficiencies in previous research using pencil-and-paper psychological tests were due largely to the fact that such variables as generation, socioeconomic status, and religious affiliation were not controlled. Since the Jewish group is not considered homogeneous, it is believed that the study of differentiation within the total group itself is justified, even before making comparisons with non-Jews. What generation level, for example, shows more maladjustment on psychological testing? Is it the immigrant generation which is uprooted and then set down in an alien milieu as a minority? Or is it their offspring, who have, perhaps, additional problems stemming from cultural conflicts between the demands of the home, on the one hand, and those of the larger society, on the other? What, then, is the status of the third generation who are likely to suffer because they bear the stigma of a minority without enjoying the benefits of a firm group identification such as their less acculturated forefathers enjoyed? The generation differences therefore loom large in the construction of any hypotheses.

Subjects

Approximately 370 students were tested; about 100 of them non-Jews. The samples were obtained from full-time Orthodox Jewish schools, private, secular, and Sunday schools, in New York City. The cooperation of seventeen institutions was required. Many schools refused to have their students tested because they disapproved of questions inquiring about religious affiliation.

In this study, students who were born abroad and who came to the United States after the age of five were considered as being first-generation. Second generation included those individuals whose parents were born abroad. The third generation was made up of students whose parents were both born in the United States. There was, however, an intermediate group between the second and third generation, given the designation of "mixed generation," where one parent was born abroad and the other in the United States. It was found that in 90 per cent of these intermediate cases the mothers were born in this country, and the fathers were born abroad.

Psychological Tests

1. *Thurstone Personality Schedule* (49). The original test included 223 items. To shorten the battery, only 90 of the most discriminatory items were selected. Thurstone used the method of internal consistency to validate the test. He selected fifty subjects from the sample who gave the highest scores (neurotic) and fifty who gave the lowest scores (non-neurotic). Using the responses of these two groups, it was possible to evaluate the discriminatory value of each item on the schedule.

2. *The Rorschach Multiple Choice Test* (24). This is the adaptation of the Rorschach Test for group administration. Three groups of ten responses are provided for each inkblot. The subject underlines the single response in each group which seems to him to be the best description. Half the responses were chosen from the records of healthy, normal individuals, and the other half from the records of persons suffering various psychological disturbances. Although the test did not prove to be too satisfactory on an individual basis, except as a screening device, significant differences were found between various groups, adjusted and maladjusted (10, 13, 40).

Both projective techniques and personality inventories have been used in the assessment of personality. Since correlations between the Rorschach and personality inventories have been rather low, it is obvious that further research as to their relationship would be helpful. The personality inventory requires the subject to report on his attitude and behavior by answering specific questions for which the answers are obvious. On the projective test, however, the subject cannot use any "censorship" to avoid unacceptable or poor responses. Since there is sometimes little relationship between the results obtained in these two tests, one concludes that the personality inventory and the Rorschach are measuring different areas of behavior or different levels of personality.

Blairs suggests that the Rorschach is a measure of "self-adjustment" or "inner adjustment," while the personality inventory should be considered as a measure of "social adjustment" (11). Allport believes that a diagnostician should use both objective and projective tests (4). He presents evidence that individuals who give "healthy" personality inventory scores may or may not produce healthy Rorschachs. Those who try to repress their problems are more likely to show maladjustment on the projective tests, consequently, while appearing normal on the personality inventory.

RESULTS

SCORES OBTAINED BY HIGH-SCHOOL STUDENTS, ACCORDING TO GENERATION LEVEL

Intragroup differences were first calculated among all the orthodox boys attending the Talmudic academies of Manhattan and Brooklyn, with the assumption that this group would be more homogeneous. However, as can be seen from Table 20-2, the first generation appears to be least adjusted on the Thurstone Personality Inventory, while the third generation seems to have the best score of adjustment (32.88 and 17.46, significant at better than the .01 level). The scores on the Rorschach show an opposite trend. It seems, therefore, that the foreign-born are least adjusted "socially" while the third generation appears to have the greatest "inner maladjustment."

The same trend is found when all Jewish boys, irrespective of their religious subgroup affiliation, are combined. With a further analysis of boys of mixed parentage, it was found that they were closer to first- and second-generation groups when the mother is American- and Orthodox-born. The mixed group also stands closer to the third generation when their mothers are Conservative or Reform. In the latter case, boys are likely to feel closer identification with the American culture through the mother's more culturally active influence.

When various generations of girls were tested, they obtained nearly identical scores on the Personality Inventory. Their Rorschach scores,

TABLE 20-2

Mean Scores Obtained by Jewish Boys on the Thurstone Personality Schedule and Rorschach Multiple Choice Test

Generation	N	Orthodox Group Mean	S.D.	t	N	Entire Samples Mean	S.D.	t
A. Thurstone Personality Schedule								
First Generation	17	32.88	11.18		17	32.88	11.18	
				.81				.22
Second Generation	28	30.32	9.39		45	29.06	10.64	
				.68				1.92
Mixed Parentage	11	27.90	10.09		29	24.17	10.86	
				2.32 *				.73
Third Generation	11	17.45	10.54		43	22.39	11.00	
TOTAL	67	28.46	10.95		134	26.35	11.08	
B. Rorschach Multiple Choice Test								
First Generation	17	7.91	5.05		17	7.91	5.05	
				.22				.38
Second Generation	28	8.30	5.51		45	8.46	5.06	
				.58				.91
Mixed Parentage	11	9.63	7.72		28	10.10	8.67	
				1.97				.90
Third Generation	10	13.35	9.46		41	11.84	6.95	
TOTAL	66	9.18	6.83		131	8.80	6.82	

* Significant at the 5 per cent level of confidence

however, showed an ascending degree of maladjustment from second to third generation, but the range of differences of group means was not so wide. These differences between boys and girls lead us to believe that the Jewish male tends to be influenced to a greater degree by social and cultural forces than Jewish females, who tend, in turn, to have a more well-defined role within the Jewish family in general.

Leon Feldman, in his survey of sex differences in college students, finds that the female Jewish student is more home-oriented, more concerned with family guidance, and at the same time less fearful of social or vocational discrimination by the larger world (14). Accordingly, she accepts and avows her Jewishness more openly than her Jewish brother at college may, and she participates more in Jewish organizational activity, feeling more secure as a Jew. Similar findings on the more favorable adjustment of women are to be seen in the studies of Abel and Hsu (1) and of Hallowell (21).

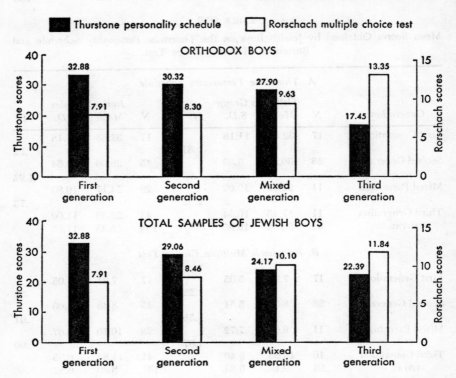

FIG. 20-1. Comparison of the mean scores obtained by various generations of Jewish boys on the Thurstone Personality Schedule, and the Rorschach Multiple Choice Test.

SOCIOECONOMIC STATUS AND TEST RESULTS

It is a well-known fact that the longer the immigrant groups have been in this country, the higher their socioeconomic status is likely to be. It could therefore be assumed that the division according to generation in the previous section would actually be analogous to a division along socioeconomic lines, since these two factors would correlate. In using the Warner classification in this study, we found that the test results were approximately the same for socioeconomic groups as when the students were divided according to generation.

To control further for the socioeconomic status variable, the boys were matched on a one-to-one basis with relation to the profession or vocation of their fathers *within* the second and third generation. In this way, two groups equated in socioeconomic status but of different *generations* were obtained. It was found that the generation differences in adjustment level *do not* disappear when the socioeconomic status is made comparable. In other words, even when controlling the latter fact, the second generation nonetheless maintains a higher neurotic score on the Personality Inventory and a lower neurotic score on the Rorschach Multiple Choice Test than do the individuals belonging to the third generation. Thus, the important factor in producing such differences is the generation and not the socioeconomic status of the group.

Scores Obtained by Orthodox, Conservative, and Reform Students

Male and female groups were divided on the basis of religious affiliation: Orthodox-Talmudical, Orthodox-coeducational, Conservative, or Reform. The differences in scores between the groups were, in general, not significant. In other words, one's specific subgroup religious affiliation has little relation to either one's "inner" or "social" adjustment.

A further test of the hypothesis that generation is the primary causative factor for differences in both types of adjustments was also examined. Third-generation boys were divided into Reform and Orthodox groupings, these being considered as extremes on the continuum of religious liberalism versus conservatism. No significant differences were revealed.

Test Results Obtained with Non-Jewish Students

Table 20-3 gives the test results of Jewish and non-Jewish students. If we compare the aggregate mean scores of non-Jewish students (29.06) on the Personality Schedule with the aggregate mean score of the total Jewish sample (26.35), the difference found is not significant, but seems to favor the Jewish group slightly. However, the widest difference was found in the Rorschach mean score, non-Jewish students giving a less neurotic mean score than the Jewish sample (6.78 and 9.80, significant at better than the .01 level). Similar trends in the results were found in comparing the aggregate mean scores of the non-Jewish girls and the aggregate mean scores of the Jewish girls. The comparisons made here included groups which are heterogeneous from the point of view of generation. In order to eliminate the factor of generation with its attendant effects on adjustment scores, long-established Protestants were compared with third-generation Jews, on the basis of the assumption that third-generation Jews had become more acculturated and therefore a better sample for comparison with the non-Jewish group. The Per-

TABLE 20-3

Comparison of Scores Obtained by Jewish and Non-Jewish Students

Religion	Thurstone Personality Schedule				Rorschach Multiple Choice Test			
	N	Mean	S.D.	t	N	Mean	S.D.	t
Boys								
Total, Non-Jewish	45	29.06	12.06		42	6.78	4.75	
				1.32				3.73 *
Total, Jewish	134	26.35	11.08		131	9.80	6.82	
Girls								
Total, Non-Jewish	44	32.06	11.80		41	5.51	3.20	
				.98				2.44 †
Total, Jewish	143	30.03	12.08		142	7.10	4.92	

* Significant at the 1% level of confidence
† Significant at the 5% level of confidence

sonality Schedule results show little difference between the two samples, while the difference in the Rorschach is maintained, as in the case when the aggregate scores were compared. In other words, although the "social adjustment" of the dominant group is similar to the "social adjustment" of the minority group, the "inner adjustment" level seems to favor the former.

DISCUSSION OF THE RESULTS

The most striking finding in this research is the ascending "inner maladjustment" shown by Jewish boys from first to third generation on the Rorschach Multiple Choice Test. Socioeconomic status and specific type of synagogue affiliation seem to have very little effect on such scores. On the other hand, the scores on the Personality Schedule follow the opposite trend, i.e., foreign-born show a greater degree of "social maladjustment" than the third-generation boys.

It seems that boys who are born abroad or whose parents are not entirely assimilated may either feel somewhat insecure in their relationship with the social world or do not strive to adopt the American norms of "social adjustment" as measured by the paper-and-pencil test, e.g., the Thurstone Personality Schedule. The third generation, on the other hand, will try to conform as much as possible to these norms. As pointed out by Margaret Mead, all Americans try to be "third generation" in general (38). Also, as Gorer states with reference to the Jewish group, "Many of the children and nearly all the grandchildren of the original immigrants were willing to abandon in a considerable degree these claims for special status, and in the greatest part gave up completely the un-American habits which were the manifestations of such claims" (18, p. 205).

Some psychologists who have studied Jewish and Gentile temperament on the personality inventories found that their Jewish groups obtained healthier scores than Gentiles. These findings, which are contrary to what might be expected from a minority group, may be attributed to what Allport has called "enhanced striving," where there is special effort not only to appear just like anyone else, but to overemphasize certain desirable characteristics and to view their handicap as an obstacle to be surmounted by an extra spurt of effort (5, p. 156).

This would tend to be reflected to a greater degree in the third-generation Jewish boy who would like to appear as "fully Americanized" as possible, and not show the least signs of weakness, dependence, or rejection. This attitude, one may reason, is emphasized by radio, television, movies, etc., where the hero is always courageous and full of initiative. As an illustration, in one question where the respondents had to state whether they had courage, only 8 percent of the third-generation boys admitted that they lacked courage, as against 35 per cent of the second-generation group.

An interesting analogy to these results is provided by a study by Wheatley and Sumner (51). They administered the Bernreuter test to a group of Negro students at Howard University. This test included many of the items on the Thurstone Personality Schedule. They discovered that the mean score obtained by the Negro students was equal to the white's mean score. This leads to the belief that for a population belonging to a minority group, and whose striving is to conform, the paper-and-pencil test does not reflect the actual degree of maladjustment but reflects, rather, a picture of what these individuals *consider* socially normal in the dominant group.

In a similar vein, Richards found that white students ranked Jews fifth in the nine groups evaluated on a social distance scale (42). Using the same social distance scale with Negro students, McDonagh and Richards (36) did not find any difference from the results obtained with a white population. Merton developed the reference-group theory which aims to systematize the determinants of the processes of such evaluation and self-appraisal of individuals who take into account the values and standards of other individuals or groups (39). This may explain the dissimilarity in personality scores between first- and third-generation Jewish boys, since the values for self-appraisal might be different in the two groups. On the other hand, for all the Negroes, the dominant group functions for them as a reference group.

It is for this very reason that the use of projective tests may have greater sensitivity in revealing inner dynamic adjustment. Since the individual does not "know" what is normal and what is abnormal, his percepts on the test therefore tend to reflect the deeper layer of his personality, which is not readily accessible to his awareness.

Allport's contribution on the subject of differences between projective and objective tests has already been mentioned. He believes it is not possible to know about the existence of a neurotic situation unless both diagnostic approaches are utilized. He states that it is not the well-integrated subject, aware of his problems, who reveals himself in projective testing, but rather the neurotic personality, who in repressing his fears and anxieties is caught off-guard by a projective method. Previous research, using solely objective tests of personality, revealed very little of significance, since anxiety might have been repressed while taking such a personality questionnaire (4). As stated before, the first-generation Jewish boys are not entirely devoid of anxiety, but contrary to the third-generation boys, they might not repress it to the same degree, since they are more inclined to recognize the overt fact of nonacceptance. Furthermore, their anxiety may be tempered by their stronger feelings of identity with their minority group which, in turn, gives them a measure of security. There was a far greater sense of "ethnic" pride among the first- and second-generation high-school students in our own studies as compared with the third-generation subjects.

Mussen gave the Thematic Apperception Test to 50 Negroes and 50 whites, and found significant differences between the two groups (41). One of these differences showed that the Negro boys' stories expressed more aggressive "press" from the environment, and further there was a mild verbal aggressive expression by heroes. These reactions may be expected from a minority group in response to the hostile discriminations they suffer.

Another study where a projective test was used to compare white and Negro reactions was conducted by Blairs (10). He found that the Negro students indicated more maladjustment with the Rorschach Multiple Choice Test than the white students. The mean scores of this study and the present one are closely similar. One may conclude that both the Negro and the Jew, as members of minority groups, suffer the "mark of oppression," to use Kardiner's terminology.

The generation differences within various Jewish groups are only matters of degree on the level of "inner adjustment," since the first-generation boys still have poorer scores on the Rorschach Multiple Choice Test than the non-Jewish group. As pointed out earlier in this discussion, there is a desire among Jewish students, particularly of the third generation, to become a part of the majority. However, since there is little willingness to condone such a "crossing of the line" by the dominant group, the American Jew develops all the symptoms characteristic of the "marginal man."

In a substudy of the present research, it was found that the identification of the third-generation Jewish boys toward their Jewish group was weaker than the identification of the first and second generations. This naturally intensifies their marginality. In the course of research, individual students were interviewed to obtain some insight into their problems from their own points of view. The following is a verbatim answer obtained from one sixteen-year-old boy. Requested to give his opinion as to the degree of adjustment and difference between first, second, and third generation, he answered as follows: "The first generation would have a problem adjusting to his environment, but the third generation also probably [in] getting accepted by everyone else. In some cases there is still a barrier, *only if it is in the mind* [italics by the author]. He might [still] find it difficult. First-generation Jews may have some difficulties with the language and money, but not on deeper problems of acceptance by the Gentiles. Therefore the third generation should be more neurotic."

It was also pointed out earlier in this chapter that previous studies using objective tests on Jews and non-Jews were inconclusive since the the differences found were negligible. But in certain instances, as we noted, Jews scored sometimes higher and sometimes lower than non-Jews. However, a more adequate examination of the test results in Table 20-1 will reveal a most interesting trend in this connection.

Until 1938, except for one study, incidentally the only one which uses a high-school sample, all the Jewish groups show poorer adjustment according to the tests. Most of the results of studies after 1938, however, show an opposite trend. In the later instances, Jews show better or at least an equal degree of *social* adjustment as do the non-Jews. We may assume that prior to 1938 a larger number of students in their early twenties or below might have come from immigrant homes and that a significant number of them might also have been foreign-born. Around 1940, the ratio of acculturated Jews was no doubt greater than in the earlier samples; as a result, the later tests show a more favorable adjustment so far as social balance is concerned.

This process of acculturation to American norms had developed well enough by 1940 so that one can see the differences. The accumulation of data of several studies throughout the years may be called a longitudinal plan of research, while the cross-sectional or transverse method has been used in the present study. Here the first- and second-generation sample shows poorer social adjustment while the third-generation one shows better social adjustment than do Gentiles.

A further study on genuine maladjustment as a result of nonacceptance by the dominant group is reported by Kluckhohn and Leighton in their study of the Navajo (29). Since the most acculturated Navajo are not received on terms of social equality, in sour disillusionment they abandon all moral codes. An earlier pertinent study is the pioneering work conducted by Hallowell among the Ojibwa Indians of Wisconsin (21). Hallowell divided his samples into three groups: 1) nonacculturated, 2) semiacculturated, and 3) entirely acculturated. It is obvious that if they were given the pencil-and-paper test of an objective questionnaire, the last group would probably show better social adjustment, since they would have a better idea of the norms of the dominant group. However, Hallowell used Davidson's signs of maladjustment on the individually administered Rorschach. He found that 56 per cent of the most-acculturated Indians fell into the poorly adjusted group, while 27 per cent of the least-acculturated Indians received the same rating. He feels that it is lack of any positive substitute for aspects of the aboriginal value system which have their core in ethicoreligious belief that is responsible for his findings on the acculturated group. Hallowell had not specifically discussed the Indian as a marginal individual, but he agrees with the writer that his own acculturated sample among Ojibwa was not received on "equal" terms by the dominant group.*

Some writers have offered suggestions to counteract the psychological effects of rejection by the dominant group. Bettelheim reports the ex-

* Personal communication.

perience of his three-year-old daughter who came home one afternoon quite upset because Nancy, her friend, refused to play with her because she was a "shoe" (9). At that early age, Bettelheim states, an explanation of the situation will not be meaningful because the concept of a minority group status is beyond the child's comprehension. Since being a "shoe" could only be interpreted as a sign of Nancy's rejection, he suggests the child can be made to feel more secure by showing that she is still accepted by other children, and still loved by everyone else.

Lewin has also been interested in how a child may be raised to withstand the realities of life without trauma. Ignoring or suppressing the unpleasantness of the situation would only make matters worse at a later period in his estimation. He gives the example of an adopted child who finally learns that he is an orphanage child. Undoubtedly, this would propel the individual into a psychic turmoil if he learned the fact too abruptly. A protected Jewish child sooner or later will discover that he is regarded as being "different." As suggested by Brown earlier, he will then suffer the consequences of such knowledge.

According to Lewin, the Jewish child who is a member of a minority group might as well learn about it at an early age. Even if there is no immediate exposure to anti-Semitism, it is bound to happen in the future. Building a positive feeling of group identity in the Jewish group may minimize the ambiguity which is characteristic of the position of the marginal individual. One of the techniques of such preparation is to discuss the Jewish problem as a social issue rather than as an individual matter. This will prevent empty forms of anger or self-pity which are likely to develop from naive exposure to anti-Semitic experiences (32).

Greenberg likewise holds a similar view. A recognition of the unfavorable attitude toward Jews and an open discussion of the discomfort resulting from it will mitigate a sense of Jewish inferiority otherwise bound to develop if there is a protracted attempt to suppress or falsify the situation (19).

BIBLIOGRAPHY

1. Abel, T. M., and Hsu, F.: "Some aspects of personality of Chinese as revealed by Rorschach test." *Journal of Projective Techniques,* 1948, vol. 12, pp. 79–93.

2. Ackerman, Nathan, and Jahoda, Marie: *Anti-Semitism and Emotional Disorder*. New York: Harper & Brothers, 1950.

3. Adorno, T. W.; Frenkel-Brunswik, E.; Levinson, D. J.; and Sanford, R. N.: *The Authoritarian Personality*. New York, Harper & Brothers, 1952.

4. Allport, Gordon: "The trend in motivational theory." *American Journal of Orthopsychiatry*, 1953, vol. 23, pp. 107–119.

5. ————: *The Nature of Prejudice*. Cambridge: Addison-Wesley Publishing Co., 1954.

6. Anastasi, A., and Foley, J. P.: *Differential Psychology*. New York: Macmillan Company, 1949.

7. Bernard, Jessie: "Biculturality, a study in social schizophrenia." In *Jews in a Gentile World* (I. Graeber and S. Britt, eds.). New York: Macmillan Company, 1942.

8. Bettelheim, Bruno, and Janowitz, Morris: *Dynamics of Prejudice*. New York: Harper & Brothers, 1950.

9. Bettelheim, Bruno: "How arm our children against anti-semitism. A psychologist's advice to Jewish parents." *Commentary*, 1951, vol. 12, pp. 209–218.

10. Blairs, G. M.: "Personality adjustment of teachers as measured by multiple choice Rorschach test." *Journal of Educational Research*, 1946, vol. 39, pp. 652–657.

11. Blairs, G. M., and Clark, R. W.: "Personality adjustment of ninth grade pupils as measured by the multiple choice Rorschach test and the California test of personality." *Journal of Educational Psychology*, 1946, vol. 37, pp. 13–20.

12. Brown, Fred: "A note on the stability and maturity of Jewish and non-Jewish boys." *Journal of Social Psychology*, 1940, vol. 12, pp. 171–175.

13. Cox, K. J.: "Can the Rorschach multiple choice test pick sales clerks?" *Personnel Journal*, 1948, vol. 1, pp. 357–363.

14. Feldman, L. A.: "The Jewish college student." *Jewish Spectator*, December, 1955, pp. 11–17.

15. Garrett, H. E.: "Jews and others; some group differences in personality, intelligence and college achievement." *Personnel Journal*, 1929, vol. 7, pp. 341–348.

16. Glazer, Nathan: "What sociology knows about American Jews." *Commentary*, 1950, vol. 9, pp. 275–284.

17. Gordon, A. I.: "Frustration and aggression among Jewish university students." *Jewish Social Studies*, 1943, vol. 5, pp. 27–42.

18. Gorer, Geoffrey: *The American People*. New York: W. W. Norton & Co., 1948.

19. Greenberg, Clement: "Self-hatred and Jewish chauvinism." *Commentary*, 1950, vol. 10, pp. 426–433.

20. Hallowell, A. I.: "Values, acculturation and mental health." *American Journal of Orthopsychiatry,* 1950, vol. 20, pp. 732–743.

21. ————: "The use of projective techniques in the study of sociopsychological aspects of acculturation. *Journal of Projective Techniques,* 1951, vol. 15, pp. 27–44.

22. Handlin, Oscar: *The Uprooted.* Boston: Little Brown & Co., 1951.

23. ————: *Adventures in Freedom. Three Hundred Years of Jewish Life in America.* New York: McGraw-Hill Book Company, 1954.

24. Harrower, M. R., and Steiner, M. E.: *Large Scale Rorschach Techniques.* Springfield, Ill.: Charles C. Thomas, 1951.

25. Haveman, Ernest, and West, P. Salter: *They Went to College.* New York: Harcourt, Brace & Co., 1952.

26. Kardiner, Abram, and Ovesey, Lionel: *The Mark of Oppression.* New York: W. W. Norton & Co., 1951.

27. Kerckhoff, Alan C., and McCormick, Thomas C.: "Marginal status and marginal personality." *Social Forces,* 1955, vol. 34, pp. 48–55.

28. Kinsey, A. Charles, et al.: *Sexual Behavior in the Human Male.* Philadelphia: W. B. Saunders Co., 1948.

29. Kluckhohn, Clyde, and Leighton, Dorothea: *The Navajo.* Cambridge: Harvard University Press, 1951.

30. Koenig, Samuel: "Methods of studying Jewish life in America." In *Yivo Annual of Jewish Social Science,* vol. II–III. New York: Yivo Publications, 1948.

31. Lewin, Kurt: "Self hatred among Jews." In *Resolving Social Conflict.* New York: Harper & Brothers, 1948, pp. 186–200.

32. ————: "Bringing up the Jewish child." In *Resolving Social Conflict.* New York: Harper & Brothers, 1948, pp. 169–185.

33. ————: "Psycho-sociological problems of a minority group." In *Resolving Social Conflict.* New York: Harper & Brothers, 1948, pp. 145–158.

34. Loewenstein, Rudolph M.: *Christians and Jews.* New York: International Universities Press, 1951.

35. Long, H. H.: "Tested personality adjustment in Jewish and non-Jewish students." *Journal of Negro Education,* 1944, vol. 13, pp. 64–69.

36. McDonagh, E. C., and Richards, E. S.: *Ethnic Relations in the U.S.A.* New York: Appleton-Century-Crofts, 1953.

37. Malzberg, Benjamin: "New data relative to incidence of mental disease among Jews." *Mental Hygiene,* 1936, vol. 20, pp. 280–291.

38. Mead, Margaret: *And Keep Your Powder Dry.* New York: William Morrow & Co., 1942.

39. Merton, R. K., and Kitt, Alice: "Contribution to the theory of reference group behavior." In *Continuities and Discontinuities in Social Research* (R. K. Merton and P. Lazarsfeld, eds.) Glencoe, Ill.: Free Press, 1950.

40. Mosak, Harold: "Performance on the Harrower-Erickson multiple choice test of patients with spinal cord injuries." *Journal of Consulting Psychology,* 1951, vol. 15, pp. 346–349.

41. Mussen, Paul H.: "Differences between the T.A.T. responses of Negro and white boys." *Journal of Consulting Psychology,* 1953, vol. 17, pp. 373–376.

42. Richards, Eugene: "Attitude of college students in the Southwest toward ethnic groups in the U.S." *Sociology and Social Research,* 1950, vol. 35, pp. 22–30.

43. Shuey, A. M.: "Personality traits of Jewish and non-Jewish students." *Archives of Psychology,* 1944, vol. 290, pp. 1–38.

44. Sperling, A. P.: "A comparison between Jews and non-Jews, with respect to several traits of personality." *Journal of Applied Psychology,* 1942, vol. 26, pp. 828–840.

45. Sukow, M., and Williamson, E. G.: "Personality traits and attitudes of Jewish and non-Jewish students." *Journal of Applied Psychology,* 1938, vol. 22, pp. 487–492.

46. Sward, Keith, and Friedman, Meyer: "Jewish temperament." *Journal of Applied Psychology,* 1935, vol. 19, pp. 70–84.

47. Sward, Keith: "Patterns of Jewish temperament." *Journal of Applied Psychology,* 1935, vol. 19, pp. 410–423.

48. Terman, Lewis M., and Oden, Melita H., et al.: *The Gifted Child Grows Up.* Vol. IV, Genetic Studies of Genius. Stanford: Stanford University Press, 1948.

49. Thurstone, L. L., and Thurstone, G. A.: "A neurotic inventory." *Journal of Social Psychology,* 1930, vol. 1, pp. 3–30.

50. Warner, W. L., and Srole, Leo: *The Social Systems of American Ethnic Groups.* New Haven: Yale University Press, 1947.

51. Wheatley, L. A., and Sumner, F. C.: "Measurement of neurotic tendency in Negro students of music." *Journal of Psychology,* 1946, vol. 22, pp. 247–252.

52. Wilson, David C., and Lantz, Edna M.: "Effect of culture change on the Negro race in Virginia. As indicated by a study of state hospital admissions." *American Journal of Psychiatry,* 1957, vol. 114, pp. 25–32.

53. Zborowski, Mark, and Herzog, E.: *Life Is with People.* New York: International Universities Press, 1952.

E. Gartly Jaco

Division of Medical Sociology
University of Texas Medical Branch

21

MENTAL HEALTH OF THE SPANISH-AMERICAN
IN TEXAS *

Of the subcultural groups maintaining a specific identity, perhaps the Spanish-speaking constitutes the largest ethnic group within the state of Texas and the entire American Southwest. The 1950 census indicated a population of more than one million individuals with Spanish surnames residing in Texas, comprising 13 per cent of the total state population (7). Sociological distinctions can be made between the Hispanos, Hispanic-American, Mexican-American, and Mexican within the Spanish-speaking aggregate (6), but for the sake of brevity all are placed under the rubric of "Mexican" in this paper, while acknowledging many social, economic, and cultural differences.

Historically, the Spanish-speaking peoples preceded the English-speaking Anglo in Texas, although arriving after the Indians. The patterns of living of the Anglo became dominant in Texas after a series of conflicts culminating in the Texas Revolution, the Mexican War, the establishment of Texas as a republic, and eventually its becoming the twenty-eighth state in the Union. Consequently, the Spanish-speaking population is historically the reverse of other subcultural groups immigrating into the United States. Another difference is the close proximity of the "mother country" of Mexico (for those other than Hispanos), which has reinforced and supported many of their cultural patterns.

The typical Mexican in Texas today personifies the persistence of a different way of life and identity from that of the predominant Anglo. He is usually bilingual, is likely to marry another of Spanish

* Support for the psychiatric survey is gratefully acknowledged from the Russell Sage Foundation and from the Hogg Foundation for Mental Health. Much of the information reported herein will be developed at greater length in a forthcoming monograph encompassing the entire psychiatric survey of Texas, now in preparation.

descent, has less than five years of formal schooling with a consequent limitation in occupational advancement and opportunity, is likely to reside in a socially segregated community, is usually a member of the Roman Catholic denomination, usually has a large number of children after marriage, his household is composed of several nuclear families of several generations, and he has a somewhat shorter life expectancy than the Anglo.

The culture of the Spanish-speaking peoples in Texas and the Southwest has been described in many studies (1, 5, 6, 8), and no attempt will be made herein to present in detail the basic components of this subcultural group. Generally, the Spanish-Americans are a modest but proud people, oriented toward the present rather than the future, more dependent upon kinsmen and *compadres* than competitive, value individuality more than individualism, and are likely to be content with existing circumstances of life, preferring to cope with rather than to control or manipulate stressful or threatening forces in the environment. Their community life is usually organized along *gemeinschaft* rather than *gesellschaft* patterns. Their family is an extended system, with a feeling of responsibility, care, and support for all their members uppermost. Emotional support, warmth, acceptance, and stability are offered their members to a much greater extent than the Anglos and many other subcultural groups in America. The Spanish-Americans and Anglo-Americans are thus more accommodated than assimilated to each other in Texas today.

The major purpose of this inquiry will be to present a general description of the incidence of major mental disorders of the Spanish-surname population of Texas, and to compare results with that of the Anglo-American and nonwhite populations in the same area in an effort to determine differences as well as similarities in the mental health picture of this contemporary subcultural group. The principal hypothesis is that the Spanish-speaking population will exhibit significant differences in both form as well as frequency of major mental disorders from other ethnic groups of the same area during the same interval of time.

METHOD

Data on diagnosed psychotic cases for the Mexican group in Texas were obtained from a survey of the incidence of these disorders recently conducted (2, 3). This survey included all inhabitants of the state of

Texas who sought psychiatric treatment for a psychosis for the first time in their lives during the two-year period of 1951–1952. Information was compiled from every psychiatrist in private practice in Texas during this time, and from all of the private, city-county, state, and Veterans Administration hospitals in Texas and surrounding states. Cases for the two-year period were averaged into an annual rate and computed for the twenty-seven economic subregions of the state. Incidence rates were adjusted for age, sex, and major ethnic composition of each of the subregions, with the 1950 population of Texas constituting the "standard population" for standardizing the rates.

Although the regular census data for Texas include the Mexican population within the category of white population, as distinguished from the nonwhite group, the necessary data on age, sex, and other socioeconomic factors studied were obtained from a special census monograph (7). Knowledge of the population of the Mexicans is therefore contingent upon the use of Spanish surnames by the census bureau in compiling their study. While an incomplete account of this group is obtained by this method, at least more than 90 per cent of the known composition and related demographic characteristics of the Mexican population can be reasonably derived.

FINDINGS

Total Rates. Of the total number of 11,298 new psychotic cases found for the two-year period, 684 (6 per cent) were Mexican, 9,557 were Anglo-Americans (84.6 per cent), and 1,057 (9.4 per cent) were nonwhite. The average annual incidence rate per 100,000 population, standardized directly for age and sex composition, was 42 for the Mexican group, 80 for the Anglos, and 56 for the nonwhite population of Texas.

Ecological Distribution. The pattern of distribution of mental disorders differed significantly between the three major ethnic groups for the twenty-seven economic subregions within the state. As illustrated in Table 21-1, although incidence rates of psychoses varied considerably for different areas within Texas, negative rank-order correlations were obtained for the average rates for the six geographic parts of the state between the three subcultural groups, all being statistically insignificant. Consequently, the ecological patterns of incidence differed markedly between the geographic areas for the different ethnic groups, suggesting that either conditions conducive to the onset of these mental dis-

TABLE 21-1

Annual Adjusted Incidence Rates of Psychoses by Geographical Areas within
the State of Texas of Mexican, Anglo-American, and Nonwhite Groups,
1951–1952, per 100,000 Population

Area, Subregion No.	Mexican	Anglo-American	Nonwhite
East	67	93	52
12	70	67	45
13	85	72	35
G	53	100	80
H	70	115	63
14	59	112	37
South	36	92	34
3	36	97	29
15	33	85	25
11	40	94	47
Central	33	94	47
D	9	114	73
7C	27	71	61
2	22	94	24
E	51	99	15
F	59	89	65
9	24	90	53
10	39	103	37
North	39	61	64
6B	0	61	109
7A	90	67	68
7B	0	54	31
8	58	68	50
B	39	58	50
C	48	58	75
Northwest	26	71	89
4	24	73	119
6A	28	68	59
West	43	63	37
5	26	65	57
A	43	81	47
1A	61	44	45
1B	42	60	0

orders affected these groups differently in different areas, or the conditions leading to obtaining psychiatric treatment varied excessively
between the different subregions for these groups.

To check the possibility that differences in psychiatric facilities between the subregions may have accounted for their variances in rates,
a rank-order correlation was computed between incidence rates and
number of psychiatric beds and psychiatrists in private practice in the

areas. However, none of the correlation values were found to be of statistical significance. Consequently, availability of treatment facilities had no effect upon the differentials in incidence rates for these groups. It should also be pointed out that a small percentage of the psychotic cases were never hospitalized, being treated either on an outpatient basis or failing to obtain actual treatment following an initial psychotic diagnosis.

Source of Treatment. In a more concerted effort to estimate a potential source of bias in rates for the three subcultural groups, the sources of psychiatric diagnosis and treatment were studied. For the entire patient population, 53 per cent went initially to a psychiatrist in private practice or to a private hospital. Among the 47 per cent obtaining publicly supported care, 4 per cent went to city-county hospitals, 7 per cent to Veterans Administration hospitals, and 36 per cent to state institutions. Within this tax-supported group of patients, one found 73 per cent of the Mexicans, 39 per cent of the Anglos, and 95 per cent of nonwhites.

Incidence rates were computed for public and private sources of treatment and adjusted for differences in age and sex distribution to obtain a clearer picture of any differences in the two major sources of treatment. Although the total private rate of 38 was only slightly higher than the public rate of 34, as shown in Table 21-2, with only one exception, the public rate was higher than the private rate for males and females in the three ethnic groups. The single exception was the extremely higher private than public rate for the Anglo females, which apparently was of sufficient enormity to raise the entire private rate for all the groups slightly above that of the total public rate.

TABLE 21-2

Annual Adjusted Incidence Rates of Psychoses by Source of Treatment of Mexican, Anglo-American and Nonwhite Groups of Texas, 1951–1952, per 100,000 Population

	Public	Private	Total
Males			
Mexican	30	10	40
Anglo-American	39	34	73
Nonwhite	57	3	60
Females			
Mexican	32	13	45
Anglo-American	25	62	87
Nonwhite	47	3	50
TOTAL	34	38	72

Differentials in the disparity between private and public rates were also exhibited between the sexes and subcultural groups. The public rate for both males and females of the Mexicans was practically identical, both the public rates being about three times greater than the private rate. The Anglo-American males exhibited only a slightly higher rate of public than private treatment, while the Anglo female had nearly a two-and-a-half times higher private than public rate. The greatest disparity between public and private rates, as anticipated, held for the nonwhite group, with both males and females having only a very small rate of private contrasted to public care.

It should be noted that although the median income level of Mexicans in Texas is the lowest of the three ethnic groups, the Spanish-speaking group was more likely to obtain private psychiatric care than the nonwhite population. It is likely that the extreme paucity of private treatment facilities for the Negroes in Texas accounted primarily for the extremely high rate of publicly supported care for this group. Needless to add, if the privately treated cases had not been included in this survey, extreme distortions in incidence rates would have been obtained for the sexes in these ethnic groups. Consequently, differences in sources of psychiatric treatment were found between the subcultural groups.

Since every possible source of psychiatric treatment was encompassed in this survey, the likelihood that differences in attitudes toward mental illness and consequent entry into treatment could account sufficiently for variations in rates for these groups was minimized. When all known sources of qualified psychiatric treatment are included in an epidemiological study of this type, any differentials in attitudes toward psychiatric illness and treatment, when such care is obtained, more likely affect than distort sufficiently the total incidence rate for such groups and socioeconomic levels. That this may be supported regarding this particular survey of Texas is the fact that more than two and a half times the number of psychotic cases would have had to be overlooked or avoided treatment among the Spanish-American group for their rate to have merely *equaled* that of the Anglo-Americans. Furthermore, over twice as many more Mexican psychotics would be needed for their rate to equal that of the nonwhite population. While there is evidence that Mexicans have a different attitude toward "Anglo-medicine" than the other groups (6), it seems unlikely, in view of the extreme disparities in rates, that the low incidence rate of such severe mental disorders as the psychoses for the Spanish-speaking population of Texas can be sufficiently accounted for in these terms. Nor does it seem feasible that there are nearly three times as many cases of psychosis among the Mexican group than our extensive survey net was able to find.

Age and Sex. Some similarities and dissimilarities were exhibited in incidence rates for various age levels between males and females of the three major ethnic groups, as shown in Table 21–3. No cases were found

TABLE 21-3

Annual Age-Specific Incidence Rates by Age and Sex for Mexican, Anglo-American, and Nonwhite Groups, per 100,000 Population, Texas, 1951–1952

	Males			Females		
Age	Mexican	Anglo-American	Non-white	Mexican	Anglo-American	Non-white
Under 15 Years	0	1	0	0	1	2
15–24 Years	36	40	59	32	52	46
25–44 Years	56	100	87	76	135	76
45–64 Years	63	128	83	64	147	74
65+ Years	82	207	148	65	155	84

under the age of fifteen for the Mexican male or females, with only a negligible rate found for the other two ethnic groups also. The greatest disparity in rates between the three groups was found for the older age ranges, with the Mexican rate for males and females over age sixty-five also considerably lower than those in the other two subcultural groups. In general, the rate for the Mexican male tended to increase steadily with advancing age while the Mexican female rate reached its peak between the ages of twenty-five and forty-four and declined slightly thereafter. On the other hand, both the Anglo-American males and females showed a sharp and consistent increase in incidence with advancing age, with essentially the same pattern holding also for the nonwhite populations. Rates for most of the various age ranges tended to be more similar between the Mexican and nonwhite females than found for the Mexican and nonwhite males. It may also be noted that the disparity between the rates of the Anglo-Americans and Mexican males and females tended to increase with each advancing age group. Furthermore, the rates for the Anglo-American males exceeded that of Mexican and nonwhite males after the age of twenty-five, while the rate for the Anglo-American females was higher than the females in the other two groups past the age of fifteen.

Incidence rates for females were found to be higher in both the Mexican and Anglo-American groups while the male rate was higher in the nonwhite population. For the entire state, the female incidence rate was significantly higher than that of the males. It should be pointed out that this is the first large-scale survey of psychoses to find a higher rate for females than males.

Diagnosis. In order to give greater stability to the identification of the various forms of mental illness, specific diagnoses were combined into three major categories: functional, old-age, and organic psychoses. The various types of schizophrenia, the affective, and involutional disorders were combined into the functional psychoses. The so-called old-age psychoses were composed of cerebral arteriosclerosis and senile dementia, and the remaining acute and chronic brain syndromes made up the organic psychotic category.

The Mexican group exhibited the lowest rates of the functional disorders of the three subcultural groups, although this differential was more apparent among the males than females, as depicted in Table 21-4. Males in the Mexican and Anglo-American groups had consider-

TABLE 21-4

Annual Adjusted Incidence Rates of Psychoses by Diagnosis of Mexican, Anglo-American and Nonwhite Groups of Texas, 1951–1952, per 100,000 Population

	Males			Females		
Psychosis	*Mexican*	*Anglo-Americans*	*Non-white*	*Mexican*	*Anglo-Americans*	*Non-white*
Functional	24	47	32	35	69	35
Schizophrenia	20	32	30	26	43	32
Affective	3	11	2	7	19	2
Involutional	1	4	1	2	7	1
Old-Age	7	13	11	5	10	10
Cerebral arterio-sclerosis	4	7	6	2	5	4
Senile dementia	3	6	3	3	4	4
Organic	8	13	15	3	7	4
Toxic	2	6	4	0	2	1
Paresis	4	2	8	1	1	3
Other	2	5	4	2	4	1

ably lower rates than their corresponding females, while the nonwhite males showed only a slightly lower rate than nonwhite females for the functional psychoses. The opposite picture was found for the old-age and organic psychoses in that the males of all three groups had higher rates of these disorders than the females. Nevertheless, the Mexicans still exhibited the lowest rates of these psychoses.

Although some differences in more specific diagnosis of mental patients exist among psychiatrists, the more detailed psychiatric syndromes are offered for whatever value they may have in Table 21-4. For schizophrenia in all forms, the Mexican population exhibited less than the other two ethnic groups for both sexes. However, the disparity was greater between the females of the subcultural groups than the males in that the rate of schizophrenia for the Anglo-American males was nearly the same as that for the nonwhite males, although still higher than that for Mexican males, whereas for the females, the Anglo-Americans had nearly twice the rate of schizophrenia than the Mexican females, with the nonwhite female falling in between.

A somewhat different picture emerges, however, for the affective psychoses, which include the various types of manic-depressive and psychotic-depressive. Both the Mexican males and females exhibited a higher incidence of these disorders than the nonwhite sexes, especially for the Mexican female, whose rate was more than twice that of the nonwhite female. Nevertheless, the Anglo-American males and females had a considerably higher rate of these psychoses than their ethnic counterparts. A similar pattern of rate differentials was also found for the involutional psychosis.

The Mexican males and females exhibited a considerable lower incidence of cerebral arteriosclerosis and senile dementia than the other two ethnic groups. Although the nonwhite group exhibited a higher incidence of these disorders than the Mexicans for both sexes, and approached the rate of the Anglo-Americans, the evidence does not support differential life expectancy as a possible reason for these rate differentials, especially since the female rates were consistently lower than that for males despite their higher life expectancy. Some interesting differentials also occurred for the specific organic psychoses, especially the toxic psychoses and general paresis, a psychosis of syphilitic infectious etiology. No cases of toxic psychoses were found for the Mexican female, while the rate for the Mexican male was one-third less than that of the Anglo-American males and half that of the nonwhite male, while the Anglo-American female rate was twice that of the nonwhite female. Conversely, the rate of general paresis among the Mexican males was twice that of the Anglo-American male, but half that of the nonwhite male, while the rates for Mexican and Anglo-American females were identical for this disorder, with nonwhite females exhibiting a rate three times higher than females in the other two groups. For the remaining acute and chronic brain syndromes, the Mexican male and female showed identical incidence rates, both of which were considerably less than the other two groups. Consequently, both the form as well as frequency of mental disorders varied considerably among the three major subcultural groups and by sex. While the over-all rates were generally lower for the Mexican group, their outstanding exceptions were found for the affective psychoses and general paresis in which their rate deviated in a higher incidence for these particular mental disorders.

Urban-Rural Residence. A major differential that has often been examined in epidemiological studies of mental disorders is the urban-rural differential in place of living of patients at the time they become mentally ill. The definition of urban and rural communities in this study was identical with that of the United States Census Bureau, with a population of 2,500 constituting the cutting point between urban and rural residence. As shown in Table 21-5, the total adjusted incidence rate for

TABLE 21-5

Annual Adjusted Incidence Rates of Psychoses by Urban-Rural Residence of Mexican, Anglo-American and Nonwhite Groups of Texas, 1951–1952, per 100,000 Population

	Urban	Rural
Males		
Mexican	63	26
Anglo-American	115	50
Nonwhite	93	46
Females		
Mexican	68	35
Anglo-American	137	52
Nonwhite	74	45
TOTAL	112	47

urban areas was nearly two and a half times greater than that of the rural. Considerably more urban cases were found than their ratio in the population would have suggested, since the Texas population was 63 per cent urban for the 1950 census period. For the males, the Mexicans exhibited a somewhat greater disparity between urban and rural rates, although the urban rate for Anglo-Americans was far greater than males of the Mexican and nonwhite groups. For the females, on the other hand, the Anglo-Americans exhibited the largest disparity between urban and rural rates, even though the urban rate for Mexican females was nearly twice higher than the rural rate.

Consequently, for both sexes in the three major ethnic groups, the incidence was considerably greater in urban than rural communities. Since it has already been shown that availability of psychiatric facilities did not affect the rates, it is likely that living in rural areas, as opposed to urban areas, was no significant deterrent in preventing one ethnic group from obtaining psychiatric care more than the others.

Interstate Migration. The factor of spatial mobility has often been regarded as significant in the incidence and prevalence of mental disorders (4). This factor will be studied only in terms of interstate migration, since census data are most readily available in this form. The non-migrant was categorized as one born in the state and becoming psychotic therein (born in Texas), while the interstate or non-Texas-born patient was defined as one born anywhere outside the state of Texas, but residing therein at the time of becoming psychotic during the two-year study interval. This factor was obtained for 73 per cent of the Mexican cases, 65 per cent of the Anglo-American, and 85 per cent of the nonwhite patients in this survey. Because of the incompleteness of this factor, some reservations may be necessary in evaluating the results.

TABLE 21-6

Annual Adjusted Incidence Rates of Psychoses by Interstate-Migration Status of Mexican, Anglo-American and Nonwhite Groups of Texas, 1951–1952, per 100,000 Population

	Native-Born	*Non-Native-Born*
Males		
Mexican	33	23
Anglo-American	53	50
Nonwhite	50	42
Females		
Mexican	34	39
Anglo-American	62	62
Nonwhite	45	49
TOTAL	53	51

For the entire number of cases, the rate for the Texas-born was slightly higher than those born elsewhere at the time of becoming psychotic, as shown in Table 21–6. For the males in all three ethnic groups, the native-born rate was higher than those born elsewhere. However,

for the Mexican and nonwhite females, the rate was slightly higher for
those born out of the state than those born within, while both native-
born and non-native-born Anglo-American females had identical rates.
However, chi-square tests of significance indicated that none of the differences between the rates of the migrant and nonmigrant groups was
significant statistically. Consequently, the differences in the rates in
terms of interstate migration are more likely due to chance variation
than any actual differences in incidence in terms of spatial mobility. Of
course, the migration differential, as measured herein, was extremely
gross in that the internal migrant differences as well as the length of stay
in Texas for those born out of the state may have exhibited a somewhat different picture. Nevertheless, these differentials taken in their
crude form indicate that when the rates are adjusted for age differentials
in terms of interstate migration, this factor was of no significance in
terms of the incidence rates of psychoses for the three major subcultural
groups.

TABLE 21-7

Annual Adjusted Incidence Rates of Psychoses by Marital Status of Mexican, Anglo-
American and Nonwhite Groups of Texas, 1951–1952, per 100,000 Population

		Males			Females		
Status	Total	Mexican	Anglo-American	Non-white	Mexican	Anglo-American	Non-white
Single	200	126	246	189	129	187	182
Married	77	27	70	53	45	109	45
Divorced	274	47	362	263	95	279	164
Widowed	111	97	125	70	63	121	71
Separated	189	24	215	125	32	234	172

Marital Status. A major index of the status of family living is that
of marital status, a factor readily obtainable in the majority of psychiatric
records. Incidence rates for the five types of marital status for the entire
state, adjusted for age, sex, and ethnic differentials, were highest for the
divorced, followed in order by the single, separated, widowed, and,
lastly, married. Significant divergencies, however, from this over-all pattern were found for the various subcultural groups and between the
sexes, as shown in Table 21–7. Both the Mexican males and females
differed in their rank-order of incidence rates for the various types of
marital status with the single Mexican males and females exhibiting
the highest rate and the separated the lowest, while the widowed Mexican

males were second in highest incidence, followed in order by the divorced and married. Among the Mexican females, the divorced came second, followed by the widowed and married.

Only the Anglo-American and nonwhite males exhibited identical rank-order with the total state picture, in terms of marital status, while the Anglo-American females showed a higher rate for the separated and less for the single than the Anglo-American males, and the nonwhite females showed their highest rate to be among the single, followed in order by the separated, divorced, widowed, and lastly, married, differing from the nonwhite male for the single, divorced, and separated.

The fact that the most significant divergencies in marital and family status of psychotic cases at the time they became mentally ill differed more for the Mexican group than the other two may be of etiological significance. Certain outstanding differences in the Mexican kinship system may possibly bear upon not only the chances of becoming psychotic, but, may also affect their likelihood of obtaining treatment. The single, having by far the highest rate for both Mexican males and females, followed closely by the widowed and divorced, indicates a relatively deviant family status of the patient at the time he became psychotic. In the status of being single, or in a home broken by death or divorce, it is likely that such family conditions were conducive either to the onset of a mental disorder or increased the likelihood of coming into psychiatric treatment. In either event, family status has considerable significance in the incidence of these disorders.

Occupation. The mode of earning a livelihood in addition to that of family status may be also regarded as a significant sociological factor that may be of etiological as well as epidemiological significance for these subcultural groups. Not only the economic role, i.e., the occupation itself, but whether or not one is employed and the differential sources of stress engendered by modes of work, as well as being out of work, were included in this study. The occupational categories used by the Census Bureau's Dictionary of Occupational Titles were employed in this survey, with the occupational category rather than the specific line of work comprising the basis of analysis. For all groups, the rate of psychoses for the unemployed was far greater than for those engaged in an occupation at the time they became psychotic. However, the finding that the professional and semiprofessional occupations showed the highest incidence rate of psychosis was unexpected, since other surveys have usually found this category of work to be extremely low for these major mental disorders. Service and manual work occupations came next, followed in order by clerical and sales jobs, agricultural, and lastly managerial, official, and proprietary occupations, as shown in Table 21–8. Among the ethnic groups, the rates for the Mexicans diverged

TABLE 21-8

Annual Adjusted Incidence Rates of Psychoses by Occupational Category of Mexican, Anglo-American and Nonwhite Groups of Texas, 1951–1952, per 100,000 Population

		Males			Females		
Category	Total Rates	Mexican	Anglo-American	Non-white	Mexican	Anglo-American	Non-white
Professional and Semiprofessional	149	65	145	177	55	193	70
Managerial, Official and Proprietary	57	36	66	35	111	55	0
Clerical-Sales	99	68	87	190	104	114	23
Service	107	74	122	89	131	96	111
Agricultural	97	51	139	102	93	70	66
Manual Work	103	62	132	108	45	103	38
Unemployed	2102	42	429	197	577	5047	475

again considerably from those of the other two groups. For the Mexican males, service workers exhibited the highest incidence rate, followed in order by clerical-sales, professional and semiprofessional, manual work, agricultural, and lastly managerial, official, and proprietary occupations. This pattern was considerably different for the Mexican female in all occupations, except service jobs, which was also highest, followed in order by managerial, official, and proprietary jobs, clerical-sales, agricultural work, professional and semiprofessional, and lastly, manual work.

Rank-order correlations between rates for the occupational categories and the subcultural groups for males and females were all insignificant. Consequently, the pattern of psychoses for the Mexican group not only diverged from the other two groups in terms of occupation, but also between the sexes within this group. It is of interest to point out that with the exception of the professional, semiprofessional, and manual work occupations, the incidence rates were higher for the Mexican female than male in all of the remaining modes of employment. In general, employment or working outside of the home may be regarded as somewhat "deviant" in the light of the typical Mexican finding that the rate for the unemployed Mexican male was extremely low compared to the other groups and sexes.

Since occupation is one index of the ability to pay for psychiatric treatment, a correlation was computed between the median income of the six occupational categories and the incidence rates for the Mexican males and females, with correlation values being extremely negligible, —.09 and —.14 for Mexican males and females, respectively. For the total incidence rates and median income of the six occupational categories, the correlation value of .20 was found, also insignificant statistically. Therefore, once again, no relationship was found between income level and the incidence rate, further supporting the contention that factors other than economic or financial were probably operating in the rate differentials found herein.

Education. Education has been regarded, sociologically, as a major channel of vertical mobility as well as an important part of the over-all dimension of status, particularly in urban communities of America. Consequently, the degree of educational attainment may be an index of acculturation as well as an effort to achieve a higher social position in the dominant Anglo culture in Texas, particularly on the part of the Spanish-speaking and nonwhite subcultural groups. Data on this factor were not obtained for all of the cases, with the most extreme shortage

TABLE 21-9

Annual Adjusted Incidence Rates of Psychoses by Education of Mexican, Anglo-American and Nonwhite Groups of Texas, 1951–1952, per 100,000 Population

| Educational Attainment | Total | *Males* | | | *Females* | | |
		Mexican	Anglo-American	Non-white	Mexican	Anglo-American	Non-white
None	105	40	129	59	44	114	85
1–4 Years	50	28	59	43	37	48	45
5–8 Years	52	34	51	59	42	56	53
9–12 Years	50	57	43	54	50	56	45
In College	71	63	62	100	42	85	55

found in private psychiatrists' files, while generally those obtaining public-supported care were more than likely to be included in the study of this factor. Thus, educational attainment was obtained for two-thirds of the Mexican and nonwhite patients in contrast to 50 per cent for the Anglo-American cases. These shortcomings should be kept in mind in analyzing this particular variable, since it is likely that the lesser educational levels may be more represented than the higher levels. In all instances, as shown in Table 21–9, no significant rank-order correlations were found between educational level and incidence rates for any of the ethnic groups and sexes. However, the direction and degree of the correlations deserve attention. For both Mexican males and females and nonwhite males, the relationship between education and incidence rate is in a *positive* direction, all others being negative. Furthermore, the correlation value for the Mexican male was the highest (.70), considerably higher than for the Spanish-American female (.12), while that of the nonwhite males was in between at .42. A negative correlation of —.40 was found for the Anglo-American males, far higher than the values of —.02 for the Anglo females and —.18 for the nonwhite females.

Also of interest is the finding that both extremes of the educational continuum, those with no education and those attending college, also exhibited the highest incidence rates compared to the more average levels of schooling. Since the median level of education is lower for the Mexican than the other groups in Texas, the relationship between the educational factor and mental disorders assumes even greater importance for this ethnic group.

DISCUSSION

Two major "unknowns" concerning the data presented herein are: 1) The actual number of psychotic members of the three ethnic groups who obtained care from other than qualified psychiatric facilities and specialists; and 2) the number of psychotic cases that were successfully concealed and failed to obtain care of any professional kind. However, because every possible qualified source of psychiatric care in Texas was encompassed, because only psychotic cases, the most severely disordered of mental conditions, were included, and because most of the differences found for the ethnic groups were of such significant magnitude, it is believed that these shortcomings can have only a minimum of effect upon the major results of this inquiry. For example, to deny the finding that the Spanish-speaking population has less psychosis than the Anglo-Americans in Texas because the former either are more prone to prevent their psychotic members from obtaining psychiatric treatment or fail to recognize psychotic symptoms more than the latter is to hold that such occurs for every three psychotic Mexicans to one Anglo-American case, and for every two Mexicans to one nonwhite psychotic person. While this ratio of "protection" from psychiatric treatment may be possible, it does not truly seem plausible that such a wide disparity could be sustained among the various subcultural groups. Furthermore, it is equally possible that factors preventing psychotic members from obtaining treatment may apply as much to the Anglo and nonwhite groups as to the Spanish-Americans.

Several psychiatrists in private practice in Texas who have treated Mexican patients have commented to this writer about the fact that frequently such patients would admit having been treated by various "folk-practitioners," such as *albolarias, curanderas,* and even *brujas* (witches) (6). However, the fact that such patients eventually came to the Anglo psychiatrist for aid, particularly those with more severe mental disturbances, indicates the lack of influence of such practitioners in minimizing the known psychotic rate of this group.

SUMMARY AND CONCLUSIONS

Evidence from anthropological and sociological studies depicts the Spanish-speaking peoples of Texas and the American Southwest as a warm, supportive, and reasonably secure subcultural group, traits not found to the same extent in other ethnic groups inhabiting the same area. The principal hypothesis that the Mexican group would exhibit differences in form and frequency of major mental disorders was tested by a recent psychiatric survey. The results indicated that:

1. The incidence rate of total psychoses for the Mexicans was considerably lower than the Anglo-American and nonwhite groups in Texas.

2. The ecological distribution of incidence rates for the subregions of the state differed significantly among the Mexican, Anglo, and nonwhite groups.

3. Availability to psychiatric treatment facilities were not significantly related to the incidence rates for subregions. Other factors and checks cast doubt on the possibility that differences among the three ethnic groups in attitudes toward psychiatric illness and sources of treatment sufficiently accounted for differentials in their rates.

4. The incidence rate of psychoses tended to increase with advancing age for the Mexican male more than the female, while both sexes of the Anglo-American and nonwhite groups showed increasing rates with aging. Rates were higher for females than males in both the Spanish-American and Anglo-American groups, while the opposite occurred for the nonwhites.

5. The incidence of functional, old-age, and organic psychoses was

lower for the Mexicans than Anglos and nonwhites. Differentials between the sexes and in each of the three subcultural groups were exhibited for the more specific diagnostic categories.

6. Urban rates were consistently higher than rural rates for all three ethnic groups and sexes, although differentials in degree of variation between these rates existed among the groups.

7. The factor of being born in Texas or an in-migrant was not significantly related to the incidence of psychoses for any of the ethnic groups.

8. Differences in rates for the three subcultural groups were found for five forms of marital status, and between the sexes in these groups.

9. Occupational differences in incidence rates were found among the three ethnic groups and by sex.

10. A positive correlation between level of education and incidence rates of psychoses was found only for the Mexican group, and was considerably more significant for Mexican males than females. For both sexes in the Anglo and nonwhite groups, education was negatively related and to a lesser degree.

11. These findings generally support the major hypothesis that the Spanish-speaking peoples exhibit differences in incidence and types of mental disorders from the other major subcultural groups of Texas, with more emphasis found upon a consistently lower rate of psychoses in general.

12. Since epidemiological data of this kind can only offer etiological hypotheses rather than proof, the influence of the subcultural system of the Spanish-speaking group in preventing major mental disorders such as the psychoses from occurring to the same extent as other groups within the same area is still subject to considerably more inquiry. In terms of existing knowledge about their subculture and the known incidence of mental disorders reported in this survey, however, it is likely that the patterns of living peculiar to the Spanish-speaking people contribute in some measure to their good mental health status.

BIBLIOGRAPHY

1. Barron, M. L., ed.: *American Minorities*. New York: Alfred Knopf, 1957.
2. Jaco, E. G.: "Incidence of psychoses in Texas, 1951–1952." *Texas State Journal of Medicine,* 1957, vol. 53, p. 86.

3. ———: "Social factors in mental disorders in Texas." *Social Problems,* 1957, vol. 4, p. 322.

4. Malzberg, B., and Lee, E. S.: *Migration and Mental Disease.* New York: Social Science Research Council, 1956.

5. Marden, C. F.: *Minorities in American Society.* New York: American Book Co., 1952.

6. Saunders, L.: *Cultural Difference and Medical Care.* New York: Russell Sage Foundation, 1954.

7. U.S. Bureau of the Census: *Persons of Spanish Surname.* Washington, D.C.: U.S. Government Printing Office, 1950 Census of Population, IV, Pt. III, Ch. C. 1950.

8. Woods, Sister F. J.: *Cultural Values of American Ethnic Groups.* New York: Harper & Brothers, 1956.

WORLD PERSPECTIVES

E. D. Wittkower

Department of Psychiatry
McGill University

and

J. Fried

Department of Sociology and Anthropology
McGill University

22

SOME PROBLEMS OF TRANSCULTURAL PSYCHIATRY *

Modern psychiatry has arrived at a stage of theoretical sophistication where the sociocultural dimension joins with the genetic, biological, and psychological interpretation of human behaviour. Valuable contributions to the field of cultural psychiatry, i.e., that branch of psychiatry which deals with the interrelationship of abnormal psychological states and sociocultural milieu, have been made in the past fifteen years. Epidemiological studies related to the ecology of city life (7, 9, 10, 22, 33), to social stratification (15, 16), to occupation (11, 16, 29), and to ethnic groups (2, 6, 18, 19, 23, 31, 36, 38, 39) have been carried out by psychiatrists and social scientists. Another important development has been the careful study of whole communities, such as the Hutterites (8) and the Stirling County [Nova Scotia] project (20, 21), the Yorkville study (28), etc., in which the factors of community social structure and culture were brought into direct relation with mental health. Still another avenue of research has been the study of the beneficial and harmful aspects of the hospital environment in the therapeutic process (4, 5, 37). Most of this literature has been ably surveyed in Arnold M. Rose, *Mental Health and Mental Disorder* (32) and M. K. Opler, *Culture, Psychiatry and Human Values* (26).

Most of the work concerned with the relationship between culture and mental health has been carried out within the boundaries of a

* This paper was originally published in *The International Journal of Social Psychiatry*, 1958, vol. III, no. 4, pp. 245–252. Reprinted by permission.

489

single country. Pioneering efforts have been made by such writers as P. K. Benedict and Jacks (1), Lin (23), and Yap (39) to compare the incidence and prevalence of mental illnesses in several cultures. Yet, for reasons which are one of the major concerns of this paper, these efforts have been rather inconclusive.

While some studies have indeed involved samples composed of representatives of different national or cultural groups, these were persons not living in the countries of their origin [cf. Hinkle's study of Chinese in New York City (13, 14), Opler and Singer's studies of Italians and Irish (27, 34), Spiegel's studies of Italians, Irish, and Yankees (35), and Roberts' and Myers' study of Irish, Italians, Negroes, and Jews (30)]. Thus, for example, a hypothetical study in New York City, contrasting Chinese with Italians or Yankees, is not the same as a comparison of mainland Chinese with Sicilian Italians or Boston Yankees.

What follows is a report on the initial results obtained from a worldwide enquiry addressed to psychiatrists and social scientists in thirty-five countries concerning the frequency and nature of mental illness in their respective countries; a discussion of possible reasons for differences noted; and some theoretical and practical conclusions regarding the possibility of future research.

Our "procedure" for collecting information took the form of a series of communications * addressed to scientists strategically placed and qualified to be able to give authoritative information concerning the area of our interest.†

To avoid misunderstandings we would like to underline that we are fully aware of the shortcomings of correspondence as a research tool and of the preliminary nature of the observations to be reported. Our aim in presenting our preliminary observations is to stimulate interest in a field of psychiatry which was hitherto been little explored.

PRELIMINARY OBSERVATIONS ††

EPIDEMIOLOGY

As regards epidemiology, two methods have commonly been used

* Letters and a brief questionnaire.

† The information thus received was organized in the form of a number of newsletters (*Newsletter on Transcultural Research in Mental Health Problems*) sent to our correspondents and available to others interested in the   ject.

†† With the exception of a few references to published   .terial taken from reprints sent by the authors, all the observations presented are based on personal communications.

for the estimation of the incidence of mental illness in the population of a given geographical unit: *1*) investigation of a sample population taken as representative of the total population; and *2*) hospital admission statistics. Some authors have combined both methods.

Difficulties which have been encountered in local community surveys include the definition of what is a case, design of reliable sampling procedures, unwillingness of the local population to cooperate, and language handicaps in countries in which the language is incompletely mastered by the investigator.

Hospital admission statistics are easily accessible but cannot be regarded as representative of incidence and prevalence of mental illness in the total culture because composition of institutionalized patients depends to a great extent on the availability of treatment facilities, on the necessity to give priority to grossly disturbed patients in countries in which treatment facilities are scarce, and on the varying degree to which mentally disturbed persons are tolerated and consequently kept in their home environment (26).

While it is difficult enough to make correct estimates regarding the incidence and prevalence of mental illness in a given geographical unit, the difficulties inherent in the task are obviously multiplied if attempts are made to assess the incidence and prevalence of mental illness within the boundaries of a given culture, and even more so on comparison of two or several cultures. Complicating factors in the last case are the introduction of such uncontrollable variables as differences in the quality of the training of psychiatric observers and differences in the clinical concepts, criteria, and labels which they use (26).

Consequently, on methodological grounds, there are no existing statistics which permit valid statistical transcultural comparisons of incidence and prevalence of mental illness. In the light of our present knowledge, approximations and impressions have to be relied upon.

A few gross examples culled from our correspondence must suffice: In contrast to the Western world, a very substantial proportion of patients treated in Indian mental hospitals suffer from psychiatric disturbances associated with nutritional deficiencies. *Cannabis indica* addiction is common in India, and opium addiction in the Far East and in some Arabic countries of the Near East. A high frequency of general paralysis of the insane (G.P.I.) has been observed in Hong Kong and a low frequency on Formosa and in India. Rarity of senile psychoses in the Chinese population has been reported from both Hong Kong and Formosa. Despite some statements to the contrary, the view is generally accepted that schizophrenia is ubiquitous. Manic-depressive psychoses seem to be especially frequent in Denmark and rare among African Negroes (3) and in Newfoundland. Obsessional neuroses have been reported as rare on Formosa and as exceedingly rare in Kenya (3) and in Kuwait. Correspondents from Ireland, Greece, and Italy report a high incidence of conversion hysteria. As regards anxiety states and psychosomatic disorders, the writer from Ireland states that, though by no means rare, they are probably fewer and less intractable in Ireland than elsewhere. Immigrants from Iraq into Israel remarkably often develop bronchial asthma. Absence of severe anxiety in clinical pictures and comparative rarity of anxiety states in out-patients have been reported from Hong Kong. Psychoneuroses are said to be rare on Formosa and have not been mentioned at all by Indian correspondents. The correspondent from Hong Kong noted a rarity of homosexuality and of other sexual perversions among the local Chinese population. The rate of perversions and of homosexuality is said to be high in Iran, and there has been "a real epidemic" of sexual crimes in the city of Sao Paulo in Brazil.

SYMPTOMATOLOGY

Any discussion of symptomatology will, regardless of the direction of the approach, run headlong into the problem of the normal-abnormal dichotomy. Both anthropologists and psychiatrists face the astonishingly difficult task of evaluating behaviour in terms of a series of factors, including its relation to accepted norms of behaviour for a given culture and the adequacy of behaviour in its social setting. A principal danger comes from mistaking the culturally defined norms of behaviour in Western culture to be ideal standards. Consequently, numerous Western scientists have been unconsciously guilty of ethnocentric prejudice, and hence of distortion, in evaluating the implications of the psychological organization of non-Western peoples.

A few observations illustrating culture-bound differences in symptomatology may be presented:

1. It has been noted that *schizophrenia* in the more primitive cultures is quieter than in the Western world. Blunting of affect, bizarreness, and other features suggesting deterioration have been described as typical of psychotic populations in Africa (1). It has been said that schizophrenia in primitive cultures is "a poor imitation of European forms" (1). According to a correspondent from India, schizophrenics in India

are less aggressive and violent than schizophrenics in the United Kingdom and probably in the United States. On the other hand, it has been reported that states of confused excitement, Carothers' "frenzied anxiety," not infrequently combined with homicidal behaviour, are more common in nonliterate psychotics than in Western patients (2, 26).

2. All observers agree that true *manic-depressive psychoses* are rare in technologically backward areas. For instance, Carothers, working in Kenya, had no case of depression in his series of 558 mentally deranged Africans other than a few involutional melancholics. In none of these were psychomotor retardation or ideas of sin or unworthiness seen. Nor was there in any of them a previous history of mental disorder. Mania of the acute and chronic form, by contrast, was fairly common (3, 12).

3. A number of *specific syndromes* have been described in various parts of the world under the names of Koro, Imu, Latah, Amok, Arctic hysteria, and Windigo psychosis. Some of these syndromes are characterized by echolalia and echopraxia with or without homicidal behaviour. In the Windigo psychosis of the Ojibway and Cree Indians of Canada, homicidal behaviour is combined with cannibalism.

REASONS FOR DIFFERENCES NOTED

There are no doubt marked differences in the frequency and nature of mental diseases in various cultures, although no methodology has yet been devised to quantify these differences in a statistically valid manner.

Explanation of some of the differences found is simple. It is obvious that in a country such as India, in which poverty and malnutrition are rampant, mental disorders due to malnutrition and avitaminosis are common; that malarial psychoses do not occur in countries without malaria; and that in countries in which expectation of life is short, senile psychoses are rarely observed.

Errors in Estimation. Open to doubt is the alleged very low incidence of psychoneuroses in African Negroes, Chinese, and Indians. It seems conceivable that the sparsity of trained psychiatrists in these countries is such, and the necessity to deal with psychiatric emergencies is so great, that the problem of psychoneuroses, which looms so large in the Western world, is of minor importance. The observation that obsessional neuroses are nonexistent in African Negroes may be correct; yet it is also possible that many milder cases of obsessive-compulsive psychoneuroses escape detection because their symptoms resemble characteristics of the cultural background itself.

Pseudo differences in incidence, as mentioned before, may come about if different diagnostic criteria and diagnostic labels are applied by psychiatrists in different countries. For instance, the relatively high figures for incidence of the manic form of manic-depressive psychoses in populations of technologically underdeveloped areas have been attributed to the tendency of local psychiatrists to diagnose states of excitement as mania rather than as catatonic excitement or schizo-affective state, as undoubtedly many psychiatrists would (1, 36). P. K. Benedict and Jacks suggest that the specific syndromes mentioned before, such as Latah, Amok, and Windigo psychosis, are culture-determined schizophrenic variations. Some of the specific syndromes, such as Koro and demoniacal possession, the Hsieh-Ping of the Chinese, have been, rightly or wrongly, regarded as hysterical in origin by local observers (23).

Sociocultural Variables. Beyond this, due consideration for sociocultural variables alone can account for differences in incidence, type, and content of psychiatric disorders on comparison of various cultures.

Various observers have commented on the paucity of content, the shallowness of affect, the lack of psychogenic precipitating factors, and of gross dilapidation of habits in schizophrenics of primitive cultures. Yap has pointed out that "this is probably true, since the richness of psychiatric symptomatology is dependent on the intellectual and cultural resources of the patient. . . . The same difference is found," he continues, "between the educated and the uneducated in any culture" (39).

Tooth suggests that the rarity of depressive states in African Negroes is related to the prophylactic catharsis provided by their culture, such as the institutionalized orgies of grief following a death (38), whereas P. K. Benedict and Jacks, contrasting the high incidence of confused excitement (often combined with homicidal behaviour) and the rarity of depressions, suggest that in nonliterates the hostility of the psychotic individual is directed *outward*, whereas in the West this hostility is more often directed *inward*. "Western culture," these writers state, "presents a significant contrast with at least many nonliterate cultures in the mechanisms of conscience (superego) formation and the extent to which supernatural authority figures are incorporated or introjected" (1).

Some cogent remarks have been made by Yap on the depressions of the Chinese. He states: ". . . there are significant differences in the incidence, intensity, and quality of the depressive illnesses in Chinese as compared with Westerners, and . . . the key to the understanding of these differences lies in the investigation of the religious background and the traditional methods of handling guilt, or, for that matter, how the guilt makes its appearance. In Chinese one would have to study specifically the practice of ancestor worship, which is of course very different from Christianity in its concepts of sin and guilt and their absolution" (39).

Various correspondents have suggested social and cultural factors as either correlated with, or causally connected to, mental illness. These include difficulties arising from the conflict between generations schooled in different values and fundamental attitudes, disturbances in family and community organization which upset traditional systems of security for the individual, dislocations of populations due to migration and attendant adjustment problems, and population pressures combined with poverty. A few examples must suffice:

1. It has been suggested that changes which affect basic cultural values, ideals, or attitudes, traditionally the core of interpersonal relations, adversely affect mental health. Thus, in Japan, Formosa, and India, where powerful traditions of family solidarity are shaken by new economic and political developments, observers are keenly appraising the results. From Japan we learn that in the rural areas the older age groups maintain powerful family solidarity with the twin values of "obligation" and "duty" guiding the relation of the individual to the social world. Such Japanese are typically overanxious and oversensitive to obligation, and this is expressed in the famous "face-saving" concept. However, rapid social and economic changes in Japan, plus the catastrophic defeat in war, have produced a split among generations, especially noticeable among the so-called "lost generation" composed of persons who were between the ages of ten and twenty years during the late war.

2. Evidence is accumulating to substantiate the hypothesis that mental health problems grow in direct relation to the disturbing of traditional bonds that hold families and communities together. It is suggested that individuals socialized under such well-knit family conditions may suffer when they are estranged from traditional systems of security arrangements previously rooted in the family.

Our research in Peru, begun in the summer of 1956 in collaboration with Dr. Seguin of the Hospital Obrero of Lima, is yielding evidence that the migrating individual from the tightly knit family background is especially vulnerable when faced with serious problems in an urban setting, when isolated from the security of his relatives.

3. This raises the extremely significant issue of the relation of migration to mental illness (25). Involved in such movements are all the stresses and difficulties inherent in the tremendous readjustments the immigrants must make to a novel and often hostile sociocultural environment. Again utilizing our Peruvian example, we note that many thousands of the native rural population of the Andean Highlands are flooding in a vast movement toward the coast. The social and economic differences between rural-Indian and urban-coastal culture are so extreme that many migrants are in fact unable to adjust, even assuming there were no serious physiological problems of adaptation to the descent from over 10,000 feet to sea level. Psychiatrically, it appears to produce a distinctive series of psychosomatic symptoms among a high proportion of these migrants.

A startlingly similar picture of the effects of migration is reported from Formosa, where mainland migrant patients show a parallel tendency to develop psychosomatic symptoms as an unconscious defense against anxiety and tension.

4. From the Gold Coast of Africa come excellent examples of the relations between culture change and mental illness. Reports describe how both the incidence and forms of mental illness differ between the more highly Europeanized African urban resident and the more tribal natives. Europeanized Negroes show little significant variation from white European norms in their mental disorders, whereas the more tribal populations undergoing severe acculturation react to stress and anxiety in culturally distinct forms.

5. Few of our correspondents, unfortunately, attempted to delineate the constellation of personality characteristics regarded as typical of the members of a given culture.

Since the shaping of the ego is largely a result of the reciprocal interaction between the human organism and its environment, and since most members of a culture experience a similar childhood environment, there are common features to their ego structures. These shared characteristics have been called "the modal personality type" by Kardiner (17) and Linton (24). It follows that we must understand what forces are responsible for the development of such specific features of character, i.e., every aspect of child-rearing practices must be investigated thoroughly from infancy through childhood.

Given these basic characteristics formed in childhood, which determine values, sentiments, and emotional responses, one can explore to what extent the social and cultural environment provides outlets, expressions, and gratification of needs, or leads to conflicts and frustrations.

This type of approach can be carried out only by workers well-versed in psychoanalytic dynamics and psychopathology. It is only through such an approach that the undoubted effects of culture change, described above, can be understood with any degree of precision.

CONCLUSIONS

The purpose of this paper has been to report preliminary observations obtained in a project concerned with transcultural psychiatric studies.

It becomes apparent that research can advance only when some homogeneity and standardization are introduced into the techniques of diagnosing and evaluating psychological states, and when coordinated and duplicated studies utilizing common methodologies are attempted across national and cultural boundaries.

Suggestive evidence has been submitted to substantiate the hypothesis that cultures differ significantly in incidence and symptomatology of mental illness. The available evidence strongly suggests that cultures differ *a*) in the amount of aggression, guilt, and anxiety generated within the structure of the life situations faced, and *b*) in the techniques used by the members of these cultures in dealing with aggression, guilt, and anxiety. These areas require further elaboration. Such sociocultural variables as family and community organization, rapid sociocultural changes, migration, population pressure, and political events are undoubtedly related to the etiology of mental illness.

Although examples have been taken predominantly from three continents—Africa, South America, and Asia—to illustrate how social, economic, and other cultural factors adversely affect mental health, it should be emphasized that the principles involved are the same when one considers similar circumstances in dealing with European or North American populations.

BIBLIOGRAPHY

1. Benedict, P. K., and Jacks, I.: "Mental illness in primitive societies." *Psychiatry*, 1954, vol. 17, p. 377.

2. Carothers, J. C.: *The African Mind in Health and Disease*. Geneva: World Health Organization, 1953. Monograph Series No. 17.

3. ———: "A study of mental derangement in Africans, and an attempt to explain its peculiarities, more especially in relation to the African attitude to life." *Psychiatry*, February 1948, vol. 11, p. 47.

4. Caudill, W.: "Perspectives on administration in psychiatric hospitals." *Administrative Science Quarterly*, 1956, vol. 1, p. 155.

5. Caudill, W.; Redlich, F. C.; Gilmore, H. R.; and Brody, W.: "Social structure and interaction processes on a psychiatric ward." *American Journal of Orthopsychiatry*, 1952, vol. 22, p. 314.

6. Dhunjiboy, J.: "Brief résumé of the types of insanity commonly met with in India." *Journal of Mental Science*, 1920, vol. 16, p. 187.

7. Dunham, H. W.: "The ecology of the functional psychoses in Chicago." *American Sociological Review*, 1937, vol. 2, p. 467.

8. Eaton, J. W., and Weil, R. J.: *Culture and Mental Disorders. A Comparative Study of the Hutterites and Other Populations*. Glencoe, Ill.: Free Press, 1955.

9. Faris, R. E. L.: "Ecological factors in human behavior." In *Personality and the Behavior Disorders* (J. McV. Hunt, ed.). New York: The Ronald Press Company, 1944.

10. Faris, R. E. L., and Dunham, H. W.: *Mental Disorders in Urban Areas*. Chicago: University of Chicago Press, 1939.

11. Frumkin, R. M.: "Occupation and major mental disorders." In *Mental Health and Mental Disorder* (A. M. Rose, ed.). New York: W. W. Norton & Company, 1955.

12. Gordon, H. L.: "Psychiatry in Kenya Colony." *Journal of Mental Science*, 1934, vol. 80, p. 167.

13. Hinkle, L. E., Jr.: "Some Relationships between Health, Personality, and Environmental Factors in a Group of Adult Chinese." Paper read at Annual Meeting of the American Psychosomatic Society, Atlantic City, May 4th and 5th, 1957.

14. Hinkle, L. E., Jr., and Wolff, H. G.: "The nature of man's adaptation to his total environment and the relation of this to illness." *A.M.A. Archives of Internal Medicine*, 1957, vol. 99, p. 442.

15. Hollingshead, A. B., and Redlich, F. C.: "Schizophrenia and social structure." *American Journal of Psychiatry*, 1954, vol. 110, p. 695.

16. ————:"Social stratification and psychiatric disorders." *American Sociological Review*, 1953, vol. 18, p. 163.

17. Kardiner, A.: *Psychological Frontiers of Society*. New York: Columbia University Press, 1945.

18. Lambo, T. A.: "Neuropsychiatric observations in the western region of Nigeria." *British Medical Journal*, 1956, vol. 2, p. 1388.

19. Lambo, T. A.: "The role of cultural factors in paranoid psychosis among the Yoruba tribe." *Journal of Mental Science*, April 1955, vol. 101, p. 239.

20. Leighton, A.: "The Stirling County Study—a brief outline." Cornell University, Ithaca, N.Y., April 1956. (Personal communication.)

21. Leighton, A.: "The Stirling County Study. A research program in social factors related to psychiatric health." In *Interrelations Between the Social Environment and Psychiatric Disorders*. New York: Milbank Memorial Fund, 1953.

22. Lemkau, P.; Tietze, C.; and Cooper, M.: "Mental hygiene problems in an urban district." *Mental Hygiene*, 1942, vol. 26, p. 275.

23. Lin, Tsung-yi: "A study of the incidence of mental disorder in Chinese and other cultures." *Psychiatry*, 1953, vol. 16, p. 313.

24. Linton, R.: *The Cultural Background of Personality*. New York: Appleton-Century-Crofts, 1945.

25. Murphy, H. B. M.: "Einwirkungen von Emigration und Flucht auf die psychische Verfassung." *Geistige Hygiene Forschung und Praxis*, 1955, 253.

26. Opler, M. K.: *Culture, Psychiatry and Human Values*. Springfield, Ill.: Charles C Thomas, 1956.

27. Opler, M. K., and Singer, J. L.: "Ethnic differences in behavior and psychopathology: Italian and Irish." *International Journal of Social Psychiatry*, 1956, vol. 2, p. 11.

28. Rennie, T. A. C.: "The Yorkville Community Mental Health Research Study." In *Interrelations Between the Social Environment and Psychiatric Disorders*. New York: Milbank Memorial Fund, 1953.

29. Rennie, T. A. C.; Srole, L.; Opler, M. K.; and Langner, T. S.: "Urban life and mental health. Socio-economic status and mental disorder in the metropolis." *American Journal of Psychiatry*, 1957, vol. 113, p. 831.

30. Roberts, B. H., and Myers, J. K.: "Religion, national origin, immigration, and mental illness." *American Journal of Psychiatry*, 1954, vol. 110, p. 759.

31. Roheim, G. "Racial differences in the neuroses and psychoses." *Psychiatry*, 1939, vol. 2–3, p. 375.

32. Rose, Arnold M. (editor): *Mental Health and Mental Disorder*. New York: W. W. Norton & Co., 1955.

33. Schroeder, C. W.: "Mental disorders in cities." *American Journal of Sociology*, 1942, vol. 47, p. 40.

34. Singer, J. L., and Opler, M. K.: "Contrasting patterns of fantasy and

motility in Irish and Italian schizophrenics." *Journal of Abnormal and Social Psychology*, 1956, vol. 53, p. 42.

35. Spiegel, J. P.: "The resolution of role conflict within the family." (Personal communication.)

36. Stainbrook, E.: "Some characteristics of the psychopathology of schizophrenic behavior in Bahian society." *American Journal of Psychiatry*, 1952, vol. 109, p. 300.

37. Stanton, A. H., and Schwartz, M. S.: *The Mental Hospital*. New York: Basic Books, 1954.

38. Tooth, G.: *Studies in Mental Illness in the Gold Coast*. London: Her Majesty's Stationery Office, 1950. Colonial Research Publications No. 6.

39. Yap, P. M.: "Mental diseases peculiar to certain cultures: A survey of comparative psychiatry." *Journal of Mental Science*, 1951, vol. 97, p. 313.

PERSONAL COMMUNICATIONS

Africa: Dr. E. F. B. Forster, Dr. G. Jahoda (Ghana); Dr. J. C. Carothers (Kenya); Dr. T. A. Lambo (Nigeria).

Asia: Dr. Luther B. Parhad (Kuwait, Arabia); Dr. Pow Meng Yap (China); Dr. E. K. Yeh, Dr. Tsung-yi Lin, Dr. Hsien Rin (Formosa); Dr. K. R. Masani, Dr. S. C. Srivastava, Dr. N. S. Vahia (India); Dr. Max Valentine (Iran); Dr. Abraham A. Weinberg (Israel); Dr. Tsuneo Muramatsu, Dr. Shogo Terashima (Japan); Dr. H. B. M. Murphy (Malaya).

Europe: Dr. Erik Stromgren (Denmark); Dr. George Spyros Philippopoulos (Greece); Dr. S. D. McGrath (Ireland); Dr. Emilio Servadio (Italy); Dr. Ornulv Odegard (Norway).

North America: Dr. J. Frazier Walsh (Canada).

South America: Dr. A. C. Pacheco e Silva (Brazil); Dr. Carlos A. Seguin (Peru).

Margaret Mead

American Museum of Natural History
New York City

and

Department of Anthropology
Columbia University

23

MENTAL HEALTH IN WORLD PERSPECTIVE

With The Third International Mental Health Congress, which met in London in the summer of 1948, the responsible aspiration for the use of the human sciences for the well-being of each individual human being in the world was finally institutionalized on an international basis. There had been international psychiatric meetings in the past—two meetings were called by the International Committee for Mental Hygiene, in Washington, D.C. in 1930, and in Paris in 1937—but this earlier movement toward internationalism was interrupted by the war. The 1948 Congress (28) represented the growth of an appreciation of the interdisciplinary nature of mental health problems, which had led in the United States to the research program of the Mental Health Section of the United States Public Health Service. The recognition by psychiatrists that much of the mental illness which they encountered in their individual patients was rooted in the wider sociocultural environment and might yield to a concerted multidisciplinary attack found expression in the organization that grew out of the 1948 Congress, the World Federation for Mental Health, with its explicit provision for membership by all the relevant professional societies and scientific groups, which would include social work, nursing, psychology, sociology, anthropology, etc., as well as national mental health associations. So an organizational base was provided for those who wished to translate the aspirations which were connected with their professional practice or their research into world-wide implications.

The world mental health approach can be seen as: *a*) a framework within which cross-cultural comparisons can be fruitfully made; *b*) a

501

form within which the knowledge gained in one part of the world, either
from old experience or new experiment, can be made available to other
parts of the world; *c*) an institutional form through which the mental
health aspects of international programs, initiated either by the United
Nations, its various specialized agencies, or by nongovernmental international organizations, can be interrelated; and *d*) a framework within
which problems that affect the whole world can be considered in world
terms by the responsibly interested people in different countries.

The first aspect, that of cross-cultural comparisons in the incidence
and prevalance of types of mental illness in different parts of the world,
can be scrutinized for the value of such comparisons in illuminating the
whole problem. It is possible, for instance, to look anew at a question
like delinquency, a major emphasis in the program of the Tenth Annual
Meeting in Copenhagen in 1957 (32), against the background of life in
cities as different as Taipei, Hong Kong, Copenhagen, Los Angeles, and
Tel Aviv. The kind of provincialism which traces juvenile delinquency to
local school legislation, the state of playgrounds, the percentage of recent
immigrants in the population, the decay of a particular form of religion,
or the evils of capitalism is corrected in such a comparison. Attention is
thereby focused at a higher level of generalization as the recognition
grows that juvenile delinquency is a phenomenon of the twentieth century in the great cities of the world, that it is related to the inability of
the agencies of education and law to provide a way of life for young
people without stigmatizing a certain percentage of them. The discussion
of some million juvenile benzedrine addicts in Japan, delivered at the
Ninth Annual Meeting in Berlin in 1956 (51), put the question of
juvenile drug addiction in the United States in a wider perspective.
Comparisons among the juveniles who affect aberrant dress and modified
transvestitism in London, in Sydney, in New York, reveal a common element in their superficially so different states, regardless of whether they
are Mexicans, Puerto Ricans, and Negroes in the United States, or young
people of pure Anglo-Saxon stock in Sydney. They are a group who see
life as a blind alley; they are in economic situations which offer them no
hope of a kind of satisfying social identity. Thus the comparative method
which has been the basis of cultural anthropology becomes a tool of
continuing usefulness in the exploration of those wider social conditions
which result in the traumatization, penalization, or sacrifice of some
segment of the population.

Just as such comparisons widen understanding of underlying conditions which militate against the attainment of mental health, so a comparative approach to practical experiences in different cultures provides a basis for improved practice. After the tragic floods in the Netherlands in 1953, the Mental Health Society in Holland was able to draw on the British experience of evacuation during World War II and persuade the authorities to refuse offers of hospitality from surrounding countries, which would have separated children from their parents, and also to advise the evacuation of rural peoples to other rural areas where they would be more at home, rather than to cities where they would be disoriented and miserable. After the devastating earthquake in Greece, mental health workers who had participated in World Federation meetings applied their knowledge of the importance of discussion and participation and so prevented a type of mass relief that would have ignored the basic needs of the people for tools and materials to deal with their threatened crops.

The influx of refugees from Hungary in the autumn of 1956 provided for another type of cooperation. The Austrian Society for Mental Health took the initiative in developing mental health services for the refugees; mental health societies in other parts of the world sent contributions. Through the World Federation for Mental Health, individuals and foundations made grants which provided for sending consultants to Vienna, helping to maintain international teams, coordinating the work with that of the World Health Organization consultant, Dr. Maria Pfister, and preparing materials on the specific problems of Hungarian culture which were used especially in the United States in the reception of the refugees. Here a problem of international scope could be dealt with both locally and cross-nationally. Specific knowledge of Hungarians and world experience of some of the problems common to all refugee groups, such as their special feeling about the first country to which they flee, could be integrated, picking up an earlier emphasis in the work of the World Federation resulting from the Vienna meeting of 1953 and the publication of H. B. M. Murphy's study of refugees (20), *Flight and Resettlement*.

The detailed history of the set of ideas which have centered about problems of mother-child relationships provides a vivid illustration of the way in which placing research and therapeutic experience within a context of social responsibility can deal with the social lag which is such a common feature of our rapidly changing civilization. The focus on mother-child relationships, including the importance of breast-feeding, the need for close proximity immediately following delivery, the need for

continuity in the relationship between an infant and a single mother or
mother surrogate, and the dangers of brief or protracted mother-child
separation during different periods of infancy were originally highlighted
in child development studies (1, 24), in the work of field anthropologists
(17), and in research by psychoanalysts on infants and children (11).
These findings were translated into demands for action, as in the Cor-
nelian Corner in Detroit, into films (see film bibliography), into more
research, and into attempts to institutionalize corrective practices, such
as the Rooming-in Program at Yale (14), itself supported by mental
health research funds from the United States Public Health Service. Then
the World Health Organization entered the picture, providing funds for
a summary monograph by John Bowlby (2), which brought together research findings on the question of separation, and sponsoring a European
Regional Seminar on Child Psychiatry in the spring of 1952, where the
research work of Sibylle Escalona on infants (12) (a U.S. Mental Health
Research Project), and the findings of the child analyst, Erik Erikson, on
a recent teaching visit to Israel, were included in the discussions (34).

In the summer of 1952, the World Federation for Mental Health, in
cooperation with the World Health Organization, sponsored a Seminar
on Mental Health and Infant Development at Chichester, England, where
specialists in the care of children from fifty-one countries spent three
weeks discussing the implications of mother-child relationships for the
mental health of children (24). This seminar was an example of the kind
of cooperation which is possible between a United Nations Agency, the
World Federation, and professionals working on basic research in human
behavior. The theme of the seminar, the mental health of children under
two, originated in an international conference during World War II
where some of the delegates from Asia had proposed beginning the discussion of child health *from* the age of two, with the comment, "Then
you know whether they are going to live or not." Selecting the period
from conception to the age of two stressed the new post-World War II
possibility for infant survival in every part of the world.

For the seminar in 1952 we had clinical studies and expository films
made by René Spitz and Katherine Wolf in the United States and Latin
America, a film made in England by James Robertson on the effects of
separation during hospitalization, and a film on the rehabilitation of an
institutionally traumatized child in France by Jenny Aubry; detailed basic
research on infants made by Sibylle Escalona; the experience of Edith
Jackson in the rooming-in experiments at Yale University hospital (14),

and the experience with cottage homes for small children in Denmark. Those countries, like the United States, France, and Great Britain, which had gone too far in developing types of hospitalization for childbirth, treatment of sick children, and care of children from broken homes, could put their experience at the disposal of the countries like Thailand which were just on the verge of building modern institutions, in the effort to prevent a wasteful repetition of the Western mistakes. The faculty and the teaching materials—multidisciplinary case histories— came from three cultures: England, France, and the United States, and gave the kind of cross-cultural validity and international atmosphere within which countries with less-developed institutions could follow leads and advice which they could view as stemming from wide experience rather than as presenting explicitly uninational models. At the same time, the methods by which the case materials had been assembled, which included selections from many of the best longitudinal studies in the United States, and the newest attempts at interdisciplinary cooperative research in France, became available as research models in other countries. Because the mental health movement is concerned with goals and presents an aspiration for the greater well-being of human beings, there can be no separation between research and practice, between learning and using information, nor between the results of some special piece of research and putting it into practice.

At Chichester it was becoming apparent that the emphasis on mother-child relationships was accompanied by a growing tendency to ignore the role of other family members, especially the father, and to ignore the idiosyncratic needs of particular mothers, or the demands of particular conditions, such as the period of rest provided at childbirth for the tired mother of small means and many children. Corrections for a too sweeping application of the new Western research were included in the work of the seminar.

Then in the early winter of 1953, the Mental Health Section of the World Health Organization sponsored a four-year Study Group in the Psychobiological Development of the Child (26), under the chairmanship of Frank Fremont-Smith, modeling its procedures upon the well-tested pattern of the interdisciplinary conferences which had been developed for the Josiah Macy, Jr. Foundation under the leadership of Lawrence K. Frank. Mr. Frank had also been chairman of the International Preparatory Commission on Mental Health, which produced the charter document for the World Congress on Mental Health in 1948 (27).

The Study Group on the Psychobiological Development of the Child took the next step by including, in addition to work in child psychiatry, anthropology, child psychology, new developments from the comparative study of the behavior of other living things (ethology), and research on the relationship between the study of the brain and behavior. This inaugurated fresh research by the Study Group on a wider biological base, on the implications of human mother-child care, and the various kinds of group processes, which has been subsequently reflected in such diverse ways as the later work of John Bowlby, case studies of group behavior of geese by Lorenz, and materials presented to the Macy Conference on Group Processes, which includes studies of mental hospitals and the psychology of brain-washing procedures (23). Four members of the original study group have been invited to the United States under the aegis of the newly established International Seminars on Mental Health of the Postgraduate Center for Psychotherapy and the World Federation for Mental Health.

Another facet of the way in which clinical findings, field research, conference procedures, and national and international action programs have interacted can be found in the growing use of the concept of identity originally developed by Erik Erikson (7) in his materials for the special Macy Conference on Health and Human Relations that was preparatory to the 1950 United States White House Conference on children. This had grown out of his work with gifted young adolescents at Stockbridge (8) combined with his studies of normal preadolescence for one of the longitudinal research projects represented also in the Chichester case histories (9), work on Russian personality for the Columbia University Research in Contemporary Cultures project (5), and participation in a series of conferences sponsored by the Macy Foundation held in Germany after the war (7). This concept of the necessary search of young people for identity, combined with my Admiralty Islands work on cultural transformation while identity of the individuals involved in the transformation was maintained (17, 18), Kenneth Soddy's work on sensorily traumatized children in England, Otto Klineberg's long years of research on problems of race and race prejudice (15), and Hans Rümke's Netherlands studies of the psychology of religions (22), formed the basis for the first publication of the Scientific Committee of the World Federation, in January, 1958, on "Identity" (33). The thinking which led up to the selection of the problem of identity as a central issue of our time also involved the Federation's adoption of a new positive approach to problems of inter-group prejudice, in which the question: *How can we develop a positive sense of identity which does not involve as an essential component the devaluation of others?* has been substituted for the traditional approach, which was: *How can we prevent or combat prejudice?* Continued interest in the problem of identity search led Erik Erikson into a study of Martin Luther (10), [a topic which had also engrossed Paul Reiter of Denmark (21), who for several years led the World Federation discussion group on leadership]. Erikson's studies of identity search by adolescents—given depth by the exploration of the relationship between Martin Luther, German culture, and the emergence of Protestantism and immediacy, by our present concern with the character of great men and the implications in a shrinking world—was again given to the whole Federation at the second Vienna meeting in 1958, that meeting itself being a response to the way in which the Austrian Society met the problem of refugees, while the problems of development and transformation became a central theme of the 1960 White House Conference on Children.

The growth of the new United Nations specialized agencies after World War II initiated a new period of governmental responsibility. The World Federation for Mental Health was inaugurated as part of the planning which went into the World Health Organization also. Four psychiatrists who had been intimately and dynamically associated with the application of wide social psychiatric insights to wartime problems, Brock Chisholm in the Canadian Army and J. R. Rees, Ronald Hargreaves, and Kenneth Soddy in the British Army, became, respectively, first Director-General of the World Health Organization, first President and later Director of the World Federation for Mental Health, first Chief of the Mental Health Section of the World Health Organization, and Scientific Director and Deputy Director of the World Federation for Mental Health. Today, the work of the Mental Health Section of the World Health Organization is under the direction of E. E. Krapf, who has been actively associated with the work of the World Federation. Otto Klineberg, formerly Director of the Tensions Project of UNESCO, is now actively planning research and leading conferences for the World Federation for Mental Health, while Brock Chisholm, formerly Director-General of the World Health Organization became the 1957–1958 President of the World Federation for Mental Health. Mottram Torre, now special consultant to the World Federation, has pioneered in problems of mental health of diplomats, technical experts, and administrators, in a variety of contexts, in government agencies, in international agencies and international conferences, combining research in this field and practice as psychiatric consultant to the United Nations Medical Service.

Thus the Mental Health movement, national and international, in its research as well as in its application, is based firmly on continuing relationships of trust among people who are willing to take responsibility for the human consequences of their professional activities.

It has been explicitly recognized that there are various kinds of effort which are more appropriate to nongovernmental agencies, and that a vigorous international voluntary association can greatly augment the efforts of governmental groups in creating climates of opinion, undertaking special projects, organizing seminars and conferences which require funds and help from a variety of sources, and taking the initiative in raising particular problems. The World Federation for Mental Health thus provides an agency through which initiation of an activity on a world scale can take place either through the action of an individual associate, through a member mental health association, through a member professional association, through the *ad hoc* discussion groups held at annual meetings, or through the initiation of international governmental agencies, in search of consultants, contract fulfillments, or cooperation in inaugurating enterprises requiring multiple sponsorship.

The report of the Preparatory Commission for the Congress in 1948 closed with a series of recommendations to the World Health Organization and UNESCO, most of which have now been at least partly carried out.

INTERNATIONAL RECOMMENDATIONS

A. United Nations

1. That immediate steps be taken to plan and establish mental health services in the occupied territory of Germany, in order to deal with the disastrous effects of present conditions there, which are a threat not only to the welfare of that country, but also to the world. Such services should include advisers to the highest authority, and working teams representing the appropriate disciplines from the occupying and neutral nations and the German people.

2. (a) That the specialised agencies of the United Nations continue to give urgent consideration to the mental health problems of displaced persons, transferred and migrating populations, homeless children, and others constituting the human aftermaths of war;

(b) That recognition be given to the initiative shown and the enormous amount of work accomplished by national and local governmental and voluntary agencies in this matter;

(c) That this work be encouraged and extended.

(d) That close contact be maintained with all such local agencies, and arrangements be made for continuous exchange of information, so that activities may become part of a co-ordinated effort;

(e) That immediate steps be taken to provide basic living requirements for all displaced persons, and protective measures adopted to minimise the adverse effects of social disturbances on mental health;

(f) That national agencies be urged to do everything possible along these lines in their own countries.

3. (a) That United Nations' organisations do everything possible to co-ordinate their activities in the interest of developing adequate mental health programmes within each member nation.

(b) That a demonstration of the integration of mental health with public health activities in a specific area, and related to a specific problem (such as child care) be undertaken, the implications of which should render more effective the extension of such combined operations;

(c) That aid in the establishment of mental health services be available to all nations, including those who by reason of limitations of size, population, or professional personnel have special need for technical advice and assistance.

4. That in order to furnish information required by agencies such as World Health Organisation, Food and Agricultural Organisation, International Labour Office, United Nations Educational Scientific and Cultural Organisation, studies be made to reveal cultural and national characteristics of the countries involved.

5. (a) That in order to ensure the best possible use of educational methods in carrying out a unified health programme, co-operation be strengthened between WHO and UNESCO;

(b) Similarly in the mental health aspects of its educational work, the ILO should enlist the co-operation of WHO and UNESCO.

6. (a) That, in view of the proven value of group discussion of inter-personal and inter-group tensions, systematic study be made as to the best methods of using this technique at the higher levels of international diplomacy.

(b) That there be convened a conference of technically qualified representatives of the social sciences and psychiatry, appointed by their governments, to enquire into existing international tensions and to make relevant proposals.

7. That a team of social scientists and psychiatrists should conduct in various parts of the world a series of conferences and study periods on human relations, to which local, governmental, educational, public health and mental health leaders would contribute.

8. (a) That the various U.N. organisations, working in co-operation with private foundations and universities, extend further the provision for international contacts among mental health specialist personnel. This could take the

form of an increase in the number of international fellowships, exchange of consultants and visiting professorships.

(b) That WHO be asked to utilise some of its fellowships for this purpose.

(c) That action be taken to evaluate the results of such procedures.

9. That in order to stimulate and to recognise outstanding leadership in the field of mental health, the United Nations consider the award of prizes for major contributions in research, scientific publication, administrative initiative, and excellence of mental health services.

10. That the UN organisations consider all possible means of integrating national loyalties to the United Nations and to the world community.

11. (a) That international as well as national governmental organisations make provision for the application of professional techniques to the selection of civil servants, especially those who play an important part in the conduct of affairs; and that provision be made for the constant improvement of these techniques.

(b) That those responsible for decisions in human affairs make use of the knowledge and methods developed by the social sciences and psychiatry; and that, to this end, governments be encouraged to incorporate into appropriate departments, teams of social scientists and psychiatrists as advisors or as members of the staff.

12. That UN organisations encourage all professional schools to give appropriate emphasis in their training programmes to mental health principles and to the contributions of the social sciences. This applies not only to those schools dealing directly with health, such as medicine and education, but also to those concerned with the circumstances of health, such as engineering and architecture.

13. (a) That studies be made of social institutions which are in process of rapid change, in order to clarify the factors contributing to, and resulting from, such change as, for example, the introduction of a system of universal education, or of personal income tax, re-housing a bombed town, industrialisation.

(b) That advantage be taken of conditions of rapid change to introduce mental health principles into the development of new services.

14. That the UN organisations encourage the inclusion of mental health activities in government education departments, in view of the established value of this practice.

15. That it be recognised that organisations or persons who display bias on the basis of race, colour, creed or economic status, are apt to be unsuitable as advisors in matters pertaining to mental health.

B. World Health Organisation

1. The successful administration of any public health programme involves the acceptance of the programme by the people on whose behalf it is administered; and hence must take into account the attitudes varying in different

cultures, which may assist or obstruct the application of scientific knowledge. This is a point at which mental health principles can find direct and useful application.

Accordingly it is recommended that adequate attention be given to mental health principles in connection with the undertakings of the World Health Organisation, in promoting maternal and child welfare, and in the control of venereal disease, tuberculosis, and malaria, all of which have mental implications in respect to causative factors, effects, and control.

2. That long-term plans for comparative studies in the field of mental health be envisaged, and steps taken immediately to facilitate such studies as:—

(a) determining the criteria by which mental ill-health might be assessed by a nation or region;

(b) securing and maintaining agreement on terminology, nomenclature, methods of survey, statistical procedures;

(c) recognising factors which are general to all countries, and those which are specific to certain regions.

In this connection, the World Federation for Mental Health and other international and national professional associations should be invited to furnish expert help where needed.

3. That the World Health Organisation call on appropriate international professional organisations (e.g. World Federation for Mental Health) for co-operation in the formulation and promulgation of principles important in promoting the healthy development of children.

4. (a) That pilot studies and demonstrations in mental health education be undertaken;

(b) That provisions be made for the widespread dissemination of mental health information, including the results of research and demonstrations;

(c) That there be international and interdisciplinary co-ordination in research effort.

5. That international congresses in all fields of health be facilitated with representation from the various professions.

6. That, as soon as is practicable, an advisory Expert Committee be established, composed of professional personnel in the field of mental health and human relations.

7. That in co-operation with professional associations in various countries, further international surveys of standards of professional training be undertaken along lines already carried out in relation to social workers, with a view to the raising of these standards throughout the world; such professional training being interpreted in the widest sense, to include as many as possible of the professions regarded as responsible for mental health.

8. That a definite minimum proportion of the total funds available for fellowships be devoted to fellowships for mental health personnel.

9. That there be undertaken studies of the differences in approach to mental health education, for each of the four groups:

(a) persons working in professions related to health;

(b) policy-making bodies;

(c) persons in the fields of radio, press, films, etc.;

(d) the general public.

C. United Nations Educational, Scientific, and Cultural Organisation

1. That the establishment be encouraged of international organisations for the social sciences and psychiatry, in order that research may be co-ordinated and the results made known.

2. That the Tensions Project serve as a co-ordinating agency in the field of group relations by:

(a) collecting the results of research in this field in various countries;

(b) making available such results to all interested;

(c) co-ordinating research along international lines;

(d) inviting the co-operation of the World Federation for Mental Health in carrying through any investigations in which both organisations are interested.

3. That co-operative surveys of national cultures look particularly for characteristics which hold promise as aids to world citizenship.

4. (a) That since the value of including mental health activities in education departments is recognised, such inclusion be encouraged and strengthened wherever possible.

(b) That similar encouragement be given to scientists in the field of education in their efforts to base educational practice on the principles of human development (27).

One of the areas which the World Federation has recognized as crucial is the whole problem of the effects of technical change. In 1949 Lawrence K. Frank, picking up a theme on which an interdisciplinary committee of the U.S. National Research Council had disbanded at the end of the war, proposed, through the Division of World Affairs of the National Committee for Mental Hygiene (which then carried on the work of the World Federation in the United States), that a manual be prepared on the mental health aspects of the changes in living habits which were going on all over the world, and were being accentuated by planned change. This original suggestion was reshaped within the Department of Social Sciences of UNESCO, and a manual was prepared by the World Federation for Mental Health on Cultural Patterns and Technical Change (16), which was later published in paper and so became available to a wide audience.

With the new activity (4) in regard to problems of atomic energy and automation, the World Federation has both taken specific initiative toward the new International Atomic Energy Agency, the World Health Organization, and UNESCO, and responded to requests for further participation. During the preparations for the First World Mental Health Year in 1960, the Federation will undertake a cross-cultural survey of attitudes toward mental illness and mental health in many countries, complementing the World Health Organization's initiation of studies in the epidemiology of mental disease. The growing emphasis on Asian and African problems has been reflected in the second project of the Scientific Committee of the World Federation, a study of the concept of mental health in different cultures, with special attention to the great world religious ideologies; and a conference in March, 1958, on Mental Health in Africa South of the Sahara, held at Bukavu in the Belgian Congo in cooperation with the Commission for Technical Coordination in Africa South of the Sahara; and a seminar in Manila, cosponsored by the World Health Organization (Western Pacific Regional Office), the Asia Foundation, the World Federation for Mental Health, the Philippine Government, the National Family Life Workshop, and the Philippines Mental Health Association, at which specialists from seventeen Asia and Southeast Asian countries will discuss changing forms of the family.

In this whole interweaving of ideas and practice, research application, and continuing responsibility, the working ties between widely scattered individuals, made possible by the newly elaborated conference method which breaks down barriers of discipline, nationality, and language, and permits a new form of rapid face-to-face communication, have been essential. In recognition of the significance of this conference method, the World Federation for Mental Health and the Macy Foundation cosponsored a conference on the Effective Functioning of Discussion Groups and Small Conferences in 1956 (3, 13).

This was preceded by a preparatory conference on problems of interpretation, which stressed the emerging role of the interpreter as a specialist in the cultures among whose members he has to facilitate communication (13).

The most frequent criticism aimed at the mental health movement is that its goals are poorly defined, ever-changing, recurrently ambiguous. This seems to me to be a characteristic intrinsic to the movement, which, because it represents the common aspiration of many groups, in many areas of life, in many countries, must always be a composite of goals, not yet envisioned in some parts of the world, already overachieved and requiring correction in others. It is primarily a great echoing system of communication through which the thought of individuals, the explicit goals of organizations, the programs of agencies, the beneficence of foundations, and the direction of research are involved in a responsible effort to use our growing scientific knowledge to meet the ever-changing problems of human beings in an interconnected world.

FILM REFERENCES

Aubry (Roudinsco), Jenny. *Monique (Maternal Deprivation in Young Children)*. 2 reels. 22 minutes. Sound. J. Aubry, Association pour la Sante Mentale de l'Enfance, 40 rue François, Paris VIII.

Escalona, S., and M. Leitch. *Eight Infants: Tension Manifestations in Response to Perceptual Stimuli*. New York University Film Library, New York. n.d.

Fries, M., and P. J. Woolf. *Series of Studies on Integrated Environment: The Interaction between Child and Environment*. (5 Films). New York University Film Library, New York.

Joselin, Arnold G. *Life Begins at Leeds*. 5 reels. 50 minutes. Sound. World Federation for Mental Health, 19 Manchester Street, London, W. 1, and Leeds University, U.K.

Robertson, James. *A Two-Year-Old Goes to Hospital*. 4 reels. 60 minutes. Sound. Tavistock Clinic, 2 Beaumont Street, London, W. 1.

Spitz, René, and Katherine A. Wolf. *The Smiling Response*. Silent. René Spitz, 1150 Fifth Avenue, New York 28, N.Y. n.d.

BIBLIOGRAPHY

1. Bakwin, H.: "Psychogenic fever in infants." *American Journal of Diseases of Children*, 1944, vol. 67, pp. 176–181.

2. Bowlby, John: *Maternal Care and Mental Health*. Geneva: World Health Organization Technical Monograph Series, no. 2, 1951. (Also in abridged version: *Child Care and the Growth of Love*. London: Penguin Books, 1953.)

3. Capes, M., ed.: *Proceedings of the International Conference on Small Groups and Group Discussions* (held at Eastbourne, England, January–February, 1956, under the auspices of the World Federation for Mental Health and the Josiah Macy, Jr. Foundation). Basic Books, 1959.

4. Chisholm, Brock: *Prescription for Survival* (Bampton Lectures). New York: Columbia University Press, 1957.

5. Erikson, Erik H.: *Childhood and Society*. New York: W. W. Norton & Co., 1950.

6. ————: "Growth and crises of the healthy personality." *Supplement No. II, Symposium of the Healthy Personality*. New York: Josiah Macy, Jr. Foundation Conference Transactions, 1950, p. 93.

7. ————: "Sense of inner identity." In *Health and Human Relations*. New

York: Blakiston Division, McGraw-Hill Book Co., published for the Josiah Macy, Jr. Foundation, 1953.

8. ———: "On the sense of inner identity." In *Psychoanalytic Psychiatry and Psychology*, vol. I, (Robert P. Knight, ed.). New York: International Universities Press, 1954, pp. 351–364.

9. ———: "Sex differences in the play configurations of American adolescents." In *Childhood in Contemporary Cultures* (Margaret Mead and Martha Wolfenstein, eds.). Chicago: University of Chicago Press, 1955, pp. 324–341. (Adapted from a larger paper published in the *American Journal of Orthopsychiatry*, 1951, vol. XXI, no. 4, pp. 667–692.)

10. ———: *Young Man Luther: An Essay in Identity and Ideology.* New York: W. W. Norton & Co., 1958.

11. Escalona, Sibylle: "The psychological situation of mother and child upon return from the hospital." In *Problems of Infancy and Childhood.* New York: Josiah Macy, Jr. Foundation. Transactions of the Third Conference, 1949.

12. ———: *Early Phases of Personality Development: A Non-normative Study of Infant Behavior.* Monographs of the Society for Research in Child Development, Inc., 1952.

13. Glenn, Edmund S.: Introduction to the Special Issue: "Interpretation and intercultural communication." *Etcetera: A Review of General Semantics*, Special Issue, March, 1958.

14. Jackson, E., and Klatskin, E. H.: "Rooming-in research project: Development of methodology of parent-child relationship in a clinical setting." In *The Psychoanalytic Study of the Child*, vol. 5. New York: International Universities Press, 1950.

15. Klineberg, Otto: *Tensions Affecting International Understanding.* New York: Social Science Research Council, Survey Research Bulletin 62, 1950.

16. Mead, Margaret, ed.: *Cultural Patterns and Technical Change.* Paris: United Nations Educational, Scientific and Cultural Organization, 1953. (Also Mentor Book, MD 134, New American Library, New York, 1955.)

17. Mead, Margaret: "Some theoretical considerations on the problem of mother-child separation." *American Journal of Orthopsychiatry*, July, 1954, vol. XXIV, no. 3.

18. ———: *New Lives for Old: Cultural Transformation—Manus, 1928–1953.* New York: William Morrow & Co., 1956.

19. ———: "Changing patterns of parent-child relations in an urban culture" (the Ernest Jones Lecture of 1957). *International Journal of Psychoanalysis*, 1957, vol. 38, no. 6.

20. Murphy, H. B. M., ed.: *Flight and Resettlement.* Paris, UNESCO, 1955.

21. Reiter, Paul Johann Stephen: *Martin Luther's Umwelt, Character und Psychose; sowie die Bedeutung dieser Factoren für seine Entwicklung und Lehre; eine Historische-Psychiatrische Studie.* Vol. I: *Die Umwelt.* Kopen-

hagen: Levin & Munksgaard———Ejnar Munksgaard, 1937. Vol. II: *Luther's Personlichkeit, Seelenleben und Krankheiten.* Kopenhagen: Ejnar Munksgaard, 1941.

22. Rümke, H. C.: *The Psychology of Unbelief.* Translated from the Dutch by M. H. C. Willems. London: Rockliff Publishing Corporation, Ltd., 1952.

23. Schaffner, Bertram, ed.: *Group Processes.* Transactions of the First Conference, 1954; published 1955. Transactions of the Second Conference, 1955; published 1956. Transactions of the Third Conference, 1956; published 1957. Transactions of the Fourth Conference, 1957; published 1959. New York: The Josiah Macy, Jr. Foundation.

24. Soddy, Kenneth, ed.: *Mental Health and Infant Development.* Proceedings of the International Seminar held by the World Federation for Mental Health at Chichester, England. 2 volumes. London: Routledge and Kegan Paul, Ltd., 1955.

25. Spitz, R. A.: "Hospitalism." In *The Psychoanalytic Study of the Child,* vol. I. New York: International Universities Press, 1945.

26. Tanner, J., and Inhelder, B., ed.: *Discussions on Child Development.* Vol. I: First Meeting of the World Health Organization Study Group on Psychobiological Development of the Child, Geneva, 1953; published 1956. Vol. II: Second Meeting, London, 1954; published 1957. Volume III: published 1958; and Vol. IV, in press. London: Tavistock Press; New York: International Universities Press.

27. World Federation for Mental Health: "Mental Health and World Citizenship: A Statement Prepared for the International Congress on Mental Health." London, 1948.

28. ———: *Proceedings of the Third International Congress on Mental Health* (J. C. Flugel, ed.). London, 1948.

29. ———: *Social Provisions for Mental Health: Proceedings of the Sixth Annual Meeting of the World Federation for Mental Health.* Vienna, 1953.

30. ———: *Family Health and the State: Proceedings of the Eighth Annual Meeting of the World Federation for Mental Health.* Istanbul, 1955.

31. ———: *Mental Health in Home and School: Proceedings of the Ninth Annual Meeting of the World Federation for Mental Health.* Berlin, 1956.

32. ———: *Growing Up in a Changing World: Proceedings of the Tenth Annual Meeting of the World Federation for Mental Health.* Copenhagen, 1957. (Not as yet available.)

33. ———: *Identity: Introductory Study No. 1 of the Scientific Committee of the Executive Board,* 1958.

34. World Health Organization: "Scandinavian Seminar on Child Psychiatry and Child Guidance Work." Report of "A Seminar on Child Psychiatry for Scandinavian Countries" held April 21 through May 2, 1952, in Lillehammer, Norway. Report issued by World Health Organization Regional Office, Geneva.

NAME INDEX

SUBJECT INDEX

Abyssinia. *See* Ethiopia
acculturation, 2, 3, 6, 25, 64
  of Arabs in Algeria, 333 ff.
  of immigrant groups, 443, 451
  among Iroquois, 94
  of Japanese-Americans, 216
  of Jews, 444, 446, 451, 452, 455, 461, 462
  and mental health, 129, 130
  among migrants in Peru, 119–37
  studies of, 428
  among Ute, 115
  See also specific group listings
acting-out, 438
adaption syndrome, 122
  among Southern Bantu (Africa), 364
adjustment, social, and generation level
      among Jews, 457–59
  and religious affiliation, 457–58
adolescence, in Singapore, 304. *See also* Lin, T. Y.
affect, lack of control, 441
affective symbolism in Arabs and Americans, 338
Africa, 5
  Algeria, 333
  Carothers' survey, 428
  Gold Coast, 496
  Kenya, 1
  South, Bushmen, 25
  Zulu, 351 ff.
African studies, 317–69
Ainu, *Imu,* 229, 493
Alaskan Eskimo mental patients, 430
  compared with, Indian mental patients, 430
  white mental patients, 430
alcohol, among Andean Indians, 131
  in Ifaluk culture, 149
alcoholic psychosis and migration, 131
alcoholics in the Zar cult, 321
alcoholism, among Chinese in New York City, 429
  chronic, 429
  among Irish, 429, 434

  among Iroquois, 66
  in Japan, 215
  rates in cultural groups, 429
Aleutian Islanders, 430
Algeria, 4
Algerians, anal sadism, 346
  culture, 333, 335 ff., 348
Alor, people of, 174
ambivalence, 427
America, 6
American Indian, studies, 21–137
American Midwest, 3
American Negro, 413. *See also* Negro
  culture, 415
American Psychiatric Association, 407, 430
  illness nomenclature, 430
Amok, 295, 493
Amsterdam, 5
Andean Indians, 120
anemia, 429
Anglo-American, studies, 373–485
anthropological field surveys, 430
  interviewing, 432
anthropologist, 11, 13, 16, 22, 39, 99, 121, 141, 375
  and acculturation, 443
  on Ifaluk, 153
  and Iroquois, 65
  theory of culture, 215
anthropology, 7, 12, 115, 428
  cultural, 7, 23
  and psychiatry, 441
  social, 366, 368
anthropophobia, Japanese syndrome, 237
anxiety, 41
  and aggression in American Negro, 420
  and ceremonialism, 289
  in Ifaluk culture, 147–49, 152
  in Irish patients, 437
  and religion in North India, 273–89
  and ritual, 273
  states, 492
Arab culture and homosexuality, 347–48
Arab personality, 333 ff.

522